CONTACTS ®

Number 91 / 2002 Published in October by The S

Tel: 020-7437 7631 Fax: 020-7437 5881 e-mail:

C000152946

Editorial & Production Kate Poynton, Kathy Norrish
Christine Barry, Hannah Frankel, Gavin May, Lisa Spezza, John Watson

CONTENTS

CONTENTS

3

Index to Advertisers

Index to Advertisers Cont'd

ABBOT MEAD VICKERS BBDO Ltd
151 Marylebone Road
London NW1 5QE
Fax: 020-7616 3600   Tel: 020-7616 3500

AKA
Gloucester Mansions
140A Shaftesbury Avenue
London WC2H 8HD
e-mail: aka@akauk.com
Fax: 020-7836 8787   Tel: 020-7836 4747

BANKS HOGGINS O'SHEA FCB
55 Newman Street
London W1P 3PG
Fax: 020-7947 8001   Tel: 020-7947 8000

BARTLE BOGLE HEGARTY
60 Kingly Street, London W1B 5DS
Fax: 020-7437 3666   Tel: 020-7734 1677

BATES Ltd
121-141 Westbourne Terrace
London W2 6JR
Fax: 020-7258 3757   Tel: 020-7262 5077

BATES TAVNER RESOURCES INTERNATIONAL Ltd
International House
World Trade Centre
1 St Katherine's Way
London E1W 1UN
Fax: 020-7702 2271   Tel: 020-7481 2000

BDH/TBWA
St Paul's,
781 Wilmslow Road
Didsbury Village
Manchester M20 2RW
e-mail: info@bdhtbwa.co.uk
Fax: 0161-908 8601   Tel: 0161-908 8600

BMP DDB Ltd
12 Bishops Bridge Road
London W2 6AA
Fax: 020-7402 4871   Tel: 020-7258 3979

BURNETT Leo Ltd
60 Sloane Avenue
London SW3 3XB
Fax: 020-7591 9126   Tel: 020-7591 9111

C.D.P.
33-34 Soho Square
London W1D 3DP
Fax: 020-7292 4010   Tel: 020-7292 4000

CIA
1 Paris Garden
London SE1 8NU
Fax: 020-7261 0188   Tel: 020-7633 9999

COGENT
Heath Farm
Hampton Lane, Meriden
West Midlands CV7 7LL
Fax: 0121-627 5038   Tel: 0121-627 5040

D'ARCY
Warwick Building
Kensington Village
Avonmore Road, London W14 8HQ
Fax: 020-7348 3855   Tel: 020-7751 1800

DEWYNTERS Plc
48 Leicester Square
London WC2H 7QD
Fax: 020-7321 0104   Tel: 020-7321 0488

DONER CARDWELL HAWKINS
26-34 Emerald Street
London WC1N 3QA
Fax: 020-7437 3961   Tel: 020-7734 0511

EURO RSCG WNEK GOSPER
11 Great Newport Street
London WC2H 7JA
Fax: 020-7465 0552   Tel: 020-7240 4111

FAULDS ADVERTISING Ltd
Sutherland House, 108 Dundas Street
Edinburgh EH3 5DQ
Fax: 0131-557 2261   Tel: 0131-557 6003

GOLLEY SLATER & PARTNERS (LONDON) Ltd
St George's House
3 St George's Place
Church Street
Twickenham TW1 3NE
Fax: 020-8892 4451   Tel: 020-8744 2630

GREY WORLDWIDE
215-227 Great Portland Street
London W1W 5PN
Fax: 020-7637 7473   Tel: 020-7636 3399

HARDSELL Ltd
(Advertising, Marketing, Design)
Unit 11-3-1, The Leathermarket
Weston Street
London SE1 3ER
e-mail: bigideas@hardsell.co.uk
Fax: 020-7403 5381   Tel: 020-7403 4037

HAYMARKET ADVERTISING Ltd
Suite 4, Victory House
99-101 Regent Street
London W1B 4EZ
e-mail: info@haymarket-advertising.co.uk
Fax: 020-7734 4835   Tel: 020-7437 7206

HOLMAN ADVERTISING Ltd
Holman House
30 Maple Street
London W1T 6HA
e-mail: holman.house@lineone.net
Fax: 020-7631 5283   Tel: 020-7637 3533

KANE Peter & COMPANY Ltd
12 Burleigh Street
London WC2E 7PX
Fax: 020-7836 4073   Tel: 020-7836 4561

LEAGAS DELANEY LONDON Ltd
1 Alfred Place
London WC1E 7EB
Fax: 020-7758 1760   Tel: 020-7758 1758

LEITH AGENCY The
The Canon Mill
1-3 Canon Street
Edinburgh EH3 5HE
Fax: 0131-557 5837   Tel: 0131-557 5840

LOWE LINTAS
Bowater House
68-114 Knightsbridge
London SW1X 7LT
Fax: 020-7584 9557   Tel: 020-7584 5033

McCABES
36 Lexington Street
London W1F 0LJ
e-mail: theatre@mccabes.co.uk
Fax: 020-7412 2020   Tel: 020-7412 2000

McCANN-ERICKSON ADVERTISING Ltd
7 Herbrand Street
London WC1N 1EX   Tel: 020-7837 3737

MEDIACOM
180 North Gower Street
London NW1 2NB
Fax: 020-7874 5999   Tel: 020-7874 5500

MOUNTAIN VIEW Ltd
279 Tottenham Court Road
London W1T 7RJ
Fax: 020-7670 3672   Tel: 020-7670 3670

MUSTOE MERRIMAN HERRING LEVY
133 Long Acre
Covent Garden
London WC2E 9AG
Fax: 020-7379 8487   Tel: 020-7379 9999

OGILVY & MATHER Ltd
10 Cabot Square
Canary Wharf
London E14 4QB
Fax: 020-7345 9000   Tel: 020-7345 3000

PARTNERS BDDH
Cupola House
London WC1E 7EB
Fax: 020-7467 9210   Tel: 020-7467 9200

PUBLICIS Ltd
82 Baker Street
London W1U 2AE
Fax: 020-7487 5351   Tel: 020-7935 4426

RAINEY KELLY CAMPBELL ROALFE YR
Greater London House
Hampstead Road
London NW1 7QP
Fax: 020-7611 6011   Tel: 020-7404 2700

RED CELL ADVERTISING Ltd
4 Flitcroft Street
London WC2H 8TB
Fax: 020-7240 9094   Tel: 020-7240 4949

RICHMOND TOWERS Ltd
26 Fitzroy Square
London W1T 6BT
Fax: 020-7388 7761   Tel: 020-7388 7421

ROOSE & PARTNERS
Holborn Hall
100 Gray's Inn Road
London WC1X 8AU
Fax: 020-7831 8761   Tel: 020-7831 7400

RPM 3
William Blake House
8 Marshall Street
London W1V 2AJ
Fax: 020-7439 8884   Tel: 020-7434 4343

SAATCHI & SAATCHI
80 Charlotte Street
London W1A 1AQ
Fax: 020-7637 8489   Tel: 020-7636 5060

SMEE'S ADVERTISING Ltd
3-5 Duke Street
Manchester Square
London W1M 6BA
Fax: 020-7935 8588   Tel: 020-7486 6644

SWK & PARTNERS Ltd
52-54 Broadwick Street
London W1F 7AQ
Fax: 020-7534 0808   Tel: 020-7534 0800

TBWA/GGT DIRECT
82 Dean Street
London W1D 3HA
Fax: 020-7434 2925   Tel: 020-7439 4282

TBWA LONDON
76-80 Whitfield Street
London W1T 4EZ
Fax: 020-7573 6667   Tel: 020-7573 6666

THEATRE DESPATCH Ltd
Azof Hall
Azof Street
London SE10 0EG
e-mail: info@theatre.org
Fax: 08700 525915   Tel: 020-8853 0750

THOMPSON J Walter CO Ltd
40 Berkeley Square
London W1J 5AL
e-mail: firstname.lastname@jwt.com
Fax: 020-7493 8432   Tel: 020-7499 4040

TMP WORLDWIDE
Chancery House
53-64 Chancery Lane
London WC2A 1QS   Tel: 020-7406 5000

TV MANAGEMENTS
Brink House
Avon Castle
Ringwood
Hants BH24 2BL   Tel: 01425 475544

WCRS
5 Golden Square
London W1F 9BS
Fax: 020-7806 5099   Tel: 020-7806 5000

YOUNG & RUBICAM Ltd
Greater London House
Hampstead Road
London NW1 7QP
Fax: 020-7611 6570   Tel: 020-7387 9366

Key to areas of specialization:
C Cabaret **F** Films **G** General **M** Musicals
Md Models **PM** Personal Managers **S** Singing
TV Television **V** Variety

For information regarding membership of the Personal Managers' Association please contact:

Personal Managers' Association Ltd
Rivercroft, 1 Summer Road
East Molesey, Surrey KT8 9LX
Tel: 020-8398 9796

* Denotes PMA Membership

1984 PERSONAL MANAGEMENT Ltd
Suite 508, Davina House
137 Goswell Road
London EC1V 7ET
Fax: 020-7250 3031   Tel: 020-7251 8046

1st FRAMEWORK
Fulcrum
19 Great Guildford Street
London SE1 9EZ
Fax: 020-7803 0531   Tel: 020-7803 0530

21ST CENTURY ACTORS MANAGEMENT
Co-operative
E10 Panther House
38 Mount Pleasant
London WC1X 0AP
e-mail: twentyfirstcenturyactors@yahoo.co.uk
Fax: 020-7833 1158   Tel: 020-7278 3438

21ST CENTURY VAUX CASTING
The Corn Exchange
Fenwick Street, Liverpool L2 7QS
e-mail: 21stcenturyvaux@beeb.net
Fax: 0151-231 1068   Tel: 0151-258 1679

2MA-MAGEE MATTHEWS ASSOCIATES
Springvale, Tutland Road
North Baddesley Hampshire SO52 9FL
e-mail: mo@2ma.co.uk
Fax: 023-8074 1355   Tel: 023-8074 1354

41 MANAGEMENT*
4th Floor, 41 St Vincent Place, Glasgow G1 2ER
e-mail: agent@41management.co.uk
Fax: 0141-248 6307   Tel: 0141-248 3891

ABBOTT June ASSOCIATES
The Courtyard, 10 York Way
King's Cross, London N1 9AA
e-mail: juneabbott@courtyardtheatre.freeserve.co.uk
Fax: 020-7833 0870   Tel: 020-7837 7826

A & B PERSONAL MANAGEMENT Ltd*
PM Write
Paurelle House, 91 Regent Street
London W1B 4EL
e-mail: billellis@aandb.co.uk
Fax: 020-7734 6318   Tel: 020-7734 6047

ACB MANAGEMENT
Riverside Studios, Crisp Road
Hammersmith, London W6 9RL
e-mail: acbmanagement@aol.com
Fax: 020-8237 1001   Tel: 020-8237 1116

ACCESS ASSOCIATES
76 Compton Street, London EC1V 0BN
e-mail: access.ppc@virgin.net   Tel: 020-7689 5903

ACROBAT PRODUCTIONS
(Artists & Advisors)
The Circus Space, Coronet Street
London N1 6HD
e-mail: info@acrobatproductions.co.uk
Tel: 020-7613 5259

ACT ONE DRAMA STUDIO & AGENCY
31 Dobbin Hill, Sheffield S11 7JA
e-mail: info@actonedrama.co.uk
Fax: 07971 112153　　　Tel: 0114-266 7209

ACT OUT AGENCY
22 Greek Street, Stockport
Cheshire SK3 8AB　　　Tel/Fax: 0161-429 7413

ACTING ASSOCIATES
PM
71 Hartham Road, London N7 9JJ
e-mail: fiona@actingassociates.co.uk
Tel/Fax: 020-7607 3562

ACTING UP NORTH
4 Hillcrest, Monk Fryston
Leeds LS25 5EX　　　Tel/Fax: 01977 681348

ACTIVATE DRAMA SCHOOL
Priestman Cottage, Sea View Road
Sunderland SR2 7UP
e-mail: activate_agcy@hotmail.com
Fax: 0191-551 2051　　　Tel: 0191-565 2345

ACTORS AGENCY
1 Glen Street, Tollcross, Edinburgh EH3 9JD
Fax: 0131-228 4645　　　Tel: 0131-228 4040

ACTORS ALLIANCE
Co-operative
Bon Marché Centre
241-251 Ferndale Road, London SW9 8BJ
e-mail: actors@actorsalliance.fsnet.co.uk
Tel/Fax: 020-7326 0070

ACTOR'S CREATIVE TEAM
Room 9, Albany House
82-84 South End
Croydon CR0 1DQ　　　Tel: 020-8239 8892

ACTORS DIRECT Ltd
Gainsborough House
109 Portland Street
Manchester M1 6DN
Fax: 0161-237 9993　　　Tel: 0161-237 1904

ACTORS FILE The
PM Co-operative
Spitfire Studios, 63-71 Collier Street
London N1 9BE
e-mail: mail@theactorsfile.co.uk
Fax: 020-7278 0364　　　Tel: 020-7278 0087

ACTORS' GROUP The (TAG)
PM
4 Newton Street, Piccadilly
Manchester M1 2AW
e-mail: agent@tagactors.co.uk
Fax: 0161-236 6935　　　Tel: 0161-228 0771

ACTORS IN SCANDINAVIA
Vuorimiehenkatu 20D
00150 Helsinki, Finland
e-mail: lauram@actors.fi
Fax: 00 358 9 68 404 422　　　Tel: 00 358 9 68 40440

Brannkyvhog 39
Stockholm, Sweden 11822

ACTORS INTERNATIONAL Ltd
Conway Hall, 25 Red Lion Square
London WC1R 4RL
e-mail: actors-international@talk21.com
Fax: 020-7831 8319　　　Tel: 020-7242 9300

ACTORS LIST The
Half Moon Chambers, Chapel Walks
Manchester M2 1HN
e-mail: elizabeth@actorslist.co.uk
Fax: 0161-832 5219   Tel: 0161-833 1605

ACTORUM Ltd
PM Co-operative
3rd Floor, 21 Foley Street
London W1W 6DR
e-mail: actorum2@ukonline.co.uk
Fax: 020-7636 6975   Tel: 020-7636 6978

AFFINITY MANAGEMENT
North Lodge, Highgate Green
Forest Row, East Sussex RH18 5AS
e-mail: crbird@2310@mistral.co.uk
                                    Tel: 01342 822685

AGENCY The
(Teri Hayden)
47 Adelaide Road, Dublin 2, Eire
e-mail: theagency@oceanfree.net
Fax: 00 353 1 6760052   Tel: 00 353 1 6618535

AIM (ASSOCIATED INTERNATIONAL MANAGEMENT)*
Nederlander House, 7 Great Russell Street
London WC1B 3NH
e-mail: info@aim.demon.co.uk
Fax: 020-7637 8666   Tel: 020-7637 1700

AIR-O-BATS
Acrobatic & Aerial Agency
84 Laburnum Avenue, Hornchurch
Essex RM12 4HA
e-mail: kda@air-o-bats.com
                                    Tel/Fax: 01708 705601

A & J MANAGEMENT
551 Green Lanes, London N13 4DR
e-mail: ajmanagement@bigfoot.com
Fax: 020-8882 5983   Tel: 020-8882 7716

ALANDER AGENCY
TV F S V
135 Merrion Avenue, Stanmore
Middlesex HA7 4RZ   Tel: 020-8954 7685

ALEXANDER PERSONAL MANAGEMENT Ltd
16 Roughdown Avenue
Hemel Hempstead
Herts HP3 9BH
e-mail: apm@onetel.net.uk
Fax: 01442 241099   Tel: 01442 252907

ALEXANDER Suzanne MANAGEMENT
London Road Business Centre
Suite 3:2, 106 London Road, Liverpool L3 5JY
e-mail: suzyalex@hotmail.com
                    Tel/Fax: 0151-608 9655

ALEXANDER'S
13 Rushcliffe Rise, Sherwood
Nottingham NG5 3HJ
e-mail: alexander's@wash-pit.demon.co.uk
Fax: 0115-840 7498   Tel: 0115-840 0354

ALL STAR SPEAKERS
100 Farm Lane, Fulham, London SW6 1QH
e-mail: laura@allstarspeakers.co.uk
Fax: 020-7385 6647   Tel: 020-7381 4693

ALLGOOD ASSOCIATES
Norris House, 46 De Vere Gardens
Cranbrook Ilford, Essex IG1 3ED
Fax: 020-8554 9322   Tel: 020-8554 5080

ALLSORTS
(Drama for Children)
(Sasha Leslie, Melissa Healy)
2 Pember Road, London NW10 5LP
e-mail: enquiries@allsorts.ltd.uk
                    Tel/Fax: 020-8969 3249

ALLSORTS THE AGENCY Ltd
1 Cathedral Street, London SE1 9DE
Fax: 020-7403 1656   Tel: 020-7403 4834

ALPHA PERSONAL MANAGEMENT Ltd
PM Co-operative
Studio B4, 3 Bradbury Street
London N16 8JN
e-mail: alphamanagement3@aol.com
Fax: 020-7241 2410   Tel: 020-7241 0077

ALRAUN Anita REPRESENTATION*
5th Floor, 28 Charing Cross Road
London WC2H 0DB
e-mail: anita@cjagency.demon.co.uk
Fax: 020-7379 6865   Tel: 020-7379 6840

ALTARAS Jonathan ASSOCIATES Ltd*
2nd Floor
13 Short's Gardens
London WC2H 9AT
e-mail: helen@jaa.ndirect.co.uk
Fax: 020-7836 6066   Tel: 020-7836 8722

ALVAREZ MANAGEMENT
86 Muswell Road, London N10 2BE
e-mail: sga@alvarezmanagement.fsnet.co.uk
Fax: 020-8444 2646   Tel:020-8883 2206

A L W ASSOCIATES
70 Mildmay Road, London N1 4NG
e-mail: alweurope@freeuk.com
Fax: 020-7254 0093   Tel: 020-7923 0027

AMBER PERSONAL MANAGEMENT Ltd
PM
28 St Margaret's Chambers
5 Newton Street
Manchester M1 1HL
e-mail: info@amberltd.co.uk
Fax: 0161-228 0235   Tel: 0161-228 0236

189 Wardour Street, London W1F 8ZD
Fax: 020-7734 9883   Tel: 020-7734 7887

AMOR REEVES MANAGEMENT
Bouverie House, 43A Effra Road, Wimbledon,
London SW19 8PS
Fax: 020-8543 1973   Tel: 020-8543 1999

ANA (Actors Network Agency)
PM Co-operative
55 Lambeth Walk
London SE11 6DX
e-mail: info@ana-actors.co.uk
Fax: 020-7735 8177   Tel: 020-7735 0999

ANDERSSEN'S
4 Rothmans Avenue
Chelmsford CM2 9UE   Tel/Fax: 01245 476187

ANDREW'S MANAGEMENT
203 Links Road
London SW17 9EP
e-mail: atj@andrewsman.fsnet.co.uk
Fax: 020-8677 8973   Tel: 020-8769 7416

ANGEL Susan & FRANCIS Kevin Ltd*
Write, no e-mails
1st Floor, 12 D'Arblay Street
London W1F 8DU
e-mail: angelpair@freeuk.com
Fax: 020-7437 1712   Tel: 020-7439 3086

ANGLO-CARIBBEAN PRODUCTIONS Ltd
1A Gambole Road
Tooting Broadway
London SW17 0QJ
e-mail: jasonyoung72@yahoo.com
Fax: 020-8801 7592   Tel: 07970 715080

ANOTHER FACE
48 Dean Street
London W1V 5HL
e-mail: info@anotherface.com
Fax: 020-7494 3300   Tel: 020-7287 1223

A.P.M. ASSOCIATES (Linda French)
(See ALEXANDER PERSONAL MANAGEMENT Ltd)

ARAENA/COLLECTIVE
10 Bramshaw Gardens,
South Oxhey
Herts WD1 6XP
e-mail: patricia@araena.watford.net
                    Tel/Fax: 020-8428 0037

ARCH CREATIVE MANAGEMENT Ltd
4, 2 St Stephen's Crescent
London W2 5QT
e-mail: md@arch123.com
                    Tel/Fax: 020-7727 2910

ARENA ENTERTAINMENT ORGANISATION
(Corporate Entertainment)
Regent's Court
39 Harrogate Road
Leeds LS7 3PD
e-mail: stars@arenaentertainments.co.uk
Fax: 0113-239 2016   Tel: 0113-239 2222

ARENA PERSONAL MANAGEMENT Ltd
Co-operative
Room 11, East Block
Panther House
38 Mount Pleasant
London WC1X 0AP
e-mail: arenapm@netscapeonline.co.uk
                    Tel/Fax: 020-7278 1661

A R G
4 Great Portland Street
London W1W 8PA
Fax: 020-7436 6700   Tel: 020-7436 6400

ARGYLE ASSOCIATES
PM (Richard Linford) (No Unsolicited Mail)
86 Goswell Road
London EC1V 7DB
e-mail: argyle.associates@virgin.net
Fax: 020-7608 1642   Tel: 020-7608 2095

ARLINGTON ENTERPRISES Ltd
1-3 Charlotte Street
London W1T 1RD
e-mail: arlington-enterprises.co.uk
Fax: 020-7580 4994   Tel: 020-7580 0702

ARRAN ASSOCIATES
112 Mount Pleasant
London EN4 9HQ
e-mail: arranassoc@netscapeonline.co.uk
Fax: 020-8447 3957   Tel: 020-8441 7348

ARTISTS INDEPENDENT NETWORK
32 Tavistock Street
London WC2E 7PB
Fax: 020-7240 9029   Tel: 020-7257 8725

Alan Cumming

Caroline Quentin

ARTS MANAGEMENT
Redroofs, Littlewick Green
Maidenhead, Berks
Fax: 01628 822461   Tel: 01628 822982

**ARTSWORLD INTERNATIONAL
MANAGEMENT Ltd**
PO Box 13759
London W2 6FG
e-mail: bob@artsworld.freeserve.co.uk
Fax: 020-7262 1459   Tel: 020-7262 1500

ASH PERSONAL MANAGEMENT
8 Valley Road, Streatham
London SW16 2XN
e-mail: ashpersonalmgmt@hotmail.com
                         Tel/Fax: 020-8677 6171

ASHCROFT Sharron MANAGEMENT Ltd
Suite D450, Dean Clough
Halifax HX3 5AX
e-mail: info@sharronashcroft.co.uk
Fax: 01422 343417   Tel: 01422 343949

ASHDOWN ASSOCIATES
Crescent Arts Centre
2-4 University Road
Belfast BT7 1NH
e-mail: ashdown.cbn.@artservicesireland.com
                         Tel/Fax: 028-9024 8861

ASQUITH & HORNER
PM Write SAE
The Studio, 14 College Road
Bromley, Kent BR1 3NS
Fax: 020-8313 0443   Tel: 020-8466 5580

Paul Blackthorne

Martiné McCutcheon

A

ASSOCIATED ARTS
(Non-Acting)
8 Shrewsbury Lane, London SE18 3JF
e-mail: karen@associated-arts.co.uk
Fax: 020-8856 8189　　Tel: 020-8856 4958

ASSOCIATED SPEAKERS
(Lecturers & Celebrity Speakers)
24A Park Road, Hayes
Middlesex UB4 8JN　　Tel: 020-8848 9048

AST MANAGEMENT
PM
Anna Scher Theatre,
70-72 Barnsbury Road
London N1 0ES
e-mail: theagency@annaschermanagement.fsnet.co.uk
Fax: 020-7833 9467　　Tel: 020-7278 2101

ATS CASTING Ltd
26 St Michaels Road, Leeds LS6 3AW
Fax: 0113-275 6422　　Tel: 0113-230 4300

AVALON MANAGEMENT GROUP Ltd
4A Exmoor Street, London W10 6BD
Fax: 020-7598 7300　　Tel: 020-7598 8000

AVENUE ARTISTES Ltd
C G TV
8 Winn Road, Southampton SO17 1EN
Fax: 023-8090 5703　　Tel: 023-8055 1000

AWA - ANDREA WILDER AGENCY
23 Cambrian Drive, Colwyn Bay
Conwy LL28 4SL
e-mail: casting@awagency.co.uk
Fax: 07092 249314　　Tel: 01492 547542

AXIS MUSIC PRODUCTIONS
(Composers of Music for Film & TV)
6 Linley Court, Rouse Gardens
London SE21 8AQ
e-mail: axis@axismusic.co.uk
Fax: 07932 033182　　Tel: 020-8670 6710

AXM
Actors' Exchange Management
PM Co-operative
206 Great Guildford Business Square
30 Great Guildford Street, London SE1 0HS
e-mail: info@axmgt.com
Fax: 020-7261 0408　　Tel: 020-7261 0400

AZA ARTISTES
(Existing Clients only)
652 Finchley Road
London NW11 7NT　　Tel: 020-8458 7288

BₐK MANAGEMENT
30 Spedan Close, Branch Hill,
Hampstead, London NW3 7XF
e-mail: bkmanagement@aol.com
　　　　　　Tel/Fax: 020-7794 8980

BALLROOM, LONDON THEATRE OF
(Ballroom/Social Dancers for Film/TV/Theatre)
24 Ovett Close, Upper Norwood
London SE19 3RX
e-mail: paulharrisdance@hotmail.com
Mobile: 07958 784462　　Tel: 020-8771 4274

B A M ASSOCIATES
1st Floor
41 Bloomfield Road
Bristol BS4 3QA
e-mail: bamassociates@aol.com
　　　　　　Tel/Fax: 0117-971 0636

BARKER Gavin ASSOCIATES Ltd*
(Gavin Barker, Michelle Burke)
2D Wimpole Street, London W1G 0EB
e-mail: gbarker@dircon.co.uk
Fax: 020-7499 3777　　Tel: 020-7499 4777

B.A.S.I.C./JD AGENCY
C V S
3 Rushden House
Tatlow Road, Glenfield
Leicester LE3 8ND   Tel/Fax: 0116-287 9594

BECKER Paul Ltd
61 Portobello Road, London W11 3DB
e-mail: info@paulbeckerltd.com
Fax: 020-7221 5030   Tel: 020-7221 3050

BELFRAGE Julian ASSOCIATES
46 Albemarle Street, London W1S 4DF
Fax: 020-7493 5460   Tel: 020-7491 4400

BENJAMIN Audrey AGENCY
278A Elgin Avenue, Maida Vale
London W9 1JR
e-mail: aud@elginavenue.fsbusiness.co.uk
Fax: 020-7266 5480   Tel: 020-7289 7180

BETTS Jorg ASSOCIATES
4th Floor, The Linen Hall,
162-168 Regent Street
London W1B 5TE
e-mail: jorgbetts@aol.com
Fax: 020-7306 3251   Tel: 020-7306 3250

BEXFIELD Glenn PERSONAL MANAGEMENT
Friese-Greene House
15-17 Middle Street
Brighton Media Centre
Brighton BN1 1AL
Fax: 01273 201118   Tel: 01273 201104

BIDDY & BUZZ Ltd
20 Buckthorn House
Longlands Road
Sidcup, Kent DA15 7NA   Tel/Fax: 020-8300 4313

BIG AGENCY The
Chequers
Station Road, Petworth
West Sussex GU28 0ES
e-mail: gib@gibenterprises.com
Fax: 01798 343611   Mobile: 07776 195357

BILL & CHRISTIAN @JB AGENCY
7 Stonehills Mansions
8 Streatham High Road
London SW16 1DD
e-mail: enquiries@jbagency.freeserve.co.uk
Fax: 020-8769 9567   Tel: 020-8677 7202

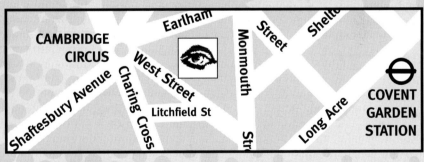
21

BILLBOARD PERSONAL MANAGEMENT
Co-operative
The Co-op Centre
11 Mowll Street
London SW9 6BG
e-mail: billboardpm@easynet.co.uk
Fax: 020-7793 0426   Tel: 020-7735 9956

BIRD AGENCY
(Personal Performance Management)
Birkbeck Centre, Birkbeck Road, Sidcup
Kent DA14 4DE
Fax: 020-8308 1370   Tel: 020-8309 7068

BLACKBURN Debra MANAGEMENT
Oak Lodge Studio
Arkley Lane, Arkley
Herts EN5 3JR
e-mail: dbm2@freeuk.com
Fax: 020-8440 7674   Tel: 020-8440 4532

BLACKBURN SACHS ASSOCIATES
88-90 Crawford Street
London W1H 2BS
e-mail: presenters@blackburnsachsassociates.com
Fax: 020-7258 6162   Tel: 020-7258 6158

B L A MANAGEMENT
(Children & Young Adults)
Performance House, 20 Passey Place
Eltham, London SE9 5DQ
e-mail: bla@dircon.co.uk
Fax: 020-8850 9944   Tel: 020-8850 9888

BLOND Rebecca ASSOCIATES
69A Kings Road, London SW3 4NX
e-mail: rebecca.blond@lineone.net
Fax: 020-7351 4600   Tel: 020-7351 4100

BLUE WAND PRODUCTIONS Ltd
PM TV F G
2nd Floor, 12 Weltje Road
London W6 9TG
e-mail: lino@bluewand.co.uk
Mobile: 07885 528743   Tel/Fax: 020-8741 20

BMA MODELS
The Stables, 5 Norcott Hall Barns, Norcott Hill
Berkhamsted, Herts HP4 1RB
e-mail: bmamodels@bmamodels.com
Fax: 01442 879879   Tel: 01442 878878

BODEN AGENCY
PM
6-12 Windmill Hill, Enfield, Middlesex EN2 6SA
e-mail: bodens2692@aol.com
Fax: 020-8367 1836   Tel: 020-8367 2692

BOOKERS UK
7 Green Avenue, Mill Hill
London NW7 4PX   Tel/Fax: 020-8201 1400

BOOKHOUSE GROUP The
2 Gill's Cottages, Rochester, Kent ME1 1BY
e-mail: mr.barnes@virgin.net
Tel/Fax: 01634 812672

BOSS MODEL MANAGEMENT Ltd
Half Moon Chambers, Chapel Walks
Manchester M2 1HN
e-mail: julie@bossagencies.co.uk
Fax: 0161-832 5219   Tel: 0161-834 3403

BOURNE Sheila MANAGEMENT*
14 Crown Road, Shoreham, Kent TN14 7TL
e-mail: sheila@bourne-uk.freeserve.co.uk
Fax: 01959 524529   Tel: 01959 524528

BOYCE Sandra MANAGEMENT*
1 Kingsway House, Albion Road
London N16 0TA
e-mail: info@sandraboyce.com
Fax: 020-7241 2313   Tel: 020-7923 0606

B.R. MANAGEMENT
7 Stonehills Mansions
8 Streatham High Road
London SW16 1DD
Fax: 020-8769 9567   Tel: 020-8677 9865

BRAIDMAN Michelle ASSOCIATES*
3rd Floor Suite
10-11 Lower John Street
London W1F 9EB
e-mail: info@braidman.com
Fax: 020-7439 3600   Tel: 020-7437 0817

BRAITHWAITE'S THEATRICAL AGENCY
8 Brookshill Avenue
Harrow Weald
Middlesex HA3 6RZ   Tel: 020-8954 5638

BREAK A LEG MANAGEMENT
Units 2/3 The Precinct
Packington Square
London N1
Fax: 020-8374 2008   Tel: 020-8341 3318

BRITT MANAGEMENT
59 Plains of Waterloo, Ramsgate
Kent CT11 8JE   Tel/Fax: 01843 850586

BROADCASTING COMPANY
Unit 23, Canalot Studios,
222 Kensal Road
London W10 5BN
Fax: 020-7460 5223   Tel: 020-7460 5222

BROOK Dolly AGENCY
PO Box 5436
Dunmow CM6 1WW
Fax: 01371 875996   Tel: 01371 875767

BROOK Valerie AGENCY
10 Sandringham Road
Cheadle Hulme, Cheshire SK8 5NH
Fax: 0161-488 4206   Tel: 0161-486 1631

BROOKS Claude ENTERTAINMENTS
1 Burlington Avenue
Slough, Berks SL1 2JY
Fax: 01753 520424   Tel: 01753 520717

BROOKS Neil MANAGEMENT
153 Rathgar Road
Rathgar, Dublin 6
e-mail: enquiries@neilbrooksmanagement.com
Fax: 00 353 1 496 6496   Tel: 00 353 1 496 6470

BROWN & SIMCOCKS*
PM Write
1 Bridgehouse Court
109 Blackfriars Road
London SE1 8HW
e-mail: barryandcarrie@lineone.net
Fax: 020-7928 1909   Tel: 020-7928 1229

BRUNSKILL MANAGEMENT Ltd*
PM M S TV Write
Suite 8A, 169 Queen's Gate
London SW7 5HE
e-mail: contact@brunskill.com
Fax: 020-7589 9460   Tel: 020-7581 3388

The Courtyard, Edenhall, Penrith,
Cumbria CA11 8ST
Fax: 01768 881850   Tel: 01768 881430

BSA Ltd
(See HARRISON Penny BSA Ltd)

BERWICK KALER

RICHARD WILSON FOR 'SHELTER'

MADELEINE HOWARD

LUKE KELLY PHOTOGRAPHY

222 St. Leonard's Road,
East Sheen,
London, SW14 7BN

TEL: 020-8878 2823

BURDETT-COUTTS ASSOCIATES*
Riverside Studios, Crisp Road
London W6 9RL
e-mail: agentcoutts@mac.com
Fax: 020-8748 0430   Tel: 020-8563 1040

BURKEMAN Brie*
14 Neville Court, Abbey Road
London NW8 9DD
e-mail: brie.burkeman@mail.com
Fax: 0709 2239111   Tel: 0709 2239113

BURNETT GRANGER ASSOCIATES*
(Barry Burnett, Lindsay Granger)
Prince of Wales Theatre
31 Coventry Street
London W1D 6AS
Fax: 020-7839 0438   Tel: 020-7839 0202

BURT Ben ASSOCIATES (BBA)
187 Wardour Street
London W1F 8ZD
e-mail: ben@benburtassociates.fsnet.co.uk
                    Tel/Fax: 020-7434 2802

C.A. ARTISTES MANAGEMENT
Md Featured Commercials
153 Battersea Rise
London SW11 1HP
e-mail: casting@caartistes.com
Fax: 020-7924 2334   Tel: 020-7223 7827

CADS MANAGEMENT
48 Lightwoods Hill, Smethwick,
West Midlands B67 5EB
e-mail: admin@cadsmanagement.co.uk
Fax: 0121-434 4909   Tel: 0121-420 1996

CAIRNS AGENCY The
Dalziel House, Garden Flat
7 Claremont Terrace, Glasgow G3 7XR
e-mail: the_cairns_agency@yahoo.com
Fax: 0141-353 6385   Tel: 0141-331 2519

C.A.L.S. CASTING
(Children & Teenagers)
Unit E2, Bellevale Shopping Centre
Liverpool L25 2RG
Mobile: 07930 889057   Tel/Fax: 0151-487 8500

CAM
PM Write
19 Denmark Street, London WC2H 8NA
e-mail: info@cam.co.uk
Fax: 020-7240 7384   Tel: 020-7497 0448

CAMBELL JEFFREY MANAGEMENT
(Set, Costume, Lighting Designers)
11A Greystone Court,
South Street, Eastbourne BN21 4LP
e-mail: cambell@theatricaldesigners.co.uk
Fax: 01323 411373   Tel: 01323 411444

CAMPBELL Alison MODEL & PROMOTION AGENCY
381 Beersbridge Road, Belfast BT5 5DT
e-mail: alison.campbell@dnet.co.uk
Fax: 028-9080 9808   Tel: 028-9080 9809

CAMPBELL ASSOCIATES
Campbell Park, Fernhurst Road,
Milland, Nr Liphook, Hants GU30 7LU
e-mail: campbellassociates@btinternet.com
Fax: 01428 741648   Tel: 01428 741005

2 Chelsea Cloisters,
Sloane Avenue, Chelsea, London SW3 3DW
Fax: 020-7584 8799   Tel: 020-7584 5586

Sam Kindred

Annette Badland

DAVID HATTON
PHOTOGRAPHY

Tel 020 8506 0514

CAPITAL ARTS THEATRICAL AGENCY
Wyllyotts Centre, Darkes Lane
Potters Bar, Herts EN6 2HN
e-mail: capitalartstheatre@genie.co.uk
Mobile: 07885 232414   Tel/Fax: 020-8449 2342

CAPITAL VOICES
(Anne Skates. Session Singers, Studio,
Stage & TV)
Brook House, 8 Rythe Road
Claygate, Surrey KT10 9DF
e-mail: capvox@aol.com
Fax: 01372 466229   Tel: 01372 466228

CARDIFF CASTING
Co-operative Actors Management
Chapter Arts Centre, Market Road
Cardiff CF5 1QE
e-mail: admin@cardiffcasting.co.uk
Fax: 029-2023 3380   Tel: 029-2023 3321

CAREY Roger ASSOCIATES*
PM
7 St George's Square, London SW1V 2HX
e-mail: rogercarey@freeuk.com
Fax: 020-7630 0029   Tel: 020-7630 6301

CAROUSEL ENTERTAINMENT & EVENT MANAGEMENT
(Acts for Corporate & Private Events)
18 Westbury Lodge Close, Pinner
Middlesex HA5 3FG
e-mail: acts@carouselentertainments.co.uk
Fax: 020-8933 1614   Tel: 020-8866 8816

CARTEURS
170A Church Road, Hove, East Sussex BN3 2DJ
Fax: 01273 770444   Tel: 01273 770445

Alfie Turco

BLACK & WHITE CASTING PHOTOGRAPHS READY WHILE YOU WAIT NO APPOINTMENT

PASSPORT PHOTO SERVICE
449 OXFORD STREET, LONDON, W.1
Telephone: 020-7629 8540
Opposite Selfridges   Est 1953

CASAROTTO MARSH Ltd
(Film Technicians)
National House
60-66 Wardour Street
London W1V 4ND
e-mail: casarottomarsh@casarotto.uk.com
Fax: 020-7287 5644   Tel: 020-7287 4450

CASAROTTO RAMSAY & ASSOCIATES Ltd*
(Writers, Directors, Producers)
National House
60-66 Wardour Street
London W1V 4ND
e-mail: agents@casarotto.uk.com
Fax: 020-7287 9128   Tel: 020-7287 4450

CASTAWAY ACTORS AGENCY
30-31 Wicklow Street
Dublin 2, Ireland
e-mail: castaway@clubi.ie
Fax: 00 353 1 6719133   Tel: 00 353 1 6719264

CASTCALL & CASTFAX
(Casting & Consultancy Service)
106 Wilsden Avenue,
Luton LU1 5HR
e-mail: casting@castcall.co.uk
Fax: 01582 480736   Tel: 01582 456213

CASTING BOOK The
Suite C4, Maidstone Business Centre
St Peter Street, Maidstone
Kent ME16 0ST
Fax: 01622 662990   Tel: 01622 765700

CASTING COUCH PRODUCTIONS Ltd
Canalot Production Studios
222 Kensal Road, London W10 5BN
e-mail: moiratownsend@yahoo.co.uk
Fax: 020-8208 2373   Tel: 020-8438 9679

CASTING DEPARTMENT The
10 Tiverton Road
London NW10 3HL
Fax: 020-8960 0410   Tel: 020-8960 0055

CASTWEB
7 St Lukes Avenue, London SW4 7LG
e-mail: castweb@netcomuk.co.uk
Fax: 020-7720 2879   Tel: 020-7720 9002

C B A INTERNATIONAL (CINDY BRACE)
166 Waverley Avenue
Twickenham TW2 6DL

31 rue Milton, 75009 Paris, France
e-mail: c_b_a@club-internet.fr
Fax: 33 148-74 51 42   Tel: 33 145 26 33 42

C C A MANAGEMENT*
PM Write (Actors and Technicians)
7 St George's Square
London SW1V 2HX
e-mail: ccamanagement@btclick.com
Fax: 020-7630 7376   Tel: 020-7630 6303

CCM
Co-operative
Panther House, 38 Mount Pleasant
London WC1X 0AP
e-mail: ccmaa@bigfoot.com
Fax: 020-7813 3103   Tel: 020-7278 0507

CDA
(See DAWSON Caroline ASSOCIATES)

CELEBRITY GROUP Ltd The
12 Nottingham Place
London W1M 3FA
e-mail: info@celebrity.co.uk
Fax: 020-7224 6060   Tel: 020-7224 5050

A

Roz Allibone

Photographic Portraits

020 8940 4390
Kew, Surrey

See my online portfolio at
www.rozallibone.com

PEARLY KING & QUEEN
01245~476187

CELEX CASTING
(Anne Sweeting)
11 Glencroft Drive, Stenson Fields
Derby DE24 3LS
e-mail: anne@celex.co.uk
Fax: 01332 232115   Tel: 01332 232445

CENTRAL AGENCY The
PM
112 Gunnersbury Avenue, London W5 4HB
e-mail: info@dorm.co.uk
Fax: 020-8992 9993   Tel: 020-8993 7441

CENTRAL LINE
PM Co-operative
11 East Circus Street, Nottingham NG1 5AF
e-mail: mailact@the-central-line.co.uk
Fax: 0115-950 8087   Tel: 0115-941 2937

CENTRE STAGE AGENCY*
7 Rutle
Circular Road
Dublin 8
e-mail: geraldinecenterstage@eircom.net
                    Tel/Fax: 00 353 1 4533599

CFA MANAGEMENT
East Trevelmond Farm
Trevelmond
Liskeard
Cornwall PL14 4LY
e-mail: frances@cornwall-film-agency.fsnet.co.uk
                    Tel/Fax: 01579 321858

CHANCE David A. ASSOCIATES
(See CINEL GABRAN MANAGEMENT)

Campbell Associates
Personal Management & Representation

Audrey Campbell
Jackie Williamson
Michelle Holmes

Campbell Park, Fernhurst Road, Milland, Nr Liphook GU30 7LU
Phone 01428 741005   Fax 01428 741648

London
2 Chelsea Cloisters, Sloane Avenue, Chelsea SW3 3DW
Phone 020 7584 5586   Fax 020 7584 8799
email: CampbellAssociates@btinternet.com

Member of the Agent's Association (Great Britain)

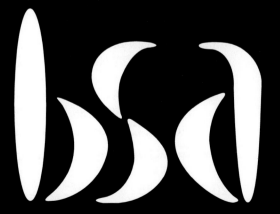

Heather Peace

Steve McFadden

Nicola Blackman

Claire Grogan
P h o t o g r a p h y

020 7272 1845

mobile 07932 635381
www.clairegrogan.co.uk
student rates

CHAPMAN AGENCY
The Link Building, Paradise Place
Birmingham B3 3HJ
e-mail: chapman@bssd.ac.uk
Fax: 0121-262 6801   Tel: 0121-262 6807

CHARLESWORTH Peter & ASSOCIATES
68 Old Brompton Road, London SW7 3LQ
Fax: 020-7589 2922   Tel: 020-7581 2478

CHARLIE COHEN MAYER
(UK and LA Talent Agency)
(Incorporating Ovitz International)
PM
121 Brecknock Road
London N19 5AE   Tel: 020-8883 4937

CHATTO & LINNIT Ltd
123A Kings Road
London SW3 4PL
Fax: 020-7352 3450   Tel: 020-7352 7722

CHURCHILL Hetty PERSONAL MANAGEMENT
Unit 306
30 Great Guildford Street
London SE1 0HS
Fax: 020-7401 3737   Tel: 020-7928 9229

CINEL GABRAN MANAGEMENT
1 Velindre Road, Whitchurch
Cardiff CF14 2TE
e-mail: enquiries@cinelgabran.co.uk
          Tel/Fax: 029-2062 0433

CIRCUIT PERSONAL MANAGEMENT Ltd
Suite 71 S.E.C., Bedford Street, Shelton
Stoke-on-Trent, Staffs ST1 4PZ
e-mail: mail@circuitpm.co.uk
Fax: 01782 264200   Tel: 01782 285388

CITY ACTORS' MANAGEMENT Ltd
PM Co-operative
24 Rivington Street
London EC2A 3DU
e-mail: info@city-actors.freeserve.co.uk
Fax: 020-7613 2656   Tel: 020-7613 2636

CITY LITES
(Performing Arts School & Casting Agency)
PO Box 29673, London E8 3FH
Mobile: 07773 865025   Tel/Fax: 020-7683 9016

C.K.K. ENTERTAINMENT
PO Box 24550, London E17 9FG
e-mail: ckk.entertainment@virgin.net
Fax: 020-8923 0983   Tel: 020-8923 0977

CLAPPERBOARD CASTING
PO Box 153, Manchester M7 4YU
Fax: 0161-792 4285   Tel: 0161-792 2277

CLARKE Jean MANAGEMENT
International House, 223 Regent Street
London W1R 7DB
Fax: 020-7495 7742   Tel: 020-7495 2424

CLARKE Rose MANAGEMENT
PO Box 23722, 3-4 Bramham Gardens
Kensington, London SW5 0WX
e-mail: roseclarkemanagement@hotmail.com
          Tel/Fax: 020-8856 2536

CLASS ACT
11 Thorn Road, Boundstone, Farnham
Surrey GU10 4TU
e-mail: classact93@hotmail.com
          Tel/Fax: 01252 792078

CLAYPOLE MANAGEMENT
PO Box 29853, Wimbledon, London SW19 7WS
e-mail: claypole_1@hotmail.com
Fax: 08701 334784   Tel: 020-8286 1171

HOBSON'S
[actors]

HOBSON'S INTERNATIONAL • **ACTORS** • KIDS • SINGERS • STUDIO • VOICES

62 Chiswick High Road	**T.** +44 (0) 20 8747 8326	**email** actors@hobsons-international.com
London W4 1SY	**F.** +44 (0) 20 8742 2237	**www** hobsons-international.com

Nyland management

20 School Lane, Heaton Chapel, Stockport SK4 5DG
Tel: 0161 442 2224 Fax: 0161 432 5406
e-mail: nylandmgmt@freenet.co.uk

CLOUD NINE AGENCY
96 Tiber Gardens, Treaty Street
London N1 0XE
e-mail: cloudnineagency@ic24.net
Tel/Fax: 020-7278 0029

CMA (COULTER MANAGEMENT AGENCY)
(Anne Coulter)
74 Victoria Crescent Road
Glasgow G12 9JN
e-mail: cmaglasgow@aol.com
Fax: 0141-579 4700   Tel: 0141-579 1400

CMP MANAGEMENT
Tandy House, 30-40 Dalling Road
London W6 0JB
e-mail: c.price@btclick.com
Fax: 020-8741 1786   Tel: 020-8741 3400

COCHRANE Elspeth PERSONAL MANAGEMENT*
PM
14/2, 2nd Floor, South Bank Commercial Centre
140 Battersea Park Road, London SW11 4NB
e-mail: elspeth@elspethcochrane.co.uk
Fax: 020-7622 5815   Tel: 020-7622 0314

COLLINS Shane ASSOCIATES*
39-41 New Oxford Street, Bloomsbury
London WC1A 1BH
e-mail: shane_collins@lineone.net
Fax: 020-7836 9388   Tel: 020-7836 9377

COLLIS MANAGEMENT
182 Trevelyan Road, London SW17 9LW
e-mail: marilyn@collismanagement.co.uk
Fax: 020-8682 0973   Tel: 020-8767 0196

COMEDY CLUB
165 Peckham Rye, London SE15 3HZ
e-mail: comedyclub@cwcom.net
Fax: 020-7732 9292   Tel: 020-7732 3434

CONTI Italia AGENCY Ltd
S M TV F Write or Phone
23 Goswell Road, London EC1M 7AJ
e-mail: sca@italiaconti36.freeserve.co.uk
Fax: 020-7253 1430   Tel: 020-7336 6122

CONWAY Clive ASSOCIATES
32 Grove Street, Oxford OX2 7JT
e-mail: clive.conway@ntlworld.com
Fax: 01865 514409   Tel: 01865 514830

CONWAY VAN GELDER Ltd*
PM
3rd Floor, 18-21 Jermyn Street
London SW1Y 6HP
Fax: 020-7287 1940   Tel: 020-7287 0077

COOKE Howard ASSOCIATES*
19 Coulson Street, Chelsea
London SW3 3NA
e-mail: mail@hca1.co.uk
Fax: 020-7591 0155   Tel: 020-7591 0144

CORNER Clive ASSOCIATES
73 Gloucester Road, Hampton
Middlesex TW12 2UQ
e-mail: corner.assoc@cwcom.net
Fax: 020-8979 4983   Tel: 020-8287 2726

CORNISH Caroline MANAGEMENT Ltd
12 Shinfield Street, London W12 0HN
e-mail: carolinecornish@aol.com
Fax: 020-8743 7887   Tel: 020-8743 7337

COULSON Lou*
1st Floor, 37 Berwick Street, London W1F 8RS
Fax: 020-7439 7569   Tel: 020-7734 9633

CRAWFORDS
2 Conduit Street, London W1S 2XB
Fax: 020-7355 1084   Tel: 020-7629 6464

CREAM THEATRICAL AGENCY The
e-mail: neil@thecreamta.freeserve.co.uk
Fax: 0709 1214326   Tel: 0709 1213303

CREATIVE MEDIA INTERNATIONAL
PM Write
22 Kingsbury Avenue, Dunstable
Bedfordshire LU5 4PU   Tel/Fax: 01582 510869

CREDITS ACTORS AGENCY Ltd
29 Lorn Road, London SW9 0AB
e-mail: credits@actors29.freeserve.co.uk
Fax: 020-7274 5849   Tel: 020-7737 0735

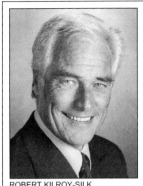

CRESCENT MANAGEMENT
PM Co-operative
10 Barley Mow Passage, Chiswick
London W4 4PH
e-mail: jennybenson@crescentmanagement.fsnet.co.uk
Fax: 020-8987 0207   Tel: 020-8987 0191

CROUCH ASSOCIATES*
PM Write
9-15 Neal Street, London WC2H 9PW
e-mail: crouchassocs@hotmail.com
Fax: 020-7379 1991   Tel: 020-7379 1684

CROUCH Sara MANAGEMENT
Suite 1, Ground Floor, 1 Duchess Street
London W1W 6AN
e-mail: saracrouch@btinternet.com
Fax: 020-7436 4627   Tel: 020-7436 4626

CROWD PULLERS
(Street Artistes)
158 Old Woolwich Road, Greenwich
London SE10 9PR
e-mail: jhole@crowdpullers.demon.co.uk
Fax: 020-8858 9045   Tel: 020-8305 0074

CRUICKSHANK Harriet*
(Directors, Designers, Choreographers)
97 Old South Lambeth Road
London SW8 1XU
Fax: 020-7820 1081   Tel: 020-7735 2933

CS EVENTS
21-37 Third Avenue, London E13 8AW
e-mail: email@csevents.co.uk
Fax: 020-8471 2111   Tel: 020-8471 3111

Lime

ACTORS AGENCY & MANAGEMENT LIMITED

T 0161 237 3300   F 0161 236 7557

54 Princess Street Manchester M1 6HS
Incorporating Manchesters most elite casting suites

C.S.A.
(Christina Shepherd Advertising)
13 Radnor Walk
London SW3 4BP
e-mail: csa@shepherdmanagement.co.uk
Fax: 020-7352 2277   Tel: 020-7352 2255

CSM (ARTISTES)
PM
St Dunstan's Hall, East Acton Lane
London W3 7EG
e-mail: carolecdleadact@aol.com
Fax: 020-8740 6542   Tel: 020-8743 9514

CURTIS BROWN GROUP Ltd*
(Actors, Producers, Directors, Set/Costume Designers)
Haymarket House, 28-29 Haymarket
London SW1Y 4SP
e-mail: cb@curtisbrown.co.uk
Fax: 020-7396 0110   Tel: 020-7396 6600

CYBER-ARTISTS 2000
In The Can Ltd, 20 Old Steine, Brighton BN1 1EL
e-mail: cyber@cyber.ndo.co.uk
                          Tel/Fax: 01273 671234

D Lisa MANAGEMENT Ltd
Unit 5, Gun Wharf, 241 Old Ford Road
London E3 5QB
e-mail: lisad@serez.co.uk
Fax: 020-8980 2211   Tel: 020-8980 0117

DALY David ASSOCIATES
586A Kings Road, London SW6 2DX
e-mail: daviddaly@associates16.freeserve.co.uk
Fax: 020-7610 9512   Tel: 020-7384 1036

DALY David ASSOCIATES (MANCHESTER)
(Clare Marshall)
16 King Street, Knutsford WA16 6DL
e-mail: claremarshall@daviddalyassociates.freeserve.co.uk
Fax: 01565 755334   Tel: 01565 631999

DALZELL & BERESFORD Ltd
26 Astwood Mews
London SW7 4DE
Fax: 020-7341 9412   Tel: 020-7341 9411

DANCERS
1 Charlotte Street, London W1T 1RD
e-mail: info@dancersagency.com
Fax: 020-7636 1657   Tel: 020-7636 1473

DARRELL Emma MANAGEMENT
(Producers, Directors & Existing Writers only)
North Vale, Shire Lane, Chorleywood
Herts WD3 5NH
e-mail: emma.mc@virgin.net
Fax: 01923 284064   Tel: 01923 284061

DAVID AGENCY The
F TV Md Write or Phone
153 Battersea Rise, London SW11 1HP
e-mail: casting@davidagency.net
Fax: 020-7924 2334   Tel: 020-7223 7720

DAVIS Dabber PRODUCTIONS
(Write or Phone)
24A Park Road, Hayes
Middlesex UB4 8JN   Tel: 020-8848 9048

DAVIS Lena, JOHN BISHOP ASSOCIATES
Cotton's Farmhouse, Whiston Road
Cogenhoe, Northants NN7 1NL
Fax: 01604 890405   Tel: 01604 891487

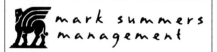

Anton Saunders

Inika Wright

David Potter
Photography

020 8442 0093
07973 579988

DAWSON Caroline ASSOCIATES*
19 Sydney Mews
London SW3 6HL
e-mail: cda@cdalondon.com
Fax: 020-7589 4800   Tel: 020-7581 8111

DEALERS AGENCY BELFAST
85 Rosebery Road
Belfast BT6 8JB
e-mail: dealers@dnet.co.uk
Mobile: 07702 183299   Tel/Fax: 028-9046 0381

DENMAN CASTING AGENCY
Burgess House
Main Street, Farnsfield
Notts NG22 8EF
Fax: 0115-947 3257   Tel: 0115-941 8421

DENMARK STREET MANAGEMENT
PM Co-operative Write SAE
Packington Bridge Workspace, Unit 11
1B Packington Square
London N1 7UA
e-mail: mail@denmarkstreet.net
Fax: 020-7354 8558   Tel: 020-7354 8555

DEREK'S HANDS AGENCY
153 Battersea Rise
London SW11 1HP
e-mail: casting@derekshands.com
Fax: 020-7924 2334   Tel: 020-7924 2484

DESMOND Ken AGENCY & MANAGEMENT
Tudor House, Catherine Road, Benfleet
Essex SS7 1HY   Tel/Fax: 01268 566916

Lindsay Duncan

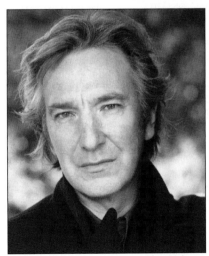

Alan Rickman

Fatimah Namdar 020 8341 1332

ANTHONY STRAEGER
PHOTOGRAPHER
TEL/FAX 020 8769 7031 MOBILE 07961 184888

de WOLFE Felix*
PM Write
Garden Offices, 51 Maida Vale, London W9 1SD
e-mail: felixdewolfe@aol.com
Fax: 020-7289 5731   Tel: 020-7289 5770

DICKINSON Julia
PM
39D Highbury New Park, Canonbury
London N5 2EN
e-mail: actorsfile@aol.com
Mobile: 07949 759468   Tel/Fax: 020-7359 1354

DIESTENFELD Lily
(Personal Manager for 45+ Playing Ages)
28B Alexandra Grove, London N12 8HG
e-mail: lilyd@talk21.com
Fax: 020-7485 1005   Tel: 020-8446 5379

DIRECT CHOICE MANAGEMENT
5 Denmark Street, London WC2H 8LP
e-mail: agents@dircon.co.uk
Fax: 020-7379 0677   Tel: 020-7240 8490

DIRECT LINE
PM (Personal Manager: Daphne Franks)
Park House, 62 Lidgett Lane
Leeds LS8 1PL
e-mail: daphne.franks@dline.org.uk
                              Tel/Fax: 0113-266 4036
St John's House, 16 St John's Vale
London SE8 4EN   Tel/Fax: 020-8694 1788

DOWNES PRESENTERS AGENCY
96 Broadway, Bexleyheath
Kent DA6 7DE
e-mail: downes@presenters.com
Fax: 020-8301 5591   Tel: 020-8304 0541

PLA

PAT LOVETT ASSOCIATES

Pat Lovett, Dolina Logan

39 Sandhurst Court, Acre Lane, London, SW2 5TX Tel: 020 7733 1110 Fax: 020 7733 4440
5 Union Street, Edinburgh, EH1 3LT Tel: 0131 478 7878 Fax: 0131 478 7070

DREW Bryan Ltd
PM Write
Mezzanine, Quadrant House
80-82 Regent Street, London W1B 5AU
e-mail: bryandrewltd@netscapeonline.co.uk
Fax: 020-7437 0561   Tel: 020-7437 2293

DSA THEATRICAL AGENCY Ltd
1 Addley Court
435 Chiswick High Road, London W4 4AU
Fax: 020-8995 1347   Tel: 020-8994 9445

EARLE Kenneth PERSONAL MANAGEMENT
214 Brixton Road, London SW9 6AP
e-mail: kennethearle@agents-uk.com
Fax: 020-7274 9529   Tel: 020-7274 1219

EARNSHAW Susi MANAGEMENT
PM
5 Brook Place, Barnet, Herts EN5 2DL
Fax: 020-8364 9618   Tel: 020-8441 5010

EASTMAN MARLEY ORGANISATION The
(Dance Agency/Choreographers)
7th Floor, 54-62 Regent Street
London W1R 5PJ
e-mail: emo.ltd@dance-agency.freeserve.co.uk
Fax: 020-7287 2844   Tel: 020-7439 4052

EBA
Rooftop Studio, Somerfield Arcade, Stone
Staffordshire ST15 8AU   Tel/Fax: 01785 761233

EDWARDS Representation Joyce
PM Write
275 Kennington Road, London SE11 6BY
e-mail: joyce.edwards@virgin.net
Fax: 020-7820 1845   Tel: 020-7735 5736

ELLIOTT AGENCY The
PO Box 2772, Lewes
Sussex BN8 4DW
e-mail: info@elliottagency.co.uk
Fax: 01273 400814   Tel: 01273 401264

ELLIS Bill Ltd
(See A & B MANAGEMENT Ltd)

EMPTAGE HALLETT*
24 Poland Street
London W1F 8QL
e-mail: michaels@emphal.demon.co.uk
Fax: 020-7287 4411   Tel: 020-7287 5511

2nd Floor
3-5 The Balcony, Castle Arcade
Cardiff CF10 2BU
e-mail: gwenprice@emphal.fsnet.co.uk
Fax: 029-2034 4206   Tel: 029-2034 4205

ENGLISH Doreen '95
Write or Phone
4 Selsey Avenue
Aldwick, Bognor Regis
West Sussex PO21 2QZ   Tel/Fax: 01243 825968

ENTERTAINMENT DIRECTORY The (TED)
21-37 Third Avenue
London E13 8AW
Fax: 020-8471 2111   Tel: 020-8471 3111

EPSTEIN June ASSOCIATES
Write
Flat 1, 62 Compayne Gardens
London NW6 3RY
e-mail: jepstein@lineone.net
Fax: 020-7328 0684   Tel: 020-7328 0864

Andrew Joseph

photographer

tel: 020 7813 1520 or 07956 544 982

www.carelesskiss.com email: andrew@carelesskiss.com

ESSANAY*
PM Write
2 Conduit Street, London W1S 2XB
Fax: 020-7355 1084   Tel: 020-7409 3526

ETHNICS ARTISTE AGENCY
118A Tonsley Heights, East Hill
Wandsworth, London SW18 2HF
Fax: 020-8874 3382   Tel: 020-8877 9324

ET-NIK CASTING AGENCY Ltd
Unit 4, 1A Hollybush Place, London E2 9QX
e-mail: mail@et-nikcasting.co.uk
Fax: 020-7739 6718   Tel: 020-7739 6738

ETTINGER BROS GROUP
(Representation & Management)
3 Church Road, Penny Lane
Liverpool L15 9EA
e-mail: ettinger@genie.co.uk
Fax: 0151-733 2468   Tel: 0151-734 2240

**EURO KIDS AND ADULTS INTERNATIONAL
CASTING AND MODEL AGENCY**
Phillips Farm, Glaziers Lane, Culcheth
Warrington WA3 4AQ
e-mail: info@eurokids.co.uk
Fax: 01925 767563   Tel: 01925 767574

EVANS Jacque MANAGEMENT Ltd
Top Floor Suite, 14 Holmesley Road
London SE23 1PJ
Fax: 020-8699 5192   Tel: 020-8699 1202

EVANS & REISS*
100 Fawe Park Road
London SW15 2EA
e-mail: marcia@evans-reiss.fsnet.co.uk
Fax: 020-8877 0307   Tel: 020-8877 3755

EVOLUTION TALENT MANAGEMENT
The Truman Brewery Building, Studio 21
91 Brick Lane
London E1 6QB
e-mail: evolutionmng@aol.com
Fax: 020-7375 2752   Tel: 020-7375 2672

FACE FACTORY
29 Abbey Business Centre, Ingate Place
London SW8 3NS
Fax: 020-7720 9871   Tel: 020-7720 9877

FACT PRESENTATIONS
97 Cloudesley Road, Islington
London N1 0EW
e-mail: factartists@onetel.net.uk
Fax: 020-7833 9373   Tel: 020-7833 9575

FARNES Norma MANAGEMENT
9 Orme Court
London W2 4RL
Fax: 020-7792 2110   Tel: 020-7727 1544

FASTCAST UK
PO Box 80
Middlesex UB5 6JU
e-mail: jackson@fastcastuk.co.uk
Mobile: 07930 612315   Tel: 020-8399 9354

FAWKES Irene MANAGEMENT
2nd Floor, 91A Rivington Street
London EC2A 3AY
e-mail: irenefawkes@fsbdial.co.uk
Fax: 020-7613 0769   Tel: 020-7729 8559

FBI AGENCY Ltd The
PO Box 250, Leeds LS1 2AZ
e-mail: j.spencer@fbi-agency.ltd.uk
                    Tel/Fax: 07050 222747

FEAST Kate MANAGEMENT*
10 Primrose Hill Studios, Fitzroy Road
London NW1 8TR
e-mail: katefeast@freeuk.com
Fax: 020-7586 9817   Tel: 020-7586 5502

FEATURES
1 Charlotte Street, London W1T 1RD
e-mail: info@features.co.uk
Fax: 020-7636 1657   Tel: 020-7637 1487

FENLON Colette PERSONAL MANAGEMENT
(Incorporating CHILTERN CASTING CHILDREN'S AGENCY)
2A Eaton Road, West Derby L12 7JJ
Fax: 0151-280 7998   Tel: 0151-259 2926

FILM RIGHTS Ltd
PM Write
South Bank Commercial Centre
140 Battersea Park Road, London SW11 4NB
Fax: 020-7720 6000   Tel: 020-7720 2000

FIRST HAND MANAGEMENT
PO Box 34610, London E17 7EX
e-mail: firsthandmgmt@slmpromotions.co.uk
Fax: 0870 135 0179   Tel: 020-8521 9783

FITZGERALD Sheridan MANAGEMENT
87 Western Road, Upton Park, London E13 9JE
Fax: 020-8470 2587   Tel: 020-8471 9814

FLETCHER ASSOCIATES
(Broadcast & Media)
25 Parkway, London N20 0XN
Fax: 020-8361 8866   Tel: 020-8361 8061

FOCUS MANAGEMENT Ltd
PM
155 Park Road, Teddington
Middlesex TW11 0BP
e-mail: focus.mgt@virginnet.co.uk
Fax: 020-8241 2447   Tel: 020-8241 2446

FREEHAND PRODUCTIONS Ltd
33-37 Hatherley Mews
Hiltongrove Business Centre
London E17 4QP
e-mail: freehanduk@yahoo.com
Fax: 020-8520 7766   Tel: 020-8520 7777

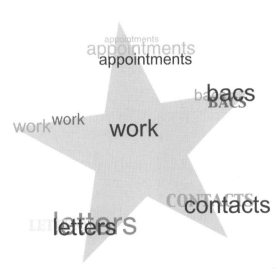

FRENCH Linda
(See ALEXANDER PERSONAL MANAGEMENT Ltd)

FRESH AGENTS
82 Queens Road, Brighton BN1 3XE
e-mail: info@freshagents.com
Fax: 01273 711778   Tel: 01273 711777

FRONTLINE MANAGMENT
PM Co-operative
Colombo Centre, 34-68 Colombo Street
London SE1 8DP
e-mail: frontlineactor@freeuk.com
                    Tel/Fax: 020-7261 9466

GAGAN Hilary ASSOCIATES*
PM
187 Drury Lane, London WC2B 5QD
e-mail: hilary@hgassoc.freeserve.co.uk
Fax: 020-7430 1869   Tel: 020-7404 8794

GALLIARD'S MANAGEMENT
(Hugh Galliard)
33 Richford Street, London W6 7HJ
e-mail: hugh@galliards.net   Tel: 020-8743 2201

GALLOWAYS ONE
15 Lexham Mews, London W8 6JW
e-mail: hugh@galloways.ltd.uk
Fax: 020-7376 2416   Tel: 020-7376 2288

GARDNER Kerry MANAGEMENT*
7 St George's Square, London SW1V 2HX
e-mail: kerrygardner@freeuk.com
Fax: 020-7828 7758   Tel: 020-7828 7748

GARRETT Michael ASSOCIATES*
23 Haymarket, London SW1Y 4DG
e-mail: enquiries@michaelgarrett.co.uk
Fax: 020-7839 4555   Tel: 020-7839 4888

tom oldham photography

020 7352 5368
07968 201 544
chaz@waitrose.com

GARRICKS*
7 Garrick Street, London WC2E 9AR
e-mail: megan@garricks.net
Fax: 020-7497 9242   Tel: 020-7240 0660

GAY Noel ARTISTS*
19 Denmark Street, London WC2H 8NA
Fax: 020-7287 1816   Tel: 020-7836 3941

GFI MANAGEMENT
(Incorporating GO FOR IT CHILDREN'S AGENCY)
47 North Lane, Teddington
Middlesex TW11 0HU
Fax: 020-8287 9405   Tel: 020-8943 1120

GILBERT & PAYNE
Suite 73-74 Kent House, 87 Regent Street
London W1B 4EH
e-mail: ee@succcesstheatrical.com
Fax: 020-7494 3787   Tel: 020-7734 7505

GLASS Eric Ltd
PM Write
28 Berkeley Square, London W1X 6HD
e-mail: eglassltd@aol.com
Fax: 020-7499 6780   Tel: 020-7629 7162

GO ENTERTAINMENTS Ltd
(Circus Artistes, Chinese State Circus,
Cirque Surreal, Bolshoi Circus)
The Arts Exchange, Congleton
Cheshire CW12 1JG
e-mail: phillipgandey@netcentral.co.uk
Fax: 01260 270777   Tel: 01260 276627

GOLDPUSH Ltd
38 Langham Street
London W1N 5RH
e-mail: razgold@goldpush.com
Fax: 020-7323 9526   Tel: 020-7323 9522

GORDON & FRENCH*
Write
12-13 Poland Street
London W1F 8QB
e-mail: mail@gordonandfrench.net
Fax: 020-7734 4832   Tel: 020-7734 4818

GOSS Gerald Ltd
Dudley House, 169 Piccadilly, London W1J 9EH
Fax: 020-7499 7227   Tel: 020-7499 7447

G.O.T. PERSONAL MANAGEMENT
1 Balliol Chambers, Hollow Lane, Herts SG4 9SB
e-mail: cast@guild-of-thieves.com
                    Tel: 01462 420400

GRANTHAM-HAZELDINE
5 Blenheim Street, London W1S 1LD
Fax: 020-7495 3370   Tel: 020-7499 4011

GRAY Darren MANAGEMENT
(Specialising in representing/promoting
Australian Artists)
2 Marston Lane, Portsmouth
Hampshire PO3 5TW
e-mail: darren.gray1@virgin.net
Fax: 023-9267 7227   Tel: 023-9269 9973

GRAY Joan PERSONAL MANAGEMENT
PM F TV
29 Sunbury Court Island
Sunbury-on-Thames
Middlesex TW16 5PP   Tel/Fax: 01932 783544

GRAYS MANAGEMENT Ltd
PM
Panther House, 38 Mount Pleasant
London WC1X 0AP
e-mail: e-mail@graysmanagement.idps.co.uk
                    Tel/Fax: 020-7278 1054

BILLY MARSH ASSOCIATES

MANAGING DIRECTOR
JAN KENNEDY

AGENT
WENDA HOLLAND

DIRECTORS
**SIR BILL COTTON CBE TONY BALL MBE
SUZANNE WESTRIP**

174-178 NORTH GOWER STREET LONDON NW1 2NB
TELEPHONE: 020 7388 6858   FAX: 020 7388 6848
E-MAIL: bmarsh@bmarsh.demon.co.uk

THE TOMMY TUCKER AGENCY

DANCERS • CHOREOGRAPHERS • MUSICAL THEATRE

Telephone 020 7370 3911 Fax 020 7370 4784 e-mail: TTTommytucker@AOL.com

GREEN & UNDERWOOD Ltd
PM Write
2 Conduit Street, London W1S 2XB
e-mail: info@greenandunderwood.com
Fax: 020-7355 1084   Tel: 020-7493 0308

GREIG Miranda ASSOCIATES Ltd
41 Beauchamp Road, London SW11 1PG
e-mail: mail@mirandagreigassoc.co.uk
Fax: 020-7652 6406   Tel: 020-7564 6000

GRESHAM Carl PRESENTATIONS
PM Write
PO Box 3, Bradford, West Yorkshire BD1 4QN
e-mail: carl@carlgresham.co.uk
Fax: 01274 370313   Tel: 01274 735880

GRIFFIN Sandra MANAGEMENT
6 Ryde Place, Richmond Road
East Twickenham, Middlesex TW1 2EH
e-mail: sgmgmt@aol.com
Fax: 020-8744 1812   Tel: 020-8891 5676

GROUP 3 ASSOCIATES
PM
79 Hornsey Road, Islington
London N7 6DJ   Tel: 020-7609 9862

HALLY WILLIAMS AGENCY The
121 Grange Road, Rathfarnham, Dublin 14
e-mail: hallywilliams@eircom.net
Fax: 00 353 14933076   Tel: 00 353 14933685

HAMILTON ASPER MANAGEMENT*
24 Hanway Street, London W1T 1UH
e-mail: info@hamiltonasper.co.uk
Fax: 020-7636 1226   Tel: 020-7636 1221

HAMMER WESTDAL*
PM Write
Unit C218, Trident Business Centre
89 Bickersteth Road, London SW17 9SH
e-mail: the@gents.co.uk
Fax: 020-8355 3480   Tel: 020-8355 3474

HANCOCK Roger Ltd*
4 Water Lane, London NW1 8NZ
e-mail: hancockltd@aol.com
Fax: 020-7267 0705   Tel: 020-7267 4418

HARLEY AGENCY The
Regent House, 291 Kirkdale, London SE26 4QD
e-mail: mail@theharleyagency.co.uk
Fax: 020-8659 8118   Tel: 020-8659 8147

HARRIS AGENCY Ltd The
52 Forty Avenue, Wembley Park
Middlesex HA9 8LQ
e-mail: sharrisltd@aol.com
Fax: 020-8908 4455   Tel: 020-8908 4451

HARRISON Penny BSA Ltd
Trinity Lodge, 25 Trinity Crescent
London SW17 7AG
e-mail: bsaltd@yahoo.co.uk
Fax: 020-8672 8971   Tel: 020-8672 0136

HARRISPEARSON
14-16 Guilford Street, London WC1N 1DW
e-mail: agent@harrispearson.co.uk
Fax: 020-7430 9890   Tel: 020-7430 9229

HATTON Richard Ltd*
29 Roehampton Gate
London SW15 5JR
Fax: 020-8876 8278   Tel: 020-8876 6699

HATTON Stephen MANAGEMENT*
PM Write
Suite 24, London Fruit & Wool Exchange
Brushfield Street, London E1 6HB
e-mail: info@shmuk.com
Fax: 020-7247 9957   Tel: 020-7377 1237

HAYDEN Teri
(See AGENCY The)

HAZEMEAD Ltd
(Entertainment Consultants)
3rd Floor, 18 Hanover Street
London W1S 1YN
Fax: 020-7629 5668   Tel: 020-7629 4817

HEATHCOTE George MANAGEMENT
58 Northdown Street, London N1 9BS
e-mail: gheathcote@freeuk.com
Fax: 020-7713 6959   Tel: 020-7713 6968

HEAVY PENCIL MANAGEMENT
PM Co-operative
BAC, Lavender Hill
London SW11 5TF
e-mail: heavy.pencil@talk21.com
Fax: 020-7924 4636   Tel: 020-7738 9574

HENRY'S AGENCY
53 Westbury, Rochford
Essex SS4 1UL
e-mail: info@henrysagency.co.uk
Fax: 01702 543654   Tel: 01702 541413

HICKS Jeremy ASSOCIATES
12 Ogle Street, London W1W 6HU
Fax: 020-7636 8880   Tel: 020-7636 8008

HILL Edward MANAGEMENT
Riverbank House
Putney Bridge Approach
London SW6 3JD
e-mail: ehill@breathe.com
Fax: 020-7371 0066   Tel: 020-7371 0666

Agent
Laura Munsterhjelm
Helsinki   +358 9 6840 440
Stockholm +46 8 5560 4200
lauram@actors.fi

HILLMAN THRELFALL
33 Brookfield, Highgate West Hill
London N6 6AT
e-mail: emma@hillmanthrelfall.net
Fax: 020-8340 9309   Tel: 020-8341 2207

HINDIN Dee ASSOCIATES
Malvern House
15-16 Nassau Street
London W1W 7AB
Fax: 020-7637 0818   Tel: 020-7637 0616

HINDIN Philip
66 Melbourne Way
Bush Hill Park, Enfield
Middlesex EN1 1XQ   Tel/Fax: 020-8366 2978

HIRED HANDS
12 Cressy Road
London NW3 2LY
e-mail: hiredhands@ukonline.co.uk
Fax: 020-7267 1030   Tel: 020-7267 9212

HOBBS Liz GROUP Ltd
(Artist Management & Public Relations)
Head Office: 68 Castlegate, Newark,
Notts NG24 1BG
e-mail: info@lizhobbsgroup.com
Fax: 01636 703343   Tel: 01636 703342

Finsbury Business Centre
40 Bowling Green Lane
London EC1R 0NE
Fax: 01636 703343   Tel: 020-7287 8870

HOBSON'S ACTORS
62 Chiswick High Road, Chiswick
London W4 1SY
e-mail: actors@hobsons-international.com
Fax: 020-8742 1511   Tel: 020-8747 8326

HOLLAND-FORD Robert
PM Write or Phone
103 Lydyett Lane, Barnton, Northwich
Cheshire CW8 4JT   Tel: 01606 76960

HOLLOWOOD Jane ASSOCIATES Ltd
50 Copperas Street
Manchester M4 1HS
e-mail: janehollowood@ukonline.co.uk
Fax: 0161-834 8333   Tel: 0161-834 8334

HOLLY Dave ARTS MEDIA SERVICES
The Annexe, 23 Eastwood Gardens, Felling
Tyne & Wear NE10 0AH
Fax: 0191-438 2722   Tel: 0191-438 2711

HOPE Sally ASSOCIATES*
108 Leonard Street
London EC2A 4XS
e-mail: s-hope@dircon.co.uk
Fax: 020-7613 4848   Tel: 020-7613 5353

HOWARD Amanda ASSOCIATES Ltd*
21 Berwick Street
London W1F 0PZ
e-mail: mail@amandahowardassociates.co.uk
Fax: 020-7287 7785   Tel: 020-7287 9277

HOWE Janet
Canal Side Chambers, The Boat Yard,
Newcastle Road, Stone
Staffordshire ST15 8JZ
Tel/Fax: 01785 818480   Tel/Fax: 01785 816888

18 The Downs, Altrincham
Cheshire WA14 2PU
e-mail: janet@jhowecasting.fsbusiness.co.uk
Mobile: 07801 942178   Tel/Fax: 0161-233 0700

Representing:-

Actors, Dancers, Choreographers, Singers and Children in all aspects of -T.V., Film, Video, Theatre, and Commercial Work. Full Production Team available for Trade, Fashion & Corporate Work. Three Fully Equipped city centre studios for all your audition requirements.

Visit our website: www.kmcagencies.co.uk

London Office:-
t: 0845 660 2459 (local rate)
f: 0870 442 1780
e: london@kmcagencies.co.uk

P.O. Box 122, 4th floor, Ghulam House
16 Blossom Street, Manchester M4 5AW
t: 0161 237 3009 f: 0161 237 9812
e: casting@kmcagencies.co.uk

All postal submissions to head office in Manchester.

HOWELL Philippa
(See PHPM)

HUGHES Jane MANAGEMENT
The Coach House
PO Box 123, Knutsford Cheshire WA16 9HX
Fax: 01565 722211   Tel: 01565 723000

HUNTER Bernard ASSOCIATES
13 Spencer Gardens, London SW14 7AH
Fax: 020-8392 9334   Tel: 020-8878 6308

I C M Ltd (INTERNATIONAL CREATIVE MANAGEMENT)*
Oxford House, 76 Oxford Street
London W1D 1BS
e-mail: casting@icmlondon.co.uk
Fax: 020-7323 0101   Tel: 020-7636 6565

ICON ACTORS MANAGEMENT
Tanzaro House, Ardwick Green North
Manchester M12 6FZ
e-mail: info@iconactors.net
Fax: 0161-273 4567   Tel: 0161-273 3344

IMA (Isabel Maria Associates)
147-153 Larkhall Lane
London SW4 6RG
e-mail: ima.agency@virgin.net
                          Tel/Fax: 020-7498 8132

I.M.L.
PM Co-operative
Oval House, 52-54 Kennington Oval
London SE11 5SW
e-mail: imllondon@hotmail.com
                          Tel/Fax: 020-7587 1080

IMPACT INTERNATIONAL MANAGEMENT
80 Netherlands Road, New Barnet
Herts EN5 1BS
e-mail: info@impactinternationalgroup.com
Fax: 020-7495 6515   Tel: 020-7495 6655

INGMAN Trevor Ltd
PM
29 Whitcomb Street
London WC2H 7EP
e-mail: info@trevoringman.com
Fax: 020-7930 4441   Tel: 020-7930 4442

INSPIRATION MANAGEMENT
PM Co-operative
Room 200, The Aberdeen Centre
22-24 Highbury Grove
London N5 2EA
e-mail: agent@inspirationmanagement.freeserve.co.uk
                          Tel/Fax: 020-7704 8497

INTER-CITY CASTING
PM
Portland Tower, Portland Street
Manchester M1 3LF
e-mail: intercity@bigfoot.com
                          Tel/Fax: 0161-226 0103

INTERNATIONAL ARTISTES Ltd*
F M PM TV
Mezzanine Floor, 235 Regent Street
London W1B 2AX
e-mail: (name)@intart.co.uk
Fax: 020-7409 2070   Tel: 020-7439 8401

INTERNATIONAL THEATRE & MUSIC Ltd
(Piers Chater Robinson)
Shakespeare House, Theatre Street
London SW11 5ND
e-mail: inttheatre@aol.com
Fax: 020-7801 6317   Tel: 020-7801 6316

IRISH ARTS NETWORK
Victor House, Marlborough Gardens
London N20 0SH
e-mail: rosemaryifbco@aol.com
                          Tel/Fax: 020-8361 0678

Paul Bradley

Rania Ajami

Rupert Whickham

regan
rimmer
management

36-38 Glasshouse St.
London W1B 5DL

t 020 7287 9005
f 020 7287 9006
e thegirls@regan-rimmer.co.uk

ITG Ltd
(International Talent Group)
1 Stedham Place, London WC1A 1HU
Fax: 020-7436 5197   Tel: 020-7436 2249

JAA
(See ALTARAS Jonathan ASSOCIATES Ltd)

JAMES Julie
Studio 1, 48 Vincent Square
London SW1P 2NR
e-mail: juliejames@btclick.com
Mobile: 07931 219054   Tel/Fax: 020-7834 0967

JAMES Susan
(See SJ MANAGEMENT)

JAMESON Joy Ltd
PM
2.19 The Plaza, 535 Kings Road
London SW10 0SZ
Fax: 020-7352 1744   Tel: 020-7351 3971

JAY Alex PERSONAL MANAGEMENT
e-mail: alex-jay-pm.freeserve.co.uk
                              Tel/Fax: 01453 872038

JB ASSOCIATES*
First Floor, 3 Stevenson Square
Manchester M1 1DN
e-mail: united_cities@compuserve.com
Fax: 0161-237 1809   Tel: 0161-237 1808

JEFFREY & WHITE MANAGEMENT*
PM
9-15 Neal Street, London WC2H 9PW
Fax: 020-7240 0007   Tel: 020-7240 7000

J.G.M.
15 Lexham Mews, London W8 6JW
e-mail: jgm@galloways.ltd.uk
Fax: 020-7376 2416   Tel: 020-7376 2414

JLM PERSONAL MANAGEMENT*
(Janet Lynn Malone, Sharon Henry)
242 Acton Lane, London W4 5DL
e-mail: jlm@skynow.net
Fax: 020-8747 8286   Tel: 020-8747 8223

JLS CASTINGS
Casting Agency & Management
14 Kings Terrace, Basford, Stoke on Trent
Staffordshire ST4 6EB
Mobile: 07957 687144   Tel/Fax: 01782 626260

J M ASSOCIATES*
(Jan Murphy)
77 Beak Street, London W1F 9ST
Fax: 020-7434 0640   Tel: 020-7434 0602

JOHNSON WHITELEY Ltd
21 Eastcastle Street, London W1W 8DD
e-mail: jwltd@freeuk.com
Fax: 020-7323 3761   Tel: 020-7323 3744

JONES Sally AGENCY The
96 Lutton Gate
Gedney Hill
Spalding, Lincs PE12 0QH
e-mail: sjonesag@aol.com   Tel: 01406 330383

JPA MANAGEMENT
30 Daws Hill Lane, High Wycombe
Bucks HP11 1PW
e-mail: jackie.palmer@btinternet.com
Fax: 01494 510479   Tel: 01494 520978

KAL MANAGEMENT
Write
95 Gloucester Road, Hampton
Middlesex TW12 2UW
e-mail: kaplan222@aol.com
Fax: 020-8979 6487   Tel: 020-8783 0039

KANAL Roberta AGENCY
82 Constance Road, Twickenham
Middlesex TW2 7JA
e-mail: roberta.kanal@cwcom.net
Tel/Fax: 020-8894 7952   Tel: 020-8894 2277

KARUSHI MANAGEMENT
17 Newburgh Street
London W1F 7RZ
Fax: 020-7434 1949   Tel: 020-7734 3884

KCPM (Kenneth Cleveland Personal Management Ltd)*
(Film, TV & Theatre Technical Personnel)
6 Ganton Street, London W1F 7QW
e-mail: kcpmail@kcpm.co.uk
Fax: 020-7734 7318   Tel: 020-7734 7304

KEAN & GARRICK
PM (Existing Clients only)
PO Box 303, Hampton TW12 3TU
Fax: 020-8979 5335   Tel: 020-8979 0900

KEARNEY Dee MANAGEMENT
Rolekall Casting, 1 Dunwood Bridge
Bridge Street, Shaw OL2 8BG
e-mail: deeluvvie@btinternet.com
                              Tel/Fax: 01706 882442

KENIS Steve & Co
Royalty House, 72-74 Dean Street
London W1D 3SG
e-mail: sk@sknco.com
Fax: 020-7287 6328   Tel: 020-7534 6001

Robert Carpenter Turner ~ Photographer

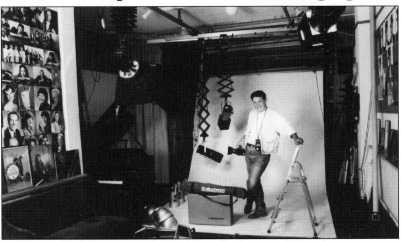

Specialist in promotional pictures for Actors and Musicians.
Portfolio/Head/full length Dance or Modelling shots. Fully equipped studio with separate changing/
make-up room. Grand piano in studio. Location work. Express 2 hour processing available. 5 minutes walk
West Hampstead tube and railway stations. Credit Cards accepted. No casual callers. Illustrated price list.

www.carpenterturner.co.uk
e-mail: robert@carpenterturner.co.uk
The Studio, 63 Hemstal Road, West Hampstead, London NW6 2AD
Telephone: 020-7624 2225   Facsimile: 020-7624 7731

KING Adrian ASSOCIATES
33 Marlborough Mansions
Cannon Hill
London NW6 1JS
e-mail: akassocs@aol.com
Fax: 020-7435 4100   Tel: 020-7435 4600

K M C AGENCIES
PO Box 122, 4th Floor, Ghulam House
16 Blossom Street
Manchester M4 5AW
e-mail: casting@kmcagencies.co.uk
Fax: 0161-237 9812   Tel: 0161-237 3009

All postal submissions to Manchester office:
e-mail: london@kmcagencies.co.uk
Fax: 0870 4421780   Tel: 0845 6602459

KNIGHT AYTON MANAGEMENT
114 St Martin's Lane
London WC2N 4BE
e-mail: info@knightayton.co.uk
Fax: 020-7836 5333   Tel: 020-7836 8333

KNIGHT Ray CASTING
21A Lambolle Place
London NW3 4PG
e-mail: casting@rayknight.co.uk
Fax: 020-7722 2322   Tel: 020-7722 1551

KREATE Ltd
Unit 201, 30 Great Guildford Street
London SE1 0HS
e-mail: kreate@btconnect.com
Fax: 020-7401 3003   Tel: 020-7401 9007

James Grant

Tashaka Francis

Joel Howard

JAMES GILL 020 7735 5632 *Photographer with Attitude & Imagination*

Loesje Sanders

AGENT FOR:
Directors, Designers, Lighting Designers, Choreographers

For more information:
Website: www.loesjesanders.com
E-mail: loesjev@aol.com
Tel: (0044) (0)1394 385260

LINKS MANAGEMENT

34-68 Colombo Street

London SE1 8DP

Tel/Fax: 020 7928 0806

e-mail: links@eidosnet.co.uk

KREMER ASSOCIATES
Cameo House, 11 Bear Street
London WC2H 7AS
e-mail: info@kremerassociates.co.uk
Fax: 020-7766 5238   Tel: 020-7930 6996

KRUGER Rolf MANAGEMENT Ltd
PM (Rachel & Rolf Kruger)
205 Chudleigh Road
London SE4 1EG
e-mail: mail@krugeractors.com
Fax: 020-8690 7999   Tel: 020-8690 7666

LADKIN Michael PERSONAL MANAGEMENT
Suite 1, Ground Floor
1 Duchess Street
London W1W 6AN
e-mail: ladkinm@aol.com
Fax: 020-7436 4627   Tel: 020-7436 4626

LAINE MANAGEMENT
131 Victoria Road
Salford M6 8LF
e-mail: lainecasting.freeserve.co.uk
Fax: 0161-787 7572   Tel: 0161-789 7775

LAINE Betty MANAGEMENT
The Studios East Street
Epsom, Surrey KT17 1HH
e-mail: enquiries@betty-laine-management.co.uk
                    Tel/Fax: 01372 721815

LAND Paulette
(Business Management)
48 Acacia Grove, New Malden, Surrey KT3 3BP
e-mail: pauletteland@free.uk.com
Fax: 020-8949 0840   Tel: 020-8949 5586

LANGFORD ASSOCIATES
17 Westfields Avenue, Barnes, London SW13 0AT
e-mail: langford@ctors.fsnet.co.uk
Fax: 020-8878 7078   Tel: 020-8878 7148

LAPATA
St Matthew's Church, St Petersburgh Place
London W2 4LA
e-mail: londonacademy.performingarts@btinternet.com
Fax: 020-7727 0330   Tel: 020-7727 0220

LEE Bernard MANAGEMENT
1 Heathside Place, Epsom Downs
Surrey KT18 5TX
e-mail: jon@blm1.freeserve.co.uk
                    Tel/Fax: 01737 354777

LEE'S PEOPLE
60 Poland Street, London W1V 3DF
e-mail: lee@lees-people.co.uk
Fax: 020-7734 3033   Tel: 020-7734 5775

LEHRER Jane ASSOCIATES*
100A Chalk Farm Road
London NW1 8EH
e-mail: janelehrer@aol.com
Fax: 020-7482 4899   Tel: 020-7482 4898

LEIGH MANAGEMENT
14 St David's Drive, Edgware HA8 6JH
Tel/Fax: 020-8951 4449   Tel: 020-8952 5536

L'EPINE SMITH & CARNEY ASSOCIATES*
PM Write
Suite 61-63, Kent House, 87 Regent Street
London W1B 4EH
e-mail: jesscarney@aol.com
Fax: 020-7434 4173   Tel: 020-7434 4143

LEWIS Tony ENTERTAINMENTS
PO Box 11268
London SW5 0ZL
Fax: 020-7373 6427   Tel: 020-7370 0416

LIME ACTORS AGENCY & MANAGEMENT Ltd
4th Floor, 54 Princess Street
Manchester M1 6HS
e-mail: debbie.pine@limemanagement.co.uk
Fax: 0161-236 7557   Tel: 0161-237 3300

LINKS MANAGEMENT
34-68 Colombo Street, London SE1 8DP
e-mail: links@eidosnet.co.uk
                    Tel/Fax: 020-7928 0806

LINKSIDE AGENCY
21 Poplar Road, Leatherhead
Surrey KT22 8SF
e-mail: linksideagency@hotmail.com
Fax: 01372 801972   Tel: 01372 802374

LITTLE ACORNS MODELLING AGENCY
London House, 271-273 King Street
Hammersmith, London W6 9LZ
Fax: 020-8408 3077   Tel: 020-8563 0773

LONDON MANAGEMENT*
2-4 Noel Street
London W1F 8GB
Fax: 020-7287 3036   Tel: 020-7287 9000

LONDON MUSICIANS Ltd
(Orchestral Contracting)
Cedar House
Vine Lane, Hillingdon
Middlesex UB10 0BX
e-mail: mail@lonmus.demon.co.uk
Fax: 01895 252556   Tel: 01895 252555

LONGTIME MANAGEMENT
(Existing Clients only)
2 Devonshire Court, Devonshire Hill Lane
London N17 7NJ   Tel/Fax: 020-8352 1467

LOOK ALIKES Ltd
17-23 Lorn Road
London SW9 0AB
e-mail: info@lookalikes.ltd.uk
Fax: 020-7274 4466   Tel: 020-7274 0666

LOOKALIKES (Susan Scott)
26 College Crescent, London NW3 5LH
e-mail: susanscott@lookalikes.freeserve.co.uk
Fax: 020-7722 8261   Tel: 020-7387 9245

LORD Annabel ASSOCIATES (ALA)
(Writers, Designers, Directors, Composers,
Lyricists, Musical Directors)
7 Camberwell Grove
London SE5 8JA
e-mail: annabel@ala.prestel.co.uk
Fax: 020-7701 9762   Tel: 020-7701 9769

LOVETT Pat ASSOCIATES
(See P.L.A.)

L.S.M.T. MANAGEMENT
83 Borough Road
London SE1 1DN
e-mail: wendylee@lsmtmanagement.fsnet.co.uk
          Tel/Fax: 020-7407 4407

LSW PROMOTIONS
181A Faunce House, Doddington Grove
Kennington, London SE17 3TB
e-mail: lswpromos@hotmail.com
          Tel/Fax: 020-7735 5911

LWA
18 Elliott Square
London NW3 3SU
Fax: 020-7586 1583   Tel: 020-7586 5867

LYNE Dennis AGENCY*
108 Leonard Street, London EC2A 4RH
e-mail: d.lyne@virgin.net
Fax: 020-7739 4101   Tel: 020-7739 6200

MAC-10 Ltd
Unit 69
2 Hellidon Close, Ardwick
Manchester M12 4AH
e-mail: info@mac-10.co.uk
Tel/Fax: 0161-275 9610   Tel: 0161-275 9510

MACNAUGHTON LORD 2000 Ltd*
(Writers, Designers, Directors,
Composers/Lyricists/Musical Directors)
Douglas House, 16-18 Douglas Street
London SW1P 4PB
e-mail: info@ml2000.org.uk
Fax: 020-7834 4949   Tel: 020-7834 4646

LEANNE WILSON

KATIE VANDYCK
Photographer
020-7733 9297

Jacob Munn

DANIEL HARWOOD-STAMPER
Photography
Tel: 020-7930 1372

MADELEY Paul PUBLICITY
17 Valley Road
Arden Park, Bredbury
Stockport, Cheshire SK6 2EA
Fax: 0161-430 4016   Tel: 0161-430 5380

MAGNET PERSONAL MANAGEMENT
Co-operative
Unit 743, The Big Peg
120 Vyse Street
Birmingham B18 6NF   Tel/Fax: 0121-628 7788

MAGNOLIA MANAGEMENT
136 Hicks Avenue, Greenford
Middlesex UB6 8HB
e-mail: magnoliamanagement@bigfoot.com
Fax: 020-8575 0369   Tel: 020-8578 2899

MAITLAND MUSIC
PM (Anne Skates)
Brook House, 8 Rythe Road
Claygate, Surrey KT10 9DF
e-mail: maitmus@aol.com
Fax: 01372 466229   Tel: 01372 466228

MAKDEE MANAGEMENT
64A Canadian Avenue
London SE6 3BP
e-mail: donka@canad.freeserve.co.uk
Tel/Fax: 020-8425 0093   Tel: 020-8695 9522

MANAGEMENT 2000
23 Alexandra Road
Mold, Flintshire CH7 1HJ
e-mail: jc@management2000.freeserve.co.uk
                          Tel/Fax: 01352 771231

MANS Johnny PRODUCTIONS Ltd
The Maltings, Brewery Road
Hoddesdon, Herts EN11 8HF
e-mail: real@legend.co.uk
Fax: 01992 470516   Tel: 01992 470907

MANSON Andrew PERSONAL MANAGEMENT*
288 Munster Road
London SW6 6BQ
e-mail: amanson@aol.com
Fax: 020-7381 8874   Tel: 020-7386 9158

MARCUS AND McCRIMMON MANAGEMENT
4 Fitzwarren Gardens, Highgate
London N19 3TP
e-mail: email@marcusandmccrimmon.com
Fax: 020-7281 3933   Tel: 020-7281 2692

MARKHAM & FROGGATT Ltd*
PM Write
4 Windmill Street, London W1P 1HF
e-mail: markham@online.rednet.co.uk
Fax: 020-7637 5233   Tel: 020-7636 4412

MARKHAM John ASSOCIATES
1A Oakwood Avenue
Purley, Surrey CR8 1AR
e-mail: j.markham.associates@lineone.net
Fax: 020-8763 8942   Tel: 020-8763 8941

MARMONT MANAGEMENT Ltd*
PM
Langham House, 308 Regent Street
London W1B 3AT
e-mail: penrose@marmont.co.uk
Fax: 020-7323 4798   Tel: 020-7637 3183

MARSH Billy ASSOCIATES Ltd*
174-178 North Gower Street, London NW1 2NB
e-mail: bmarsh@bmarsh.demon.co.uk
Fax: 020-7388 6848   Tel: 020-7388 6858

MARSH Sandra MANAGEMENT
(Film Technicians)
c/o Casarotto Marsh Ltd, National House
60-66 Wardour Street
London W1V 4ND
e-mail: casarottomarsh@casarotto.uk.com
Fax: 020-7287 5644   Tel: 020-7287 4450

MARSHALL Ronnie AGENCY
S F M PM TV Write or Phone
66 Ollerton Road
London N11 2LA   Tel/Fax: 020-8368 4958

MARSHALL Scott*
PM TV Write or phone
44 Perryn Road, London W3 7NA
e-mail: smpm@scottmarshall.co.uk
Fax: 020-8740 7342   Tel: 020-8749 7692

MARTIN Carol PERSONAL MANAGEMENT
19 Highgate West Hill, London N6 6NP
Fax: 020-8340 4868   Tel: 020-8348 0847

MARTIN-SMITH MANAGEMENT Nigel
54 Princess Street
Manchester M1 6HS
Fax: 0161-236 7557   Tel: 0161-228 6444

MAY John
Garden Flat
6 Westbourne Park Villas, London W2 5EA
e-mail: john@johnmayagent.freeserve.co.uk
Fax: 020-7229 9828   Tel: 020-7221 7917

MAY Teresa MODEL MANAGEMENT
PO Box 23418, London SE26 5ZS
e-mail: teresamay@modelmanagement.co.uk
                           Tel: 01622 765700

MAYER Cassie Ltd*
11 Wells Mews
London W1T 3HD   Tel: 020-7462 0040

MBA
(Formerly MGA Mahoney Associates)
Concorde House
18 Margaret Street, Brighton BN2 1TS
e-mail: mga.concorde@virgin.net
Fax: 01273 685971   Tel: 01273 685970

McCORQUODALE Anna PERSONAL MANAGEMENT
43 St Maur Road, London SW6 4DR
e-mail: amc@netcomuk.co.uk
Fax: 020-7371 9048   Tel: 020-7731 1721

McINTOSH RAE MANAGEMENT*
Write SAE
Thornton House, Thornton Road
London SW19 4NG
e-mail: mcinrae@talk21.com
Fax: 020-8944 6624   Tel: 020-8944 6688

McKENNA Deborah Ltd
(Celebrity Chefs & Television Writers)
Claridge House
29 Barnes High Street, London SW13 9LW
e-mail: info@deborahmckenna.com
Fax: 020-8392 2462   Tel: 020-8876 7566

McKINNEY MACARTNEY MANAGEMENT Ltd
(Technicians)
The Barley Mow Centre
10 Barley Mow Passage
London W4 4PH
e-mail: fkb@mmtechsrep.demon.co.uk
Fax: 020-8995 2414   Tel: 020-8995 4747

McLEAN Bill PERSONAL MANAGEMENT Ltd
PM Write
23B Deodar Road
London SW15 2NP   Tel: 020-8789 8191

McLEOD HOLDEN ENTERPRISES Ltd
Priory House
1133 Hessle High Road
Hull HU4 6SB
e-mail: peter.mcleod@mcleod-holden.com
Fax: 01482 353635   Tel: 01482 565444

McREDDIE Ken Ltd*
PM
91 Regent Street, London W1B 4EL
Fax: 020-7734 6530   Tel: 020-7439 1456

MCS AGENCY
47 Dean Street, London W1D 5BE
e-mail: info@mcs-group.freeserve.co.uk
Fax: 020-7734 9996   Tel: 020-7734 9995

THEATRICAL AGENTS

ACTORS

DANCERS

SINGERS

MODELS

PRESENTERS

CHOREOGRAPHERS

Success

SUITE 73-74 KENT HOUSE

87 REGENT STREET

LONDON W1B 4EH

TEL: 020 7734 3356

FAX: 020 7494 3787

e-mail: ee@successtheatrical.com

MEDIA LEGAL
PM F TV Voice-overs (Existing Clients only)
83 Clarendon Road, Sevenoaks
Kent TN13 1ET   Tel: 01732 460592

MEDIA MODELLING & CASTING AGENCY
53 Astley Avenue, Dover, Kent CT16 2PP
e-mail: info@mediamodels.net
Mobile: 07713 158355   Tel: 01304 204715

MERCURY ENTERTAINMENTS GROUP
Unit 3, The Fishergate Centre
4 Fishergate, York YO10 4FB   Tel: 01904 541800

MIDLANDS CASTING
23 Woodlands Grove, Isleworth
Middlesex TW7 6NS
Fax: 020-8847 4265   Tel: 020-8560 8795

MILLENNIUM ARTISTES MANAGEMENT Ltd
(Personal Management & Event Co-ordinators)
PO Box 2001, Caterham, Surrey CR3 6UA
e-mail: mam.ltd@lineone.net
                    Tel/Fax: 01883 347790

MILNER David MANAGEMENT
1A Pollards Row, Bethnal Green, London E2 6NA
e-mail: agntdm@netscapeonline.co.uk
Fax: 020-7613 0780   Tel: 020-7613 4041

MINT MANAGEMENT
8A Barry Road, London SE22 0HU
e-mail: mintman@freenetname.co.uk
Fax: 020-8693 2976   Tel: 020-8637 0351

MK MANAGEMENT
49 Lavender Gardens, London SW11 1DJ
e-mail: hannah@mkmanagement.co.uk
Fax: 020-7924 5175   Tel: 020-7564 2508

M.K.A.
11 Russell Kerr Close, Chiswick
London W4 3HF
e-mail: mka.agency@virgin.net
Fax: 020-8994 2992   Tel: 020-8994 1619

ML 2000 Ltd
(See MACNAUGHTON LORD 2000 Ltd)

MONTAGU ASSOCIATES
3 Bretton House, Fairbridge Road
London N19 3HP
Fax: 020-7263 3993   Tel: 020-7263 3883

MOORE ACTORS
71 Buttermere Road, Ashton-under-Lyne
Manchester OL7 9EW
e-mail: mooreactors@btinternet.com
Fax: 0161-330 6626   Tel: 0161-355 7341

MORE MANAGEMENT
21 Brittany Road, Worthing
West Sussex BN14 7DY
e-mail: kylanik@freeuk.com
Fax: 01903 202246   Tel: 01903 538877

MORGAN & GOODMAN
Mezzanine, Quadrant House
80-82 Regent Street
London W1B 5RP
e-mail: mg1@btinternet.com
Fax: 020-7494 3446   Tel: 020-7437 1383

MOSS Jae ENTERPRISES
Riverside House, Feltham Avenue
Hampton Court, Surrey KT8 9BJ
e-mail: jmossent@aol.com
Fax: 020-8979 9631   Tel: 020-8979 3459

MPC ENTERTAINMENT
G Write or Phone
MPC House 15-16 Maple Mews
Maida Vale, London NW6 5UZ
e-mail: mpc@mpce.com
Fax: 020-7624 4220   Tel: 020-7624 1184

MUGSHOTS AGENCY
(Amanda Ashed, Tina Pelini)
20 Greek Street, London W1D 4DU
Fax: 020-7437 0308   Tel: 020-7437 2275

MURPHY Elaine ASSOCIATES
310 Aberdeen House
22-24 Highbury Grove
London N5 2EA
e-mail: emurphy@freeuk.com
Fax: 020-7704 8039   Tel: 020-7704 9913

MUSIC INTERNATIONAL
M
13 Ardilaun Road, London N5 2QR
e-mail: music@musicint.demon.co.uk
Fax: 020-7226 9792   Tel: 020-7359 5183

MYERS MANAGEMENT
63 Fairfields Crescent
London NW9 0PR   Tel/Fax: 020-8204 8941

NARROW ROAD COMPANY*
22 Poland Street, London W1F 8QH
e-mail: agents@narrowroad.co.uk
Fax: 020-7439 1237   Tel: 020-7434 0406

NASH INTERNATIONAL
135 Epping New Road
Buckhurst Hill, Essex IG9 5TZ
e-mail: nashinternational@msn.com
Fax: 020-8559 0974   Tel: 020-8559 1696

NCI MANAGEMENT
2nd Floor
51 Queen Anne Street
London W1M 0HS
Fax: 020-7935 1258   Tel: 020-7224 3960

NEVS AGENCY
Regal House, 198 Kings Road
London SW3 5XP
Fax: 020-7352 6068   Tel: 020-7352 4886

NEW CASEY AGENCY
The Annexe, 129 Northwood Way
Middlesex HA6 1RF   Tel: 01923 823182

NICHOLSON Jackie ASSOCIATES
PM
Suite 30, 1st Floor, Kent House, 87 Regent Street
London W1B 4EH
Fax: 020-7434 0445   Tel: 020-7434 0441

NOEL CASTING
(Specialising in Character Actors and Ethnic
and Asian Actors)
Suite 501, International House
223 Regent Street, London W1B 2QD
e-mail: kingnoel/177@hotmail.com
Fax: 020-7544 1090   Tel: 020-7544 1010

NORTH OF WATFORD ACTORS AGENCY
Co-operative
Bridge Mill, Hebden Bridge
West Yorks HX7 8EX
e-mail: northofwatford@ukonline.co.uk
Fax: 01422 846503   Tel: 01422 845361

NORTH ONE MANAGEMENT
18 Ashwin Street, London E8 3DL
e-mail: actors@northone.co.uk
Fax: 020-7249 9989   Tel: 020-7254 9093

Northern Lights Management

Personal representation of Actors from the North and in the North

Agents: Maureen Magee and Angie Forrest

Dean Clough, Halifax, West Yorkshire HX3 5AX

Tel: 01422 382203
Fax: 01422 330101

email: NLManagement@aol.com

NORTHERN DRAMA
PO Box 27, Tadcaster, North Yorks LS24 9XS
e-mail: alyson@connew.com
Tel/Fax: 01937 530600

NORTHERN LIGHTS MANAGEMENT
PM
Dean Clough, Halifax
West Yorks HX3 5AX
e-mail: nlmanagement@aol.com
Fax: 01422 330101　　　Tel: 01422 382203

NORTHERN PROFESSIONALS
(Casting, Technicians, Action Safety,
Boat & Diving Equipment Hire)
21 Cresswell Avenue, North Shields
Tyne & Wear NE29 9BQ
e-mail: bill.gerard@northpro83.freeserve.co.uk
Fax: 0191-296 3243　　　Tel: 0191-257 8635

NORWELL LAPLEY ASSOCIATES
Lapley Hall, Lapley
Staffs ST19 9JR
e-mail: norwelllapley@freeuk.com
Fax: 01785 841992　　　Tel: 01785 841991

NOW YOU'RE TALKING
(After Dinner Speakers & Celebrities)
Stone Cottage, Ireby, Carnforth
Lancs LA6 2JQ
e-mail: speakers@nyt.co.uk　　　Tel: 01524 242221

NSM
(Natasha Stevenson Management)
The Nightingale Centre, 8 Balham Hill
London SW12 9EA
e-mail: nsm@netcomuk.co.uk
Fax: 020-8772 0111　　　Tel: 020-8772 0100

NUTOPIA PERSONAL MANAGEMENT
8, 132 Charing Cross Road
London WC2H 0LA　　　Tel/Fax: 020-8882 6299

NYLAND MANAGEMENT Ltd
20 School Lane, Heaton Chapel
Stockport SK4 5DG
e-mail: nylandmgmt@freenet.co.uk
Fax: 0161-432 5406　　　Tel: 0161-442 2224

OFF THE KERB PRODUCTIONS
22 Thornhill Crescent, London N1 1BJ
e-mail: info@offthekerb.co.uk
Fax: 020-7700 4646　　　Tel: 020-7700 4477

3rd Floor, Hammer House
113-117 Wardour Street, London W1F 0UN
e-mail: offthekerb@aol.com
Fax: 020-7437 0647　　　Tel: 020-7437 0607

OPERA & CONCERT ARTISTS
M Opera
75 Aberdare Gardens
London NW6 3AN
Fax: 020-7372 3537　　　Tel: 020-7328 3097

ORDINARY PEOPLE Ltd
8 Camden Road, London NW1 9DP
e-mail: info@ordinarypeople.co.uk
Fax: 020-7267 5677　　　Tel: 020-7267 7007

O'REILLY Dee MANAGEMENT Ltd
PM
112 Gunnersbury Avenue
London W5 4HB
e-mail: info@dorm.co.uk
Fax: 020-8992 9993　　　Tel: 020-8993 7441

ORIENTAL CASTING AGENCY Ltd (Peggy Sirr)
Afro/Asian Artists Write or Phone
1 Wyatt Park Road, Streatham Hill
London SW2 3TN
e-mail: peggy.sirr@btconnect.com
Fax: 020-8674 9303　　　Tel: 020-8671 8538

ORION PRODUCTIONS & CASTING AGENCY
DBH House, Boundary Street
Liverpool L5 9YJ　　　Tel/Fax: 0151-482 5565

OTTO PERSONAL MANAGEMENT Ltd
PM Co-operative
The Printer's Loft, 111 Arundel Lane
Sheffield S1 4RF
e-mail: ottopm@hotmail.com
Fax: 0114-275 0550　　　Tel: 0114-275 2592

OUT & OUT ENTERTAINMENTS
(Actors, Entertainers & DJ's)
21-37 Third Avenue, London E13 8AW
e-mail: info@oao.co.uk
Fax: 020-8471 2111　　　Tel: 020-8471 3111

PAN ARTISTS AGENCY
Ingleby, 1 Hollins Grove, Sale, Cheshire M33 6RE
e-mail: bookings@panartists.freeserve.co.uk
Fax: 0161-973 9724　　　Tel: 0161-969 7419

PANTO PEOPLE
3 Rushden House, Tatlow Road
Glenfield, Leicester LE3 8ND
Tel/Fax: 0116-287 9594

PARAMOUNT INTERNATIONAL MANAGEMENT
Talbot House
204-226 Imperial Drive, Harrow
Middlesex HA2 7HH
e-mail: mail@theatreuk.com
Fax: 020-8868 6475　　　Tel: 020-8429 3179

Anthony Topham

Juliet Fitzgerald

Paul Ritter

Chloe Newsome

SIMON ANNAND

P h o t o g r a p h e r

020-7241 6725
Mobile: 07970 932 553

Concessions available

Angela Cameron

PARK MANAGEMENT Ltd
PM Co-operative
Studio 5A, Disney Place House
14 Marshalsea Road
London SE1 1HL
e-mail: park_management@hotmail.com
Fax: 020-7357 0047   Tel: 020-7357 0024

PARR & BOND
The Tom Thumb Theatre
Eastern Esplanade Cliftonville
Kent CT9 2LB   Tel: 01843 221791

PAUL Yvonne MANAGEMENT Ltd
10 Tiverton Road
London NW10 3HL
Fax: 020-8960 0410   Tel: 020-8960 0022

P B J MANAGEMENT Ltd*
(Comedy)
7 Soho Street, London W1D 3DQ
e-mail: general@pbjmgt.co.uk
Fax: 020-7287 1191   Tel: 020-7287 1112

PBR MANAGEMENT
1st Floor, 26 Foubert's Place, London W1F 7PP
e-mail: pbrmanagement@aol.com
Fax: 020-7494 9029   Tel: 020-7494 9030

PC THEATRICAL & MODEL AGENCY
(Large Database of Twins)
10 Strathmore Gardens, Edgware
Middlesex HA8 5HJ
e-mail: twinagy@aol.com
Fax: 020-8933 3418   Tel: 020-8381 2229

PELHAM ASSOCIATES
Brighton Media Centre, 9-12 Middle Street
Brighton BN1 1AL
e-mail: agent@pelhamassociates.co.uk
Fax: 01273 202492   Tel: 01273 323010

PEMBERTON ASSOCIATES*
193 Wardour Street, London W1F 8ZF
e-mail: general@pembertonassociates.com
Fax: 020-7734 2522   Tel: 020-7734 4144

Suite 35-36 Barton Arcade, Deansgate
Manchester M3 2BH
Fax: 0161-835 3319   Tel: 0161-832 1661

PEPPERPOT PROMOTIONS
(Bands)
Suite 20B, 20-22 Orde Hall Street
London WC1N 3JW
e-mail: chris@pepperpot.co.uk
Fax: 01255 473107   Tel: 020-7405 9108

PERFORMANCE ACTORS AGENCY
PM Co-operative
137 Goswell Road
London EC1V 7ET
e-mail: performance@p-a-a.co.uk
Fax: 020-7251 3974   Tel: 020-7251 5716

PERFORMERS DIRECTORY
(Actors, Dancers, Models and Extras)
PO Box 29942
London SW6 1FL
e-mail: performersdirectory@yahoo.com
Tel: 020-7384 0445

PERFORMING ARTS*
(Directors/Designers/Choreographers/Lighting
Designers)
6 Windmill Street, London W1T 2JB
e-mail: info@performing-arts.co.uk
Fax: 020-7631 4631   Tel: 020-7255 1362

PERRY George
(See PROFILE MANAGEMENT)

PERSONAL APPEARANCES
20 North Mount, 1147-1161 High Road,
Whetstone N20 0PH
e-mail: pers.appearances@talk21.com
Tel/Fax: 020-8343 7748

PFD*
PM
Drury House, 34-43 Russell Street
London WC2B 5HA
e-mail: postmaster@pfd.co.uk
Fax: 020-7836 9544   Tel: 020-7344 1010

PHILLIPS Frances*
89 Robeson Way
Borehamwood, Herts WD6 5RY
e-mail: derekphillips@talk21.com
Tel: 020-8236 0766   Tel/Fax: 020-8343 7919

PHPM
(Philippa Howell Personal Management)
184 Bradway Road, Sheffield S17 4QX
e-mail: philippa@phpm.freeserve.co.uk
Tel/Fax: 0114-235 3663

PHYSICALITY Ltd*
(Physical Artistry Specialists)
265-267 Ilford Lane, Ilford
Essex IG1 2SD
e-mail: info@physicality.co.uk
Fax: 020-8491 2801   Tel: 020-8491 2800

PHYSICK Hilda
PM Write
78 Temple Sheen Road
London SW14 7RR
Fax: 020-8876 5561   Tel: 020-8876 0073

PICCADILLY MANAGEMENT
PM (Personal Manager: Juliet Russell)
Unit 131, 23 New Mount Street
Manchester M4 4DE
e-mail: piccadilly.management@virgin.net
Fax: 0161-953 4001   Tel: 0161-953 4057

PICOT Nic ENTERTAINMENT AGENCY
25 Highfield, Carpenders Park WD1 5DY
e-mail: nic@nicpicot.co.uk
Fax: 020-8421 2500   Tel: 020-8421 2700

PINEAPPLE AGENCY
159-161 Balls Pond Road
London N1 4BG
Fax: 020-7241 3006   Tel: 020-7241 6601

P.L.A. (LOVETT Pat ASSOCIATES)
39 Sandhurst Court, Acre Lane
London SW2 5TX
e-mail: pla.london@blueyonder.co.uk
Fax: 020-7733 4400   Tel: 020-7733 1110

5 Union Street, Edinburgh EH1 3LT
e-mail: pla.edinburgh@blueyonder.co.uk
Fax: 0131-478 7070   Tel: 0131-478 7878

PLATER Janet MANAGEMENT Ltd
D Floor
Milburn House, Dean Street
Newcastle-upon-Tyne NE1 1LF
e-mail: magpie@tynebridge.demon.co.uk
Fax: 0191-221 2491   Tel: 0191-221 2490

PLUNKET GREENE Ltd
(In conjunction with James Sharkey Assoc Ltd)
(Existing Clients only)
PO Box 8365, London W14 0GL
Fax: 020-7603 2221   Tel: 020-7603 2227

POLLYANNA MANAGEMENT Ltd
PO Box 30661
London E1W 3GG
e-mail: pollyanna-mgmt@yahoo.co.uk
Fax: 020-7480 6761   Tel: 020-7702 1937

POOLE Gordon AGENCY Ltd
The Limes, Brockley
Bristol BS48 3BB
e-mail: agents@gordonpoole.com
Fax: 01275 462252   Tel: 01275 463222

POWELL Claire PERSONAL MANAGEMENT
(Existing Clients only)
27 Ravenslea Road
London SW12 8SL
e-mail: cppmagency@hotmail.com
                    Tel/Fax: 020-8673 9959

POWER MODEL MANAGEMENT CASTING AGENCY
The Royal, 25 Bank Plain
Norwich NR2 4SF
e-mail: powermodelmanagement@btinternet.com
Fax: 01603 621101   Tel: 01603 621100

POWER PROMOTIONS
PO Box 61, Liverpool L13 0EF
e-mail: tom@powerpromotions.co.uk
                    Tel/Fax: 0151-230 0070

PPM - Polo Piatti Management
(No Unsolicited Mail)
157 Capel Road
London E7 0JT   Tel/Fax: 020-8478 2101

PREGNANT PAUSE AGENCY
(Pregnant Models, Dancers, Actresses)
11 Matham Road
East Molesey KT8 0SX
e-mail: info@pregnantpause.co.uk
Fax: 020-8783 0337   Tel: 020-8979 8874

PRICE GARDNER MANAGEMENT
85 Shorrolds Road
London SW6 7TU
e-mail: info@pricegardner.com
Fax: 020-7381 3288   Tel: 020-7610 2111

PRICHARD Peter at INTERNATIONAL ARTISTES Ltd
Mezzanine Floor, 235 Regent Street
London W1B 2AX
e-mail: maria@intart.co.uk
Fax: 020-7409 2070   Tel: 020-7352 6417

PRIDE ARTIST MANAGEMENT
The Burnside Centre, Burnside Crescent
Middleton, Manchester M24 5NN
e-mail: artistes@prideradio.co.uk
                    Tel/Fax: 0161-643 6266

PRINCIPAL ARTISTES
PM Write
4 Paddington Street, Off Baker Street
London W1M 3LA
Fax: 020-7486 4668   Tel: 020-7224 3414

PRO ACRO
(Circus Skills & Speciality Acts)
Spring Vale, Tutland Road, North Baddesley
Hants SO52 9FL
e-mail: mo@2ma.co.uk
Fax: 023-8074 1355   Tel: 023-8074 1354

Bill Nighy

David Koppel
Portraits & Production Photography
Tel: 020 8349 0001
Mobile: 07831 838378

Lara Belmont

DANCERS

1 Charlotte Street, London W1T 1RD
Tel (020) 7636 1473   Fax (020) 7636 1657   Email: info@danceragency.com

PROFILE MANAGEMENT
(George Perry)
70 Leslie Road, East Finchley
London N2 8BJ
e-mail: georgeperryprofile@hotmail.com
Fax: 020-8365 2732   Tel: 020-8442 0584

PROTOCOL
2/7 Harbour Yard, Chelsea Harbour
London SW10 0XD
e-mail: stars@protocoltalent.com
Fax: 020-7349 1533   Tel: 020-7349 8877

PURPLE PROMOTIONS AGENCY
1 Cathedral Street, Norwich
Norfolk NR1 1LU   Tel: 01603 614104

PVA MANAGEMENT Ltd
Hallow Park, Worcester WR2 6PG
e-mail: clients@pva.co.uk
Fax: 01905 641842   Tel: 01905 640663

QDOS Ltd
8 King Street, Covent Garden
London WC2E 8HN
e-mail: info@qdosentertainment.plc.uk
Fax: 020-7240 4956   Tel: 020-7240 5052

QUADRAPHOLD MANAGEMENT
(Andy Ball)
Queens Chambers
Queen Street, Blackpool
Lancashire FY1 1PD
e-mail: info@quadraphold.com
Fax: 01253 290019   Tel: 01253 311112

QUICK Nina ASSOCIATES
(See TAYLOR Brian - QUICK Nina ASSOCIATES)

RAGE MODELS
(Young Adults Fashion)
Tigris House, 256 Edgware Road
London W2 1DS
e-mail: info@ugly.org
Fax: 020-7402 0507   Tel: 020-7262 0515

RAINBOW REPRESENTATION
45 Nightingale Lane, Crouch End
London N8 7RA
e-mail: rainbowrp@ukgateway.net
                    Tel/Fax: 020-8341 6241

RATTLEBAG ACTORS AGENCY Ltd
PM
Everyman Theatre Annexe, 13-15 Hope Street
Liverpool L1 9BH
e-mail: actors@rattlebag.co.uk
Fax: 0151-709 0773   Tel: 0151-708 7273

RAVENSCOURT MANAGEMENT
Tandy House, 30-40 Dalling Road
London W6 0JB
e-mail: ravenscourt@hotmail.com
Fax: 020-8741 1786   Tel: 020-8741 0707

RAY'S NORTHERN CASTING AGENCY
7 Wince Close, Alkrington, Middleton
Manchester M24 1UJ   Tel/Fax: 0161-643 6745

RAZZAMATAZZ MANAGEMENT
Crofters, East Park Lane, New Chapel
Surrey RH7 6HS
e-mail: mcgrogan@tinyworld.co.uk
Fax: 01342 835433   Tel: 01342 835359

RBM
PM (Comedy)
3rd Floor, 18 Broadwick Street
London W1V 1FG
e-mail: info@rbmcomedy.com
Fax: 020-7287 5020   Tel: 020-7287 5010

REACTORS AGENCY
1 Eden Quay
Dublin 1
Fax: 00 353 1 8783182   Tel: 00 353 1 8786833

RE.ANIMATOR MANAGEMENT
(Representation for Dancers)
Wimbledon Theatre, The Broadway
London SW19 1QG
e-mail: re.animator@virgin.net
Fax: 020-8542 8081   Tel: 020-8542 9763

REA Tano PERSONAL MANAGEMENT
PM (Singers)
58 Alexandra Road
London NW4 2RY
Fax: 020-8203 1064   Tel: 020-8203 1747

REDDIN Joan
PM Write
Hazel Cottage
Frogg's Island, Wheeler End Common
Bucks HP14 3NL   Tel: 01494 882729

REDROOFS ASSOCIATES
Littlewick Green, Maidenhead, Bucks SL6 3QY
Fax: 01628 822461   Tel: 01628 822982

REDWAY John ASSOCIATES (in association
with A.I.M.)
Nederlander House, 7 Great Russell Street
London WC1B 3NH
e-mail: info@aim.demon.co.uk
Fax: 020-7637 8666   Tel: 020-7637 1700

REGAN RIMMER MANAGEMENT
(Leigh-Ann Regan & Debbie Rimmer)
36-38 Glasshouse Street
London W1B 5DL
e-mail: thegirls@regan-rimmer.co.uk
Fax: 020-7287 9006   Tel: 020-7287 9005

REGENCY AGENCY
F TV
25 Carr Road, Calverley
Leeds LS28 5NE   Tel: 0113-255 8980

REPRESENTATION JOYCE EDWARDS
(See EDWARDS Representation Joyce)

REYNOLDS Sandra MODEL & CASTING AGENTS
Md F TV
50 Fitzroy Street, London W1T 5BT
e-mail: tessa@sandrareynolds.co.uk
Fax: 020-7387 5848   Tel: 020-7387 5858

35 St Georges Street, Norwich NR3 1DA
Fax: 01603 219825   Tel: 01603 623842

RICHARDS Lisa
46 Upper Baggot Street, Dublin 4
e-mail: lisar@iol.ie
Fax: 00 353 1 6603545   Tel: 00 353 1 6603534

RICHARDS Stella MANAGEMENT
(Existing Clients only)
42 Hazlebury Road
London SW6 2ND
Fax: 020-7731 5082   Tel: 020-7736 7786

RIDGEWAY MANAGEMENT
Fairley House, Andrews Lane
Cheshunt, Herts EN7 6LB
e-mail: info@ridgewaystudios.co.uk
Fax: 01992 633844   Tel: 01992 633775

RK COMMERCIALS
G Md
205 Chudleigh Road, London SE4 1EG
e-mail: rkcommercials@krugeractors.com
Fax: 020-8690 7999   Tel: 020-8690 6542

RKM
(See KRUGER Rolf MANAGEMENT Ltd)

ROBSON NEWMAN MANAGEMENT
14 Ritz Buildings
Church Road, Tunbridge Wells
Kent TN1 1HP
Fax: 01892 514173   Tel: 01892 524122

ROGUES & VAGABONDS MANAGEMENT Ltd
PM Co-operative
The Print House,
18 Ashwin Street, London E8 3DL
e-mail: rogues.vagabonds@virginnet.co.uk
Fax: 020-7249 8564   Tel: 020-7254 8130

ROGUE ACTORS MANAGEMENT
1-4 Pope Street
London Bridge
London SE1 3PR
e-mail: simonramuk@yahoo.co.uk
Mobile: 07909 695492   Tel/Fax: 020-7378 9104

ROLE MODELS
12 Cressy Road
London NW3 2LY
Fax: 020-7267 1030   Tel: 020-7284 4337

ROSEBERY MANAGEMENT Ltd
PM Co-operative
Diorama Arts Centre, 34 Osnaburgh Street
London NW1 3ND
e-mail: roseberymgmt@netscapeonline.co.uk
Fax: 020-7692 3065   Tel: 020-7813 1026

impact
INTERNATIONAL MANAGEMENT
Professional Entertainment Solutions

Actors
Models
Singers
Promotion
Commercial & Industrial
Film & Video
Choreographers
Dancers
Inhouse Production

Tel: +44 (0) 20 7495 6655 • Fax: +44 (0) 20 7495 6515 • Email: info@impactinternationalgroup.com

---

ROSEMAN ORGANISATION The
Suite 9, The Power House
70 Chiswick High Road
London W4 1SY
e-mail: info@therosemanorganisation.co.uk
Fax: 020-8742 0554   Tel: 020-8742 0552

ROSS BROWN ASSOCIATES
PM
Rosedale House
Rosedale Road, Richmond
Surrey TW9 2SZ
e-mail: rossbrownassoc@freeuk.com
Fax: 020-8940 4121   Tel: 020-8332 9193

ROSSMORE PERSONAL MANAGEMENT
Rossmore Road
Marylebone
London NW1 6NJ
e-mail: rossmore@freeuk.com
Fax: 020-7258 0124   Tel: 020-7258 1953

ROYCE MANAGEMENT
34A Sinclair Road
London W14 0NH
Fax: 020-7371 4985   Tel: 020-7602 4992

RUBICON MANAGEMENT
27 Inderwick Road
Crouch End
London N8 9LB   Tel/Fax: 020-8374 1836

RUBY TALENT
Apartment 9
Goldcrest Building
1 Lexington Street
London W1F 9TA
e-mail: tara@ruby-talent.co.uk
Fax: 020-7439 1649   Tel: 020-7439 4554

RWM MANAGEMENT
The Aberdeen Centre
22-24 Highbury Grove
London N5 2EA
e-mail: rwm.mario-kate@virgin.net
Fax: 020-7226 3371   Tel: 020-7226 3311

SANDERS Loesje*
(Designers, Directors, Choreographers, Lighting
Designers)
Pound Square
1 North Hill
Woodbridge
Suffolk IP12 1HH
e-mail: loesjev@aol.com
Fax: 01394 388734   Tel: 01394 385260

SANGWIN Maggi MANAGEMENT
(In association with The W6 Agency)
11 Devonshire Mews
Chiswick
London W4 2HA
e-mail: maggisangwin@lineone.net
Fax: 020-8994 7778   Tel: 020-8994 7878

SARABAND ASSOCIATES
(Sara Randall, Bryn Newton, Christina Beyer)
265 Liverpool Road
London N1 1LX
Fax: 020-7609 2370   Tel: 020-7609 5313

SBS Ltd (The Casting Information Service)
Suite 1, 16 Sidmouth Road
London NW2 5JX
e-mail: sbsltd@talk.com
Fax: 020-8459 7442   Tel: 020-8459 2781

SCA MANAGEMENT
TV F S M Write or Phone
23 Goswell Road
London EC1M 7AJ
e-mail: sca@italiaconti36.freeserve.co.uk
Fax: 020-7253 1430   Tel: 020-7336 6122

SCHNABL Peter
The Barn House, Cutwell, Tetbury
Gloucestershire GL8 8EB
Fax: 01666 502998   Tel: 01666 502133

SCOT-BAKER AGENCY
35 Caithness Road
Brook Green
London W14 0JA
e-mail: scot.baker@btinternet.com
Fax: 020-7603 7698   Tel: 020-7603 9988

SCOTT-PAUL YOUNG ERTAINMENTS Ltd
Northern Lights House
110 Blandford Road North
Langley, Nr Windsor
Berks SL3 7TA
e-mail: 72016.2712@compuserve.com
Fax: 01753 810961   Tel: 01753 693250

SCOTT Tim PERSONAL MANAGEMENT
Unit 5
The Cloisters Business Centre
8 Battersea Park Road
London SW8 4BG
e-mail: tim.scott2@virgin.net
Fax: 020-7498 2942   Tel: 020-7978 1352

Acrobatic And Aerial Agency
Unique - Talent - of human capabilities

AIR-O-BATS

E-mail: kda@air-o-bats.com
www.air-o-bats.co.uk

84 Laburnum Ave. Hornchurch. Essex. RM12 4HA
Tel/Fax: 01708 705601

SCREENLITE AGENCY
Shepperton Film Studios
Shepperton, Middlesex TW17 0QD
e-mail: screenlite@dial.pipex.com
Fax: 01932 572507 Tel: 01932 562611 Ext 2271

SCRIMGEOUR Donald ARTISTS AGENCY
(Dance)
49 Springcroft Avenue, London N2 9JH
e-mail: vwest@dircon.co.uk
Fax: 020-8883 9751 Tel: 020-8444 6248

SECOND SKIN AGENCY
50 Elmwood Road, Chiswick, London W4 3DZ
e-mail: jenny@secondskin.freeserve.co.uk
Tel/Fax: 020-8994 9864

SEDGWICK Dawn (MANAGEMENT)
3 Goodwins Court, Covent Garden
London WC2N 4LL
Fax: 020-7240 0415 Tel: 020-7240 0404

SEE INTERNATIONAL Ltd
(Formerly International World of Sport)
PO Box 14, Bognor Regis
West Sussex PO22 7JW
Fax: 01243 868907 Tel: 01243 868397

SEQUINS THEATRICAL AGENCY
Winsome, 8 Summerhill Grove
Bush Hill Park
Enfield EN1 2HY Tel: 020-8360 4015

SHALIT ENTERTAINMENT Ltd
Cambridge Theatre
Seven Dials, Covent Garden
London WC2H 9HU
e-mail: info@shalit.co.uk
Fax: 020-7379 3238 Tel: 020-7379 3282

SHAPER Susan MANAGEMENT
Queens House, 1 Leicester Place
London WC2H 7BP
e-mail: ssm5@altavista.net
Fax: 020-7534 3317 Tel: 020-7534 3316

SHAW Vincent ASSOCIATES Ltd
20 Jay Mews, London SW7 2EP
e-mail: vincentshaw@clara.net
Fax: 020-7225 1079 Tel: 020-7581 8215

SHEDDEN Malcolm MANAGEMENT
1 Charlotte Street, London W1T 1RD
Fax: 020-7636 1657 Tel: 020-7636 1876

SHEPHERD MANAGEMENT Ltd
13 Radnor Walk, London SW3 4BP
e-mail: info@shepherdmanagement.co.uk
Fax: 020-7352 2277 Tel: 020-7352 2200

SHEPHERD Elizabeth AGENCY
29 Eversley Crescent, London N21 1EL
e-mail: elizabeth.esa@bigfoot.com
Fax: 020-8364 1624 Tel: 020-8364 0598

SHOWBUSINESS ENTERTAINMENT & TELEVISION CASTING AGENCY
The Bungalow, Chatsworth Avenue
Long Eaton, Nottingham NG10 2FL
Fax: 0115-946 1831 Tel: 0115-973 5445

SHOWSTOPPERS!
(Entertainments & Management)
42 Foxglove Close, Witham
Essex CM8 2XW
e-mail: mail@showstoppers-group.com
Fax: 01376 510340 Tel: 01376 518486

SILVESTER MANAGEMENT
24 Lake View, Edgware HA8 7RU
e-mail: silvestermgmt@freeuk.com
Fax: 020-8958 7711 Tel: 020-8958 5555

SIMONES INTERNATIONALE
(Model & Artistes Management & Agency)
PO Box 15154
London W5 3FW Tel/Fax: 020-8861 3900

SIMPSON FOX ASSOCIATES Ltd*
(Directors, Designers, Choreographers)
52 Shaftesbury Avenue, London W1D 6LP
e-mail: cary@simpson-fox.demon.co.uk
Fax: 020-7494 2887 Tel: 020-7434 9167

SINGER Sandra ASSOCIATES
21 Cotswold Road, Westcliff on Sea
Essex SS0 8AA
e-mail: sandra.singer@virgin.net
Fax: 01702 339393 Tel: 01702 331616

SINGERS' AGENCY The
PM M G
16 Harris Lane, Shenley, Radlett
Herts WD7 9EB
e-mail: davidburn@btinternet.com
Fax: 01923 859636 Tel: 01923 852175

SIRR Peggy
(See ORIENTAL CASTING AGENCY Ltd)

SJ MANAGEMENT
15 Maiden Lane
London WC2E 7NA
e-mail: sj@susanjames.demon.co.uk
Fax: 020-7836 5724 Tel: 020-7836 5723

SO DAM TUFF Ltd
41 Paradise Walk
Chelsea, London SW3 4JL
e-mail: tiger@sodamtuff.com
Fax: 020-7352 0001 Tel: 020-7351 0111

SOLOMON ARTISTES MANAGEMENT INTERNATIONAL
30 Clarence Street, Southend-on-Sea
Essex SS1 1BD
e-mail: info@solomon-artistes.co.uk
Fax: 01702 392385 Tel: 01702 392370

SOPHIE'S PEOPLE
60 Tottenham Court Road
London W1T 2EW
e-mail: sophies.people@btinternet.com
Fax: 020-736 2600 Tel: 020-7636 2333

SOUTH WEST MANAGEMENT & CASTING CO Ltd
The Courtyard, Whitchurch
Ross-on-Wye HR9 6DA
e-mail: agent@southwestcastingco.uk
Fax: 01600 891099 Tel: 01600 892005

SPARE PARTS
(Body Parts Specialists)
153 Battersea Rise
London SW11 1HP
Fax: 020-7924 2334   Tel: 020-7924 2484

SPEAK Ltd
140 Devonshire Road, Chiswick
London W4 2AW
e-mail: speak@dircon.co.uk
Fax: 020-8742 1333   Tel: 020-8742 1001

SPEAKERS CORNER
(Speakers & Cabaret for the Corporate Market)
Tigana House, Catlins Lane, Pinner
Middlesex HA5 2AG
e-mail: info@speakerscorner-uk.com
Fax: 020-8868 4409   Tel: 020-8866 8967

SPHINX MANAGEMENT & ENTERTAINMENT AGENCY
Unity House, 2 Unity Place
Westgate, Rotherham
South Yorks S60 1AR
Fax: 01709 369990   Tel: 01709 820379

SPIRE CASTING
PO Box 372
Chesterfield S41 0XW
e-mail: spirecasting@aol.com
                         Tel: 01246 224798

SPLITTING IMAGES LOOKALIKE AGENCY
29 Mortimer Court
Abbey Road
London NW8 9AB
e-mail: info@splitting-images.com
Fax: 020-8809 6103   Tel: 020-7286 8300

SPORTABILITY Ltd
(Sporting Personalities)
Unit 2, 23 Green Lane
Dronfield
Derbyshire S18 2LL
Fax: 01246 290520   Tel: 01246 292010

SPORTS WORKSHOP PROMOTIONS Ltd
(Sports Models)
PO Box 878, Crystal Palace
National Sports Centre
London SE19 2BH
e-mail: info@sportspromotions.co.uk
Fax: 020-8776 7772   Tel: 020-8659 4561

SPYKER Paul MANAGEMENT
1-2 Henrietta Street, Covent Garden
London WC2E 8PS
e-mail: info@pspy.com
Fax: 020-7379 8282   Tel: 020-7379 8181

STACEY Barrie PROMOTIONS
Apartment 8
132 Charing Cross Road
London WC2H 0LA
Fax: 020-7836 2949   Tel: 020-7836 4128

STAFFORD Helen MANAGEMENT
14 Park Avenue, Bush Hill Park, Enfield
Middlesex EN1 2HP
e-mail: helen.stafford@myself.com
Fax: 020-8482 0371   Tel: 020-8360 6329

STAGE CENTRE MANAGEMENT Ltd
PM Co-operative
41 North Road
London N7 9DP
e-mail: stagecentre@ukgateway.net
Fax: 020-7609 0213   Tel: 020-7607 0872

Anne Marie Shevlin

Aldo Williams

Carlos Lopez-Real

Ricky Groves

Rebecca Jane

Jeremy Rendell Photography

Studio: 020 7566 0024
Mobile: 07860 277 411
www.jeremyrendell.com
jeremy@rendell-photo.demon.co.uk

Multicultural artiste representation

- ACTORS •
- MODELS •
- SINGERS •
- DANCERS •
- CHOREOGRAPHERS •

Unit 4, 1a Hollybush Place, London, E2 9QX   Tel: 020 7739 6738   Fax: 020 7739 6718
E-mail: mail@et-nikcasting.co.uk   Web: www.et-nikcasting.co.uk

STARLINGS THEATRICAL AGENCY
45 Viola Close
South Ockendon
Essex RM15 6JF
e-mail: juliecartercar24w@supanet.com
Mobile: 07941 653463   Tel: 01708 859109

STARNOWSKI Richard MANAGEMENT
4th Floor, 20-24 Kirby Street
London EC1N 8TS
Fax: 020-7242 8125   Tel: 020-7242 5542

STATUS CASTING AGENCY
PO Box 19259
London NW10 8FF
Fax: 020-8965 2600   Tel: 020-8838 3554

STEVENSON Natasha MANAGEMENT
(See NSM)

STIVEN CHRISTIE MANAGEMENT
(Incorporating The Actors Agency of Edinburgh)
80A Dean Street
London W1D 3SN
Tel/Fax: 020-7434 4430   Tel: 07000 228677(ACTORS)

1 Glen Street
Tollcross
Edinburgh EH3 9JD
Fax: 0131-228 4645   Tel: 0131-228 4040

ST. JAMES'S MANAGEMENT
PM Write SAE
19 Lodge Close
Stoke D'Abernon, Cobham
Surrey KT11 2SG
Fax: 01932 860444   Tel: 01932 860666

STONE Annette ASSOCIATES*
2nd Floor, 22 Great Marlborough Street
London W1V 1AF
Fax: 020-7434 2346   Tel: 020-7734 0626

STONE Ian ASSOCIATES
4 Masons Avenue, Croydon
Surrey CR0 9XS
Fax: 020-8680 9912   Tel: 020-8667 1627

STONE Richard PARTNERSHIP The*
PM
2 Henrietta Street
London WC2 8PS
e-mail: all@richstonepart.co.uk
Fax: 020-7497 0869   Tel: 020-7497 0849

STORM ARTISTS MANAGEMENT
First Floor
47 Brewer Street
London W1F 9UF
e-mail: info@stormartists.co.uk
Fax: 020-7437 4314   Tel: 020-7437 4313

STORM FORCE COMMUNICATIONS Ltd
(Ian Richardson & Tony Williamson)
Dudswell Lane, Berkhamsted
Herts HP4 3TQ
e-mail: ian.storm@btinternet.com
Fax: 01442 879954   Tel: 01442 879082

STREETJAM
(Dancers, Choreographers)
95 Blenheim Gardens, Brixton Hill
London SW2 5BA
Fax: 020-8671 4330   Tel: 020-8671 4618

STUART MANAGEMENT Ltd
169 Hamlet Court Road
Westcliff-on-Sea
Essex SS0 7EL
e-mail: darren@stuartmgt.freeserve.co.uk
Fax: 01702 394301   Tel: 01702 394300

**STUNTMAN AND SHOWMANS
PROMOTIONS Ltd**
BSA House
249 Barking Road, East Ham
London E6 1LB   Tel: 020-8472 8301

SUCCESS
Suite 74, 3rd Floor, Kent House
87 Regent Street
London W1B 4EH
e-mail: ee@successtheatrical.com
Fax: 020-7494 3787   Tel: 020-7734 3356

SUCCESSFUL CHOICE
13 Cambridge Drive, Lee Green
London SE12 8AG   Tel: 020-8852 4955

SUMMERS Mark MANAGEMENT
14 Russell Garden Mews
London W14 8EU
e-mail: mark@marksummers.com
Fax: 020-7602 9994   Tel: 020-7603 1979

SUMMERTON Michael MANAGEMENT Ltd
PM M C
Mimosa House, Mimosa Street
London SW6 4DS
Fax: 020-7731 0103   Tel: 020-7731 6969

SWEENEY MANAGEMENT
Ramillies House
1-2 Ramillies Street, London W1F 7LN
e-mail: info@sweeneymanagement.co.uk
Fax: 020-7437 2080   Tel: 020-7287 0900

T.A. MANAGEMENT
18 Kingsdale Gardens, Notting Hill
London W11 4TZ
e-mail: tamanagement@hotmail.com
                    Tel/Fax: 020-7603 3471

TALENT ARTISTS Ltd*
4 Mews House, Princes Lane
London N10 3LU
e-mail: talent.artists@virgin.net
Fax: 020-8444 3353   Tel: 020-8444 4088

TALKBACK MANAGEMENT*
20-21 Newman Street
London W1P 3HB
Fax: 020-7861 8061   Tel: 020-7861 8060

TAM MANAGEMENT
192 Derby Lane, Stoneycroft
Liverpool L13 6QQ
Mobile: 07870 807723   Tel/Fax: 0151-259 6017

TAYLOR MANAGEMENT
31B Cranbrook Park, Wood Green
London N22 5NA
Fax: 020-8809 4417   Tel: 020-8826 0839

TAYLOR Brian - QUICK Nina ASSOCIATES*
50 Pembroke Road, Kensington
London W8 6NX
e-mail: briantaylor@nqassoc.freeserve.com.uk
Fax: 020-7602 6301   Tel: 020-7602 6141

TCG ARTIST MANAGEMENT
Garden Studios, 11-15 Betterton Street
London WC2H 9BP
e-mail: enquiries@tcgartistmanagement.co.uk
Fax: 020-7470 8857   Tel: 020-7470 8856

TELFORD Paul MANAGEMENT
PM
23 Noel Street, London W1V 3RD
e-mail: paul@telford-mgt.demon.co.uk
Fax: 020-7434 1200   Tel: 020-7434 1100

THEATRE EXPRESS PERFORMING ARTS AGENCY
                    Tel/Fax: 01608 676024

THOMAS & BENDA ASSOCIATES Ltd
Top Floor, 15-16 Ivor Place
London NW1 6HS   Tel/Fax: 020-7723 5509

THOMPSON Jim
Herricks, School Lane, Arundel
West Sussex BN18 9DR
e-mail: jim@jthompson42.freeserve.co.uk
Fax: 01903 885887   Tel: 01903 885757

Lisa Shelley

Gerald Kyd

FEATURES

1 Charlotte Street London W1T 1RD
Tel: (020) 7637 1487 Fax: (020) 7636 1657 E-mail address: info@features.co.uk

THOMPSON Peggy OFFICE The
PM
1st and 2nd Floor Offices
296 Sandycombe Road
Kew
Richmond
Surrey TW9 3NG
Fax: 020-8332 1127   Tel: 020-8332 1003

THORNTON AGENCY
(Specialist Agency for Small People)
72 Purley Downs Road
Croydon CR2 0RB
e-mail: thorntons.leslie@tinyworld.co.uk
Fax: 020-7385 6647   Tel: 020-8660 5588

THRESH Melody MANAGEMENT ASSOCIATES Ltd (MTM)
MTM House
29 Ardwick Green North
Ardwick
Manchester M12 6DL
e-mail: melody.thresh@melody-thresh-management.co.uk
Fax: 0161-273 5455   Tel: 0161-273 5445

THURSTONS PERSONAL MANAGEMENT
4 Park Gate
Mount Avenue
London W5 1PX
e-mail: jtashton@yahoo.com
Fax: 020-8930 8162   Tel: 020-8248 6574

TINKER Victoria MANAGEMENT
(Technical, Non-Acting)
Birchenbridge House
Brighton Road
Mannings Heath, Horsham
West Sussex RH13 6HY   Tel/Fax: 01403 210653

TINSELTOWN ARTS AGENCY
44-46 St John Street
London EC1M 4DT
e-mail: info@tinseltown.co.uk
Fax: 020-7253 5400   Tel: 020-7689 7860

TONER CASTING Ltd
The Attic, 6th Floor, Hanover House
Hanover Street
Liverpool L1 3DZ
e-mail: tonercasting@hotmail.com
Fax: 0151-707 8414   Tel: 0151-708 6400

TOP CATS PROMOTIONS & MODELS
Llantrisant Road
Capel Llanilltern
Cardiff CF5 6JR
e-mail: topcatspromotions@btinternet.com
Fax: 029-2089 0996   Tel: 029-2089 0800

TOP MODELS Ltd
57 Holland Park
London W11 3RS
Fax: 020-7243 6046   Tel: 020-7243 6042

TOTS-TWENTIES
Suite 3, Ground Floor
Clements Court
Clements Lane
Ilford, Essex IG1 2QY
e-mail: sara@tots-twenties.co.uk
Fax: 020-8553 1880   Tel: 020-8478 1848

TRAIN HOUSE The
27 Prospect Road, Long Ditton
Surrey KT6 5PY
e-mail: agents@trainhouse.demon.co.uk
Fax: 020-8873 2782   Tel: 020-8873 7932

TRENDS
54 Lisson Street
London NW1 5DF
e-mail: info@trendsgroup.co.uk
Fax: 020-7258 3591   Tel: 020-7723 8001

TROLAN Gary MANAGEMENT
PM Write
30 Burrard Road
London NW6 1DB
e-mail: garytrolanmgmt@aol.com
Tel/Fax: 020-7794 4429   Tel: 020-7431 4367

Beverley Klein

Benedict Cumberbatch

Montserrat Lombard

TROUPERS.COM
Unit 62, Maltings Yard
Walton Road, Wavendon
Milton Keynes MK17 8LW
e-mail: info@troupers.com
Fax: 01908 586979   Tel: 01908 282925

TUCKER Tommy AGENCY
Suite 66, 235 Earls Court Road
London SW5 9FE
e-mail: tttommytucker@aol.com
Fax: 020-7370 4784   Tel: 020-7370 3911

TV MANAGEMENTS
Brink House, Avon Castle, Ringwood
Hants BH24 2BL
Fax: 01425 480123   Tel: 01425 475544

TWINS
(See PC THEATRICAL & MODEL AGENCY)

TWINS & TRIPLETS
(Identical Babies, Children, Teenagers & Adults
for Film/Television)
Holmhurst Road
Upper Belvedere DA17 6HW
e-mail: action@infomet.co.uk
Mobile: 07703 754187   Tel/Fax: 01322 440184

TWIST & FLIC Ltd
(Sports Agent)
The Studio, 3 Thornlaw Road
London SE27 0SH
e-mail: info@sportsmodels.com
                              Tel/Fax: 020-8761 7100

TWO'S COMPANY
244 Upland Road
London SE22 0DN
e-mail: 2scompany@britishlibrary.net
Fax: 020-8299 3714   Tel: 020-8299 4593

UGLY MODELS
Tigris House, 256 Edgware Road
London W2 1DS
e-mail: info@ugly.org
Fax: 020-7402 0507   Tel: 020-7402 5564

UNIQUE MANAGEMENT GROUP
Avon House, Kensington Village,
Avonmore Road
London W14 8TS
e-mail: jcarlton@uniquegroup.co.uk
Fax: 020-7371 5352   Tel: 020-7371 5353

UNITED COLOURS OF LONDON Ltd
1 Penylan Place, Edgware
Middlesex HA8 6EN
e-mail: richard@united-colours.com
Fax: 020-8952 1892   Tel: 020-8952 2941

UPBEAT MANAGEMENT
(Theatre Touring & Events - No Actors)
Sutton Business Centre, Restmor Way
Wallington SM6 7AH
e-mail: info@upbeat.co.uk
Fax: 020-8669 6752   Tel: 020-8773 1223

VACCA Roxane MANAGEMENT*
73 Beak Street
London W1R 3LF
e-mail: roxane@rvmanagement.fsnet.co.uk
Fax: 020-7734 8086   Tel: 020-7734 8085

VAGABOND HEART
2 Grassmere Road
Hornchurch, Essex RM11 3DP
e-mail: vagabondheart@virgin.net
                              Tel: 01708 781994

VALLE ACADEMY THEATRICAL AGENCY The
The Rosedale Old Cestrians Club
Andrews Lane, Cheshunt
Herts EN7 6TB
e-mail: agency@valleacademy.co.uk
Fax: 01992 622868   Tel: 01992 622861

VIDAL-HALL Clare*
(Directors, Designers, Choreographers, Lighting
Designers)
28 Perrers Road, London W6 0EZ
e-mail: clarevidalhall@email.com
Fax: 020-8741 9459   Tel: 020-8741 7647

VILLIERS & HUDSON Ltd
(Lucy Villiers & Nancy Hudson)
3rd Floor
50 South Molton Street
London W1K 5SB
e-mail: vilhud@freeuk.com
Fax: 020-7499 0884   Tel: 020-7499 5548

VINE Michael ASSOCIATES
(Light Entertainment)
29 Mount View Road
London N4 4SS
e-mail: mpvine@aol.com
Fax: 020-8348 3277   Tel: 020-8348 5899

W6 AGENCY The
11 Devonshire Mews
Chiswick, London W4 2HA
e-mail: thew6agency@lineone.net
Fax: 020-8994 7778   Tel: 020-8994 7575

WADE Thelma PERSONAL MANAGEMENT*
54 Harley Street
London W1G 5PZ
e-mail: tandtwade@hotmail.com
Fax: 020-7580 2337   Tel: 020-7580 9860

WALMSLEY Peter ASSOCIATES
(Agent's Locum/Assistant. No Representation)
37A Crimsworth Road
London SW8 4RJ
e-mail: pwalmsley1@supanet.com
Mobile: 07778 347312   Tel: 020-7787 6419

WARING & McKENNA*
22 Grafton Street
London W1S 4EX
e-mail: dj@waringandmckenna.demon.co.uk
Fax: 020-7409 7932   Tel: 020-7491 2666

WEEKS Kimberley MANAGEMENT
116 Earlham Grove
Forest Gate
London E7 9AS   Tel: 020-8519 4473

WELCH Janet PERSONAL MANAGEMENT
24 Red Lion Street
Richmond, Surrey TW9 1RW
Fax: 020-8332 6568   Tel: 020-8332 6544

WEST CENTRAL MANAGEMENT
Co-operative
Room 4, East Block
38 Mount Pleasant
London WC1X 0AP
e-mail: west.central@virgin.net
                              Tel/Fax: 020-7833 8134

ANDY MARTIN
PHOTOGRAPHER & FILM/TV D.O.P.

STUDIO & LOCATION

01727 843036 ~ 07850 303143

(North London & Hertfordshire)

Tony Adams

WHATEVER ARTISTS MANAGEMENT Ltd
1 York Street
London W1U 6PA
e-mail: wam@agents-uk.com
Fax: 020-7487 3311   Tel: 020-7487 3111

WHITEHALL ARTISTS
10 Lower Common South
London SW15 1BP
e-mail: mwhitehall@email.msn.com
Fax: 020-8788 2340   Tel: 020-8785 3737

WILD THEATRICAL MANAGEMENT
Bretons Manor
411 Rainham Road, Rainham
Essex RM12 7LP
e-mail: wildtm@lineone.net
                    Tel/Fax: 020-7071 0317

WILDE Vivien Ltd*
193 Wardour Street
London W1V 3FA
e-mail: vivien.wilde@virgin.net
Fax: 020-7439 1941   Tel: 020-7439 1940

WILKINSON David ASSOCIATES*
115 Hazlebury Road
London SW6 2LX
Fax: 020-7371 5161   Tel: 020-7371 5188

WILLOW PERSONAL MANAGEMENT
(Specialist Agency for Short Actors)
151 Main Street
Yaxley, Peterborough
Cambs PE7 3LD
e-mail: info@willowmanagement.co.uk
                    Tel: 01733 240392

WILLS Newton MANAGEMENT
The Studios
17 Church Street, Belton
Rutland LE15 9JU
e-mail: csocci@compuserve.com
                    Tel/Fax: 01572 717314

WIZARD MANAGEMENT
5 Clare Lawn
London SW14 8BH
e-mail: attwiz@aol.com
Fax: 020-8878 3821   Tel: 020-8876 0406

WYMAN Edward AGENCY
F TV (English & Welsh Language)
67 Llanon Road, Llanishen
Cardiff CF14 5AH
e-mail: edwardwymanagency@ukonline.co.uk
Fax: 029-2075 2444   Tel: 029-2075 2351

WYPER Carolynne MANAGEMENT
2 Kimberley Road
London NW6 7SG
e-mail: info@soundtrackcwm.co.uk
Fax: 020-7328 1444   Tel: 020-7328 8211

YELLOW BALLOON PRODUCTIONS Ltd
Freshwater House
Outdowns, Effingham
Surrey KT24 5QR
e-mail: yellowbal@aol.com
Fax: 01483 281502   Tel: 01483 281500

YEOH Eddie MANAGEMENT
37 Falmouth Gardens
Redbridge, Essex IG4 5JU
Fax: 020-8550 0348   Tel: 020-8550 9994

YOUNG April Ltd
11 Woodlands Road, Barnes
London SW13 0JZ
Fax: 020-8878 7017   Tel: 020-8876 7030

ZAHL Ann PERSONAL MANAGEMENT
57 Great Cumberland Place
London W1H 7LJ
Fax: 020-7262 4143   Tel: 020-7724 3684

ZAHRA & REMICK
F TV Theatre
186 Albert Road
London N22 7AH   Tel/Fax: 020-8889 6225

ZWICKLER Marlene & ASSOCIATES
2 Belgrave Place
Edinburgh EH4 3AN   Tel/Fax: 0131-343 3030

ACT ONE
Drama Studio & Agency

Children & adults up to 30 yrs. available for tv, theatre,
radio, films, commercials, voice overs, corporate videos etc.

31 Dobbin Hill, Sheffield, S11 7JA.
tel **0114 2667209** *mobile* **07971 850617**
fax **07971 112153**
email **casting@actonedrama.co.uk**
web **www.actonedrama.co.uk**

t.a.a.
the arts academy
Represent highly talented
and trained children
including
GEORGINA SHERRINGTON
star of:
'The Worst Witch'
& 'Wyrdsister'
the arts academy
15 Lexham Mews
London W8 6JW
Tel: 020 7376 0267
Fax: 020 7376 2416

2 KIDZ ACTORS in association with TIPTOES THEATRE SCHOOL
Tiptoes House, 2 Collingwood Place
Layton, Blackpool FY3 8HU
Tel: 01253 302616   Tel: 01253 302614

ABACUS AGENCY
Milton Brook Cottage, Westcott Road
Dorking RH4 3PU
e-mail: abacusue@aol.com
Fax: 01306 877813   Tel: 01306 877144

ACADEMY MANAGEMENT
41 Worcestershire Lea, Warfield, Berks RG42 3TQ
Fax: 01344 426410   Tel: 01344 426313

ACT ONE DRAMA STUDIO & AGENCY
31 Dobbin Hill,, Sheffield S11 7JA
e-mail: casting@actonedrama.co.uk
Fax: 07971 112153   Tel: 0114-266 7209

ACT OUT AGENCY
22 Greek Street, Stockport
Cheshire SK3 8AB   Tel/Fax: 0161-429 7413

ACTIVATE DRAMA SCHOOL
(Drama School and Agency)
Priestman Cottage, Sea View Road
Sunderland SR2 7UP
e-mail: activate_agcy@hotmail.com
Fax: 0191-551 2051   Tel: 0191-565 2345

AFFINITY MODELLING & CASTING
(Babies, Children & Teenagers)
16 Paddock Gardens, East Grinstead
Sussex RH19 4AE
e-mail: linscan@aol.com
Fax: 01342 326655   Tel: 01342 311425

AGENCY K-BIS
Clermont Hall, Cumberland Road, Brighton BN1 6SL
e-mail: k-bis@zoom.co.uk   Tel/Fax: 01273 564366

A & J MANAGEMENT
551 Green Lanes, London N13 4DR
e-mail: ajmanagement@bigfoot.com
Fax: 020-8882 5983   Tel: 020-8882 7716

ALEXANDER Suzanne MANAGEMENT
London Road Business Centre
Suite 3:2, 106 London Road, Liverpool L3 5JY
e-mail: suzyalex@hotmail.com
                          Tel/Fax: 0151-608 9655

ALLSORTS (Drama for Children)
(Sasha Leslie, Melissa Healy)
2 Pember Road, London NW10 5LP
e-mail: enquiries@allsorts.ltd.uk
                          Tel/Fax: 020-8969 3249

ANDREWS Amanda AGENCY
30 Caverswall Road, Blythe Bridge
Stoke-on-Trent
Staffordshire ST11 9BG   Tel/Fax: 01782 393889

ANGEL EYES MODELLING AND CASTING AGENCY Ltd
11 The Vale, Acton, London W3 7SH
e-mail: achtarshazy@aol.com
Fax: 020-8743 9828   Tel: 020-8746 1194

ANNA'S MANAGEMENT
(Formerly of ALADDIN'S CAVE)
25 Tintagel Drive, Stanmore, Middlesex HA7 4SR
Mobile: 07973 688917   Tel/Fax: 020-8958 7636

A PLUS
(Acting and Modelling Agency)
54 Grove Park, London SE5 8LG
e-mail: janekidsplus@aol.com
Mobile: 07759 944215   Tel/Fax: 020-7737 3901

ARAENA/COLLECTIVE
10 Bramshaw Gardens, South Oxhey
Herts WD1 6XP   Tel/Fax: 020-8428 0037

ARRAN KIDZ
112 Mount Pleasant, London EN4 9HQ
e-mail: arranassoc@netscapeonline.co.uk
Fax: 020-8447 3957   Tel: 020-8441 7348

ARTS ACADEMY The (T.A.A.)
15 Lexham Mews, London W8 6JW
Fax: 020-7376 2416   Tel: 020-7376 0267

ASHCROFT ACADEMY OF DRAMATIC ART
Bellenden Old School
Bellenden Road
London SE15 4DG   Tel/Fax: 020-8693 8088

AST MANAGEMENT
Anna Scher Theatre, 70-72 Barnsbury Road
London N1 0ES
e-mail: theagency@annaschermanagement.fsnet.co.uk
Fax: 020-7833 9467   Tel: 020-7278 2101

AWA - ANDREA WILDER AGENCY
23 Cambrian Drive
Colwyn Bay, Conwy LL28 4SL
e-mail: casting@awagency.co.uk
Fax: 07092 249314   Tel: 01492 547542

BARDSLEY'S Pamela UNIQUE AGENCY
1 Birkdale Mews
15A Liverpool Road
Birkdale Southport
Merseyside PR8 4AS   Tel/Fax: 01704 566771

B.L.A. THEATRE SCHOOL
(Stage School & Agency)
Performance House, 20 Passey Place
London SE9 5DQ
e-mail: bla@dircon.co.uk
Fax: 020-8850 9944   Tel: 020-8850 9888

Annabelle Tarrant as 'Alice Watts' - Coronation Street.

Tuesdays Child
Television & Model Agency
(Est. 1976)

Children from Manchester,
Merseyside, Nottingham,
Birmingham & Yorkshire
from Birth - 18 years

Tel: 01625 501765 *and* **612244 (4 lines)**
www.tuesdayschildagency.co.uk
Email: bookings@tuesdayschildagency.co.uk

JACKIE PALMER AGENCY

30 Daws Hill Lane
High Wycombe, Bucks
Office 01494 520978
Fax 01494 510479
E-mail jackie.palmer@btinternet.com

Well behaved, natural children,
teenagers and young adults.
All nationalities, many bi-lingual.
Acrobatics are a speciality.
Pupils regularly appear in
West End Theatre, including
RSC, Royal National Theatre and
in Film and Television.

We are just off the M40
within easy reach of London, Oxford,
Birmingham and the South West.

Licensed tutors and chaperones

JIGSAW ARTS MANAGEMENT

Jigsaw Arts Management is a theatrical agency representing children and young people who have been selected from Jigsaw Performing Arts Schools.

For further information, please contact Jigsaw Arts on 020 8447 4530
64-66 High Street Barnet Hertfordshire EN5 5SJ

BODEN AGENCY
6-12 Windmill Hill, Enfield
Middlesex EN2 6SA
e-mail: bodens2692@aol.com
Fax: 020-8367 1836   Tel: 020-8367 2692

BONNIE KIDS
8 Church Road, Teddington
Middlesex TW11 8PB
e-mail: bonniekids@touchdownpromotions.co.uk
Fax: 020-8943 1024   Tel: 020-8977 5471

BOURNEMOUTH YOUTH THEATRE The (BYT)
14 Cooper Dean Drive
Bournemouth BH8 9LN
e-mail: klair@thebyt.co.uk
Fax: 01202 255826   Tel: 01202 780210

BRIGHT SPARKS THEATRE SCHOOL & AGENCY
16 Wellfield Road, London SW16 2BP
Fax: 020-8677 8659   Tel: 020-8769 3500

BRUCE & BROWN
203 Canalot Studios, 222 Kensal Road
London W10 5BN
Fax: 020-8964 0457   Tel: 020-8968 5585

BUBBLEGUM
Ealing Studios, Ealing Green
London W5 5EP
e-mail: kids@bubblegummodels.com
Fax: 020-8758 8664   Tel: 020-8758 8678

BYRON'S CASTING
(Children, Babies & Teenagers)
North London Performing Arts Centre
76 St James Lane, Muswell Hill
London N10 3DF
e-mail: nlpac@compuserve.com
Fax: 020-8444 4040   Tel: 020-8444 4445

C.A.L.S. CASTING
(Children & Teenagers)
Unit E2, Bellevale Shopping Centre
Liverpool L25 2RG
Mobile: 07930 889057   Tel/Fax: 0151-487 8500

CAPITAL ARTS
Wyllyotts Centre
Darkes Lane, Potters Bar, Herts EN6 2HN
e-mail: capitalartstheatre@genie.co.uk
Mobile: 07885 232414   Tel/Fax: 020-8449 2342

CARR Norrie MODEL AGENCY
Holborn Studios
49-50 Eagle Wharf Road, London N1 7ED
e-mail: info@norriecarr.com
Fax: 020-7253 1772   Tel: 020-7253 1771

CARTEURS THEATRICAL AGENCY
170A Church Road, Hove, East Sussex BN3 2DJ
e-mail: www@stonelandsschool.co.uk
Fax: 01273 770444   Tel: 01273 770445

C D G AGENCY
11 Princes Park Parade, Hayes
Middlesex UB3 1LA
e-mail: peterwareham@princespark.freeserve.co.uk
                                  Tel/Fax: 020-8581 4545

CENTRE STAGE MANAGEMENT
The Croft, 7 Cannon Road, Southgate
London N14 7HE
e-mail: carole@centrestageuk.com
Fax: 020-8886 7555   Tel: 020-8886 4264

CHILDREN OF LONDON ACTING & MODEL AGENCY
The Playhouse, 273 Malden Road, Surrey KT3 6AH
e-mail: childrenoflondon@compuserve.com
Fax: 020-8949 0522   Tel: 020-8949 0450

LINTON MANAGEMENT

In association with Coral Godby Theatre Workshop providing training to over 1300 members

representing

Children of all ages and young adults

available for

TV, Film, Theatre, Radio, Commercials, Voice overs etc.

Complimentary audition facilities and casting workshop available
Licenced Chaperones and Tutors supplied
Photo Directory & full cv's available on request

Tel: 0161 761 2020   Fax: 0161 761 1999

Established 1991

3 The Rock

Bury BL9 OJP

Boden Agency

Children & Teenagers Available
Stage, TV, Films

Tel: 020-8367 2692 (3 lines) Fax: 020-8367 1836
E-mail: Bodens2692@aol.com
6-12 WINDMILL HILL, ENFIELD EN2 6SA

Established
1979

CHILDSPLAY THE CHILDREN'S AGENCY
1 Cathedral Street, London SE1 9DE
Fax: 020-7403 1656   Tel: 020-7403 4834

CHRYSTEL ARTS AGENCY
15 Churchill Road, Edgware
Middlesex HA8 6NX
e-mail: chrystelarts@talk21.com
                              Tel: 020-8952 1281

CITY LITES
PO Box 29673, London E8 3FH
e-mail: gulcan@freeuk.com
Mobile: 07773 353645   Tel/Fax: 020-7683 9016

CLAPPERBOARD CASTING
(Main Agents for Stagecoach Schools)
PO Box 153, Manchester M7 4YU
Fax: 0161-792 4285   Tel: 0161-792 2277

CLARKE Rose MANAGEMENT & THEATRE SCHOOL
PO Box 23722, 3-4 Bramham Gardens
Kensington, London SW5 0WX
e-mail: roseclarkemanagement@hotmail.com
                              Tel/Fax: 020-8856 2536

CLOUD NINE AGENCY
96 Tiber Gardens, Treaty Street, London N1 0XE
e-mail: cloudnineagency@ic24.net
                              Tel/Fax: 020-7278 0029

COLIN'S PERFORMING ARTS AGENCY
(Colin's Performing Arts Ltd)
The Studios, 219B North Street, Romford
Essex RM1 4QA
e-mail: admin@colinsperformingarts.co.uk
Fax: 01708 766077   Tel: 01708 766444

COLLINS STUDENT MANAGEMENT
St Dunstan's Hall
East Acton Lane
London W3 7EG
e-mail: collinsstudents@aol.com
Fax: 020-8740 6542   Tel: 020-8743 9514

CONTI Italia AGENCY Ltd
23 Goswell Road
London EC1M 7AJ
e-mail: sca@italiaconti36.freeserve.co.uk
Fax: 020-7253 1430   Tel: 020-7336 6122

D & B MANAGEMENT & THEATRE SCHOOL
470 Bromley Road
Bromley, Kent BR1 4PN
Fax: 020-8697 8100   Tel: 020-8698 8880

DENNING Sylvia REPRESENTATION
The Studio, 1 Queensland Avenue
London SW19 3AD
e-mail: sylviadenning@bestshot.org.uk
                           Tel/Fax: 020-8540 1238

DIMPLES MODEL & CASTING ACADEMY
Suite 2, 2nd Floor, Magnum House
33 Lord Street, Leigh, Lancs WN7 1BY
e-mail: dimples_m_c_a@btinternet.com
Fax: 01942 262232   Tel: 01942 262012

EARNSHAW Susi MANAGEMENT
5 Brook Place
Barnet, Herts EN5 2DL
Fax: 020-8364 9618   Tel: 020-8441 5010

ENGLISH Doreen '95
(Gerry Kinner)
4 Selsey Avenue, Aldwick, Bognor Regis
West Sussex PO21 2QZ   Tel: 01243 825968

**EUROKIDS & ADULTS INTERNATIONAL CASTING
& MODELLING AGENCY**
The Warehouse Studio
Glaziers Lane, Culcheth
Warrington, Cheshire WA3 4AQ
e-mail: info@eurokids.co.uk
Fax: 01925 767563   Tel: 01925 767574

EXTRAS UNLIMITED
14 Russell Garden Mews, London W14 8EU
e-mail: mark@marksummers.com
Fax: 020-7602 9994   Tel: 020-7603 9995

FBI AGENCY Ltd The
PO Box 250, Leeds LS1 2AZ
e-mail: j.spencer@fbi-agency.ltd.uk
                           Tel/Fax: 07050 222747

**FIORENTINI Anna THEATRE & FILM SCHOOL &
AGENCY**
87 Glyn Road, Hackney
London E5 0JA
e-mail: info@annafiorentini.co.uk
                           Tel: 020-8985 3795

FOOTSTEPS THEATRE SCHOOL CASTING
55 Pullan Avenue, Eccleshill
Bradford BD2 3RP   Tel/Fax: 01274 637429

FOX Betty STAGE SCHOOL
The Friends Institute, 220 Moseley Road
Birmingham B12 0DG
e-mail: bettyfox.school@virgin.net
                           Tel/Fax: 0121-440 1635

GLYNNE Frances MANAGEMENT
11 High Ash Avenue
Leeds LS17 8RS
e-mail: franandmo@cwctv.net
Fax: 0113-295 9408   Tel: 0113-266 4286

ACTIVATE
YOUR IMAGINATION
Drama School and Agency

Actors, Extras, Chaperones and tutors with all round training for Theatre, T.V., Film and Commercial work

Contact: Lesley McDonough

Priestman Cottage, Sea View Road, Sunderland SR2 7UP

Tel: 0191 565 2345   Mob: 07989 365737

http://www.lineone.net/~lesley.mcdonough

Fax: 0191 551 2051   e-mail: activate_agcy@hotmail.com

KIDS PLUS / A PLUS
Acting & Modelling Agency

Kids Plus - children birth - 16 yrs
A Plus - young adults 16-26 yrs

Films, TV, Commercials, Photographic, Theatre

We have close links with local drama schools and most of our children attend regular acting classes

Casting Directory is available on request

Tel/Fax: 020 7737 3901
web: www.kidsplusuk.com
email: janekidsplus@aol.com
54 Grove Park, London SE5 8LG

GO FOR IT CHILDREN'S AGENCY
(Children & Teenagers)
47 North Lane, Teddington
Middlesex TW11 0HU
e-mail: info@goforittheatreschool.co.uk
Fax: 020-8287 9405   Tel: 020-8943 1120

GOBSTOPPERS MANAGEMENT
50 Bencroft Road, Hemel Hempstead
Herts HP2 5UY
e-mail: chrisgobstoppers@hotmail.com
Mobile: 07961 372319   Tel: 01442 269543

GOLDSTONE Samantha MANAGEMENT
10 Hillingdon Road, Whitefield
Manchester M45 7QN
e-mail: samantha.goldstone@btinternet.com
Tel/Fax: 0161-280 7678

G. P. ASSOCIATES
4 Gallus Close, Winchmore Hill, London N21 1JR
e-mail: clients@gpassociates.co.uk
Fax: 020-8882 9189   Tel: 020-8886 2263

GRAYSTONS
845 Green Lanes, Winchmore Hill
London N21 2RX
e-mail: graystons@btinternet.com
Fax: 020-8364 2009   Tel: 020-8360 5700

GREVILLE Jeannine THEATRICAL AGENCY
Melody House, Gillotts Corner
Henley-on-Thames, Oxon RG9 1QU
Fax: 01491 411533   Tel: 01491 572000

HARLEQUIN STUDIOS AGENCY FOR CHILDREN
223 Southcoast Road, Peacehaven
East Sussex BN10 8LB   Tel: 01273 581742

THE ANNA FIORENTINI
THEATRE & FILM SCHOOL & AGENCY

(Winner of the Shell LiveWire Award)

Representing 7 - 16 year olds

Situated in the East End of London

Students have Saturday classes in:

*Film Acting *Drama *Singing *Dance
*Set/Costume Design

Wally Foster Centre, Marsh Hill, Homerton Road, London E9 5QB

Tel/Fax: *Mobile:*
020 7682 1403   07779 125095

www.annafiorentini.co.uk

HARRIS AGENCY Ltd The
52 Forty Avenue, Wembley Park
Middlesex HA9 8LQ
e-mail: sharrisltd@aol.com
Fax: 020-8908 4455   Tel: 020-8908 4451

HEWITT PERFORMING ARTS
160 London Road, Romford, Essex RM7 9QL
e-mail: hewittcontrol@aol.com
                              Tel: 01708 727784

HOBSON'S KIDS
62 Chiswick High Road, London W4 1SY
e-mail: gaynor@hobsons-international.com
Fax: 020-8742 2237   Tel: 020-8747 8474

HORNIMANS MANAGEMENT
92 Malham Road, Forest Hill
London SE23 1AN   Tel/Fax: 020-8291 6944

HOWE Janet CHILDREN'S CASTING & MODELLING AGENCY
18 The Downs, Altrincham, Cheshire WA14 2PU
e-mail: janet@jhowecasting.fsbusiness.co.uk
Mobile: 07801 942178   Tel/Fax: 0161-233 0700

Canal Side Chambers, The Boat Yard,
Newcastle Road, Stone, Staffs ST15 8JZ
Tel/Fax: 01785 816888   Tel/Fax: 01785 816840

INTER-CITY KIDS
Portland Tower, Portland Street
Manchester M1 3LF
e-mail: intercity@bigfoot.com
                              Tel/Fax: 0161-226 0103

JABBERWOCKY AGENCY
(Representing Pineapple Performing Arts School and Woolborough Academy of Performing Arts, Children & Teenagers 6 Months -18 Years)
Wood Pecker Barn, Wickhurst Farm
Lamberhusrt, Kent TN3 8BH
e-mail: janella00@aol.com
Mobile: 07884 431724   Tel/Fax: 01892 890499

JB ASSOCIATES
3 Stevenson Square
Manchester M1 1DN
e-mail: united_cities@compuserve.com
Fax: 0161-237 1809   Tel: 0161-237 1808

JIGSAW ARTS MANAGEMENT
(Representing Children and Young People from Jigsaw Performing Arts Schools)
64-66 High Street, Barnet
Hertfordshire EN5 5SJ   Tel: 020-8447 4530

JUNO CASTING AGENCY
(in association with Drama Studio Edinburgh)
19 Belmont Road
Edinburgh EH14 5DZ
e-mail: 106347.3507@compuserve.com
Fax: 0131-453 3108   Tel: 0131-453 3284

KIDS LONDON
67 Dulwich Road, London SE24 0NJ
e-mail: kids.london@virgin.net
Fax: 020-7924 9584   Tel: 020-7924 9595

KIDS PLUS
(Acting & Modelling Agency)
54 Grove Park
London SE5 8LG
e-mail: janekidsplus@aol.com
Mobile: 07759 944215   Tel/Fax: 020-7737 3901

KIDZ PROFESSIONAL MODEL & CASTING AGENCY
500A Manchester Road East
Manchester M38 9NS
e-mail: info@kidzltd.com
Fax: 0161-799 6000   Tel: 08702 416260

K M C AGENCIES AND THEATRE SCHOOL
PO Box 122, 4th Floor, Ghulam House
16 Blossom Street, Manchester M4 5AW
e-mail: kids@kmcagencies.co.uk
Fax: 0161-237 9812   Tel: 0161-237 3009

KRACKERS KIDS THEATRICAL AGENCY
6/7 Electric Parade
Seven Kings Road
Ilford, Essex IG3 8BY
e-mail: krackerskids@hotmail.com
Tel/Fax: 01708 502046

LAINE Betty MANAGEMENT
The Studios, East Street
Epsom, Surrey KT17 1HH
e-mail: enquiries@betty-laine-management.co.uk
Tel/Fax: 01372 721815

L.A. KIDS
248 Station Road, Edgware, Middlesex HA8 7AU
Fax: 020-8958 2000   Tel: 020-8958 7799

LAMONT CASTING AGENCY
94 Harington Road, Formby, Liverpool
e-mail: diane@lamontcasting.co.uk
Fax: 01704 872422   Tel: 01704 877024

LINTON MANAGEMENT
3 The Rock, Bury BL9 0JP
e-mail: linman@amserve.net
Fax: 0161-761 1999   Tel: 0161-761 2020

LITTLE ACORNS
London House, 271-273 King Street
London W6 9LZ
e-mail: acorns@dircon.co.uk
Fax: 020-8408 3077   Tel: 020-8563 0773

Alex Wilson (Andrex Commercial 2001)

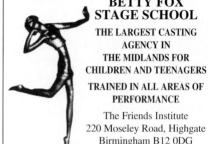
**LITTLE ADULTS ACADEMY & MODELLING
AGENCY Ltd**
Studio 11
Suite 13 Essex House
375-377 High Street
Stratford, London E15 4QZ
e-mail: donna@littleadults.demon.co.uk
Fax: 020-8519 9797   Tel: 020-8519 9755

LITTLE GEMS
11 Thorn Road, Boundstone, Farnham
Surrey GU10 4TU
e-mail: littlegems@hotmail.com
Mobile: 07960 978439   Tel/Fax: 01252 792078

LITTLE WOTSITZ CHILDREN'S TALENT AGENCY
MC House 1st Floor
2 St Mark's Place
London SW19 7ND
e-mail: lwotsitz@aol.com   Tel/Fax: 020-8947 9147

LIVE WIRE CHILDREN'S THEATRE
52 Cherry Avenue
Oldham OL8 2HS
e-mail: livewiresscotland@genie.co.uk
    Tel: 0161-345 8237

LIVEWIRES CASTING AGENCY
PO Box 23199
Edinburgh EH7 5AH
e-mail: livewiresscotland@genie.co.uk
Fax: 0131-557 2437   Tel: 0131-557 2647

MOVIE MITES AGENCY
30 Spedan Close
Branch Hill, Hampstead
London NW3 7XF
e-mail: movimites@aol.com
Fax: 020-7794 0771   Tel: 020-7431 5698

MOXEY CASTING
34 Davenport Road, Felpham
West Sussex PO22 7JS
e-mail: amandamoxey@hotmail.com
Mobile: 07860 717713   Tel: 01243 869566

MRS WORTHINGTON'S
16 Ouseley Road
London SW12 8EF   Tel/Fax: 020-8767 6944

NEXT GENERATION
26 Devonshire Way, Shirley, Croydon CRO 8BR
e-mail: nextgeneration27@aol.com
    Tel/Fax: 020-8406 9805

NOEL CASTING
(Specialising in Character Actors and
Ethnic and Asian Actors)
Suite 501, International House
223 Regent Street, London W1B 2QD
e-mail: kingnoel/177@hotmail.com
Fax: 020-7544 1090   Tel: 020-7544 1010

NORTHERN FILM & DRAMA
PO Box 27, Tadcaster, North Yorks LS24 9XS
e-mail: alyson@connew.com
    Tel/Fax: 01937 530600

O'FARRELL STAGE SCHOOL
36 Shirley Street, Canning Town
London E16 1HU   Tel: 020-7511 9444

ORR THEATRE DANCE CENTRE & AGENCY
20 Bembridge Drive, Bolton BL3 1RJ
e-mail: barbara@orrdance.co.uk
Fax: 01204 388317   Tel: 01204 579842

PALMER Jackie AGENCY
30 Daws Hill Lane, High Wycombe
Bucks HP11 1PW
e-mail: jackie.palmer@btinternet.com
Fax: 01494 510479   Tel: 01494 520978

PATMORE Sandra SCHOOL AND AGENCY
(Dancing, Drama & Acrobatic)
173 Uxbridge Road, Rickmansworth
Herts WD3 2DW   Tel/Fax: 01923 772542

PC THEATRICAL & MODEL AGENCY
10 Strathmore Gardens, Edgware
Middlesex HA8 5HJ
e-mail: twinagy@aol.com
Fax: 020-8933 3418   Tel: 020-8381 2229

PHA YOUTH
Tanzaro House
Ardwick Green North
Manchester M12 6FZ
e-mail: info@pha-agency.co.uk
Fax: 0161-273 4567   Tel: 0161-273 4444

PLAYCAST
(Drama for Children)
1B Station Road, Hampton Wick
Kingston KT1 4HG
e-mail: dragondrama@hotmail.com
                              Tel/Fax: 020-8943 1504

POLLYANNA CHILDREN'S AGENCY
PO Box 30661
London E1W 3GG
e-mail: pollyanna-mgmt@yahoo.co.uk
Fax: 020-7480 6761   Tel: 020-7702 1937

**POWER CHILDREN MODEL MANAGEMENT
CASTING AGENCY**
The Royal, 25 Bank Plain
Norwich NR2 4SF
e-mail: powermodelmanagement@btinternet.com
Fax: 01603 621101   Tel: 01603 621100

PRIDE ARTIST MANAGEMENT
The Burnside Centre, Burnside Crescent,
Middleton, Manchester M24 5NN
e-mail: artistes@prideradio.co.uk
                              Tel/Fax: 0161-643 6266

RASCALS MODEL AGENCY
13 Jubilee Parade, Snakes Lane East
Woodford Green, Essex IG8 7QG
e-mail: kids@rascals.co.uk
Fax: 020-8559 1035   Tel: 020-8504 1111

RAVENSCOURT MANAGEMENT
Tandy House, 30-40 Dalling Road
London W6 0JB
e-mail: ravenscourt@hotmail.com
Fax: 020-8741 1786   Tel: 020-8741 0707

REDROOFS ASSOCIATES
Littlewick Green, Maidenhead
Berks SL6 3QY   Tel: 01628 822982

REEL KIDS
(Children 0-16 years)
99 Vellum Drive, Carshalton, Surrey SM5 2TU
Fax: 020-8286 3243   Tel: 020-8286 2906

REYNOLDS THEATRICAL AGENCY
Westgate House, Spital Street
Dartford, Kent DA1 2EH
e-mail: info@reynoldsgroup.co.uk
Fax: 01634 329079   Tel: 01322 277200

**RIDGEWAY STUDIOS SCHOOL OF
PERFORMING ARTS**
Fairley House, Andrews Lane, Cheshunt
Herts EN7 6LB
e-mail: info@ridgewaystudios.co.uk
Fax: 01992 633844   Tel: 01992 633775

S.A.M. YOUTH AGENCY
London Road Business Centre
Suite 3:2, 106 London Road
Liverpool L3 5JY   Tel/Fax: 0151-608 9655

SAM'S KIDS MODELLING AND CASTING AGENCY
69 Corporation Street
Sheffield S3 8RG
e-mail: elaine@samskids.com
Fax: 0114-276 6365   Tel: 0114-276 7787

SCALLYWAGS AGENCY
1 Cranbrook Rise
Ilford, Essex IG1 3QW
e-mail: kids@scallywags.co.uk
Fax: 020-8924 0262   Tel: 020-8518 1133

SCREAM MANAGEMENT
3 Mersey Road, Blackpool, Lancashire FY4 1EN
e-mail: info@screamltd.fsnet.co.uk
                              Tel/Fax: 01253 298602

SHARONA STAGE SCHOOL AGENCY & MANAGEMENT
82 Grennell Road, Sutton
Surrey SM1 3DN
Fax: 020-8395 0009   Tel: 020-8642 9396

SINGER Sandra ASSOCIATES
21 Cotswold Road, Westcliff on Sea
Essex SS0 8AA
e-mail: sandra.singer@virgin.net
Fax: 01702 339393   Tel: 01702 331616

SMITH Elisabeth Ltd
81 Headstone Road, Harrow
Middlesex HA1 1PQ
e-mail: models@elisabethsmith.com
Fax: 020-8861 1880   Tel: 020-8863 2331

SMITH Robert AGENCY The
The Courtyard, Whitchurch
Ross-on-Wye HR9 6DA
e-mail: agent@southwestcasting.co.uk
Fax: 01600 891099   Tel: 01600 891160

SOLE FILE THEATRICAL AGENCY The
(Children & Young Adults)
151A Field End Road, Eastcote
Middlesex HA5 1QL
e-mail: sole.file@virgin.net
Fax: 020-8901 4001   Tel: 020-8901 4097

SPEAKE Barbara AGENCY
East Acton Lane, London W3 7EG
e-mail: speakekids1@aol.com
Fax: 020-8740 6542   Tel: 020-8743 6096

STAGE 01 THEATRE SCHOOL & AGENCY
32 Westbury Lane
Buckhurst Hill, Essex IG9 5PL
e-mail: stage01@lineone.net
Mobile: 07939 121154   Tel/Fax: 020-8506 0949

STAGE 84 YORKSHIRE SCHOOL OF PERFORMING ARTS
Old Bell Chapel, Town Lane, Bradford
West Yorks BD10 8PR
Mobile: 07785 244984   Tel: 01274 569197

STAGE PLUS AGENCY
Park Meadow House, Wycombe Road
Princes Risborough
Bucks HP27 0DH   Tel: 01844 342137

STAGECOACH AGENCY
The Courthouse, Elm Grove
Walton-on-Thames, Surrey KT12 1LZ
e-mail: mail@stagecoach.co.uk
Fax: 01932 222894   Tel: 01932 254333

STARLINGS THEATRICAL AGENCY
45 Viola Close
South Ockendon
Essex RM15 6JF
e-mail: juliecartercar24w@supanet.com
Mobile: 07941 653463   Tel: 01708 859109

STARSHINE CHILDREN'S THEATRE WORKSHOP & AGENCY
St Helier Congregational Church
Green Lane, Morden
Surrey SM4   Mobile: 07939 398630

STEVENS Dacia
Glenavon Lodge, Lansdowne Road
South Woodford
London E18 2BE   Tel: 020-8989 0166

STONELANDS SCHOOL OF BALLET & THEATRE ARTS
170A Church Road, Hove
East Sussex BN3 2DJ
e-mail: www@stonelandsschool.co.uk
Fax: 01273 770444   Tel: 01273 770445

SUMMERS Mark MANAGEMENT & AGENCY
14 Russell Garden Mews
London W14 8EU
e-mail: mark@marksummers.com
Fax: 020-7602 9994   Tel: 020-7603 9995

SUPERARTS AGENCY
26-28 Ambergate Street
London SE17 3RX   Tel/Fax: 020-7735 4975

SWEENEY TEENS AND TODS
Ramillies House, 1-2 Ramillies Street
London W1V 1DF
e-mail: teens&tods@sweeneymanagement.co.uk
Fax: 020-7437 2080   Tel: 020-7287 0900

T.A.A.
(See ARTS ACADEMY The)

TANWOOD
46 Bath Road, Swindon
Wilts SN1 4AY
Fax: 01793 643219   Tel: 01793 523895

THEATRE ARTS (WEST LONDON)
18 Kingsdale Gardens, Notting Hill
London W11 4TZ
e-mail: theatreartswestlondon@hotmail.com
Tel/Fax: 020-7603 3471

THEATRE EXPRESS PERFORMING ARTS AGENCY
Tel/Fax: 01608 676024

THOMPSON Jim CHILDREN'S SECTION
(Jenny Donnison)
Herricks, School Lane, Arundel
West Sussex BN18 9DR
Fax: 01903 885887   Tel: 01903 885757

TOP-SPOTS AGENCY
(Commercials, Films, Babies to Adults)
314 Haydons Road, Wimbledon
London SW19 8JZ
Fax: 020-8543 5511   Tel: 020-8543 7766

TOTS-TWENTIES AGENCY
Suite 3 Ground Floor, Clements Court
Clements Lane, Ilford, Essex IG1 2QY
e-mail: sara@tots-twenties.co.uk
Fax: 020-8553 1880   Tel: 020-8478 1848

TROUPERS.COM
Unit 62, Maltings Yard
Walton Road, Wavendon
Milton Keynes MK17 8LW
e-mail: info@troupers.com
Fax: 01908 586979   Tel: 01908 282925

Childsplay
★★★
The Children's Agency
BABIES, CHILDREN & TEENAGERS
for
MODELLING, ACTING & PERFORMING

T: 020 7403 4834
F: 020 7403 1656
e-mail: childsplaylondon@aol.com

Angel Eyes LTD
Modelling & Casting Agency

We represent from newborn babies, toddlers, children and teenagers and up to 40 yrs old. We do all extractions from ORIENTAL, ASIAN, AFRICAN and EUROPEAN. All models can act and dance, all well-spoken English and some bi-lingual. Languages include: Arabic, Spanish, Urdu, French, Hindi, Italian and Gujarati. All reliable and available for: TV, Photography, Films, Commercials, Extras, Theatre and Fashion. So if you are looking for excellent service, reliable models and actors who take direction well and show dedication to their roles please call us.

11 The Vale, London W3 7SH
Tel: 020 8746 1194

TRULY SCRUMPTIOUS Ltd
The Worx, 16-24 Underwood Street
London N1 7JQ
e-mail: bookings@trulyscrumptious.co.uk
Fax: 020-7251 5767   Tel: 020-7608 3806

TUESDAYS CHILD
Gateway House
Watersgreen, Macclesfield
Cheshire SK11 6LH
e-mail: bookings@tuesdayschildagency.co.uk
Tel/Fax: 01625 501765   Tel: 01625 612244

TWINS
(See PC THEATRICAL & MODEL AGENCY)

TWINS & TRIPLETS
(Identical Babies, Children, Teenagers & Adults for Film/Television)
Holmhurst Road, Upper Belvedere
Kent DA17 6HW
e-mail: action@infomet.co.uk
Mobile: 07703 754187   Tel/Fax: 01322 440184

VALLE ACADEMY THEATRICAL AGENCY The
The Rosedale Old Cestrians Club
Andrews Lane
Cheshunt
Herts EN7 6TB
Fax: 01992 622868   Tel: 01992 622861

VISIONS AGENCY
Foxbury Studios
39A Foxbury Road, Bromley
Kent BR1 4DG
e-mail: frances.cooper@talk21.com
Tel/Fax: 020-8466 7782

WHITEHALL PERFORMING ARTS CENTRE
Rayleigh Road, Leigh-on-Sea
Essex SS9 5UU   Tel/Fax: 01702 529290

WHIZZ KIDS STAGE & SCREEN AGENCY
3 Marshall Road
Cambridge CB1 7TY
e-mail: marshallcam@msn.com
Fax: 01223 512431   Tel: 01223 512423

WYSE AGENCY
1 Hill Farm Road, Whittlesford
Cambs CB2 4NB
e-mail: frances.wyse@btinternet.com
Fax: 01223 839414   Tel: 01223 832288

YOUNG ACTORS FILE The
39D Highbury New Park
Canonbury
London N5 2EN
e-mail: actorsfile@aol.com
Mobile: 07949 759468   Tel/Fax: 020-7359 1354

YOUNG STARGAZERS
Stonesthrow
18 Thornham Close
Clayton Newcastle, Staffs ST5 4LR
e-mail: info@young-stargazers.freeserve.co.uk
Fax: 01782 610363   Tel: 01782 751900

YOUNG 'UNS AGENCY
Sylvia Young Theatre School, Rossmore Road,
Marylebone, London NW1 6NJ
e-mail: younguns@freeuk.com
Fax: 020-7723 1040   Tel: 020-7723 0037

✳ **Livewires Casting Agency** *Edinburgh & Glasgow* ✳

Tel: 0131 557 2647   Fax: 0131 557 2437

Best Young Actors - 4 To 24
Recruited from Scotland's Acting Schools, Drama - Workshops and Youth Theatre Groups

---

Casting Agency & Management
2

2 KIDZ ACTORS
IN ASSOCIATION WITH

TIPTOES
THEATRE SCHOOL

REPRESENTING CHILDREN & TEENAGERS FOR FILM-TV-STAGE

Tiptoes House
2 Collingwood Place
Layton Blackpool
Lancs FY3 8HU

Tel 01253 302614
Fax 01253 302610

A LITTLE EXTRA
7 Tregoze Way, The Prinnels
Swindon, Wiltshire SN5 6NW
e-mail: swindonextra@aol.com
Mobile: 07949 759468   Tel/Fax: 0870 2412761

ALLSORTS THE AGENCY Ltd
1 Cathedral Street, London SE1 9DE
Fax: 020-7403 1656   Tel: 020-7403 4834

ATS CASTING Ltd
26 St Michael's Road
Leeds LS6 3AW
Fax: 0113-275 6422   Tel: 0113-230 4300

AVENUE ARTISTES Ltd
8 Winn Road
Southampton SO17 1EN
Fax: 023-8090 5703   Tel: 023-8055 1000

AWA - ANDREA WILDER AGENCY
23 Cambrian Drive, Colwyn Bay
Conwy LL28 4SL
e-mail: casting@awagency.co.uk
Fax: 07092 249314   Tel: 01492 547542

BALDIES CASTING AGENCY
(The only agency purely for bald people)
6 Marlott Road, Poole
Dorset BH15 3DX
Mobile: 07860 290437   Tel: 01202 666001

BRISTOL EXTRA SERVICE TEAM (B.E.S.T.)
(Ernest Jones) (Film & TV Actors, Extras,
Speciality Artists)
21 Ellesmere, Thornbury, Near Bristol BS35 2ER
Mobile: 07951 955759   Tel/Fax: 01454 411628

BROADCASTING
Unit 23 Canalot Studios
222 Kensal Road
London W10 5BN
Fax: 020-7460 5223   Tel: 020-7460 5222

BROMLEY CASTING
(Film & TV)
77 Widmore Road
Bromley BR1 3AA
e-mail: admin@bromleycasting.tv
                Tel/Fax: 020-8466 8239

BROOK Dolly CASTING AGENCY
PO Box 5436
Dunmow CM6 1WW
Fax: 01371 875996   Tel: 01371 875767

CAMCAST
Laragain, Upper Banavie, Fort William
Inverness-shire PH33 7PB
e-mail: anne@camcast.co.uk
Fax: 01397 772456   Tel: 01397 772523

CELEX CASTING & MANAGEMENT
(Children available)
11 Glencroft Drive, Stenson Fields
Derby DE24 3LS
e-mail: anne@celex.co.uk
Fax: 01332 232115   Tel: 01332 232445

CHRISTIAN'S CHARACTERS
50 Newland Terrace, Queenstown Road
Battersea, London SW8 3RN
e-mail: christianscharacters@showground.net
                Tel/Fax: 020-7720 0682

BROMLEY CASTING
FILM & T.V. EXTRAS AGENCY

Providing quality Background Artists
to the U.K. Film & T.V. Industry
Full details available from website

Tel/Fax: 020 8466 8239
WWW. BROMLEYCASTING.TV

BROMLEY CASTING
77 Widmore Road, Bromley BR1 3AA
Credits: Channel X, BBC, Bazal, C4 etc

JANET HOWE AGENCY
Walk-ons/Extras/Crowd Artists
24 Hour Service

Manchester Office - 0161 2330700
Staffordshire Office - 01785 818480/816888

Recent Credits:-
**Doctors, Casualty,
Sunday Bloody Sunday,
John Lennon, Cold Feet**

E-mail: janet@jhowecasting.fsbusiness.co.uk

CORNWALL FILM AGENCY
East Trevelmond Farm, Trevelmond
Liskeard, Cornwall PL14 4LY
e-mail: frances@cornwall-film-agency.fsnet.co.uk
Tel/Fax: 01579 321858

CROWDS
Unit 23 Canalot Studio, 222 Kensal Road
London W10 5BN
Fax: 020-7460 5223   Tel: 020-7460 5222

CYBER ARTISTS 2000
In the Can Ltd, 20 Old Steine
Brighton BN1 1EL
e-mail: cyber@cyber.ndo.co.uk
Tel/Fax: 01273 671234

DAVID AGENCY The
153 Battersea Rise
London SW11 1HP
e-mail: casting@davidagency.net
Fax: 020-7924 2334   Tel: 020-7223 7720

**EUROKIDS AND ADULTS INTERNATIONAL
CASTING AND MODEL AGENCY**
The Warehouse
Glaziers Lane, Culcheth Studio
Warrington, Cheshire WA3 4AQ
e-mail: info@eurokids.co.uk
Fax: 01925 767563   Tel: 01925 767574

EXTRAS UNLIMITED
14 Russell Garden Mews
London W14 8EU
e-mail: mark@marksummers.com
Fax: 020-7602 9994   Tel: 020-7603 9995

EXTRAS UP NORTH
9 Bulay Road
Huddersfield HD1 3NH
Fax: 01484 483100   Tel: 01484 483019

EXTRASPECIAL Ltd
38 Commercial Street
London E1 6LP
e-mail: info@extraspecial2000.com
Fax: 020-7375 1466   Tel: 020-7375 1400

FACES (CASTING AGENCY) Ltd
95 Ditchling Road
Brighton, East Sussex BN1 4ST
Fax: 01273 689021   Tel: 01273 571989

FBI AGENCY Ltd The
PO Box 250
Leeds LS1 2AZ
e-mail: j.spencer@fbi-agency.ltd.uk
Tel/Fax: 07050 222747

FBI Ltd
21 Eastcastle Street
London W1N 7PA
e-mail: fbi@dircon.co.uk
Fax: 020-7636 3392   Tel: 020-7636 2992

FLOSS EXTRAS
14 Ritz Buildings, Church Road
Tunbridge Wells
Kent TN1 1HP
e-mail: floss.extras@newmangroup.co.uk
Fax: 01892 514173   Tel: 01892 524122

G2
15 Lexham Mews
London W8 6JW
e-mail: g2@galloways.ltd.uk
Fax: 020-7376 2416   Tel: 020-7376 2133

GUYS & DOLLS CASTING
Trafalgar House
Grenville Place, Mill Hill
London NW7 3SA
Fax: 020-8381 0087   Tel: 020-8906 4144

HOWE Janet CASTING AGENCY
Canal Side Chambers, The Boat Yard,
Newcastle Road, Stone, Staffs ST15 8JZ
e-mail: janet@jhowecasting.fsbusiness.co.uk
Tel/Fax: 01785 818480   Tel/Fax: 01785 816888

18 The Downs, Altrincham, Cheshire WA14 2PU
Mobile: 07801 942178   Tel/Fax: 0161-233 0700

J B AGENCY Ltd
7 Stonehill Mansions, 8 Streatham High Road
London SW16 1DD
e-mail: tonyjb@globalnet.co.uk
Tel: 020-8769 0123   Tel: 020-8677 5151

KNIGHT Ray CASTING
21A Lambolle Place
Belsize Park
London NW3 4PG
e-mail: casting@rayknight.co.uk
Fax: 020-7722 2322   Tel: 020-7722 4111

KREATE Ltd
Unit 201, 30 Great Guildford Street
London SE1 0HS
e-mail: kreate@btconnect.com
Fax: 020-7401 3003   Tel: 020-7401 9007

LEE'S PEOPLE
60 Poland Street
London W1V 3DF
e-mail: lee@lees-people.co.uk
Fax: 020-7734 3033   Tel: 020-7734 5775

LEMON CASTINGS
23 Lucas Road, Farnworth
Bolton BL4 9RP
e-mail: andreaking@lemoncastings6.fsnet.co.uk
Mobile: 07752 455510   Tel/Fax: 01204 456253

MIDLANDS CASTING
23 Woodlands Grove, Isleworth
Middlesex TW7 6NS
Fax: 020-8847 4265   Tel: 020-8560 8795

NEMESIS AGENCY
54 Princess Street
Manchester M1 6HS
Fax: 0161-236 1771   Tel: 0161-237 1515

NIDGES CASTING AGENCY
Half Moon Chambers
Chapel Walks
Manchester M2 1HN
e-mail: moneypenny@nidgescasting.co.uk
Fax: 0161-832 5219   Tel: 0161-832 8259

**NORTHERN PROFESSIONALS CASTING
COMPANY**
21 Cresswell Avenue
North Shields
Tyne & Wear NE29 9BQ
e-mail: bill.gerard@northpro83.freeserve.co.uk
Fax: 0191-296 3243   Tel: 0191-257 8635

ORIENTAL AFRO ASIAN ARTISTS
4th Floor
20-24 Kirby Street
London EC1N 8TS
Fax: 020-7242 8125   Tel: 020-7242 5542

ORIENTAL CASTING AGENCY Ltd (Peggy Sirr)
(Afro/Asian Artists)
1 Wyatt Park Road
Streatham Hill
London SW2 3TN
e-mail: peggy.sirr@btconnect.com
Fax: 020-8674 9303   Tel: 020-8671 8538

ORION CASTING AGENCY
DBH House
Boundary Street
Liverpool L5 9YJ   Tel/Fax: 0151-482 5565

PC THEATRICAL & MODEL AGENCY
10 Strathmore Gardens, Edgware
Middlesex HA8 5HJ
e-mail: twinagy@aol.com
Fax: 020-8933 3418   Tel: 020-8381 2229

PHA CASTING
Tanzaro House
Ardwick Green North
Manchester M12 6FZ
e-mail: info@pha-agency.co.uk
Fax: 0161-273 4567   Tel: 0161-273 4444

PHOENIX AGENCY
1A Cornwallis Crescent
Clifton, Bristol BS8 4PL
Fax: 0117-973 4160   Tel: 0117-973 1100

POWER CASTING AGENCY
The Royal, 25 Bank Plain
Norwich NR2 4SF
e-mail: powermodelmanagement@btinternet.com
Fax: 01603 621101   Tel: 01603 621100

ELLIOTT AGENCY

The Top Specialists for Professional Actors (Contract & Walk on)

The Elliott Agency, PO Box 2772, Lewes, Sussex BN8 4DW, UK

Tel: 00 44 (0)1273 401264 Fax: 00 44 (0)1273 400814 Internet: www.elliottagency.co.uk

PRAETORIAN ASSOCIATES
(Specialist Extras)
2 Old Brompton Road, Suite 501
London SW7 3DG
e-mail: info@praetorianasc.com
Fax: 020-8923 7177   Tel: 020-8923 9075

PRIDE ARTIST MANAGEMENT
The Burnside Centre
Burnside Crescent, Middleton
Manchester M24 5NN
e-mail: extras@prideradio.co.uk
                          Tel/Fax: 0161-643 6266

REYNOLDS Sandra MODEL & CASTING AGENTS
35 St Georges Street
Norwich NR3 1DA
e-mail: tessa@sandrareynolds.co.uk
Fax: 01603 219825   Tel: 01603 623842

50 Fitzroy Street, London W1T 5BT
Fax: 020-7387 5848   Tel: 020-7387 5858

RUBICON ARTISTS AGENCY
27 Inderwick Road, Crouch End
London N8 9LB   Tel/Fax: 020-8374 1836

SCOTLAND'S ASIAN, AFRO-CARIBBEAN & CHINESE DIRECTORY
(Directory for Scotland - Subash Singh Pall & Surinder Kaw Hoonjan)
Ardoch House, 25 Ardoch Street
Glasgow G22 5QG
e-mail: krantimedia_comm@hotmail.com
Mobile: 07931 142932   Tel/Fax: 0141-585 3317

SKYBLUE CASTING Ltd
38 Commercial Street, London E1 6LP
e-mail: info@skybluecasting.com
Fax: 020-7375 1466   Tel: 020-7375 1400

SMITH Robert AGENCY
The Courtyard, Whitchurch
Ross-on-Wye HR9 6DA
e-mail: agent@southwestcasting.co.uk
Fax: 01600 891099   Tel: 01600 891160

SO DAM TUFF Ltd
41 Paradise Walk, Chelsea
London SW3 4JL
e-mail: tiger@sodamtuff.com
Fax: 020-7352 0001   Tel: 020-7351 0111

SWEENEY MODS
Ramillies House, 1-2 Ramillies Street
London W1V 1DF
e-mail: mods@sweeneymanagement.co.uk
Fax: 020-7437 2080   Tel: 020-7287 0900

THRESH Melody MANAGEMENT ASSOCIATES Ltd (MTM)
MTM House
29 Ardwick Green North
Manchester M12 6DL
melody.thresh@melody-thresh-management.co.uk
Fax: 0161-273 5455   Tel: 0161-273 5445

TONER CASTING Ltd
The Attic, 6th Floor, Hanover Street
Liverpool L1 3DZ
e-mail: tonercasting@hotmail.com
Fax: 0151-707 8414   Tel: 0151-708 6400

TOP-SPOTS AGENCY
(Commercials, Films, Babies to Adults)
314 Haydons Road, Wimbledon
London SW19 8JZ
Fax: 020-8543 5511   Tel: 020-8543 7766

TROUPERS.COM
Unit 62 Maltings Yard
Walton Road, Wavendon
Milton Keynes MK17 8LW
e-mail: info@troupers.com
Fax: 01908 586979   Tel: 01908 282925

UGLY ENTERPRISES Ltd
Tigris House, 256 Edgware Road
London W2 1DS
e-mail: info@ugly.org
Fax: 020-7402 0507   Tel: 020-7402 5564

UNITED COLOURS OF LONDON Ltd
4th Floor, 20-24 Kirby Street
London EC1N 8TS
Fax: 020-7242 5542   Tel: 020-7242 8125

VITAL EXTRAS
PO Box 26441, London SE10 9GZ
e-mail: vitalproductions@aol.com
                          Tel/Fax: 020-8316 4497

YOUNG ACTORS FILE The
39D Highbury New Park, Canonbury
London N5 2EN
e-mail: actorsfile@aol.com
Mobile: 07949 759468   Tel/Fax: 020-7359 1354

YOUNG STARGAZERS
Stonesthrow, 18 Thornham Close, Clayton
Newcastle, Staffs ST5 4LR
e-mail: info@young-stargazers.freeserve.co.uk
Fax: 01782 610363   Tel: 01782 751900

'Faces' (Casting Agency) Ltd

Manager ~ **Nicholas Groush**

95 Ditchling Road, Brighton, East Sussex BN1 4ST

Tel: 01273 571989/01273 329436 Fax: 01273 689021 Mobile: 07788 600877

SAMUEL FRENCH LTD

Publishers of Plays • Agents for the Collection of Royalties
Specialist Booksellers
52 Fitzroy Street London W1T 5JR
Tel 020 7255 4300 (Bookshop) 020 7387 9373 (Enquiries)
Fax 020 7387 2161 www.samuelfrench-london.co.uk
e-mail: theatre@samuelfrench-london.co.uk

For information regarding membership of the
Personal Managers' Association please contact:
   Personal Managers' Association Ltd
   ⌐Rivercroft, 1 Summer Road
   East Molesey, Surrey KT8 9LX
   Tel: 020-8398 9796
* Denotes PMA Membership

A & B PERSONAL MANAGEMENT Ltd*
Paurelle House, 91 Regent Street
London W1B 4EL
e-mail: billellis@aandb.co.uk
Fax: 020-7734 6318   Tel: 020-7734 6047

ABNER STEIN
10 Roland Gardens
London SW7 3PH
e-mail: abner@abnerstein.co.uk
Fax: 020-7370 6316   Tel: 020-7373 0456

ACTAC
7 Isles Court, Ramsbury
Wiltshire SN8 2QW
Fax: 01672 520166   Tel: 01672 520274

AGENCY (LONDON) Ltd The*
24 Pottery Lane, Holland Park
London W11 4LZ
e-mail: info@theagency.co.uk
Fax: 020-7727 9037   Tel: 020-7727 1346

A.J. ASSOCIATES
Dept C, Higher Healey House
Higherhouse Lane, White Coppice
Chorley, Lancs PR6 9BT
e-mail: ajassociates@tinyworld.co.uk
Fax: 01257 274130   Tel: 01257 273148

A M HEATH & Co Ltd
(Fiction & Non Fiction only)
79 St Martin's Lane
London WC2N 4RE
Fax: 020-7497 2561   Tel: 020-7836 4271

BLAKE FRIEDMANN
(Novels, TV/Film Scripts)
122 Arlington Road
London NW1 7HP
e-mail: julian@blakefriedmann.co.uk
Fax: 020-7284 0442   Tel: 020-7284 0408

BRITTEN Nigel MANAGEMENT*
Garden Studios
11-15 Betterton Street
Covent Garden, London WC2H 9BP
e-mail: nbm@mcmail.com
Fax: 020-7866 8110   Tel: 020-7379 0344

BRODIE Alan REPRESENTATION Ltd*
(Incorporating Michael Imison Playwrights)
211 Piccadilly
London W1J 9HF
e-mail: info@alanbrodie.com
Fax: 020-7917 2872   Tel: 020-7917 2871

BRYANT Peter (WRITERS)
94 Adelaide Avenue
London SE4 1YR
Fax: 020-8692 9107   Tel: 020-8691 9085

CANN Alexandra REPRESENTATION*
First Floor, 12 Abingdon Road
London W8 6AF
e-mail: alexcann@cannrep.demon.co.uk
Fax: 020-7938 4228   Tel: 020-7938 4002

CASAROTTO RAMSAY & ASSOCIATES Ltd*
National House
60-66 Wardour Street
London W1V 4ND
e-mail: agents@casarotto.uk.com
Fax: 020-7287 9128   Tel: 020-7287 4450

CLOWES Jonathan Ltd*
10 Iron Bridge House
Bridge Approach
London NW1 8BD
Fax: 020-7722 7677   Tel: 020-7722 7674

COCHRANE Elspeth PERSONAL MANAGEMENT*
14/2, 2nd Floor
South Bank Commercial Centre
140 Battersea Park Road
London SW11 4NB
Fax: 020-7622 5815   Tel: 020-7622 0314

CREATIVE MEDIA INTERNATIONAL
(No unsolicited scripts,
first instance sypnopsis only)
22 Kingsbury Avenue, Dunstable
Bedfordshire LU5 4PU   Tel/Fax: 01582 510869

CURTIS BROWN GROUP Ltd*
Haymarket House, 28-29 Haymarket
London SW1Y 4SP
e-mail: cb@curtisbrown.co.uk
Fax: 020-7396 0110   Tel: 020-7396 6600

DAISH Judy ASSOCIATES Ltd*
2 St Charles Place
London W10 6EG
Fax: 020-8964 8966   Tel: 020-8964 8811

de WOLFE Felix*
Manfield House, Garden Offices
51 Maida Vale
London W9 1SD
e-mail: felixdewolfe@aol.com
Fax: 020-7289 5731   Tel: 020-7289 5770

DREW Bryan Ltd
Mezzanine, Quadrant House
80-82 Regent Street
London W1B 5AU
e-mail: bryandrewltd@netscapeonline.co.uk
Fax: 020-7437 0561   Tel: 020-7437 2293

E.A. MANAGEMENT
Westwynds House
Laleham Reach
Chertsey KT16 8RT
Fax: 01932 561236   Tel: 01932 561234

FARNES Norma MANAGEMENT
9 Orme Court
London W2 4RL
Fax: 020-7792 2110   Tel: 020-7727 1544

FILLINGHAM Janet ASSOCIATES
52 Lowther Road
London SW13 9NU
e-mail: jfillassoc@aol.com
Fax: 020-8748 7374   Tel: 020-8748 5594

FILM RIGHTS Ltd
South Bank Commercial Centre
140 Battersea Park Road
London SW11 4NB
e-mail: information@filmrights.ltd.uk
Fax: 020-7720 6000   Tel: 020-7720 2000

FITCH Laurence Ltd
South Bank Commercial Centre
140 Battersea Park Road
London SW11 4NB
Fax: 020-7720 6000   Tel: 020-7720 2000

FOSTER Jill Ltd*
9 Barb Mews
London W6 7PA
Fax: 020-7602 9336   Tel: 020-7602 1263

FRENCH Samuel Ltd*
52 Fitzroy Street, Fitzrovia, London W1T 5JR
e-mail: theatre@samuelfrench-london.co.uk
Fax: 020-7387 2161   Tel: 020-7387 9373

FUTERMAN, ROSE & ASSOCIATES
(TV/Film/Stageplay Scripts)
17 Deanhill Road
London SW14 7DQ
Fax: 020-8286 4861   Tel: 020-8286 4860

GILLIS Pamela MANAGEMENT
46 Sheldon Avenue
London N6 4JR
Fax: 020-8341 5564   Tel: 020-8340 7868

GLASS Eric Ltd
28 Berkeley Square
London W1X 6HD
e-mail: eglassltd@aol.com
Fax: 020-7499 6780   Tel: 020-7629 7162

HALL Rod AGENCY Ltd The*
7 Goodge Place
London W1T 4SF
e-mail: office@rodhallagency.com
Fax: 020-7637 0807   Tel: 020-7637 0706

HAMILTON ASPER MANAGEMENT*
24 Hanway Street
London W1T 1UH
e-mail: info@hamiltonasper.co.uk
Fax: 020-7636 1226   Tel: 020-7636 1221

HANCOCK Roger Ltd*
4 Water Lane
London NW1 8NZ
e-mail: hancockltd@aol.com
Fax: 020-7267 0705   Tel: 020-7267 4418

HATTON Richard Ltd*
29 Roehampton Gate
London SW15 5JR
Fax: 020-8876 8278   Tel: 020-8876 6699

HENSHAW Michael
3 Stucley Place, London NW1 8NS
Fax: 020-7267 7960   Tel: 020-7267 1311

HIGHAM David ASSOCIATES Ltd*
5-8 Lower John Street, Golden Square
London W1F 9HA
Fax: 020-7437 1072   Tel: 020-7434 5900

HOSKINS Valerie ASSOCIATES
20 Charlotte Street
London W1T 2NA
e-mail: vha@vhaassociates.co.uk
Fax: 020-7637 4493   Tel: 020-7637 4490

HOWARD Amanda ASSOCIATES Ltd*
21 Berwick Street
London W1F 0PZ
Fax: 020-7287 7785   Tel: 020-7287 9277

HURLEY LOWE MANAGEMENT*
36 Redcliffe Road
London SW10 9NJ
Fax: 020-7351 1033   Tel: 020-7352 6878

**I C M Ltd (INTERNATIONAL CREATIVE
MANAGEMENT)***
Oxford House, 76 Oxford Street
London W1D 1BS
Fax: 020-7323 0101   Tel: 020-7636 6565

IMISON Michael PLAYWRIGHTS Ltd
(See BRODIE Alan REPRESENTATION Ltd)

INTERNATIONAL ARTISTES Ltd*
Mezzanine Floor, 235 Regent Street
London W1B 2AX
e-mail: (name)@intart.co.uk
Fax: 020-7409 2070   Tel: 020-7439 8401

JOHNSON John Ltd
Clerkenwell House
45-47 Clerkenwell Green
London EC1R 0HT   Tel: 020-7251 0125

KANAL Roberta
82 Constance Road, Twickenham
Middlesex TW2 7JA
Fax: 020-8894 7952   Tel: 020-8894 2277

KASS Michelle ASSOCIATES*
36-38 Glasshouse Street
London W1B 5DL
Fax: 020-7734 3394   Tel: 020-7439 1624

LE BARS Tessa MANAGEMENT*
(Existing Clients Only)
54 Birchwood Road
Petts Wood, Kent BR5 1NZ
e-mail: tlbm@cwcom.net
Mobile: 07860 287255   Tel/Fax: 01689 837084

LONDON MANAGEMENT*
2-4 Noel Street, London W1F 8GB
Fax: 020-7287 3036   Tel: 020-7287 9000

LORD Annabel ASSOCIATES (ALA)
(Writers, Designers, Directors,
Composers, Lyricists, Musical Directors)
7 Camberwell Grove, London SE5 8JA
e-mail: annabel@ala.prestel.co.uk
Fax: 020-7701 9762   Tel: 020-7701 9769

LOWE Ian
Glan Dulas, Cusop, Hay-on-Wye
Hereford HR3 5RQ
e-mail: ianlowe@scripts-uk.demon.co.uk
                          Tel/Fax: 01497 821780

MACNAUGHTON LORD 2000 Ltd*
Douglas House, 16-18 Douglas Street
London SW1P 4PB
e-mail: info@ml2000.org.uk
Fax: 020-7834 4949   Tel: 020-7834 4646

MANN Andrew Ltd*
1 Old Compton Street, London W1D 5JA
Fax: 020-7287 9264   Tel: 020-7734 4751

MANS Johnny PRODUCTIONS Ltd
The Maltings, Brewery Road, Hoddesdon
Herts EN11 8HF
Fax: 01992 470516   Tel: 01992 470907

MARJACQ SCRIPTS Ltd
34 Devonshire Place
London W1G 6JW
e-mail: enquiries@marjacq.com
Fax: 020-7935 9115   Tel: 020-7935 9499

MARVIN Blanche*
21A St Johns Wood High Street
London NW8 7NG
e-mail: blanchemarvin@madasafish.com
                          Tel/Fax: 020-7722 2313

M.B.A. LITERARY AGENTS Ltd*
62 Grafton Way, London W1P 5LD
e-mail: agent@mbalit.co.uk
Fax: 020-7387 2042   Tel: 020-7387 2076

McLEAN BILL PERSONAL MANAGEMENT Ltd
23B Deodar Road
London SW15 2NP   Tel: 020-8789 8191

ML 2000 Ltd
(See MACNAUGHTON LORD 2000 Ltd)

MORRIS William AGENCY (UK) Ltd*
52-53 Poland Street, London W1F 7LX
Fax: 020-7534 6900   Tel: 020-7534 6800

NARROW ROAD COMPANY*
(Richard Ireson)
182 Brighton Road
Coulsdon, Surrey CR5 2NF
e-mail: narrowroad@freeuk.com
Fax: 020-8763 9329   Tel: 020-8763 9895

P F D*
Drury House, 34-43 Russell Street
London WC2B 5HA
Fax: 020-7836 9539   Tel: 020-7344 1000

POLLINGER Laurence Ltd
9 Staple Inn, Holborn, London WC1V 7QH
e-mail: laurencepollinger@compuserve.com
Fax: 020-7242 5737   Tel: 020-7404 0342

RADALA & ASSOCIATES
17 Avenue Mansions, Finchley Road
London NW3 7AX
Fax: 020-7431 7636   Tel: 020-7794 4495

ROSICA COLIN Ltd
1 Clareville Grove Mews
London SW7 5AH
Fax: 020-7244 6441   Tel: 020-7370 1080

RUPERT CREW Ltd
(No Plays, Films or TV scripts)
1A King's Mews
London WC1N 2JA
e-mail: rupertcrew@compuserve.com
Fax: 020-7831 7914   Tel: 020-7242 8586

SAYLE AGENCY The*
11 Jubilee Place
London SW3 3TD
e-mail: info@thesayleagency.co.uk
Fax: 020-7823 3363   Tel: 020-7823 3883

SEIFERT DENCH ASSOCIATES*
24 D'Arblay Street, London W1F 8EH
Fax: 020-7439 1355   Tel: 020-7437 4551

SHARLAND ORGANISATION Ltd*
The Manor House, Manor Street, Raunds
Northants NN9 6JW
e-mail: tsoshar@aol.com
Fax: 01933 624860   Tel: 01933 626600

SHAW Vincent ASSOCIATES Ltd
20 Jay Mews, London SW7 2EP
e-mail: vincentshaw@clara.net
Fax: 020-7225 1079   Tel: 020-7581 8215

SHEIL LAND ASSOCIATES Ltd*
(Literary, Theatre & Film)
43 Doughty Street, London WC1N 2LF
e-mail: info@sheilland.co.uk
Fax: 020-7831 2127   Tel: 020-7405 9351

SOMMERFIELD Ltd
35 Old Queen Street, London SW1H 9JD
Fax: 020-7654 5226   Tel: 020-7222 9070

STEINBERG Micheline PLAYWRIGHTS*
409 Triumph House, 187-191 Regent Street
London W1R 7WF
e-mail: steinplays@aol.com
Fax: 020-7287 4384   Tel: 020-7287 4383

STEVENS Rochelle & Co*
2 Terretts Place, Upper Street, London N1 1QZ
Fax: 020-7354 5729   Tel: 020-7359 3900

THEATRE OF LITERATURE
(c/o Calder Publications)
51 The Cut
London SE1 8LF   Tel: 020-7633 0599

THURLEY J M MANAGEMENT
30 Cambridge Road, Teddington
Middlesex TW11 8DR
e-mail: jmthurley@aol.com
Fax: 020-8943 2678   Tel: 020-8977 3176

WARE Cecily LITERARY AGENTS*
19C John Spencer Square, London N1 2LZ
Fax: 020-7226 9828   Tel: 020-7359 3787

WATT A P Ltd*
20 John Street, London WC1N 2DR
e-mail: apw@apwatt.co.uk
Fax: 020-7831 2154   Tel: 020-7405 6774

WEINBERGER Josef Ltd*
12-14 Mortimer Street
London W1T 3JJ
e-mail: general.info@jwmail.co.uk
Fax: 020-7436 9616   Tel: 020-7580 2827

ALEXANDER PERSONAL MANAGEMENT Ltd
16 Roughdown Avenue, Hemel Hempstead
Hertfordshire HP3 9BH
e-mail: apm@onetel.net.uk
Fax: 01442 241099   Tel: 01442 252907

A.P.M. (Linda French)
(See ALEXANDER PERSONAL MANAGEMENT Ltd)

ARLINGTON ENTERPRISES Ltd
1-3 Charlotte Street
London W1T 1RD
e-mail: info@arlington.enterprises.co.uk
Fax: 020-7580 4994   Tel: 020-7580 0702

AST MANAGEMENT Ltd
70-72 Barnsbury Road, London N1 0ES
e-mail: theagency@annaschermanagement.fsnet.co.uk
Fax: 020-7833 9467   Tel: 020-7278 2101

BLACKBURN SACHS ASSOCIATES
88-90 Crawford Street, London W1H 2BS
e-mail: presenters@blackburnsachsassociates.com
Fax: 020-7258 6162   Tel: 020-7258 6158

BURNETT GRANGER ASSOCIATES Ltd
Prince of Wales Theatre, 31 Coventry Street
London W1D 6AS
Fax: 020-7839 0438   Tel: 020-7839 0434

CAMERON Sara MANAGEMENT
At Take Three Management
110 Gloucester Avenue, Primrose Hill
London NW1 8HX
e-mail: sara@take3mgt.demon.co.uk
Fax: 020-7209 3770   Tel: 020-7209 3777

CANTOR WISE REPRESENTATION
At Take Three Management
110 Gloucester Avenue, Primrose Hill
London NW1 8HX
e-mail: melanie@take3mgt.demon.co.uk
Fax: 020-7209 3770   Tel: 020-7209 3777

CELEBRITY GROUP Ltd The
12 Nottingham Place
London W1M 3FA
e-mail: info@celebrity.co.uk
Fax: 020-7224 6060   Tel: 020-7224 5050

CHASE PERSONAL MANAGEMENT
The Barn, Hulseheath Lane
Mere, Cheshire WA16 6PR
e-mail: sue@sammon.fsnet.co.uk
Mobile: 07775 683955   Tel: 01565 830052
London Office: Tel: 020-7351 3244
Manchester Office: Tel: 0161-819 1162

COMEDY CLUB
165 Peckham Rye, London SE15 3HZ
e-mail: comedyclub@cwcom.net
Fax: 020-7732 9292   Tel: 020-7732 3434

CRAWFORDS
2 Conduit Street, London W1S 2XB
e-mail: cr@fords.com
Fax: 020-7355 1084   Tel: 020-7629 6464

CURTIS BROWN GROUP Ltd
(Sue Freathy, Julian Beynon)
Haymarket House, 28-29 Haymarket
London SW1Y 4SP
e-mail: presenters@curtisbrown.co.uk
Fax: 020-7396 0110   Tel: 020-7396 6600

CYBER ARTISTS 2000
In the Can Ltd, 20 Old Steine
Brighton BN1 1EL
e-mail: cyber@cyber.ndo.co.uk
Tel/Fax: 01273 671234

DAVID ANTHONY PROMOTIONS
PO Box 286, Warrington, Cheshire WA2 8GA
e-mail: dap@dial.pipex.com
Fax: 01925 416589   Tel: 01925 632496

DOWNES PRESENTERS AGENCY
96 Broadway, Bexleyheath, Kent DA6 7DE
e-mail: downes@presentersagency.com
Fax: 020-8301 5591   Tel: 020-8304 0541

DYNAMIC FX Ltd
(Magical Effect Designers & Performers)
Regent House, 291 Kirkdale
London SE26 4QD
e-mail: mail@dynamicfx.co.uk
Fax: 020-8659 8118   Tel: 020-8659 8130

EARNSHAW Susi MANAGEMENT
5 Brook Place, Barnet, Herts EN5 2DL
Fax: 020-8364 9618   Tel: 020-8441 5010

EVANS Jacque MANAGEMENT Ltd
Top Floor Suite, 14 Holmesley Road
London SE23 1PJ
e-mail: jacque@jemltd.demon.co.uk
Fax: 020-8699 5192   Tel: 020-8699 1202

EXCELLENT TALENT COMPANY The
53 Goodge Street, London W1T 1TG
e-mail: ruth@excellentvoice.co.uk
Fax: 020-7636 1631   Tel: 020-7636 1636

FBI AGENCY Ltd The
PO Box 250, Leeds LS1 2AZ
e-mail: j.spencer@fbi-agency.ltd.uk
Tel/Fax: 07050 222747

FLETCHER ASSOCIATES
(Broadcast & Media)
25 Parkway, London N20 0XN
Fax: 020-8361 8866   Tel: 020-8361 8061

FOX ARTIST MANAGEMENT Ltd
Concorde House, 101 Shepherds Bush Road
London W6 7LP
e-mail: fox.artist@btinternet.com
Fax: 020-7603 2352   Tel: 020-7602 8822

GAY Noel ARTISTS
19 Denmark Street
London WC2H 8NA
Fax: 020-7287 1816   Tel: 020-7836 3941

GLASS Eric Ltd
28 Berkeley Square
London W1X 6HD
e-mail: eglassltd@aol.com
Fax: 020-7499 6780   Tel: 020-7629 7162

GRANT James MANAGEMENT
Syon Lodge, 201 London Road, Isleworth
Middlesex TW7 5BH
e-mail: enquiries@jamesgrant.co.uk
Fax: 020-8232 4101   Tel: 020-8232 4100

GRIFFIN Sandra MANAGEMENT
6 Ryde Place, Richmond Road
East Twickenham, Middlesex TW1 2EH
e-mail: sgmgmt@aol.com
Fax: 020-8744 1812   Tel: 020-8891 5676

GURNETT J. PERSONAL MANAGEMENT Ltd
2 New Kings Road
London SW6 4SA
e-mail: mail@jgpm.co.uk
Fax: 020-7736 5455   Tel: 020-7736 7828

HICKS Jeremy ASSOCIATES
12 Ogle Street
London W1W 6HU
Fax: 020-7636 8880   Tel: 020-7636 8008

HOBBS Liz GROUP Ltd
Finsbury Business Centre
40 Bowling Green Lane
London EC1R 0NE
e-mail: info@lizhobbsgroup.com
Fax: 01636 703343   Tel: 020-7287 8870

Head Office: 68 Castlegate, Newark
Notts NG24 1BG
Fax: 01636 703343   Tel: 01636 703342

HUGHES Jane MANAGEMENT
The Coach House
PO Box 123, Knutsford
Cheshire WA16 9HX
Fax: 01565 722211   Tel: 01565 723000

IVELAW-CHAPMAN Julie
The Chase, Chaseside Close
Cheddington, Beds LU7 0SA
e-mail: jic@collectopsworldwide.co.uk
Fax: 01296 662451   Tel: 01296 662441

JAYMEDIA
(Nigel Jay)
112 Beech Avenue, Rode Heath, Alsager
Cheshire ST7 3JD
e-mail: media@jaymedia.co.uk
Fax: 0870 1209079   Tel: 01270 884453

JLA (Jeremy Lee Associates Ltd)
13 Short's Gardens, Covent Garden
London WC2H 9AT
e-mail: management@jla.co.uk
Fax: 020-7240 0371   Tel: 020-7240 0413

KNIGHT AYTON MANAGEMENT
114 St Martin's Lane, London WC2N 4BE
e-mail: info@knightayton.co.uk
Fax: 020-7836 8333   Tel: 020-7836 5333

LADKIN Michael PERSONAL MANAGEMENT
Suite 1, Ground Floor, 1 Duchess Street
London W1W 6AN
Fax: 020-7436 4627   Tel: 020-7436 4626

MARKS PRODUCTIONS Ltd
2 Gloucester Gate Mews
London NW1 4AD
Fax: 020-7486 2165   Tel: 020-7486 2001

MARSH Billy ASSOCIATES Ltd
174-178 North Gower Street, London NW1 2NB
e-mail: bmarsh@bmarsh.demon.co.uk
Fax: 020-7388 6848   Tel: 020-7388 6858

MILES John ORGANISATION
Cadbury Camp Lane, Clapton-in-Gordano
Bristol BS20 7SB
e-mail: john@johnmiles.org.uk
Fax: 01275 810186   Tel: 01275 854675

MPC ENTERTAINMENT
MPC House, 15-16 Maple Mews, London NW6 5UZ
e-mail: mpc@mpce.com
Fax: 020-7624 4220   Tel: 020-7624 1184

NCI MANAGEMENT Ltd
2nd Floor, 51 Queen Anne Street
London W1M 0HS
e-mail: nicola@nci-management.com
Fax: 020-7935 1258   Tel: 020-7224 3960

NOEL John MANAGEMENT
2nd Floor, 10A Belmont Street
London NW1 8HH
e-mail: john@johnnoel.com
Fax: 020-7428 8401   Tel: 020-7428 8400

OFF THE KERB PRODUCTIONS
3rd Floor, Hammer House
113-117 Wardour Street
London W1F 0UN
e-mail: offthekerb@aol.com
Fax: 020-7437 0647   Tel: 020-7437 0607

22 Thornhill Crescent
London N1 1BJ
e-mail: info@offthekerb.co.uk
Fax: 020-7700 4646   Tel: 020-7700 4477

PHA CASTING
Tanzaro House, Ardwick Green North
Manchester M12 6FZ
e-mail: mail@pha-agency.co.uk
Fax: 0161-273 4567   Tel: 0161-273 4444

PRINCESS TALENT MANAGEMENT
Newcombe House
45 Notting Hill Gate
London W11 3LQ
e-mail: talent@princess.uk.com
Fax: 020-7908 1934   Tel: 020-7243 5100

PVA MANAGEMENT Ltd
Hallow Park, Hallow
Worcester WR2 6PG
e-mail: clients@pva.co.uk
Fax: 01905 641842   Tel: 01905 640663

QDOS Ltd
8 King Street, Covent Garden
London WC2E 8HN
e-mail: info@qdosentertainment.plc.uk
Fax: 020-7240 4956   Tel: 020-7240 5052

QUADRAPHOLD MANAGEMENT
Queens Chambers
Queen Street, Blackpool
Lancashire FY1 1PD
e-mail: info@quadraphold.com
Fax: 01253 290019   Tel: 01253 311112

RAZZAMATAZZ MANAGEMENT
Crofters, East Park Lane, New Chapel
Surrey RH7 6HS
e-mail: mcgrogan@tinyworld.co.uk
Fax: 01342 835433   Tel: 01342 835359

RK COMMERCIALS
205 Chudleigh Road
London SE4 1EG
e-mail: rkcommercials@krugeractors.com
Fax: 020-8690 7999   Tel: 020-8690 6542

ROSEMAN ORGANISATION The
Suite 9, The Power House
70 Chiswick High Road
London W4 1SY
e-mail: info@therosemanorganisation.co.uk
Fax: 020-8742 0554   Tel: 020-8742 0552

RUBY TALENT
Apartment 9, Goldcrest Building
1 Lexington Street
London W1F 9TA
e-mail: tara@ruby-talent.co.uk
Fax: 020-7439 1649   Tel: 020-7439 4554

SEVERN MANAGEMENT SERVICES
16 Graham Crescent, Rubery
Birmingham B45 9DD
Fax: 0121-693 0180   Tel: 0121-693 0190

SHAW Vincent ASSOCIATES Ltd
20 Jay Mews
London SW7 2EP
e-mail: vincentshaw@clara.net
Fax: 020-7225 1079   Tel: 020-7581 8215

SINGER Sandra ASSOCIATES
21 Cotswold Road, Westcliff on Sea
Essex SS0 8AA
e-mail: sandra.singer@virgin.net
Fax: 01702 339393   Tel: 01702 331616

SOUTHWEST MANAGEMENT AND CASTING Ltd
The Courtyard, Whitchurch
Ross-on-Wye HR9 6DA
e-mail: agent@southwestcasting.co.uk
Fax: 01600 891099   Tel: 01600 892005

SPEAK-EASY Ltd
1 Dairy Yard, High Street
Market Harborough
Leics LE16 7NL
e-mail: enquiries@speak-easy.co.uk
Fax: 01858 461994   Tel: 0870 0135126

STORM ARTISTS MANAGEMENT
47 Brewer Street
London W1F 9UF
e-mail: info@stormartists.co.uk
Fax: 020-7437 4314   Tel: 020-7437 4313

TAKE THREE MANAGEMENT
110 Gloucester Avenue, Primrose Hill
London NW1 8HX
e-mail: info@take3mgt.demon.co.uk
Fax: 020-7209 3770   Tel: 020-7209 3777

TALKBACK MANAGEMENT
20-21 Newman Street
London W1P 3HB
Fax: 020-7861 8061   Tel: 020-7861 8060

THEATRE TOURS INTERNATIONAL
The Bull Theatre, 68 The High Street
Barnet
Herts EN5 5SJ
e-mail: mail@theatretoursinternational.com
Fax: 020-8449 5252   Tel: 020-8449 7800

UNIQUE MANAGEMENT GROUP
Avon House, Kensington Village
Avonmore Road
London W14 8TS
e-mail: jcarlton@uniquegroup.co.uk
Fax: 020-7371 5352   Tel: 020-7371 5353

VAGABOND HEART
2 Grassmere Road
Hornchurch, Essex RM11 3DP
e-mail: vagabond@virgin.net   Tel: 01708 781994

VENTURE ARTISTES
PO Box 299
Oxford OX2 6LN
e-mail: venture-artistes@msn.com
Fax: 07000 402002   Tel: 07000 402001

V R M
PO Box 82, Altrincham
Cheshire WA15 0QD
Fax: 0161-928 7849   Tel: 0161-928 3222

WHATEVER ARTISTS MANAGEMENT
1 York Street, London W1U 6PA
e-mail: wam@agents-uk.com
Fax: 020-7487 3311   Tel: 020-7487 3111

WILLCOCKS John MEDIA AGENCY Ltd
34 Carisbrook Close, Enfield
Middlesex EN1 3NB
Fax: 020-8292 5060   Tel: 020-8364 4556

WINSLETT Dave ASSOCIATES
6 Kenwood Ridge, Kenley
Surrey CR8 5JW
e-mail: winslett@agents-uk.com
Fax: 020-8668 9216   Tel: 020-8668 0531

WYPER Carolynne MANAGEMENT
2 Kimberley Road
London NW6 7SG
e-mail: info@soundtrck.cwm.co.uk
Fax: 020-7328 1444   Tel: 020-7328 8211

AD VOICE
Oxford House, 76 Oxford Street, London W1D 1BS
Fax: 020-7323 0101   Tel: 020-7323 2345

ANOTHER TONGUE VOICES Ltd
48 Dean Street, London W1V 5HL
e-mail: info@anothertongue.com
Fax: 020-7494 3300   Tel: 020-7494 0300

ASQUITH & HORNER
Write SAE
The Studio, 14 College Road
Bromley, Kent BR1 3NS
Fax: 020-8313 0443   Tel: 020-8466 5580

BURNETT GRANGER ASSOCIATES Ltd
Prince of Wales Theatre, 31 Coventry Street
London W1D 6AS
e-mail: bgavo@waitrose.com
Fax: 020-7839 0438   Tel: 020-7839 0434

CALYPSO VOICES
25-26 Poland Street, London W1F 8QN
e-mail: calypso@calypsovoices.com
Fax: 020-7437 0410   Tel: 020-7734 6415

CASTAWAY
3 Kingly Street, London W1B 5PD
e-mail: sheila@castaway.org.uk
Fax: 020-7287 2202   Tel: 020-7439 7414

CONWAY VAN GELDER Ltd
(Kate Plumpton)
3rd Floor, 18-21 Jermyn Street, London SW1Y 6HP
e-mail: kate@conwayvg.co.uk
Fax: 020-7494 3324   Tel: 020-7287 0077

CREATIVE CASTING
65 Hazelbank Terrace, Edinburgh EH11 1SL
e-mail: creativecasting@hotmail.com
Tel: 0131-478 5455

CYBER ARTISTS 2000
In the Can Ltd, 20 Old Steine, Brighton BN1 1EL
e-mail: cyber@cyber.ndo.co.uk
Tel/Fax: 01273 671234

DREW Bryan Ltd
Mezzanine, Quadrant House
80-82 Regent Street, London W1B 5AU
e-mail: bryandrewltd@netscapeonline.co.uk
Fax: 020-7437 0561   Tel: 020-7437 2293

EVANS O'BRIEN
115 Humber Road, London SE3 7LW
e-mail: eobvoice@dircon.co.uk
Fax: 020-8293 7066   Tel: 020-8293 7077

EXCELLENT VOICE COMPANY
53 Goodge Street, London W1T 1TG
e-mail: info@excellentvoice.co.uk
Fax: 020-7636 1631   Tel: 020-7636 1636

FOREIGN VERSIONS Ltd
(Translation)
Bakerloo Chambers, 304 Edgware Road
London W2 1DY
e-mail: info@foreignversions.co.uk
Fax: 020-7723 5018   Tel: 020-7723 5744

GAY Noel VOICES
19 Denmark Street, London WC2H 8NA
Fax: 020-7287 1816   Tel: 020-7836 3941

GORDON & FRENCH
12-13 Poland Street, London W1F 8QB
e-mail: mail@gordonandfrench.net
Fax: 020-7734 4832   Tel: 020-7734 4818

HOBSON'S SINGERS
62 Chiswick High Road, London W4 1SY
e-mail: singers@hobsons-international.com
Fax: 020-8742 1511   Tel: 020-8747 8324

TALKING HEADS

THE VOICE AGENCY

Ask About Our In-House ISDN Studio for Bookings/Auditions

Our extensive selection of voices includes:

Animation • Characters • Broadcasters
Sports Personalities • Presenters • Actors
Regional • Atlantic • Foreign • Documentary

ALL VOICES AVAILABLE ON CD

88-90 CRAWFORD STREET
LONDON W1H 2BS
TELEPHONE: 020 7258 6161 FAX: 020 7258 6162
E-MAIL: voices@talkingheadsvoices.com
WEBSITE: talkingheadsvoices.com

HOBSON'S VOICES
62 Chiswick High Road, London W4 1SY
e-mail: voices@hobsons-international.com
Fax: 020-8742 1511   Tel: 020-8995 3628

HOPE Sally ASSOCIATES
108 Leonard Street, London EC2A 4XS
e-mail: s-hope@dircon.co.uk
Fax: 020-7613 4848   Tel: 020-7613 5353

HOWARD Amanda ASSOCIATES
21 Berwick Street, London W1F 0PZ
e-mail: mail@amandahowardassociates.co.uk
Fax: 020-7287 7785   Tel: 020-7287 9277

INTERNATIONAL ARTISTES VOICE OVERS
(Nicola Sandon)
Mezzanine Floor, 235 Regent Street
London W1B 2AX
e-mail: nikki@intart.co.uk
Fax: 020-7409 2665   Tel: 020-7434 7820

KANAL Roberta
82 Constance Road, Twickenham
Middlesex TW2 7JA
e-mail: roberta.kanal@cwcom.net
Fax: 020-8894 7952   Tel: 020-8894 2277

LIP SERVICE
4 Kingly Street, London W1B 5PE
e-mail: bookings@lipservice.co.uk
Fax: 020-7734 3373   Tel: 020-7734 3393

LONDON MANAGEMENT
2-4 Noel Street, London W1F 8GB
Fax: 020-7287 3036   Tel: 020-7287 9000

MANSON Andrew
(Genuine Americans only)
288 Munster Road, London SW6 6BQ
e-mail: amanson@aol.com
Fax: 020-7381 8874   Tel: 020-7386 9158

MARKHAM & FROGGATT Ltd
4 Windmill Street, London W1P 1HF
e-mail: fiona@online.rednet.co.uk
Fax: 020-7637 5233   Tel: 020-7636 4412

MBA
3rd Floor Suite, 10-11 Lower John Street
London W1F 9EB
e-mail: info@braidman.com
Fax: 020-7439 3600   Tel: 020-7437 0817

McREDDIE Ken Ltd
91 Regent Street
London W1B 4EL
Fax: 020-7734 6530   Tel: 020-7439 1456

NATURAL VOICE
2 Meard Street, London W1 5AR
Fax: 020-7439 0582   Tel: 020-7439 0581

NOEL John MANAGEMENT
2nd Floor, 10A Belmont Street
London NW1 8HH
e-mail: john@johnnoel.com
Fax: 020-7428 8401   Tel: 020-7428 8400

NUTOPIA VOICES
Number 8, 132 Charing Cross Road
London WC2H 0LA
e-mail: pferisnutopia@netscapeonline.co.uk
Tel/Fax: 020-8882 6299

P F D
Drury House, 34-43 Russell Street
London WC2B 5HA
Fax: 020-7836 9539   Tel: 020-7344 1000

RABBIT VOCAL MANAGEMENT
2nd Floor, 18 Broadwick Street, London W1F 8HS
e-mail: info@rabbit.uk.net
Fax: 020-7287 6566   Tel: 020-7287 6466

RHUBARB
9-15 Neal Street, Covent Garden
London WC2H 9PW
e-mail: enquiries@rhubarb.co.uk
Fax: 020-7836 0444   Tel: 020-7836 1336

SOMMERFIELD Ltd
35 Old Queen Street, London SW1H 9JD
Fax: 020-7654 5226   Tel: 020-7222 9070

SPEAK Ltd
140 Devonshire Road, Chiswick
London W4 2AW
e-mail: speak@dircon.co.uk
Fax: 020-8742 1333   Tel: 020-8742 1001

SPEAK-EASY Ltd
1 Dairy Yard, High Street, Market Harborough
Leicestershire LE16 7NL
e-mail: enquiries@speak-easy.co.uk
Fax: 01858 461994   Tel: 0870 0135126

SPEAKERS CORNER AT CRAWFORDS
2 Conduit Street, London W1S 2XB
e-mail: vo@crawfords.tv
Fax: 020-7355 1084   Tel: 020-7629 6464

STONE Richard PARTNERSHIP The
2 Henrietta Street, London WC2E 8PS
e-mail: all@richstonepart.co.uk
Fax: 020-7497 0869   Tel: 020-7497 0849

SUMMERS Mark MANAGEMENT & AGENCY
14 Russell Garden Mews, London W14 8EU
e-mail: info@marksummers.com
Fax: 020-7602 9994   Tel: 020-7603 1979

TALKIES Ltd
Ground Floor, 3 Charlotte Mews, London W1P 1LN
e-mail: beth@talkies.ltd.uk   Tel: 020-7323 6883

TALKING HEADS
88-90 Crawford Street
London W1H 2BS
e-mail: voices@talkingheadsvoices.com
Fax: 020-7258 6162   Tel: 020-7258 6161

TERRY Sue VOICES Ltd
18 Broadwick Street, London W1F 8HS
Fax: 020-7434 2042   Tel: 020-7434 2040

TONGUE & GROOVE
3 Stevenson Square, Manchester M1 1DN
e-mail: info@tongueandgroove.co.uk
Fax: 0161-237 1809   Tel: 0161-228 2469

VOCAL POINT
25 Denmark Street, London WC2H 8NJ
e-mail: enquiries@vocalpoint.net
Fax: 020-7419 0699   Tel: 020-7419 0700

VOICE & SCRIPT INTERNATIONAL
Aradco House, 132 Cleveland Street
London W1T 6AB
e-mail: info@v-s-i.com
Fax: 020-7692 7711   Tel: 020-7692 7700

VOICE BOX
PO Box 82, Altrincham, Cheshire WA15 0QD
Fax: 0161-928 7849   Tel: 0161-928 3222

VOICE SHOP
Bakerloo Chambers, 304 Edgware Road
London W2 1DY
e-mail: voiceshop@compuserve.com
Fax: 020-7706 1002   Tel: 020-7402 3966

VOICE SQUAD
24 Hawgood Street, London E3 3RU
e-mail: bookem@voicesquad.com
Fax: 020-7537 2839   Tel: 020-7517 3550

VOICEBANK, THE IRISH VOICE OVER AGENCY
The Barracks
76 Irishtown Road, Dublin 4, Ireland
e-mail: voicebank@voicebank.ie
Fax: 00 353 1 6607850   Tel: 00 353 1 6687234

VOICECALL
100 Fawe Park Road, London SW15 2EA
e-mail: penny@evans-reiss.fsnet.co.uk
Fax: 020-8877 0307   Tel: 020-8874 1793

VOICES Ltd
2 Kirkgate Lane, Wighton, Wells-next-the-Sea
Norfolk NR23 1PL
Fax: 01328 820951   Tel: 01328 820950

YAKETY YAK
8 Bloomsbury Square, London WC1A 2NE
e-mail: yakyak@netcomuk.co.uk
Fax: 020-7404 6109   Tel: 020-7430 2600

A1 ANIMALS
(Farm, Domestic & Exotic Animals)
Folly Farm, Folly Lane, Bramley, Hants RG26 5BD
e-mail: info@a1animals.freeserve.co.uk
Fax: 01256 880653   Tel: 01256 880993

ABNALLS HORSES
Abnalls Farm, Cross in Hand Lane, Lichfield
Staffs WS13 8DZ
e-mail: wofford@iname.com
Fax: 01543 417226   Tel: 01543 417075

ALTERNATIVE ANIMALS
(Animatronics/Taxidermy)
28 Greaves Road, High Wycombe
Bucks HP13 7JU
e-mail: animalworld@bushinternet.com
Fax: 01494 441385   Tel: 01494 448710

AMAZING STUNT DOGS
18 Rosewood Avenue, Kingsway, Rugby
Warwickshire CV22 5PJ
e-mail: karen@amazingstuntdogs.freeserve.co.uk
Mobile: 07759 804813   Tel: 01788 812703

ANIMAL ACTING
(Stunts, Prop, Horse-Drawn Vehicles)
15 Wolstenvale Close, Middleton
Manchester M24 2HP   Tel/Fax: 01752 894250

ANIMAL ACTORS
95 Ditching Road, Brighton
Sussex BN1 4ST   Tel: 020-8654 0450

ANIMAL AMBASSADORS
Old Forest, Hampstead Norreys Road
Hermitage, Berks RG18 9SA
     Tel/Fax: 01635 200900

ANIMAL ARK
(Animals & Animal Prop Shop)
Studio, 29 Somerset Road
Brentford, Middlesex TW8 8BT
e-mail: info@animal-ark.co.uk
Fax: 020-8560 5762   Tel: 020-8560 3029

ANIMAL ARRANGERS
(Animal Suppliers & Co-ordinators)
19 Greaves Road, High Wycombe
Bucks HP13 7JU
e-mail: 07956564715@one2one.net
Fax: 01494 441385   Tel: 01494 442750

ANIMAL CASTING
111 Tilehurst Road, Earlsfield SW18 3EX
e-mail: silcresta@aol.com
Mobile: 07956 246450   Tel/Fax: 020-8874 9530

ANIMAL EXTRAS
(Donkeys, Ponies, Farm Animals etc)
Lower Maidenland, St Kew, Bodmin
Cornwall PL30 3HA   Tel/Fax: 01208 841710

ANIMAL WELFARE FILMING FEDERATION
Suite 501 International House
223 Regent Street
London W1R 8QD   Mobile: 07798 831768

ANIMAL WORLD
19 Greaves Road, High Wycombe
Bucks HP13 7JU
e-mail: animalworld@bushinternet.com
Fax: 01494 441385   Tel: 01494 442750

ANIMALATION
16 Wiltshire Avenue, Crowthorne
Berks RG45 6NG
Fax: 01344 779437   Tel: 01344 775244

ANIMALS GALORE
208 Smallfield Road, Horley, Surrey RH6 9LS
Fax: 01342 841546   Tel: 01342 842400

ANIMALS O KAY
3 Queen Street, Chipperfield
Kings Langley, Herts WD4 9BT
e-mail: kay@animalsokay.com
Fax: 01923 269076   Tel: 01923 291277

ANTHEA'S EQUINES
(BHS Approved, Large Schooled Quality Horses,
Ponies, Cobs, for Film)
Wildwoods Riding Centre, Ebbisham Lane
Walton-on-the-Hill, Surrey KT20 5BH
e-mail: info@wildwoodsriding.co.uk
Tel/Fax: 01737 814872   Tel: 01737 812146

A-Z ANIMALS Ltd
The Bell House, Bell Lane, Fetcham
Surrey KT22 9ND
e-mail: xlence@a-zanimals.com
Fax: 01372 377666   Tel: 01372 377111

A-Z DOGS
The Bell House, Bell Lane, Fetcham
Surrey KT22 9ND
e-mail: xlence@a-zanimals.com
Fax: 01372 377666   Tel: 020-7248 6222

BOORMAN-WOODS Sue
(Specialising in Domestic Cats, Rodents, Poultry
& Farm Stock)
White Rocks Farm, Underriver
Sevenoaks, Kent TN15 0SL
Fax: 01732 763767   Tel: 01732 762913

BUGS & THINGS
28 Greaves Road
High Wycombe, Bucks HP13 7JU
e-mail: 07956564715@one2one.net
Fax: 01494 441385   Tel: 01494 448710

CANINE FILM ACADEMY The
57C Cheapside Road, Ascot, Berks SL5 7QR
e-mail: katie.cfa@virgin.net
Mobile: 07767 341424   Tel: 01344 291465

CAVALRY & OTHER HORSES
(James Mackie)
Cownham Farm, Broadwell, Moreton in Marsh
Gloucestershire GL56 0TT
e-mail: jamesmackie@cownham.fsnet.co.uk
Fax: 01451 832442   Tel: 01451 830294

CHEESEMAN Virginia
3 Sutton Road, Heston
Hounslow, Middlesex TW5 0PG
e-mail: vcheeseman@aol.com
Tel/Fax: 020-8572 0414

CLIFT Pauline
15 Gwendale, Pinkneys Green
Maidenhead, Berks SL6 6SH
e-mail: paulineclift@lineone.net
Tel/Fax: 01628 788564

COTSWOLD FARM PARK
(Rare Breeds Survival Centre)
Guiting Power, Cheltenham
Gloucestershire GL54 5UG   Tel: 01451 850307

CREATURE FEATURE
(Animal Agent)
Gubhill Farm, Ae
Dumfries, Scotland DG1 1RL
e-mail: david@creaturefeature.co.uk
Mobile: 07770 774866   Tel/Fax: 01387 860648

DUDLEY Yvonne
(Glamour Dog)
55 Cambridge Park
Wanstead, London E11 2PU   Tel: 020-8989 1528

EAST NOLTON RIDING STABLES
Nolton, Nr Newgale, Haverfordwest
Pembrokeshire SA62 3NW
Fax: 01437 710967   Tel: 01437 710360

FILM HORSES
(Horses, Saddlery, Equestrian Centre)
Glennifer Stables, Drift Road, Hawthorn Hill
Maidenhead, Berks SL6 3ST
Mobile: 07831 629662   Tel/Fax: 01628 673042

FREE ANIMAL CONSULTANT SERVICES
28 Greaves Road
High Wycombe, Bucks HP13 7JU
Fax: 01494 441385   Tel: 08000 749383

GET STUFFED
(Taxidermy)
105 Essex Road, London N1 2SL
e-mail: taxidermy@thegetstuffed.co.uk
Fax: 020-7359 8253   Tel: 020-7226 1364

GRAY Robin COMMENTARIES
(Equestrian Equipment)
Comptons, Isington
Alton, Hants GU34 4PL   Tel: 01420 23347

HEATHER'S HEAVY HORSES
Botany Bay Farm, The Ridgeway, Enfield
Middlesex EN2 8AP   Tel/Fax: 020-8364 5979

HORSEPOWER
(Hilary Parren)
Bekesbourne Stables, Aerodrome Road,
Bekesbourne, Kent CT4 5EX   Tel: 01227 830910

KNIGHTS OF ARKLEY The
Glyn Sylen Farm, Five Roads
Llanelli SA15 5BJ
e-mail: knights@arkley.totalserve.co.uk
Tel/Fax: 01269 861001

McLEOD Janis
(Dogs, Specialists in Theatre, also TV & Film Dogs)
10 Edinburgh Road, Wallasey
Merseyside CH45 4LR
e-mail: janswonderdogs@aol.com
Mobile: 07818 263147   Tel/Fax: 0151-200 7174

MILLENNIUM BUGS
(Live Insects)
28 Greaves Road
High Wycombe, Bucks HP13 7JU
e-mail: graham.smith19@virgin.net
Fax: 01494 441385   Tel: 01494 446130

MORTON Geoff
(Shire Horse & Equipment)
Hasholme Carr Farm, Holme on Spalding Moor,
York YO43 4BD   Tel: 01430 860393

OTTERS
(Tame Otters, Daphne & Martin Neville)
Baker's Mill, Frampton Mansell
Stroud, Glos GL6 8JH
e-mail: martin.neville@ukgateway.net
Tel: 01285 760234

PATCHETTS EQUESTRIAN CENTRE
Hillfield Lane, Aldenham
Watford, Herts WD2 8DP
Fax: 01923 859289   Tel: 01923 855776

PROP FARM Ltd
(Pat Ward)
Grange Farm, Elmton, Nr Creswell, North
Derbyshire S80 4LX
e-mail: pat/les@propfarm.free-online.co.uk
Fax: 01909 723465   Tel: 01909 723100

RATS!
(Trained Fancy Rats and Handler)
e-mail: esbat@blueyonder.co.uk
Tel: 020-8683 2173

RICHMOND PARK STABLES
291 Park Road, Kingston on Thames KT2 5LW
e-mail: wraithrider@hotmail.com
Mobile: 07740 636098   Tel: 020-8546 8437

ROCKWOOD ANIMALS ON FILM
Lewis Terrace, Llanbradach, Caerphilly CF83 3JZ
e-mail: rockwood@globalnet.co.uk
Mobile: 07973 930983   Tel: 029-2088 5420

SCHOOL OF NATIONAL EQUITATION Ltd
(Sam Humphrey)
Bunny Hill Top, Costock, Loughborough LE12 6XE
e-mail: sam@bunny-hill.co.uk
Fax: 01509 856067   Tel: 01509 852366

STUDIO & TV HIRE
(Stuffed Animal Specialists)
3 Ariel Way, Wood Lane
White City, London W12 7SL
Fax: 020-8740 9662   Tel: 020-8749 3445

STUNT DOGS
3 The Chestnuts, Clifton
Deddington, Oxon OX15 0PE
e-mail: gill@eurostuntdogs.co.uk
Tel/Fax: 01869 338546

SUZANNE'S RIDING SCHOOL
(Rural Surroundings)
Copse & Brookshill Farms, Brookshill Drive, Harrow
Weald, Middlesex HA3 6SB
Fax: 020-8420 6461   Tel: 020-8954 3618

TATE Olive
(Trained Dogs & Cats)
49 Upton Road, Bexleyheath, Kent DA6 8LW
Mobile: 07710 933163   Tel/Fax: 020-8303 0683

TATE'S Nigel DOGSTARS
17 Papion Grove, Walderslade Woods
Chatham, Kent ME5 9BS
e-mail: animals@dogstars.co.uk
Fax: 01634 327447   Tel: 01634 869634

THORNE'S OF WINDSOR
(Beekeeping and Other Insect Suppliers)
Oakley Green Farm, Oakley Green
Windsor, Berks SL4 4PZ
e-mail: mattallan@aol.com
Fax: 01753 830605   Tel: 01753 830256

WELLINGTON RIDING
Basingstoke Road, Heckfield RG27 0LJ
Fax: 0118-932 6661   Tel: 0118-932 6308

WHITE DOVE COMPANY Ltd The
(Provision of up to 100 Doves)
The Dovecote, 9-11 High Beech Road
Loughton, Essex IG10 4BN
e-mail: thewhitedovecompany@lineone.net
Fax: 020-8502 2461   Tel: 020-8508 1414

WOLF AND HOUND SPECIALISTS The
Butler's Farm, Beenham, Reading
Berks RG7 5NT   Tel: 0118-971 3330

ARTS COUNCIL OF WALES - MID & WEST WALES OFFICE
Ceredigion, Camarthenshire
Pembrokeshire, Powys
Swansea, Neath, Port Talbot
6 Gardd Llydaw
Jackson's Lane
Carmarthen SA31 1QD
Fax: 01267 233084   Tel: 01267 234248

ARTS COUNCIL OF WALES - NORTH WALES
Anglesey, Gwynedd, Conwy,
Denbighshire, Flintshire, Wrexham
36 Prince's Drive
Colwyn Bay
Conwy LL29 8LA
e-mail: information@ccc-acw.org.uk
Fax: 01492 533677   Tel: 01492 533440

EAST ENGLAND ARTS
Norfolk, Suffolk, Bedfordshire,
Cambridgeshire, Essex,
Hertfordshire and the unitary
authorities of Luton, Peterborough,
Southend-on-Sea and Thurrock
Cherry Hinton Hall
Cherry Hinton Road
Cambridge CB1 8DW
e-mail: info@eearts.co.uk   Tel: 01223 215355

EAST MIDLANDS ARTS
Derbyshire (excluding High Peak District),
Leicestershire, Lincolnshire, Rutland,
Northamptonshire, Nottinghamshire
Mountfields House
Epinal Way
Loughborough
Leics LE11 0QE
Fax: 01509 262214   Tel: 01509 218292

LONDON ARTS BOARD
The arts funding and development agency
for the 32 London boroughs and the
Corporation of London
2 Pear Tree Court
London EC1R 0DS
e-mail: info@lonab.co.uk
Fax: 020-7608 4100   Tel: 020-7608 6100

NORTH WEST ARTS BOARD
Greater Manchester,
Merseyside, Lancashire,
Cheshire & High Peak District of Derbyshire
Manchester House
22 Bridge Street
Manchester M3 3AB
e-mail: info@nwarts.co.uk
Fax: 0161-834 6969   Tel: 0161-834 6644

NORTHERN ARTS
Cumbria, Teesside, Durham,
Northumberland, Tyne and Wear
Central Square
Forth Street
Newcastle-upon-Tyne NE1 3PJ
e-mail: info@northernarts.org.uk
Fax: 0191-230 1020   Tel: 0191-255 8500

SOUTH EAST ARTS
Kent, Surrey, East Sussex & West Sussex
and the unitary authorities of
Brighton & Hove and Medway
Union House, Eridge Road
Tunbridge Wells, Kent TN4 8HF
Fax: 0870 2421259   Tel: 01892 507200

SOUTH WEST ARTS
The unitary authorities of Bristol, Bath,
Torbay, Plymouth and the counties of
Devon, Cornwall, Gloucestershire,
Somerset and Dorset
(except Bournemouth, Christchurch & Poole)
Bradninch Place
Exeter, Gandy Street
Devon EX4 3LS
e-mail: info@swa.co.uk
    Tel: 01392 218188

SOUTHERN ARTS
Buckinghamshire, Hampshire,
Isle of Wight, Oxfordshire, Wiltshire,
County areas of Berkshire and SE Dorset
13 St Clement Street
Winchester
Hants SO23 9DQ
e-mail: info@southernarts.co.uk
Fax: 01962 861186   Tel: 01962 855099

WEST MIDLANDS ARTS
Herefordshire, Worcestershire,
Staffordshire, Warwickshire and Shropshire,
Stoke on Trent, Telford and Wrekin
& districts of Birmingham, Coventry
Dudley, Sandwell, Solihull,
Walsall & Wolverhampton
82 Granville Street
Birmingham B1 2LH
e-mail: info@west-midlands-arts.co.uk
Fax: 0121-643 7239   Tel: 0121-631 3121

YORKSHIRE ARTS
Yorkshire & Humberside
21 Bond Street
Dewsbury
West Yorks WF13 1AX
e-mail: info@yarts.co.uk
Fax: 01924 466522   Tel: 01924 455555

ALDERSHOT
West End Centre (SA)
Queens Road, Aldershot
Hants GU11 3JD
Tel: 01252 408040   BO: 01252 330040

ANDOVER
Cricklade Theatre
Charlton Road, Andover, Hants SP10 1EJ
Arts Administrator: Holly Bednal
e-mail: hbednal@cricklade.ac.uk
                          Tel/Fax: 01264 365698

BAMPTON
West Ox Arts
WOA Gallery, Market Square
Bampton, Oxfordshire OX18 2JH
Administrator: Sally Proctor   Tel: 01993 850137

BANGOR
Theatr Gwynedd, Ffordd Deiniol
Bangor Gwynedd LL57 2TL
e-mail: theatr@globalnet.co.uk
BO: 01248 351708   Admin: 01248 351707

BEDHAMPTON
(See HAVANT)

BILLERICAY
Billericay Arts Association
The Fold, 72 Laindon Road
Billericay, Essex CM12 9LD
Secretary: Edmond Philpott   Tel: 01277 659286

BINGLEY
Bingley Arts Centre
Main Street, Bingley
West Yorkshire BD16 2LZ
Head of Halls: Mark Davies   Tel: 01274 751576

BIRMINGHAM
The Custard Factory
Gibb Street, Digbeth
Birmingham B9 4AA
e-mail: post@custardfactory.com
Fax: 0121-604 8888   Tel: 0121-693 7777

BIRMINGHAM
Midlands Arts Centre (MAC)
Cannon Hill Park, Birmingham B12 9QH
Director: Dorothy Wilson
BO: 0121-440 3838   Admin: 0121-440 4221

BOSTON
Blackfriars Arts Centre (EMA)
Spain Lane, Boston
Lincolnshire PE21 6HP
e-mail: admin@blackfriarsarts.demon.co.uk
Fax: 01205 358855   Tel: 01205 363108

BRACKNELL
South Hill Park Arts Centre
Bracknell, Berkshire RG12 7PA
Chief Executive: Ron McAllister
e-mail: southhillpark.org.uk
Fax: 01344 411427   Tel: 01344 484858

BRADFORD
Theatre in the Mill, University of Bradford
Richmond Road, Bradford
West Yorkshire BD7 1DP
Artistic Director: Andrew Loretto
e-mail: theatre-manager@brad.ac.uk
                          Tel: 01274 233188

BRAINTREE
The Town Hall Centre (EEA)
Market Square, Braintree, Essex CM7 3YG
General Manager: Jean Grice
                          Tel: 01376 557776

BRENTFORD
Watermans (LA)
40 High Street, Brentford
Middlesex TW8 0DS
Fax: 020-8232 1030
BO: 020-8232 1010   Admin: 020-8232 1020

BRIDGWATER
Bridgwater Arts Centre (SWA)
11-13 Castle Street, Bridgwater
Somerset TA6 3DD   Tel: 01278 422700

BRIGHTON
Gardner Arts Centre
University of Sussex, Falmer
Brighton BN1 9RA
Director: Sue Webster
Fax: 01273 678551
BO: 01273 685861   Admin: 01273 685447

BRISTOL
Arnolfini
16 Narrow Quay, Bristol BS1 4QA
Operations Manager: Polly Cole
Director: Caroline Collier
e-mail: arnolfini@arnolfini.demon.co.uk
Fax: 0117-925 3876   Tel: 0117-929 9191

BUILTH WELLS
Wyeside Arts Centre (ACW)
Castle Street, Builth Wells
Powys LD2 3BN
Fax: 01982 553995   Tel: 01982 553668

BURTON UPON TRENT
The Brewhouse
Union Street, Burton upon Trent
Staffs DE14 1EB
Director: Clive Lyttle
General Manager: Mike Mear
e-mail: info@brewhouse.co.uk
Fax: 01283 515106
BO: 01283 516030   Admin: 01283 567720

BURY
The Met Arts Centre
Market Street, Bury, Lancs BL9 0BW
Director: Ged Kelly
e-mail: mail@metarts.demon.co.uk
Fax: 0161-763 5056
BO: 0161-761 2216   Admin: 0161-761 7107

CANNOCK
Prince of Wales Centre
Church Sreet, Cannock, Staffs WS11 1DE
General Manager: Richard Kay
                          Tel: 01543 466453

CARDIFF
Chapter Arts Centre
Market Road, Canton, Cardiff CF5 1QE
Theatre Programmer: James Tyson
BO: 029-2030 4400   Admin: 029-2031 1050

CHESTERFIELD
The Arts Centre (EMA)
Chesterfield College, Infirmary Road
Chesterfield, Derbyshire S41 7NG
Co-ordinator: Bernie Hayter
                          Tel/Fax: 01246 500578

CHIPPING NORTON
The Theatre (SA)
2 Spring Street
Chipping Norton, Oxon OX7 5NL
Director: Tamara Malcolm
General Manager: Chris Durham
e-mail: admin@chippingnortontheatre.co.uk
Fax: 01608 642324
BO: 01608 642350   Admin: 01608 642349

CHRISTCHURCH
The Regent Centre (SA)
51 High Street, Christchurch, Dorset BH23 1AS
General Manager: David Hopkins
e-mail: info@regentcentre.co.uk
Fax: 01202 479952
BO: 01202 499148   Admin: 01202 479819

CIRENCESTER
Brewery Arts
Brewery Court, Cirencester
Glos GL7 1JH
Artistic Director: Dan Scrivener
e-mail: admin@breweryarts.freeserve.co.uk
Fax: 01285 644060
BO: 01285 655522   Admin: 01285 657181

COLCHESTER
Colchester Arts Centre (EEA)
Church Street, Colchester
Essex CO1 1NF
Director: Anthony Roberts
e-mail: colchester.artscentre@virgin.net
                          Tel: 01206 500900

CORNWALL
Sterts Open Air Theatre
Upton Cross, Liskeard
Cornwall PL14 5AZ
Tel/Fax: 01579 362962   Tel/Fax: 01579 362382

COVENTRY
Warwick Arts Centre
University of Warwick, Coventry CV4 7AL
Director: Alan Rivett
e-mail: arts.centre@warwick.ac.uk
BO: 024-7652 4524   Admin: 024-7652 3734

CUMBERNAULD
Cumbernauld Theatre
Kildrum, Cumbernauld G67 2BN
Administrator: Debbie Murdoch
Artistic Director: Simon Sharkey
Fax: 01236 738408
BO: 01236 732887   Admin: 01236 737235

DARLINGTON
Darlington Arts Centre
Vane Terrace, Darlington
County Durham DL3 7AX
BO: 01325 486555   Admin: 01325 483271

DORCHESTER
Dorchester Arts Centre
School Lane, The Grove, Dorchester
Dorset DT1 1XR
Director: Sharon Hayden
e-mail: enquiries@dorchesterarts.org.uk
                          Tel: 01305 266926

DORSET
Bryanston Arts Centre
Blandford Forum, Dorset DT11 0PX
Administrator: Sarah Moore
e-mail: bac@bryanston.co.uk
Fax: 01258 484506   Tel: 01258 456533

EDINBURGH
Netherbow: Scottish Storytelling Centre
The Netherbow, 43-45 High Street
Edinburgh EH1 1SR
Director: Dr Donald Smith
e-mail: netherbow-storytelling@dial.pipex.com
                          Tel: 0131-556 9579

EDINBURGH
Theatre Workshop
34 Hamilton Place, Edinburgh EH3 5AX
Director: Robert Rae
Fax: 0131-220 0112   Tel: 0131-225 7942

EPSOM
Playhouse (SEA)
Ashley Avenue
Epsom, Surrey KT18 5AL
Venues Manager: Trevor Mitchell
e-mail: tmitchell@epsom-ewell.gov.uk
Fax: 01372 726228
BO: 01372 742555   Admin: 01372 742226

EVESHAM
Evesham Arts Centre (WMA)
Victoria Avenue, Evesham
Worcestershire WR11 4QH
Lauri Griffith-Jones
BO: 01386 45567
Theatre: 01386 48883   Director: 01386 446067

EXETER
Exeter Phoenix
Bradninch Place
Gandy Street
Exeter, Devon EX4 3LS
Business Manager: Anthony Doherty
e-mail: admin@exeterphoenix.org.uk
Fax: 01392 667599
BO: 01392 667080   Admin: 01392 667060

FAREHAM
Ashcroft Arts Centre (SA)
Osborn Road, Fareham
Hants PO16 7DX
Director: Steve Rowley
e-mail: asharts@globalnet.co.uk
Fax: 01329 825661
BO: 01329 310600   Tel: 01329 235161

FROME
Merlin Theatre (SWA)
Bath Road, Frome
Somerset BA11 2HG
e-mail: info@merlintheatre.fsnet.co.uk
BO: 01373 465949   Admin: 01373 461360

GAINSBOROUGH
Trinity Arts Centre
Trinity Street, Gainsborough
Lincolnshire DN21 2AL
e-mail: info@trinityarts.demon.co.uk
Fax: 01427 811198
BO: 01427 810710   Admin: 01427 810298

GREAT TORRINGTON
The Plough Arts Centre (SWA)
9-11 Fore Street, Great Torrington
Devon EX38 8HQ
e-mail: beaford_arts@hotmail.com
BO: 01805 624624   Admin: 01805 622552

HARLECH
Theatr Ardudwy (ACW)
Harlech, Gwynedd LL46 2PU
Theatre Director: Glyn L Williams
BO: 01766 780667

HAVANT
Havant Arts Centre
East Street, Havant
Hants PO9 1BS
Director: Paul Sadler
e-mail: havarts@dircon.co.uk
Fax: 023-9249 8577
BO: 023-9247 2700   Admin: 023-9248 0113

HEMEL HEMPSTEAD
Old Town Hall Arts Centre (EEA)
High Street, Hemel Hempstead
Herts HP1 3AE
General Manager: Alison Young
e-mail: othadmin@dacovum.gov.uk
BO: 01442 228091   Admin: 01442 228095

HEXHAM
Queen's Hall (NA)
Beaumont Street
Hexham, Northumberland NE46 3LS
Artistic Director: Geof Keys
e-mail: boxoffice@queenshall.co.uk
Fax: 01434 652478   Tel: 01434 652476

HORSHAM
Horsham Arts Centre (SEA)
North Street, Horsham
West Sussex RH12 1RL
General Manager: Mick Gattrell
Fax: 01403 211502   Tel: 01403 259708

HUDDERSFIELD
Kirklees (various venues)
Kirklees Cultural Services
Red Doles Lane
Huddersfield HD2 1YF
Head of Performing Arts: Glenis Burgess
BO: 01484 223200   Admin: 01484 226300

INVERNESS
Eden Court Theatre
Bishop's Road
Inverness IV3 5SA
Director: Colin Marr
e-mail: admin@eden-court.co.uk
BO: 01463 234234   Admin: 01463 239841

JERSEY
Jersey Arts Centre
Phillips Street, St Helier
Jersey JE2 4SW
Director: Daniel Austin
Deputy Director: Sarah Johnson
Fax: 01534 726788
BO: 01534 700444   Admin: 01534 700400

KENDAL
Brewery Arts Centre (NA)
Highgate, Kendal
Cumbria LA9 4HE
Chief Executive: Sam Mason
BO: 01539 725133   Admin: 01539 722833

KING'S LYNN
Kings' Lynn Arts Centre (EEA)
27-29 Kings Street, King's Lynn
Norfolk PE30 1HA
Fax: 01553 762141
BO: 01553 764864   Tel: 01553 765565

KING'S LYNN
Corn Exchange
Tuesday Market Place
King's Lynn, Norfolk PE30 1JW
Marketing Manager: Suzanne Hopp
e-mail: suzanne.hopp@west-norfolk.gov.uk
Fax: 01553 762141
BO: 01553 764864   Tel: 01553 765565

LEICESTER
Phoenix Arts Centre
21 Upper Brown Street
Leicester LE1 5TE
Director: Rachael Thomas
e-mail: rachael@phoenix.org.uk
BO: 0116-255 4854   Admin: 0116-224 7700

LICHFIELD
Lichfield District Arts Association
Donegal House, Bore Street
Lichfield WS13 6NE
Administrator: Brian Pretty
Fax: 01543 308211   Tel: 01543 262223

LIVERPOOL
Bluecoat Arts Centre (NWA)
School Lane, Liverpool L1 3BX
Director: Bryan Biggs
e-mail: admin@bluecoatartscentre.com
Tel: 0151-709 5297

LONDON
BAC
Lavender Hill, Battersea
London SW11 5TN
e-mail: mailbox@bac.org.uk
Fax: 020-7978 5207
BO: 020-7223 2223   Admin: 020-7223 6557

LONDON
The Bull (Theatre, Gallery & Studios)
68 High Street, Barnet
London EN5 5SJ
e-mail: admin@thebull.org.uk
Fax: 020-8364 9037
BO: 020-8449 0048   Admin: 020-8449 5189

LONDON
Chats Palace
42-44 Brooksby's Walk, London E9 6DF
Administrator: Leanne Montgomery
BO: 020-8986 6714   Admin: 020-8533 0227

LONDON
Cockpit Theatre
Gateforth Street, London NW8 8EH
Fax: 020-7258 2921
BO: 020-7258 2925   Admin: 020-7258 2920

LONDON
The Drill Hall
16 Chenies Street
London WC1E 7EX
e-mail: admin@drillhall.co.uk   Tel: 020-7631 1353

LONDON
Hoxton Hall Arts Centre (LA)
130 Hoxton Street, London N1 6SH
Theatre Manager: Carola Palacion
e-mail: office@hoxtonhall.dabsol.co.uk
Fax: 020-7729 3815
BO: 020-7739 5431   Admin: 020-7684 0060

LONDON
Institute of Contemporary Arts
The Mall, London SW1Y 5AH
Head of Live Arts: Andrew Missingham
e-mail: performingarts@ica.org.uk
Fax: 020-7306 0122
Admin: 020-7930 0493   BO: 020-7930 3647

LONDON
Islington Arts Factory
2 Parkhurst Road, London N7 0SF
e-mail: islington@artsfactory.fsnet.co.uk
Fax: 020-7700 7229   Tel: 020-7607 0561

LONDON
Jacksons Lane
269A Archway Road, London N6 5AA
Fax: 020-8348 2424
BO: 020-8341 4421   Admin: 020-8340 5226

LONDON
The Nettlefold
West Norwood Library Centre
1 Norwood High Street, London SE27 9JX
Manager: Jean Wilson
Fax: 020-7926 8071   Tel/BO: 020-7926 8070

LONDON
October Gallery
24 Old Gloucester Street, London WC1N 3AL
Contact: Chili Hawes
e-mail: info@theoctobergallery.com
Fax: 020-7405 1851   Tel: 020-7242 7367

LONDON
Oval House (LA)
52-54 Kennington Oval
London SE11 5SW
Director: Deborah Bestwick
e-mail: info@ovalhouse.com   Tel: 020-7582 0080

LONDON
Riverside Studios (LA)
Crisp Road, Hammersmith, London W6 9RL
e-mail: online@riversidestudios.co.uk
Fax: 020-8237 1001
BO: 020-8237 1111   Tel: 020-8237 1000

LONDON
Polish Social & Cultural Association (LA)
238-246 King Street, London W6 0RF
Arts Co-ordinator: A Ostaszewski
    Tel: 020-8741 1940

LOWESTOFT
Seagull Theatre (EA)
Morton Road, Lowestoft, Suffolk NR33 0JH
Advisory Drama Teacher: Sandra Redfell
Fax: 01502 515338   Tel: 01502 562863

MAIDENHEAD
Norden Farm Centre for The Arts
Altwood Road, Maidenhead SL6 4PF
Director: David Hill
e-mail: admin@nordenfarm.org
Fax: 01628 682525
BO: 01628 788997   Admin: 01628 682555

MAIDSTONE
Corn Exchange Complex
Earl Street, Maidstone, Kent ME14 1PL
Commercial Manager: Mandy Hare
Fax: 01622 602194
BO: 01622 758611   Admin: 01622 753922

MANCHESTER
The Forum (NWA)
Civic Centre Complex, Wythenshawe
Manchester M22 5RX
BO: 0161-437 9663   Admin: 0161-935 4073

MANCHESTER
Green Room (NWA)
54-56 Whitworth Street West
Manchester M1 5WW
Artistic Director: Garfield Allen
e-mail: greenroom@easynet.co.uk
Fax: 0161-950 5776
BO: 0161-950 5900   Admin: 0161-950 5777

MANSFIELD
New Perspectives Theatre Company
The Old Library, Leeming Street
Mansfield, Notts NG18 1NG
e-mail: info@newperspectives.co.uk
    Tel: 01623 635225

MILFORD HAVEN
Torch Theatre
St Peter's Road, Milford Haven
Pembrokeshire SA73 2BU
Artistic Director: Peter Doran
e-mail: torchtheatre@cwcom.net
Fax: 01646 698919
BO: 01646 695267   Admin: 01646 694192

NEWPORT (Isle of Wight)
Quay Arts
Sea Street, Newport Harbour
Isle of Wight PO30 5BD
Fax: 01983 526606
BO: 01983 528825   Tel: 01983 822490

NORWICH
Norwich Arts Centre
Reeves Yard, St Benedicts Street
Norwich, Norfolk NR2 4PG
Director: Pam Reekie
e-mail: pam.reekie@norwichartscentre.co.uk
BO: 01603 660352   Admin: 01603 660387

NUNEATON
Nuneaton Arts Centre
Pool Bank Street, Nuneaton CV11 5DB
Chairman: Tony Deeming
e-mail: abbey.theatre@btinternet.com
    Tel: 024-7632 7359

PLYMOUTH
Plymouth Arts Centre
38 Looe Street, Plymouth
Devon PL4 0EB
Director: Ian Hutchinson
e-mail: arts@plymouthac.org.uk
Fax: 01752 206118   Tel: 01752 206114

POOLE
Poole Arts Centre (SA)
Kingland Road, Poole
Dorset BH15 1UG
BO: 01202 685222   Admin: 01202 665334

RADLETT
The Radlett Centre
1 Aldenham Avenue
Radlett, Herts WD7 8HL
Fax: 01923 857592   Tel: 01923 857546

ROTHERHAM
Rotherham Theatres
Walker Place, Rotherham
South Yorkshire S65 1JH
Strategic Leader Culture/Leisure/Lifelong
Learning : Phil Rodgers
BO: 01709 823621   Admin: 01709 823641

SALISBURY
Salisbury Arts Centre (SA)
Bedwin Street, Salisbury, Wiltshire SP1 3UT
e-mail: info@salisburyarts.co.uk
Fax: 01722 331742
BO: 01722 321744   Admin: 01722 430700

SHREWSBURY
Shrewsbury & District Arts Association (WMA)
The Gateway, Chester Street
Shrewsbury
Shropshire SY1 1NB
e-mail: migrate124@aol.com   Tel: 01743 355159

SOUTHPORT
Southport Arts Centre (NWA)
Lord Street, Southport
Merseyside PR8 1DB
e-mail: artsop@seftonarts.co.uk
BO: 01704 540011   Admin: 01704 540004

STAFFORD
Stafford Gatehouse Theatre (WMA)
Eastgate Street, Stafford ST16 2LT
General Manager: Daniel Shaw
e-mail: gatehouse@staffordbc.gov.uk
                                    Tel: 01785 253595

STAMFORD
Stamford Arts Centre (EEA)
27 St Mary's Street, Stamford
Lincolnshire PE9 2DL
General Manager: David Popple
Fax: 01780 766690
BO: 01780 763203   Admin: 01780 480846

STIRLING
MacRobert Arts Centre
University of Stirling, Stirling FK9 4LA
Director: Liz Moran   Tel: 01786 467155

SWANSEA
Taliesin Arts Centre (WWA)
University of Wales Swansea
Singleton Park, Swansea SA2 8PZ
General Manager: Sybil Crouch
e-mail: s.e.crouch@swansea.ac.uk
                                    Tel: 01792 295438

SWINDON
Wyvern Theatre
Theatre Square, Swindon
Wiltshire SN1 1QN
BO: 01793 524481   Admin: 01793 535534

TAMWORTH
Tamworth Arts Centre & Assembly Rooms
Church Street, Tamworth
Staffordshire B79 7BX
BO: 01827 709618   Tel: 01827 709620

TAUNTON
Brewhouse (SWA)
Coal Orchard, Taunton
Somerset TA1 1JL
Artistic Director: Glenys Gill
e-mail: brewhouse@btconnect.co.uk
Fax: 01823 323116
BO: 01823 283244   Admin: 01823 274608

TOTNES
Dartington Arts (SWA)
Dartington Hall, Totnes
Devon TQ9 6DE
Manager: Paul Goddard
e-mail: admin@dartingtonarts.co.uk
BO: 01803 847070   Admin: 01803 847074

TUNBRIDGE WELLS
Trinity Theatre & Arts Centre
Church Road, Tunbridge Wells
Kent TN1 1JP
Artistic Director: Tim Arthur
Executive Director: Helen Winning
BO: 01892 678678   Admin: 01892 678670

ULEY
Prema
South Street, Uley, Nr Dursley, Glos GL11 5SS
Director: Gordon Scott
e-mail: info@prema.demon.co.uk
Fax: 01453 860123   Tel: 01453 860703

VALE OF GLAMORGAN
St Donats Arts Centre (ACW)
St Donats Castle
The Vale of Glamorgan CF61 1WF
Artistic Director: David Ambrose
Fax: 01446 799101   Tel: 01446 799099

WAKEFIELD
Wakefield Arts Centre (YA)
Wakefield College, Thornes Park Centre
Thornes Park, Horbury Road
Wakefield WF2 8QZ
Facilities Officer: Carole Clark
e-mail: info@wake-theatre.demon.co.uk
                                    Tel: 01924 789824

WALLSEND
Buddle Arts Centre (NA)
258B Station Road, Wallsend
Tyne & Wear NE28 8RG
Contact: Geoffrey A Perkins
Fax: 0191-200 7142   Tel: 0191-200 7132

WASHINGTON
The Arts Centre Washington (NA)
Biddick Lane, Fatfield, District 7
Washington, Tyne & Wear NE38 8AB
Fax: 0191-219 3466   Tel: 0191-219 3455

WELLINGBOROUGH
The Castle
Castle Way, Wellingborough
Northants NN8 1XA
Executive Director: Graham Brown
Artistic Director: David Bown
e-mail: info@thecastle.org.uk
Fax: 01933 229888   Tel: 01933 229022

WHITSTABLE
Whitstable Community Arts Centre
The Re-Assembly Rooms
Horsebridge Road, Whitstable
Kent CT5 1BU
e-mail: slappers@whitstable2000.fsnet.co.uk
                                    Tel/Fax: 01227 263733

WIMBORNE
Layard Theatre
Canford School, Canford Magna
Wimborne, Dorset BH21 3AD
Director of Drama: Stephen Hattersley
Administrator: Christine Haynes
e-mail: layardtheatre@canford.com
Fax: 01202 849134
BO: 01202 849134   Admin: 01202 841254

WINCHESTER
Tower Arts Centre, Romsey Road
Winchester, Hampshire SO22 5PW
Director: John Tellett   Tel: 01962 867986

WINDSOR
Windsor Arts Centre (SA)
St Leonard's Road, Windsor, Berks SL4 3BL
Director: Debbie Stubbs
e-mail: admin@windsorartscentre.org
Fax: 01753 621527
BO: 01753 859336   Admin: 01753 859421

WOLVERHAMPTON
Afro-Caribbean Cultural Centre (WMA)
2 Clarence Street, Wolverhampton WV1 4JH
Arts Co-ordinator: CJ Antonio
                                    Tel: 01902 420109

WREXHAM
Wrexham Arts Centre (ACW)
Rhosddu Road, Wrexham LL11 1AU
e-mail: arts.centre@wrexham.gov.uk
Fax: 01978 292611   Tel: 01978 292093

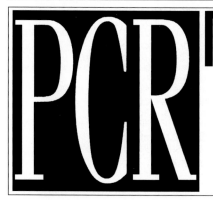

Advanced casting information. Breakdowns covering theatre, television, films and commercials. Early leads and unique free telephone information service for subscribers. Who's Where indices including casting directors. Over 30 years PCR has built up an unbeatable network of leads and information. Subscribing costs only £27.50 for 5 weekly issues. Every Monday direct to you by post.

Editorial Office:
PCR P.O. Box 11, London N1 7JZ
020-7566 8282
Subscription Office:
PCR P.O. Box 100, Broadstairs, Kent CT10 1UJ
01843 860885
www.pcrnewsletter.com

For information regarding membership of the Casting Directors' Guild please contact
PO Box 34403
London W6 0YG
Tel/Fax: 020-8741 1951

ADAMSON Joanne CASTING
15 Northview Terrace
Leeds LS28 6HY
e-mail: watts07@hotmail.com
Tel/Fax: 0113-257 9039

AILION Pippa
3 Towton Road
London SE27 9EE
Tel/Fax: 020-8670 4816   Tel: 020-8761 7095

ALEXANDER Pam
Granada Television, Quay Street
Manchester M60 9EA   Tel: 0161-832 7211

ALL DIRECTIONS OF LONDON PERSONAL MANAGEMENT & CASTINGS
7 Rupert Court, Off Wardour Street
London W1D 6EB   Tel: 020-7437 5879

ANDREW Dorothy CASTING
Campus Manor, Childwall Abbey Road,
Childwall, Liverpool L16 0JP
Fax: 0151-722 9079   Tel: 0151-722 9122

APPS Greg
(See PROTOTYPE CASTING)

ARNELL Jane
Flat 2, 39 St Peter's Square
London W6 9NN

BAIN James
Granada Television, Quay Street
Manchester M60 9EA   Tel: 0161-827 2129

BALDIES CASTING AGENCY
(The only agency purely for bald people)
6 Marlott Road, Poole, Dorset BH15 3DX
Mobile: 07860 290437   Tel: 01202 666001

BARBOUR Penny
Rosemary Cottage, Fontridge Lane,
Etchingham, East Sussex TN19 7DD

BARNES Michael CDG
25 Old Oak Road, London W3 7HN
Fax: 020-8742 9385   Tel: 020-8749 1354

BARTLETT Carolyn CDG
22 Barton Road
London W14 9HD

BEARDSALL Sarah CDG
11 Goodwins Court, London WC2N 4LL
e-mail: casting@beardsall.com

BEATTIE Victoria
(See BIG FISH CASTING)

BERRIE Gillian
(See BIG FISH CASTING)

BERTRAND Leila CASTING
53 Hormead Road, London W9 3NQ
e-mail: leila.bertrand@virgin.net
Tel: 020-8964 0683

BEWICK Maureen CASTING
104A Dartmouth Road, London NW2 4HB
Tel: 020-8450 1604

BIG FISH CASTING
(Victoria Beattie & Gillian Berrie)
2nd Floor, 95-107 Lancefield Street
Glasgow G3 8JD
Fax: 0141-248 6147   Tel: 0141-204 5207

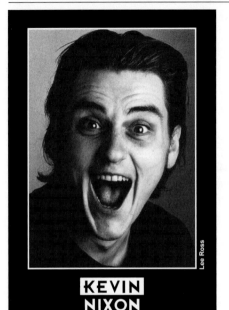

KEVIN NIXON

p h o t o g r a p h y

Spotlight, Publicity & Promotion

020 8340 4598
mobile: 07973 760 590

Lee Ross

BILL The - PEARSON TV PRODUCTIONS Ltd
Bosun House
1 Deer Park Road, Merton
London SW19 3TL   Tel: 020-8540 0600

BIRD Sarah
PO Box 32658
London W14 0XA
Fax: 020-7602 8601   Tel: 020-7371 3248

BOOTH Stephanie
52 Bates Road
Brighton BN1 6PG   Tel/Fax: 01273 500202

BOULTING Lucy CDG
Riverbank House
1 Putney Bridge Approach
London SW6 3JD
Fax: 020-7371 0066   Tel: 020-7351 0606

BRACKE Siobhan CDG
Basement Flat, 22A The Barons
St Margaret's TW1 2AP   Tel: 020-8891 5686

BROADCASTING
(Lesley Beastall & Sophie North)
23 Canalot Studios, 222 Kensal Road
London W10 5BN
Fax: 020-8968 6462   Tel: 020-7460 5220

BRUFFIN Susie CDG
133 Hartswood Road
London W12 9NG   Tel: 020-8740 9895

BRUSCHELLE Barbara
(See CASTING UNLIMITED UK & LA)

BRYDEN Kate
Unit 7, 93 Paul Street
London EC2A 4NY
e-mail: katebrydencasting@hotmail.com
Fax: 020-7251 9255   Tel: 020-7684 0465

BULLIVANT Malcom CDG
9 Montrose Villas, Hammersmith Terrace
London W6 9TT
Fax: 020-8748 1793   Tel: 020-8748 4146

BUTCHER Linda
39 Arlington Road, Surbiton
Surrey KT6 6BW
Fax: 020-8390 9777   Tel: 020-8399 7373

CAIRD LITTLEWOOD CASTING
(Angela Caird)
PO Box MT 86, Leeds LS17 8YQ
e-mail: cairdlitt@aol.com
Fax: 0113-266 6068   Tel: 0113-288 8014

C.A.L.S. CASTING
(Children & Teenagers)
Unit E2, Bellevale Shopping Centre
Liverpool L25 2RG
Mobile: 07930 889057   Tel/Fax: 0151-487 8500

CANDID CASTING
2nd Floor
111-113 Great Titchfield Street
London W1W 6RY
e-mail: mail@candidcasting.co.uk
Fax: 020-7636 5522   Tel: 020-7636 6644

CANNON DUDLEY & ASSOCIATES
43A Belsize Square
London NW3 4HN
e-mail: casting@dudley.dircon.co.uk
Fax: 020-7433 3599   Tel: 020-7433 3393

CARLING Di CASTING CDG
1st Floor, 49 Frith Street
London W1D 4SG
Fax: 020-7287 6844   Tel: 020-7287 6446

Jacqueline Charlesworth

Tim Birkett
Photography

07798 522884
020 7564 7044

Pamela Merrick

Tom Hollander

Kim Thomson

Martin Shaw

Charlie Carter
020 7751 0575

CARLTON TELEVISION
35-38 Portman Square, London W1H 0NU
Fax: 020-7612 7528   Tel: 020-7486 6688

CARROLL Anji CDG
109 Ritherdon Road, London SW17 8QH
Fax: 020-8772 6408   Tel: 020-8772 9806

CASTING ANGELS The
(London & Paris)
Suite 4, The Studio, 14 College Road
Bromley, Kent BR1 3NS   Tel/Fax: 020-8313 0443

CASTING.COM (UK)
4th Floor, 6 Hanover Street, London W1 9HH
e-mail: info@castingco.com
Fax: 020-7491 9097   Tel: 020-7491 9098

CASTING COMPANY The
(Michelle Guish CDG)
22 Great Malborough Street, London W1F 7HU
e-mail: michguish@dial.pipex.com
Fax: 020-7434 2346   Tel: 020-7734 4954

CASTING CONNECTION The
(Michael Syers)
Northern Office: Dalrossie House
16 Victoria Grove, Stockport, Cheshire SK4 5BU
Fax: 0161-442 7280   Tel: 0161-432 4122

All mail, fax & telephone calls to the Northern
Office. London Office: Garden Studios
11-15 Betterton Street, London WC2H 9BP

CASTING COUCH PRODUCTIONS Ltd
(Moira Townsend)
Canalot Production Studios
222 Kensal Road, London W10 5BN
e-mail: moiratownsend@yahoo.co.uk
Fax: 020-8208 2373   Tel: 020-8438 9679

CASTING DIRECTORS The
(Gillian Hawser & Caroline Hutchings)
24 Cloncurry Street, London SW6 6DS
e-mail: carohutchings@hotmail.com
Fax Gillian: 020-7731 0738
Fax Caroline: 020-8336 1067   Tel: 020-7731 5988

CASTING UNLIMITED (LONDON)
14 Russell Garden Mews, London W14 8EU
e-mail: info@castingdirector.co.uk
Fax: 020-7602 9994   Tel: 020-7603 1979

CASTING UNLIMITED (LOS ANGELES)
45181/2 Hazeltine Avenue
Sherman Oaks, Los Angeles CA 91423
e-mail: info@castingdirector.co.uk

CATLIFF Suzy CDG
e-mail: suzy.catliff@ukgateway.net
Fax: 020-7602 8601   Tel: 020-7371 3248

CELEBRITY GROUP Ltd The
12 Nottingham Place, London W1M 3FA
e-mail: info@celebrity.co.uk
Fax: 020-7224 6060   Tel: 020-7224 5050

CHARD Alison CDG
23 Groveside Court
Lombard Road
Battersea, London SW11 3RQ
e-mail: alisonchard@castingdirector.freeserve.co.uk
                              Tel/Fax: 020-7223 9125

CHARKHAM CASTING (Beth Charkham)
Suite 5.1, Moray House
23-31 Great Titchfield Street, London W1P 7FE
Fax: 020-7436 4943   Tel: 020-7436 4842

CLARK Andrea
(See ZIMMERMANN Jeremy CASTING)

COLLINS Jayne CASTING
38 Commercial Street, London E1 6LP
e-mail: info@jaynecollinscasting.com
Fax: 020-7422 0015   Tel: 020-7422 0014

CORDORAY Lin
66 Cardross Street
Hammersmith
London W6 0DR

COTTON Irene CDG
25 Druce Road, London SE21 7DW
e-mail: olicot@talk21.com
Tel/Fax: 020-8299 2787   Tel: 020-8299 1595

CRAMPSIE Julia
(See EASTENDERS CASTING)

CROCODILE CASTING COMPANY The
(C. Gibbs & T. Saban)
9 Ashley Close, Hendon, London NW4 1PH
e-mail: croccast@aol.com
Fax: 020-8203 7711   Tel: 020-8203 7009

CROWE Sarah CASTING
24 Poland Street, London W1V 3DD
e-mail: sarah@crowecasting.demon.co.uk
Fax: 020-7287 2147   Tel: 020-7734 5464

CROWLEY POOLE CASTING
11 Goodwins Court, London WC2N 4LL
Fax: 020-7379 5971   Tel: 020-7379 5965

CROWLEY Suzanne CDG
(See CROWLEY POOLE CASTING)

CYBER ARTISTS 2000
In the Can Ltd, 20 Old Steine, Brighton BN1 1EL
e-mail: cyber@cyber.ndo.co.uk
                              Tel/Fax: 01273 671234

DAVIES Jane CASTING Ltd
(Jane Davies CDG & John Connor)
PO Box 680, Sutton, Surrey SM1 3ZG
e-mail: jdcastingltd@cs.com
Fax: 020-8644 9746   Tel: 020-8715 1036

DAVIS Leo (Miss)
(JUST CASTING)
128 Talbot Road, London W11 1JA
Fax: 020-7792 3043   Tel: 020-7229 3471

DAVIS Noel CASTING
Flat 6, 160 Gloucester Road, London SW7 4QF

DAVY Gary CDG
3rd Floor, 2 Henrietta Street, London WC2E 8PS
e-mail: garydavy@dircon.co.uk
Fax: 020-7836 0881   Tel: 020-7836 0880

DAY Kate CDG
Pound Cottage, 27 The Green South
Warborough, Oxon OX10 7DR
                              Tel/Fax: 01865 858709

DE FREITAS Paul CDG
2 Conduit Street, London W1S 2XB

DE FREITAS Paul CDG
2 Conduit Street, London W1S 2XB

DEITCH Jane
DG03, BBC Centre House, 56 Wood Lane
London W12 7SB
Fax: 020-8576 4947   Tel: 020-8225 6417

DENMAN CASTING (Jack)
Burgess House, Main Street, Farnsfield
Notts NG22 8EF   Tel/Fax: 01623 882272

DOWD Kate
Chelsea Chambers, 262A Fulham Road
London SW10 9EL
Fax: 020-7352 6997   Tel: 020-7352 1086

DRURY Malcolm CDG
34 Tabor Road
London W6 0BW   Tel: 020-8748 9232

DUDLEY Carol CDG
(See CANNON DUDLEY & ASSOCIATES)

DUFF Julia CDG
11 Goodwins Court, London WC2N 4LL
Fax: 020-7379 5971   Tel: 020-7240 4554

DUFF Maureen CDG
(See STEVENS Gail CASTING)

DUFFY Jennifer CDG
42 Old Compton Street, London W1D 4TX
Fax: 020-7287 7752   Tel: 020-7287 7751

EAST Irene CASTING CDG
40 Brookwood Avenue, Barnes
London SW13 0LR
e-mail: irneast@aol.com   Tel: 020-8876 5686

EASTENDERS CASTING
BBC Elstree Centre, Clarendon Road
Borehamwood
Herts WD6 1JF   Tel: 020-8228 7777

EASTON Andrew
51 Links Road
London SW17 9EE   Tel: 020-8767 1623

EMMERSON Chloe
110 Goldhawk Road
London W12 8HD   Tel/Fax: 020-8749 0439

ENGLAND Liz CASTING CDG
34 Connaught Street, London W2 2AF

EVANS Karen
Carlton Television, 35-38 Portman Square
London W1H 0NU

EVANS Kate
(See KATE & ALI CASTING)

EVANS Richard CDG
10 Shirley Road, London W4 1DD
e-mail: info@rec.freeuk.com
Fax: 020-8742 1010   Tel: 020-8994 6304

FALLON & POLENTARUTTI CDG
Top Floor, 37 Berwick Street, London W1F 8RS
Fax: 020-7734 3549   Tel: 020-7734 1819

FARRON Val CDG
1 Victoria Parade, Sandycombe Road, Kew
Richmond TW9 3NB   Tel: 020-8948 6622

FEARNLEY Ali
(See KATE & ALI CASTING)

FIELDEN Ann CDG
5 Rectory Lane, London SW17 9PZ
Fax: 020-8672 4803   Tel: 020-8767 3939

FIELDEN Cornelia
Waterside, 99 Rotherhithe Street
London SE16 4NF
Fax: 020-7394 0016   Tel: 020-7394 1444

FIGGIS Susie
19 Spencer Rise
London NW5 1AR   Tel: 020-7482 2200

MICHELLE LIVINGSTONE

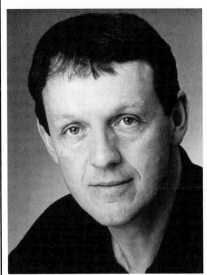

KEVIN WHATELY

JOHN FLETCHER

PHOTOGRAPHER

020-8203-4816

FILDES Bunny CASTING CDG
56 Wigmore Street
London W1   Tel: 020-7935 1254

FINCH Nikki
London Weekend TV
South Bank Television Centre, London SE1 9LT

FINCHER Sally CDG
Carlton Television
35-38 Portman Square, London W1H 0NU

FOENANDER Allan
59 North Eyot Gardens, St Peters Square
London W6 9NL
Fax: 020-8748 9628   Tel: 020-8748 9641

FOTHERGILL Janey CASTING
18-21 Jermyn Street
London SW1Y 6HP   Tel: 020-7287 6562

FOX Celestia
5 Clapham Common Northside
London SW4 0QW
e-mail: celestia.fox@virgin.net

FRAZER Janie CDG
London Weekend TV, South Bank
Television Centre, London SE1 9LT
e-mail: janie.frazer@granadamedia.com
          Tel: 020-7261 3848

FRISBY Jane CASTING CDG
51 Ridge Road, London N8 9LJ
e-mail: j.frisbycast@amserve.net

FUNNELL Caroline CDG
25 Rattray Road, London SW2 1AZ
Fax: 020-7326 1713   Tel: 020-7326 4417

GALLIE Joyce
37 Westcroft Square, London W6 0TA

GANE CASTING
(Natasha Gane)
12 Mill Lane, London NW6 1NS
e-mail: natasha@ganecasting.com
Fax: 020-7916 3446   Tel: 020-7916 2098

GB CASTING UK Ltd (Karin Grainger)
1 Charlotte Street, London W1P 1DH
e-mail: kggbuk@lineone.net
Fax: 020-7255 1899   Tel: 020-7636 2437

GILLHAM Tracey
(Entertainment - Comedy)
BBC Television Centre, Wood Lane
London W12 7RJ
e-mail: tracey.gillham@bbc.co.uk
Fax: 020-8576 4414   Tel: 020-8225 7585

GOLD Nina CDG
10 Kempe Road, London NW6 6SJ
e-mail: nina@ninagold.co.uk
Fax: 020-8968 6777   Tel: 020-8960 6099

GRAYBURN Lesley CDG
74 Leigh Gardens, London NW10 5HP
Fax: 020-8969 2846   Tel: 020-8969 6112

GREEN Jill
Fax: 020-7580 6048   Tel: 020-7580 6037

GREENE Francesca CASTING
79 Ashworth Mansions, London W9 1LN
Fax: 020-7266 9001   Tel: 020-7286 5957

GRESHAM Marcia CDG
3 Langthorne Street, London SW6 6JT
          Tel: 020-7381 2876

GROSVENOR CASTING
(Angela Grosvenor CDG)
27 Rowena Crescent, London SW11 2PT
Fax: 020-7652 6256   Tel: 020-7738 0449

GUISH Michelle CDG
(See CASTING COMPANY The)

HALL Janet
1 Shore Avenue, Shaw, Oldham OL2 8DA
e-mail: hallcastings@netscapeonline.co.uk
Mobile: 07780 783489   Tel: 01706 291459

HALL Pippa
(Children & Teenagers only)
205C Camberwell Grove, London SE5 8JU
e-mail: pippahall.casting@virgin.net
                              Tel/Fax: 020-7733 5780

HAMMOND Louis
39 Queensmill Road, London SW6 6JP

HANCOCK Gemma CDG
(See RSC CASTING DEPARTMENT)

HANSEN CASTING BUREAU Ltd
PO Box 22695
London NW3 2HL   Tel: 020-7267 8357

HARRISON Louise
44 Tytherton Road
London N19 4QA   Tel/Fax: 020-7263 6882

HAUSSMAN Ashley CASTING
c/o Serious Pictures
1A Rede Place, London W2 4TU
e-mail: haussman-casting@hotmail.com
                              Tel: 020-7792 4477

HAWSER Gillian CASTING
24 Cloncurry Street, London SW6 6DS
e-mail: gillian.hawser@virgin.net
Fax: 020-7731 0738   Tel: 020-7731 5988

HAYFIELD Judi
Granada Television, Quay Street
Manchester M60 9EA   Tel: 0161-832 7211

HENDERSON Anne CASTING Ltd CDG
93 Kelvin Road, Highbury
London N5 2PL

HICKLING Matthew
(Drama Series)
Room N412, BBC Elstree Centre
Clarendon Road
Borehamwood, Herts WD6 1JF
e-mail: matthew.hickling@bbc.co.uk
Fax: 020-8228 8311   Tel: 020-8228 8285

HILL Serena CDG
Royal National Theatre, Upper Ground
South Bank, London SE1 9PX
Fax: 020-7452 3340   Tel: 020-7452 3333

HILTON Carrie
HG4, Aberdeen Centre
22-24 Highbury Grove, London N5 2EA
Fax: 020-7359 5378   Tel: 020-7226 8897

HOOTKINS Polly CDG
PO Box 25191, London SW1V 2WN
e-mail: polly@clara.net
Fax: 020-7828 5051   Tel: 020-7233 8724

HORAN Julia
6 Evangelist Road
London NW5 1UB   Tel: 020-7267 5261

HOWE Gary
34 Orbit Street, Roath
Cardiff CF24 0JX   Tel: 029-2033 1341

HUBBARD CASTING
(Ros Hubbard, John Hubbard
Dan Hubbard CDG, Amy MacLean)
2nd Floor, 19 Charlotte Street, London W1T 1RL
e-mail: email@hubbardcasting.com
Fax: 020-7636 7117   Tel: 020-7636 9991

HUBBARD CASTING (DUBLIN)
c/o Irish Film Centre
6 Eustace Street
Temple Bar, Dublin 2

Yvonne Kaziro

ANGUS DEUCHAR
Photographer

020 8286 3303
Mobile. 07973 600728

www.ActorsPhotos.co.uk

Gerard Horan

HUGHES Sarah
Stephen Joseph Theatre, Westborough,
Scarborough, North Yorkshire YO11 1JW
Tel: 01723 370540

HUGHES Sylvia
Casting Suite, The Deanwater, Wilmslow Road,
Woodford, Cheshire SK7 1RJ
Fax: 01565 723707   Tel: 01565 722707

HUTCHINGS Caroline
PO Box 1119, Kingston & Surbiton KT2 7WY
e-mail: carohutchings@hotmail.com
Fax: 020-8336 1067   Mobile: 07768 615343

JACKSON Sue
Yorkshire Television, The TV Centre, Leeds LS3 1JS

JAFFA SILLS CASTING
67 Starfield Road, London W12 9SN
e-mail: jaffasills@supaworld.com
Fax: 020-8743 9561   Tel: 020-7565 2877

JAFFREY Jennifer
136 Hicks Avenue, Greenford
Middlesex UB6 8HB
e-mail: magnoliamanagement@bigfoot.com
Fax: 020-8575 0369   Tel: 020-8578 2899

JAMES Julie CASTING
Studio 1, 48 Vincent Square
London SW1P 2NR
e-mail: juliejames@btclick.com
Mobile: 07931 219054   Tel/Fax: 020-7834 0967

JAY Jina CASTING CDG
1st & 2nd Floor, 50 Chiswick High Road
London W4 1SZ
Fax: 020-8994 1113   Tel: 020-8995 9090

JENKINS Lucy
74 High Street, Hampton Wick
Kingston-upon-Thames KT1 4DQ
e-mail: lucy@littlejenkins.freeserve.co.uk
Fax: 020-8977 0466   Tel: 020-8943 5328

JN CASTING & PRODUCTION
Apt B, 109 Englefield Road
London N1 3LH
e-mail: james@jncasting.co.uk
Fax: 020-7359 3529   Tel: 020-7354 5511

JOHN Priscilla CDG
PO Box 22477, London W6 0GT
Fax: 020-8741 4005   Tel: 020-8741 4212

JOHNSON Alex CASTING
18 Kildare Terrace, London W2 5LX
Fax: 020-7229 1665   Tel: 020-7229 8779

JOHNSON Marilyn CDG
1st Floor, 11 Goodwins Court
London WC2N 4LL
e-mail: marilynjohnson@lineone.net
Fax: 020-7497 5530   Tel: 020-7497 5552

JONES Doreen CDG
PO Box 22478, London W6 0WJ
Fax: 020-8748 8533   Tel: 020-8746 3782

JONES Sam CDG
193 Wardour Street, London W1F 8ZF
e-mail: get@samjones.co.uk
Fax: 020-7439 1941   Tel: 020-7494 3284

JONES Sue
10 Nightingale Road, London NW10 4RH
Fax: 020-8838 1130   Tel: 020-8838 5153

KATE & ALI CASTING
1st Floor, 26 Goodge Street, London W1P 1FG
e-mail: kateali.casting@virgin.net
Fax: 020-7636 8080   Tel: 020-7636 4040

KEOGH Beverley
Brunel House, 4th Floor, 54 Princess Street
Manchester M1 6HS
Fax: 0161-236 1960   Tel: 0161-236 1900

KESTER Gaby
(See CASTING COMPANY The)

KESTON Sam
(Children, Young People, Families)
Fax: 01628 822461   Tel: 01628 822982 Ext 4

KOREL Suzy CDG
20 Blenheim Road, London NW8 0LX
e-mail: suzykorel@genie.co.uk
Fax: 020-7372 3964   Tel: 020-7624 6435

KYLE Greg CASTING
The Summerhouse, Thames House
54 Thames Street, Hampton TW12 2DX
Fax: 020-8274 8423   Tel: 020-8274 8096

LAUREN GOLDWYN CASTING Inc
14 Dean Street
London W1D 3RS
e-mail: realcreate@aol.com
Fax: 020-7437 4221   Tel: 020-7437 4188

LAYTON & NORCLIFFE CASTING
(Belinda Norcliffe, Claudie Layton &
Alix Charpentier)
Unit 232, Canalot Studios, 222 Kensal Road
London W10 5BN
e-mail: lnc@mother-goose.demon.co.uk
Fax: 020-8968 1330   Tel: 020-8964 2055

LESSALL Matthew
Unit 5, Gun Wharf, 241 Old Ford Road
London E3 5QB
e-mail: lessallcasting@hotmail.com
Fax: 020-8980 2211   Tel: 020-8980 0117

LEVINSON Sharon
30 Stratford Villas, London NW1 9SG
e-mail: sharonlev@aol.com
Fax: 020-7916 5872   Tel: 020-7485 2057

LINDSAY-STEWART Karen CDG
PO Box 2301, London W1A 1PT
e-mail: klindsaystewart@btinternet.com
Fax: 020-7439 0548   Tel: 020-7439 0544

LIP SERVICE CASTING
(Voice-Overs only)
4 Kingly Street, London W1B 5PE
e-mail: castings@lipservice.co.uk
Fax: 020-7734 3373   Tel: 020-7734 3393

LISNEY Julia CDG
501A Battersea Park Road, London SW11 4LW

MacGABHANN Dorothy
15 Sandycove Avenue East
Sandycove, Co. Dublin
Fax: 00 353 1 2846865   Tel: 00 353 1 2807242

MARSHALL Sophie
Royal Exchange Theatre Company
St Ann's Square, Manchester M2 7DH
Fax: 0161-832 0881   Tel: 0161-833 9333

McCANN Joan CDG
11 Oldfield Road
London N16 0RR   Tel: 020-7923 0648

McLEOD Carolyn CASTING
PO Box 25602
London N15 3AS   Tel/Fax: 0704 4001720

McMURRICH Chrissie
16 Spring Vale Avenue, Brentford
Middlesex TW8 9QH   Tel: 020-8568 0137

McSHANE Sooki
8A Piermont Road, East Dulwich
London SE22 0LN   Fax: 020-8693 7411

McWILLIAMS Debbie
13A Lambs Conduit Passage
London WC2R 4RH
e-mail: debbiemcwilliams@hotmail.com
Fax: 020-7495 2620   Tel: 020-7495 2520

MELA WHITE
29 Talbot Road, Twickenham, Middlesex TW2 6SJ

MOISELLE Frank
7 Corrig Avenue
Dun Laoghaire, Co. Dublin
Fax: 00 353 1 2803277   Tel: 00 353 1 2802857

MOISELLE Nuala
7 Corrig Avenue
Dun Laoghaire, Co. Dublin
Fax: 00 353 1 2803277   Tel: 00 353 1 2802857

MORRIS Jacqui
(See MUGSHOTS CASTING STUDIO)

MORRISON Melika
12A Rosebank, Holyport Road
London SW6 6LG   Tel/Fax: 020-7381 1571

MUGSHOTS CASTING STUDIO
20 Greek Street, London W1D 4DU
Fax: 020-7437 0308   Tel: 020-7437 2275

NEEDLEMAN Sue
19 Stanhope Gardens
London NW7 2JD
Fax: 020-8959 0225   Tel: 020-8959 1550

NOEL CASTING
(Specialising in Character Actors
and Ethnic and Asian Actors)
Suite 501, International House
223 Regent Street, London W1B 2QD
e-mail: kingnoel/177hotmail.com
Fax: 020-7544 1090   Tel: 020-7544 1010

O'BRIEN Debbie
72 High Street, Ashwell, Nr Baldock
Herts SG7 5NS
Fax: 01462 743110   Tel: 01462 742919

BRENDA
FRICKER

JOANNE
FARRELL

DANIEL
BROCKLEBANK

OCEAN CASTING
(Sherrie Mead)
43 Bathgate Road, Wimbledon, London SW19 5PW
e-mail: oceancasting@hotmail.com
Fax: 020-8944 9854   Tel: 020-8947 2235

O'CONNOR Pam
26 Millgreen Road, Welwyn Garden City
Herts AL7 3XF
Fax: 01707 894313   Tel: 01707 336773

PAGE HALL CASTING
PO Box 2944
London W1A 6ET   Tel: 020-7224 1093

PALMER Helena
(See CANNON DUDLEY & ASSOCIATES)

PARRISS Susie CASTING CDG
PO Box 25796, London SW19 8WS
Fax: 020-8944 9553   Tel: 020-8944 9552

PEARCE WOOLGAR CASTING
(Formerly Jill Pearce Casting)
(Prop. Francesca Woolgar CDG)
6 Langley Street, London WC2H 9JA
Fax: 020-7379 8250   Tel: 020-7240 0316

PETTS & CLAY CASTING
(Tree Petts & Sarah Clay)
14 Balfour Road, London N5 2HB
e-mail: pettsandclay@ukgateway.net
Fax: 020-7704 6774   Tel: 020-7288 0953

PLANTIN Kate
37 Albany Mews
Kingston-upon-Thames, Surrey KT2 5SL
e-mail: kateplantin@hotmail.com
Fax: 020-8549 7299   Tel: 020-8546 4577

POOLE Gilly CDG
(See CROWLEY POOLE CASTING)

PROCTOR Carl
15B Bury Place, London WC1A 2JB
Fax: 020-7916 2533   Tel: 020-7681 0034

PROTOTYPE CASTING (MELBOURNE)
The Melbourne Film Studios, 117 Rouse Street
Port Melbourne, Vic 3207, Australia
e-mail: greg@prototypecasting.com.au
Fax: 00 61 3 9646 8705   Tel: 00 61 3 9646 8777

PROTOTYPE CASTING (SYDNEY)
Fox Studios Australia, FSA #20
Driver Avenue, Moore Park NSW 1363
e-mail: greg@prototypecasting.com.au
Fax: 02 9383 4404   Tel: 02 9383 4400

PRYOR Andy CDG
Top Floor, 13 Radnor Walk, London SW3 4BP
Fax: 020-7351 2882   Tel: 020-7351 2880

RE:ACTORS
(Workshops & Showcases)
15 Montrose Walk, Weybridge, Surrey KT13 8JN
e-mail: michael@reactors.co.uk
Fax: 01932 830248   Tel: 01932 888885

REICH Liora
25 Manor Park Road
London N2 0SN   Tel: 020-8444 1686

REYNOLDS Simone CDG
60 Hebdon Road, London SW17 7NN

REYNOLDS Thalia
Room 603, BBC Victoria Road
172-178 Victoria Road, Acton, London W3 6UL

RHODES JAMES Kate
HG04, The Aberdeen Centre
22-24 Highbury Grove, London N5 2EA
e-mail: katekrj@aol.com
Fax: 020-7359 5378   Tel: 020-7704 8186

ROBERTSON Sasha
19 Wendell Road, London W12 9RS
e-mail: sasha.robertson@virgin.net
Fax: 020-8740 1396   Tel: 020-8740 0817

RODRIGUEZ Corinne
11 Lytton Avenue
London N13 4EH   Fax: 020-8886 5564

ROFFE Danielle CASTING CDG
38-42 Whitfield Street, London W1P 5RF
e-mail: drccasting@msn.com
Fax: 020-7323 3184   Tel: 020-7323 3181

ROYAL SHAKESPEARE COMPANY
(Casting Director: John Cannon CDG,
Deputy Casting Director: Ginny Schiller)
Barbican Theatre, Silk Street, London EC2Y 8BQ
Fax: 020-7628 2812   Tel: 020-7628 3351

RSC CASTING DEPARTMENT
Barbican Theatre, Silk Street, London EC2Y 8BQ
Fax: 020-7628 2812   Tel: 020-7628 3351

SBS Ltd
(The Casting Information Service)
Suite 1, 16 Sidmouth Road, London NW2 5JX
e-mail: sbsltd@talk.com
Fax: 020-8459 7442   Tel: 020-8459 2781

SCOTT Laura CDG
56 Rowena Crescent, London SW11 2PT
e-mail: lscott@dircon.co.uk
Fax: 020-7924 1907   Tel: 020-7978 6336

SEECOOMAR Nadira
PO Box 167, Twickenham TW1 2UP
Fax: 020-8744 1274   Tel: 020-8892 8478

SELWAY Mary CDG
c/o Twickenham Studios, St Margaret's
Twickenham TW1 2AW   Tel: 020-8607 8888

COLIN WILLIAMS
Black & White Portrait Photographer
Website: www.photocol.co.uk
Mobile:07957188983

| Fiona Kay-Mitchell 2001 | Rachel Hollyhead 2001 | Perry Douglin 2001 |

SHAW Philip
Suite 476, 2 Old Brompton Road
South Kensington, London SW7 3DQ
e-mail: hadespluto@aol.com
Fax: 020-8408 1193   Tel: 020-8715 8943

SHEPHERD Debbie CASTING
Suite 16, 63 St Martin's Lane, London WC2N 4JS
e-mail: info@debbieshepherdcasting.co.uk
Fax: 020-7240 4640   Tel: 020-7240 0400

SINGER Sandra ASSOCIATES
21 Cotswold Road, Westcliff on Sea
Essex SS0 8AA
e-mail: sandra.singer@virgin.net
Fax: 01702 339393   Tel: 01702 331616

SMITH Michelle CDG
220 Church Lane, Woodford, Stockport SK7 1PQ
Fax: 0161-439 0622   Tel: 0161-439 6825

SMITH Suzanne CDG
138 Haverstock Hill
London NW3 2AY
e-mail: zan@dircon.co.uk
Fax: 020-7483 2202   Tel: 020-7722 2085

SPON Wendy CDG
c/o ACT Productions
20-22 Stukeley Street
London WC2B 5LR   Tel: 020-7438 9599

STARK CASTING
Mobile: 07956 150689   Tel: 020-8806 6644

STEVENS Gail CASTING CDG
7 Garrick Street
London WC2E 9AR
Fax: 020-7379 3909   Tel: 020-7379 3877

| KELLY PHILPOTT | ALEX VASSI | TAMARA PETERS |

Van Ost & Millington Casting
Twenty Three Years of Award Winning Commercials Across Europe
Specialists in Beauty & Comedy
Tel 020 7436 9838   Fax 020 7436 9858

STEVENSON Sam
103 Whitecross Street, London EC1Y 8JD
e-mail: samstevenson@blueyonder.co.uk

STEWART Amanda CASTING
Studio One, 4 Fleet Road
London NW3 2QS   Tel: 020-7485 7973

STOLL Liz CDG
24 Corinne Road, Tufnell Park
London N19 5EY   Tel: 020-7700 0724

STREETCAST
(Jo Curtis)
14 Scott Ellis Gardens, London NW8 9HD
e-mail: jo@streetcast.co.uk
Fax: 020-7242 6200   Mobile: 07870 661682

STYLE Emma CDG
97 Third Avenue, London W10 4HS
Fax: 020-8960 8323   Tel: 020-8969 5099

SUMMERS Mark (LONDON)
(See CASTING UNLIMITED LONDON)

SUMMERS Mark (LOS ANGELES)
(See CASTING UNLIMITED LOS ANGELES)

SWAYNE Tom
First Floor, 1 Estelle Road
London NW3 2JX
Fax: 020-7482 6168   Tel: 020-7267 7421

SYERS Michael
(See CASTING CONNECTION The)

SYSON Lucinda CDG
11 Goodwins Court, London WC2N 4LL
Fax: 020-7379 5971   Tel: 020-7379 4868

TABAK Amanda CDG
(See CANDID CASTING)

TEECE Shirley
106 North View Road
London N8 7LP   Tel: 020-8347 9241

TITCHMARSH Gill CDG
Chestnut Cottage
Church Square, Chertsey Road
Shepperton TW17 9LA
Fax: 01932 242098   Tel: 01932 225727

TOBIAS SHAW Rose
219 Liverpool Road
London N1 1LX   Fax: 020-7609 9028

TOPOLSKI Tessa
25 Clifton Hill, London NW8 8JY

TOPPS CASTING
(Nicola Topping)
The Media Centre
7 Northumberland Street, Huddersfield HD1 1RL
e-mail: nicci.toppscasting@ntlbusiness.com
Fax: 01484 361001   Tel: 01484 511988

TREVELLICK Jill CDG
123 Rathcoole Gardens
London N8 9PH
e-mail: jilltrevellick@lineone.net
Fax: 020-8348 7400   Tel: 020-8340 2734

TREVIS Sarah CDG
c/o Twickenham Studios, St Margaret's
Twickenham TW1 2AW   Tel: 020-8607 8888

VAGABOND HEART
2 Grassmere Road
Hornchurch
Essex RM11 3DP   Tel: 01708 781994

VAN OST & MILLINGTON CASTING
(Valerie Van Ost & Andrew Millington)
3rd Floor, 9/10 Market Place
London W1N 7AG
Fax: 020-7436 9858   Tel: 020-7436 9838

VAUGHAN Sally
2 Kennington Park Place
London SE11 4AS   Tel: 020-7735 6539

VITAL PRODUCTIONS
PO Box 26441
London SE10 9GZ
e-mail: vitalproductions@aol.com
                         Tel/Fax: 020-8316 4497

VOSSER Anne CASTING
PO Box 203, Aldershot GU12 4YB
e-mail: vossercasting@ntlworld.com
Fax: 01252 404716   Tel: 01252 404715

WEST June
Granada Television, Quay Street
Manchester M60 9EA
e-mail: samantha.tully@granadamedia.com
                         Tel: 0161-832 7211

WESTERN Matt CASTING
4th Floor, 193 Wardour Street
London W1V 3FA
e-mail: mattwestern@lineone.net
Fax: 020-7439 1941   Tel: 020-7434 1230

WHALE Toby CDG
80 Shakespeare Road
London W3 6SN
e-mail: toby@whalecasting.com
Fax: 020-8993 8096   Tel: 020-8993 2821

WHITINGHAM Ian
c/o IWT Broadcasting
1 Barker Steet, Chelsea, London SW10 9EN
e-mail: ianwhittingham@hotmail.com
Fax: 020-7854 1973   Tel: 020-7351 9385

WOODHAMS Keith CASTING
20 Lowther Hill
London SE23 1PY
e-mail: kwoodhams@mcmail.com
Fax: 020-8314 1950   Tel: 020-8314 1677

WOOLGAR Francesca CDG
(See PEARCE WOOLGAR CASTING)

ZIMMERMANN Jeremy CASTING
Clareville House
26-27 Oxendon Street
London SW1Y 4EL
Fax: 020-7925 0708   Tel: 020-7925 0707

Concert & Exhibition Halls

ACCESS STUDIOS
8-10 Creekside, London SE8 3DX
e-mail: info@accessstudios.com
Fax: 0870 1205658   Tel: 020-7231 6185

AMADEUS CENTRE The
50 Shirland Road, London W9 2JA
e-mail: amadeuscentre.co.uk
Fax: 020-7266 1225   Tel: 020-7286 1686

B A C
Battersea Old Town Hall, Lavender Hill, Battersea
London SW11 5TN   Tel: 020-7326 8211

BARBICAN CENTRE
Barbican, Silk Street, London EC2Y 8DS
Fax: 020-7920 9648   Tel: 020-7638 4141

BIRMINGHAM SYMPHONY HALL
Broad Street, Birmingham B1 2EA
e-mail: symphonyhall@necgroup.co.uk
BO: 0121-780 3333   Tel: 0121-200 2000

BLACKHEATH HALLS
23 Lee Road, Blackheath, London SE3 9RQ
e-mail: mail@blackheathhalls.com
Fax: 020-8852 5154   BO: 020-8463 0100

CENTRAL HALL - WESTMINSTER
Storey's Gate, Westminster, London SW1H 9NH
e-mail: events@wch.co.uk   Tel: 020-7222 8010

EARL'S COURT & OLYMPIA EXHIBITION CENTRES
Earl's Court Exhibition Centre, Warwick Road
London SW5 9TA
e-mail: marketing@eco.co.uk   Tel: 020-7385 1200

FAIRFIELD HALLS
Park Lane, Croydon CR9 1DG
BO: 020-8688 9291   Tel: 020-8681 0821

FERNEHAM HALL
Osborn Road, Fareham, Hants PO16 7DB
e-mail: boxoffice@fareham.gov.uk
                           Tel: 01329 824864

GORDON CRAIG THEATRE
Stevenage Arts & Leisure Centre
Lytton Way, Stevenage, Herts SG1 1LZ
e-mail: gordoncraig@stevenage-leisure.co.uk
BO: 08700 131030   Tel: 01438 242642

HEXAGON The
Queen's Walk, Reading RG1 7UA
e-mail: boxoffice@readingarts.com
Fax: 0118-939 0028   BO: 0118-960 6060

LONDON ARENA EXHIBITION CENTRE
Limeharbour, London E14 9TH
Fax: 020-7538 5572   Tel: 020-7538 8880

MINERVA STUDIO THEATRE
Oaklands Park, Chichester, West Sussex PO19 4AP
Fax: 01243 787288   Tel: 01243 784437

NATIONAL CONCERT HALL OF WALES The
St David's Hall, The Hayes, Cardiff CF10 1SH
Fax: 029-2087 8599   Tel: 029-2087 8500

OLYMPIA EXHIBITION CENTRES
Hammersmith Road, Kensington, London W14 8UX
Fax: 020-7598 2500   Tel: 020-7385 1200

RIVERSIDE STUDIOS
Crisp Road, London W6 9RL
e-mail: info@riversidestudios.co.uk
Fax: 020-8237 1001   Tel: 020-8237 1000

ROYAL ALBERT HALL
Kensington Gore, London SW7 2AP
e-mail: admin@royalalberthall.com
Fax: 020-7823 7725   Tel: 020-7589 3203

SOUTH BANK CENTRE
including The Royal Festival Hall
Queen Elizabeth Hall, Purcell Room & Hayward
Gallery, South Bank Centre, London SE1 8XX
BO: 020-7960 4242   Tel: 020-7921 0601

ST JOHN'S
Smith Square, London SW1P 3HA
Fax: 020-7233 1618   Tel: 020-7222 1061

**WEMBLEY CONFERENCE & EXHIBITION CENTRE
& WEMBLEY ARENA**
Wembley, London HA9 0DH
BO: 020-8902 0902   Admin: 020-8902 8833

WIGMORE HALL
36 Wigmore Street, London W1U 2BP
e-mail: info@wigmore-hall.org.uk   BO: 020-7935 2141

Concert Promoters & Agents

AMP ARTISTE MANAGEMENT PRODUCTIONS
Level 2, 32-38 Osnaburgh St, London NW1 3ND
Fax: 020-7224 0111   Tel: 020-7224 1992

ASKONAS HOLT Ltd (Classical Music)
Lonsdale Chambers
27 Chancery Lane, London WC2A 1PF
e-mail: info@askonasholt.co.uk
Fax: 020-7400 1799   Tel: 020-7400 1700

AVALON PROMOTIONS Ltd
4A Exmoor Street, London W10 6BD
Fax: 020-7598 7334   Tel: 020-7598 7333

BARRUCCI LEISURE ENTERPRISES Ltd (Promoters)
45-47 Cheval Place, London SW7 1EW
e-mail: barruccci@barrucci.com
Fax: 020-7581 2509   Tel: 020-7225 2255

BLOCK Derek ARTISTES AGENCY
Douglas House
3 Richmond Buildings, London W1D 3HE
e-mail: dbaa@derekblock.demon.co.uk
Fax: 020-7434 0200   Tel: 020-7434 2100

HOBBS Liz EVENTS
Finsbury Business Centre
40 Bowling Green Lane, London EC1R 0NE
e-mail: events@lizhobbsgroup.com
Fax: 01636 703343   Tel: 020-7287 8870
68 Castlegate, Newark NG24 1BG
e-mail: info@lizhobbsgroup.com
Fax: 01636 703343   Tel: 01636 703342

HOCHHAUSER Victor
4 Oak Hill Way, London NW3 7LR
Fax: 020-7431 2531   Tel: 020-7794 0987

IMG ARTS & ENTERTAINMENT
Pier House
Strand on the Green, Chiswick, London W4 3NN
Fax: 020-8233 5001   Tel: 020-8233 5000

LEWIS Tony ENTERTAINMENTS
PO Box 11268, London SW5 0ZL
Fax: 020-7373 6427   Tel: 020-7370 0416

McINTYRE Phil PROMOTIONS Ltd
2nd Floor, 35 Soho Square, London W1D 3QX
e-mail: reception@pmcintyre.co.uk
Fax: 020-7439 2280   Tel: 020-7439 2270

MILLENNIUM ARTISTES MANAGEMENT Ltd
(Personal Management & Event Co-ordinators)
PO Box 2001, Caterham, Surrey CR3 6UA
e-mail: mamlimited@aol.com
                           Tel/Fax: 01883 347790

RBM
(Comedy)
3rd Floor, 18 Broadwick Street, London W1V 1FG
Fax: 020-7287 5020   Tel: 020-7287 5010

RIGOLETTO Ltd
4 Wigton Court, Wigton Lane
Leeds LS17 8SB   Tel: 0113-269 3720

S.F.X.
35-36 Grosvenor Street, London W1K 4QX
Fax: 020-7529 4301   Tel: 020-7529 4300

ZANDER Peter CONCERT MANAGEMENT
22 Romilly Street, London W1D 5AG
e-mail: peterzan.berlin@virgin.net
                           Tel: 020-7437 4767

121

ABLE SECURITY
117 Waverley Road, Plumstead
London SE18 7TH   Tel/Fax: 020-8317 6899

ACTORS' CONSULTANCY SERVICE
(MOMI ACTS. Andrew Ashmore
Live Interpretation in Museums & Historic Sites)
Museum of the Moving Image, South Bank
Waterloo, London SE1 8XT
e-mail: andrew.ashmore@bfi.org.uk
                              Tel: 020-7815 1336

ACTOR'S 'ONE-STOP' SHOP The
(Showreels, Photographs & CV's)
54 Belsize Avenue, London N13 4TJ
e-mail: info@actorsone-stopshop.com
Fax: 020-8482 7723   Tel: 020-8888 7006

AGENT FILE
(Software for Agents)
25 Belfast Road
Stoke Newington, London N16 6UN
e-mail: steven@agentfile.com
Mobile: 07951 150714   Tel: 07050 683662

AON Ltd (Trading as AON/ALBERT G. RUBEN)
(Insurance Brokers)
Pinewood Studios, Pinewood Road
Iver, Bucks SL0 0NH
e-mail: ann.short@ars.aon.co.uk
Fax: 01753 653152   Tel: 01753 658200

ARTON Michael Ph.D.
(Historical Research, Technical Advisor)
122 Sunningfields Road, London NW4 4RE
e-mail: michael@arton.freeserve.co.uk
                              Tel/Fax: 020-8203 2733

ARTS CLINIC The
(Psychological Counselling
Personal & Professional Development)
14 Devonshire Place, London W1G 6HX
e-mail: mail@artsclinic.co.uk
Fax: 020-7224 6256   Tel: 020-7935 1242

ARTS COUNSEL (Mary Connolly)
(Theatre Administration & Fundraising)
2 Paston Place, Kemp Town, Brighton BN2 1HA
e-mail: mary@artsco.freeserve.co.uk
Fax: 01273 673693   Tel: 01273 682406

ASPEY ASSOCIATES
(Management & Team Training, Counselling,
Human Resources)
8 Bloomsbury Square, London WC1A 2LQ
e-mail: hr@aspey.com
Fax: 020-7405 5541   Tel: 020-7405 0500

ATKINS Chris & COMPANY
(Accountants & Business Consultants)
Astra House, Arklow Road, London SE14 6EB
e-mail: chris.atkins@virgin.net Tel: 020-8691 4100

BERGER Harvey FCA
(Chartered Accountant)
18 Chalk Lane, Cockfosters
Barnet, Herts EN4 9HJ
e-mail: harvey.berger@tesco.net
                              Tel/Fax: 020-8449 9328

BEST IMPRESSION
(Image Consultancy)
36 Sandhill Oval, Alwoodley
Leeds LS17 8EA   Tel: 0113-268 6393

BIG PICTURE
(Part-time Work in Computer Retail Industry)
13 Netherwood Road, London W14 0BL
e-mail: inch@ebigpicture.co.uk
                              Tel: 020-7371 4455

BLACKMORE Lawrence
(Production Accountant)
Suite 5, 26 Charing Cross Road
London WC2H 0DG
Fax: 020-7836 3156   Tel: 020-7240 1817

BOWKER ORFORD
(Chartered Accountants)
15-19 Cavendish Place, London W1G 0DD
Fax: 020-7580 3909   Tel: 020-7636 6391

BREBNER ALLEN TRAPP
(Chartered Accountants)
180 Wardour Street, London W1F 8LB
e-mail: partners@brebner.co.uk
Fax: 020-7287 5315   Tel: 020-7734 2244

BRECKMAN & COMPANY
(Chartered Accountants)
49 South Molton Street
London W1K 5LH   Tel: 020-7499 2292

BRITISH ASSOCIATION FOR DRAMA THERAPISTS The
41 Broomhouse Lane, London SW6 3DP
e-mail: gillian@badth.demon.co.uk
                              Tel/Fax: 020-7731 0160

BROOK-REYNOLDS Natalie
(Freelance Stage Manager, Plays, Musicals,
Concerts. Equity, BECTU, SMA Member)
e-mail: nataliee5@aol.com
Mobile: 07976 234840   Tel: 020-8350 0877

BURGESS Chris
(Counselling for Performing Artists)
81 Arne House, Tyers Street
London SE11 5EZ   Tel: 020-7582 8229

BYFORD Simon
(Production Management Services)
22 Freshfield Place, Brighton
East Sussex BN2 2BN
e-mail: byford@compuserve.com
Fax: 01273 606402   Tel: 01273 623972

LOOKING FOR AN ACCOUNTANT? SOMEONE YOU CAN RELATE TO AND WHO UNDERSTANDS YOUR BUSINESS?

Our medium-sized accountancy practice based in the heart of London's Soho has a dedicated team offering comprehensive specialist advice to all those operating in and around film, theatre, television and all associated services and industries. Our client list covers the whole spectrum of individuals and companies operating in the media and entertainment sectors including those just starting out to well established industry names.

We pride ourselves in providing a fast and efficient service for all financial needs coupled with a specialist knowledge and understanding developed over many years experience, including:

- **Preparing personal and business accounts and plans.**

- **Raising finance for new business ventures, new homes or simply living.**

- **Specialist tax advice including VAT and also help with investment, pension and mortgage choices.**

- **Bookkeeping and payroll services.**

Call Simon Cryer, José Goumal or Michael Burton for a confidential and no obligation free initial discussion.

Registered to carry on audit work and authorised to carry on investment business by the Institute of Chartered Accountants in England and Wales.

The Quadrangle, 180 Wardour Street, London W1F 8LB
Tel 020 7734 2244 Fax 020 7287 5315
http://www.brebner.co.uk
E-Mail: partners@brebner.co.uk

Brebner Allen Trapp   Chartered Accountants

CASTLE MAGICAL SERVICES
(Magical Consultants, Michael Shepherd)
Broompark, 131 Tadcaster Road
Dringhouses, York YO24 1QJ
e-mail: michaelofcastle@aol.com
Tel/Fax: 01904 709500

CAULKETT Robin Dip.S.M., M.I.I.R.S.M.
(Abseiling, Rope Work)
1 Station Road, Newnham-on-Severn
Glos GL14 1BZ   Tel: 01594 825865

CELEBRITY CHEFS
c/o Sandra Singer Associates
21 Cotswold Road, Westcliff on Sea
Essex SS0 8AA
e-mail: sandra.singer@virgin.net
Fax: 01702 339393   Tel: 01702 331616

COMPAGNIE LIAN
(Artist Promotion, Image Consultancy
Copy Writing, Full Translation Services)
2 Ravenscourt Park, London W6 0TH
e-mail: compagnielian9@hotmail.com
Tel: 020-8563 0220

COURTENAY Julian
(NLP Master Practitioner
MANLP Mental Fitness UK)
42 Langdon Park Road, London N6 5QG
e-mail: info@mentalfitness.uk.com
Tel: 020-8348 9033

DICKSON Terance & ASSOCIATES
(Project & General Management)
Unit 1, Michael Manley Industrial Estate
Stewarts Road, London SW8 4UB
e-mail: sales@terrydickson.com
Fax: 020-7498 9844   Tel: 020-7622 7630

DIGITAL SUPPORT Ltd
(Training, Recruitment & Development)
2nd Floor, Hanover House, Coombe Road
Kingston-upon-Thames, Surrey KT2 7AZ
e-mail: info@digitalsupport.co.uk
Fax: 020-8546 2684   Tel: 020-8549 4477

DRAMATURGY
(Production & Literary Dramaturgy)
139B Tooting Bec Road, London SW17 8BW
e-mail: hanna.slattne@dramaturgy.co.uk
Tel: 020-8767 6004

DREAM
(Reflexology, Head, Neck & Shoulder
Massage in the Workplace)
79B Anson Road, Tufnell Park, London N7 0AS
e-mail: dreamtherapies@hotmail.com
Mobile: 07973 731026

EAGLES Steve
(International Sharpshooter & Firearms Lecturer)
Wivenhoe, 46 Hartwood Road, Southport
Merseyside PR9 9AW
e-mail: sn03@dial.pipex.com
Mobile: 07721 464611   Tel/Fax: 01704 547884

EARLE Kenneth PERSONAL MANAGEMENT
214 Brixton Road, London SW9 6AP
Fax: 020-7274 9529   Tel: 020-7274 1219

EDWARDS Simon (PEOPLE FOR BUSINESS Ltd)
(Hypnotherapy for Professionals in Film,
TV and Theatre)
15 Station Road, Quainton, Nr Aylesbury
Bucks HP22 4BW
e-mail: simongedwards@genie.co.uk
Mobile: 07889 333680   Tel: 01296 651259

ENTERTRAIN UK Ltd
18 Runnymede House, Courtlands, Sheen Road
Richmond TW10 5AY
Mobile: 07740 802602   Tel: 020-8241 0207

EQUITY INSURANCE SERVICES
131-133 New London Road
Chelmsford, Essex CM2 0QZ
Fax: 01245 491641   Tel: 01245 357854

EXECUTIVE AUDIO VISUAL
(Showreels for Actors & Presenters)
80 York Street
London W1H 1QW   Tel/Fax: 020-7723 4488

FACADE
(Creation and Production of Musicals)
43A Garthorne Road
London SE23 1EP   Tel: 020-8699 8655

FAITH Gordon BA DHC MCHC (UK)
(Hypnotherapy, Obstacles to Performing,
Positive Affirmation, Focusing)
1 Wavel Mews, Priory Road
London NW6 3AB   Tel: 020-7328 0446

FIELD Bobbie
(Arranger & Composer)
c/o Sandra Singer Associates, 21 Cotswold
Road, Westcliff on Sea, Essex SS0 8AA
e-mail: sandra.singer@virgin.net
Fax: 01702 339393   Tel: 01702 331616

FILMANGEL
(Film Finance & Script Services)
110 Trafalgar Road, Portslade
East Sussex BN41 1GS
e-mail: filmangels@freenetname.co.uk
Fax: 01277 05451   Tel: 01273 277333

FITNESS COACH The
(Jamie Baird)
6 Mysor Road, London SW11 5SB
e-mail: jamie@thefitnesscoach.co.uk
Tel: 07970 782476

FORD Jonathan & Co
(Chartered Accountants)
9 Victoria Street
Rainhill, Merseyside L35 0LB
e-mail: jford@jonathanford.co.uk   Tel: 0151-426 4512

FREE ELECTRON
(Website Design)
45 Alpha Street, Slough, Berks SL1 1RA
e-mail: mikelynn@globalnet.co.uk
Tel/Fax: 01753 693074

**GILMOUR (HEALING) CENTRE
INTERNATIONAL The**
(Spiritual Healing, Counselling, Paranormal
Investigator)
(See SINGER Sandra PUBLIC RELATIONS)

GORDON LEIGHTON
(Chartered Accountants, Business Advisers)
50 Queen Anne Street, London W1G 9HQ
e-mail: gl@gordonl.com
Fax: 020-7487 2566   Tel: 020-7935 5737

HALL Francesca Cert. Dip. IATE. UKCP reg
(Creative Arts Counsellor & Psychotherapist)
68 Tavistock Crescent, Notting Hill
London W11 1AL   Tel: 020-7243 8355

HAMMOND John B. Ed (Hons) ICHFST
(Fitness Consultancy, Sports & Relaxation
Massage)
4 Glencree, Billericay, Essex CM11 1EB
Mobile: 07703 185198   Tel/Fax: 01277 632830

HARDSELL Ltd
(Advertising, Marketing, Design)
The Leathermarket (11-3-1), Weston Street
London SE1 3ER
e-mail: bigideas@hardsell.co.uk
Fax: 020-7403 5381   Tel: 020-7403 4037

HARVEY MONTGOMERY Ltd
(Chartered Accountants)
3 The Fairfield, Farnham, Surrey GU9 8AH
e-mail: harveyca@btconnect.com
Fax: 01252 734394   Tel: 01252 734388

HERITAGE RAILWAY ASSOCIATION
7 Robert Close, Potters Bar
Herts EN6 2DH   Tel: 01707 643568

HOMEMATCH PROPERTY FINANCE
(Mortgages for Entertainers)
6 Shaw Street, Worcester WR1 3QQ
e-mail: chrisjcatchpole@aol.com
Fax: 01905 22121   Tel: 01905 22007

HONRI Peter
(Music Hall Consultant)
1 Evingar Road, Whitchurch
Hants RG28 7EY   Tel: 01256 892161

HUSSEY Daniel
(International Paranormal Occult Investigator & Consultant)
PO Box 24250, London SE9 3ZH
e-mail: enquiries@paranormaloccultinvestigator.com
Mobile: 07764 428318   Tel: 020-8378 6844

HYPNOTHERAPY
13 Cliveden Court, London Road
Brighton, East Sussex BN1 6UB
Fax: 01273 882095   Tel: 01273 506912

HYPNOTHERAPY & PSYCHOTHERAPY
(Including Performance Improvement,
Karen Mann DCH DHP)
1A Wedderburn House, Wedderburn Road
Hampstead
London NW3 5QR   Tel: 020-7794 5843

IMAGE DIGGERS
(Slide/Stills/Audio/Video Library & Theme
Research)
618B Finchley Road, London NW11 7RR
e-mail: ziph@appleonline.net
                        Tel/Fax: 020-8455 4564

IMPACT AGENCY
(Public Relations)
3 Bloomsbury Place, London WC1A 2QL
Fax: 020-7580 7200   Tel: 020-7580 1770

I R A - INDEPENDENT REVIEWS ARTS SERVICES
(Stories from World of Film/Art/Showbiz)
12 Hemingford Close, London N12 9HF
Mobile: 07956 212916   Tel/Fax: 020-8343 7437

JACKSON Kim
(Arts Education Consultancy)
1 Mellor Road, Leicester LE3 6HN
e-mail: mellor@ntlworld.com   Tel: 0116-233 8432

JFL
(Recruitment Consultants)
47 New Bond Street
London W1S 1DJ   Tel: 020-7493 8824

KELLER Don
(Marketing Consultancy & Project Management)
65 Glenwood Road, Harringay, London N15 3JS
e-mail: donkeller@waitrose.com
Fax: 020-8809 6825   Tel: 020-8800 4882

KERR John CHARTERED ACCOUNTANTS
369-375 Eaton Road, West Derby
Liverpool L12 2AH
Fax: 0151-228 3792   Tel: 0151-228 8977

KIEVE Paul
(Magical Effects for Theatre & Film)
23 Terrace Road, South Hackney
London E9 7ES   Tel/Fax: 020-8985 6188

KOHUT Donnie
(Image Consultant)
36 Sandhill Oval
Leeds LS17 8EA   Tel: 0113-268 6393

**KRAFT Susannah THEATRE ADMINISTRATION
(SKTA)**
(Tours and Administration for Small/Middle Scale
Theatre Companies)
28 Bournevale Road, London SW16 2BA
e-mail: s-nskraft@online.rednet.co.uk
Fax: 020-7564 8138   Tel: 020-8677 7952

LAMBOLLE Robert
(Script Evaluation/Editing)
618B Finchley Road, London NW11 7RR
e-mail: ziph@appleonline.net
                        Tel/Fax: 020-8455 4564

LARK INSURANCE BROKING GROUP
(Insurance Brokers)
Wigham House, Wakering Road
Barking, Essex IG11 8PJ
Fax: 020-8557 2430   Tel: 020-8557 2300

LEIGHTON Gordon
50 Queen Anne Street, London W1G 9HQ
e-mail: markg@gordonl.com
Fax: 020-7487 2566   Tel: 020-7935 5737

LINGUA FRANCA
(French Dialogue & Script Translators/Subtitlers)
12 Ack Lane West, Cheadle Hulme
Cheshire SK8 7EL   Tel: 0161-485 3357

LOCATION TUTORS NATIONWIDE
(Fully Qualified/ Experienced Support Teachers,
Covering all Key Stages in National Curriculum)
16 Poplar Walk, Herne Hill, London SE24 0BU
Fax: 020-7207 8794   Tel: 020-7978 8898

LOVE Billie HISTORICAL PHOTOGRAPHS
(Picture Research. Formerly 'Amanda' Theatrical
Portraiture)
3 Winton Street, Ryde
Isle of Wight PO33 2BX   Tel: 01983 812572

MEDIA LEGAL
(Education Services)
83 Clarendon Road, Sevenoaks
Kent TN13 1ET   Tel: 01732 460592

MESURE Steve
(Science Theatre Practitioners)
10 Warren Drive, Chelsfield, Kent BR6 6EX
e-mail: stevmesure@ic24.net   Tel: 01689 812200

MILDENBERG Vanessa
(Choreographer of Theatre)
c/o Cassandra UK, Contact Clare Bloomer
Top Flat, 79 Brondesbury Villas
London NW6 6AG
e-mail: cassandraprod@hotmail.com
Mobile: 07796 264828   Tel: 020-7372 0733

**MILITARY ADVISORY & INSTRUCTION
SPECIALISTS**
(John Sessions) (Advice on Weapons, Drill,
Period to Present. Ex Army Instructors)
e-mail: mais@ntlworld.com   Tel: 01904 491198

MILLARTARIA
(Period & Contemporary Military Researcher
& Advisor, Major Simon Millar)
Gateways Cottage, Donhead St Mary
Shaftesbury, Dorset SP7 9DJ
Fax: 01747 829227   Tel: 01747 829120

MILLER ALLAN Ann
(Private Lessons, Consultancy, Choreography)
The Belly Dance Centre, Mayfield
5 Rother Road, Seaford
East Sussex BN25 4HT
e-mail: annrusty@hotmail.com
                        Tel: 01323 899083

MORGAN Jane ASSOCIATES
(Marketing, Publicity & Press)
8 Heathville Road, London N19 3AJ
e-mail: morgans@dircon.co.uk
Fax: 020-7263 9877   Tel: 020-7263 9867

MORTON THORNTON
(Chartered Accountants)
Torrington House, 47 Holywell Hill, St Albans,
Hertfordshire AL1 1HD
e-mail: mt@mortonthornton.co.uk
Fax: 01727 861052   Tel: 01727 838255

NEATE Rodger PRODUCTION MANAGEMENT
15 Southcote Road, London N19 5BJ
e-mail: rneate@dircon.co.uk
Fax: 020-7697 8237   Tel: 020-7609 9538

NEOVISION
(Location & Production Services)
46 rue de Berne, 1201 Geneva, Switzerland
e-mail: lmouchet@worldcom.ch
                        Tel: (41 79) 357 5417

NETWORK The
(Close Protection & Investigative Services)
29 Queensdown Road, London E5 8NN
e-mail: rbc@thenetwork.demon.co.uk
Fax: 08700 543693   Mobile: 07803 207550

NORTON Michael R
(Implant/Reconstructive Dentistry)
78 Harley Street, London W1G 7HJ
e-mail: nortonimplants@compuserve.com
Fax: 020-7580 9119   Tel: 020-7580 9009

tarlo lyons

For all your legal requirements, contact Simon Meadon at:

Tarlo Lyons, Watchmaker Court,
33 St. John's Lane,
LONDON EC1M 4DB

Telephone: 020 7405 2000
email: simon.meadon@tarlolyons.com

Visit our website at www.tarlolyons.com

NUMBERCRUNCHERS ACCOUNTING SERVICES
29 Dudley Road, Tunbridge Wells, Kent TN1 1LE
e-mail: numbercrunchers@lineone.net
Tel/Fax: 01892 511035

NWA-UK HAMMERLOCK
(Advice on Wrestling Events & Promotion)
PO Box 282, Ashford, Kent TN23 7ZZ
e-mail: nwa-uk@nwa-wrestling.com
Fax: 0709 1131003   Tel: 0709 1131002

NYMAN LIBSON PAUL
(Chartered Accountants)
Regina House, 124 Finchley Road
London NW3 5JS
e-mail: entertainment@nymanlibsonpaul.co.uk
Fax: 020-7431 1109   Tel: 020-7794 5611

PARKER John SCRIPTWRITING
21 Hindsley's Place
London SE23 2NF   Tel: 020-8244 5816

PEAK PERFORMANCE TRAINING
(Tina Reibl, Hypnotherapy, NLP,
Success Strategies)
97A High Street, Maidenhead, Berks
e-mail: tina.reibl@tesco.net   Tel: 01628 633509

POLAND DENTAL STUDIOS
(Film/Stage Dentistry)
1 Devonshire Place, London W1N 1PA
Fax: 020-7486 3952   Tel: 020-7935 6919

PRESTIGE INSURANCE
Garrick House, 161 High Street, Hampton Hill
Middlesex TW12 1NG
Fax: 020-8941 1394   Tel: 020-8941 8099

PRIDE MEDIA ASSOCIATION Ltd
(Alternative Therapies,
Psychic & Paranormal Phenomena)
The Burnside Centre, 38 Burnside Crescent
Middleton, Manchester M24 5NN
e-mail: pma@prideradio.co.uk
Tel/Fax: 0161-643 6266

PRYCE Jacqui-Lee
(Personal Trainer, Boxing,
Muay-Thai & Kick-Boxing)   Mobile: 07930 304809

RETROGRAPH ARCHIVE Ltd
(Nostalgia Picture Consultants 1880-1970)
164 Kensington Park Road
Notting Hill, London W11 2ER
e-mail: retropix1@aol.com
Fax: 020-7229 3395   Tel: 020-7727 9378

ROBERT CARTER
(Solicitor)
8 West Street, London WC2H 9NG
Fax: 020-7836 2786   Tel: 020-7836 2785

SHAW Bernard
(Recording, Directing Voice Tapes)
Horton Manor, Canterbury CT4 7LG
e-mail: bernard@bernardshaw.co.uk
Tel/Fax: 01227 730843

SHAYLE Mark
(Production Management,
Ideal Production Services)
94 Gordon Road, London SE15 3RP
e-mail: m-shayle@dircon.co.uk
Fax: 020-7564 3147   Tel: 020-7564 3384

SINGER Sandra PUBLIC RELATIONS
(Entertainers, Promotions Staff & Events)
21 Cotswold Road, Westcliff-on-Sea
Essex SS0 8AA
e-mail: sandra.singer@virgin.net
Fax: 01702 339393   Tel: 01702 331616

SPEAKERPOWER.CO.UK
48 Fellows Road, London NW3 3LH
e-mail: barbara@speakerpower.co.uk
Fax: 020-7722 5255   Tel: 020-7586 4361

SPENCER Ivor
(Professional Toastmaster,
Events Organiser & Head Butler)
12 Little Bornes, Dulwich, London SE21 8SE
e-mail: ivor@ivorspencer.com
Fax: 020-8670 0055   Tel: 020-8670 8424

SPORTS WORKSHOP PROMOTIONS Ltd
(Production Advisors, Sport, Stunts, Safety)
PO Box 878, Crystal Palace National Sports
Centre, London SE19 2BH
e-mail: info@sportspromotions.co.uk
Fax: 020-8776 7772   Tel: 020-8659 4561

STAGE CRICKET CLUB
(Cricketers & Cricket Club)
39-41 Hanover Steps, St George's Fields
Albion Street, London W2 2YG
e-mail: brianjfilm@aol.com
Fax: 020-7262 5736   Tel: 020-7402 7543

STUNT ACTION SPECIALISTS
110 Trafalgar Road, Portslade
East Sussex BN41 1GS
Fax: 01273 708699   Tel: 01273 411862

SUMMERS David & COMPANY
(Chartered Accountants)
131 Salusbury Road, London NW6 6RG
e-mail: accountants@davidsummers.co.uk
Fax: 020-7372 6752   Tel: 020-7328 4861

TAKE FIVE CASTING STUDIO
(Showreels)
25 Ganton Street, London W1F 9BP
Fax: 020-7287 3035   Tel: 020-7287 2120

**TANI MORENA, SPANISH CHOREOGRAPHY
FOR PROFESSIONALS**
(Theatre, Opera, Ballet)   Tel: 020-8452 0407

TARLO LYONS
(Solicitors)
Watchmaker Court, 33 St John's Lane
London EC1M 4DB
e-mail: info@tarlo-lyons.com
Fax: 020-7814 9421   Tel: 020-7405 2000

TARRY Angela
(Clairvoyant & Aura Photography)
c/o Sandra Singer Associates
21 Cotswold Road, Westcliff on Sea
Essex SS0 8AA
Fax: 01702 339393   Tel: 01702 331616

TAX FILES (UK)
Suite 123-124, Salisbury House
163-164 London Wall, London EC2M 5ST
Fax: 020-7628 2577   Tel: 020-7628 1464

TAYLOR Charlotte
(Stylist/Props Buyer)
18 Eleanor Grove, Barnes, London SW13 0JN
Mobile: 07836 708904   Tel/Fax: 020-8876 9085

TAYLOR Chris
(Arts Administration & Marketing)
1 Chichester Terrace, Brighton BN2 1FG
e-mail: christine@mistral.co.uk
Fax: 01273 675922   Tel: 01273 625132

TELESCRIPT Ltd
The Barn, Handpost Farmhouse, Maidens Green,
Berkshire RG42 6LD
Fax: 01344 890655   Tel: 01344 890470

THEPORTFOLIOSPECIALISTS.COM
(Media Consultants)
Birmingham City Centre, Stephenson Street
Birmingham B2 4DH
e-mail: info@theportfoliospecialists.com
Tel/Fax: 0121-249 2763

THEATRE FORCE
22 Brownhill Lane, Holmbridge, Holmfirth
West Yorkshire HD9 2QW
e-mail: info@theatreforce.com   Tel: 01484 688219

THEATRE PROJECTS CONSULTANTS
4 Apollo Studios, Charlton Kings Road
London NW5 2SW
Fax: 020-7284 0636   Tel: 020-7482 4224

THEATRICAL DENTISTRY
(Richard D Casson)
6 Milford House, 7 Queen Anne Street
London W1G 9HN
e-mail: casson@dircon.co.uk
                        Tel/Fax: 020-7935 8854

THORNTON W. M.
(Military Adviser & Researcher)
37 Wolsey Close, Southall, Middlesex UB2 4NQ
e-mail: maitland@thornton44.fsnet.co.uk
                        Tel: 020-8574 4425

TODS MURRAY WS
(Richard Findlay Entertainment Lawyer)
66 Queen Street, Edinburgh EH2 4NE
e-mail: richard.findlay@todsmurray.com
Fax: 0131-225 3676   Tel: 0131-226 4771

TOUCHWOOD PRODUCTION STUDIO
(Voice-Over Showreels, Digital Editing etc)
Knightsbridge House
229 Acton Lane, Chiswick London W4 5DD
Fax: 020-8995 2144   Tel: 020-8995 3232

TRUEWAYS FENG SHUI
(Tasha Sangster,
Feng Shui for Homes & Businesses)
                        Tel: 020-7403 6564

UK ARTS-EXPLORE
(Developing and co-ordinating arts,
cultural and heritage initiatives)
The Media Centre, 7 Northumberland Street
Huddersfield HD1 1RL
e-mail: info@ukarts-explore.com
                        Tel: 01484 350031

UPFRONT TELEVISION Ltd
(Celebrity)
39-41 New Oxford Street, London WC1A 1BN
e-mail: upfront@btclick.com
Fax: 020-7836 7701   Tel: 020-7836 7702

VENTURINO Antonio
(Commedia dell' Arte & Mask Specialist
& Movement Director)
Coup de Masque, 97 Moore Road
Mapperley, Nottingham NG3 6EJ
e-mail: a-and-t@coup-de-masque.fsnet.co.uk
                        Tel/Fax: 0115-985 8409

VITAL TOUCH The
(On-Site Massage Company)
56A Highbury Park, London N5 2XG
e-mail: suzi@thevitaltouch.com
                        Tel: 020-8451 5500

WARING Elizabeth
(Counsellor for Emotional Problems)
9 Ashley Court, Grand Avenue
Sussex BN3 2NP   Tel: 01273 739351

WHITE Leonard
(Production & Script Consultant)
Highlands, 40 Hill Crest Road, Newhaven
Brighton, East Sussex BN9 9EG
                        Tel/Fax: 01273 514473

WILD DREAM CONSULTANCY
(Achievement Training, Confidence Class,
Personal Development)   Tel: 020-8374 3924

WITCH FINDER GENERAL (Occult Consultants)
BCM AKADEMIA, London WC1N 3XX
e-mail: esbat@blueyonder.co.uk
                        Tel: 020-8683 2173

WYKEHAMS RELOCATION (Relocation Services)
6 Kendrick Place
Reece Mews, London SW7 3HF
Fax: 020-7589 8886   Tel: 020-7581 1935

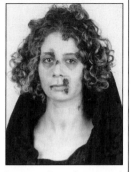

ROSEMARIE SWINFIELD
make-up designer

Rosie's Make-up Box
6 Brewer Street, Soho, London W1R 3FS

Author of:

* Stage Make-Up Step By Step
* Period Make-Up For The Stage
* Hair And Wigs For The Stage

Also

Courses, Workshops & Seminars Worldwide

Tel: 07976-965520 Fax: 020-8390 7773 e-mail: rosemarie@rosiesmake-up.co.uk www.rosiesmake-up.co.uk

---

1ST CROWN
(Suppliers of T-Shirts, Baseball Caps for Crew,
Publicity and Workwear)
3 Austin Court, London Road
Kent TN16 1HE   Mobile: 07903 941150

ACADEMY COSTUMES Ltd
50 Rushworth Street
London SE1 0RB
e-mail: academyco@aol.com
Fax: 020-7928 6287   Tel: 020-7620 0771

ANELLO & DAVIDE Ltd
Shop: 47 Beauchamp Place
Chelsea, London SW3 1NX
Fax: 020-7225 3375   Tel: 020-7225 2468

ANELLO & DAVIDE Ltd
(Bespoke, Bridal, Dance & Theatrical Footwear)
28C Standard Road
London NW10 6EU
Fax: 020-8963 1214   Tel: 020-8963 1220

ANGELS
(Fancy Dress & Revue)
119 Shaftesbury Avenue
London WC2H 8AE
e-mail: party@fancydress.com
Fax: 020-7240 9527   Tel: 020-7836 5678

ANGELS PARIS
(Costume and Uniform Hire)
Cap 18, 189 Rue d'Aubervilles
75018 Paris, France
e-mail: angels@angels.fr
Fax: 00 33 1 44 729060   Tel: 00 33 1 44 728282

ANGELS THE COSTUMIERS
40 Camden Street
London NW1 0EN
e-mail: angels@angels.uk.com
Fax: 020-7383 5603   Tel: 020-7387 0999

ANGELS WIGS
(Wig Hire/Makers, Facial Hair Suppliers)
40 Camden Street
London NW1 0EN
e-mail: wigs@angels.uk.com
Fax: 020-7383 5603   Tel: 020-7387 3999

ANICHINI Carlo
(Hairdresser)
14 Piccadilly Arcade
London SW1Y 6NH   Tel: 020-7493 5692

ARMS & ARCHERY
(Armour, Weaponry, Chainmail,
Period Costumes)
The Coach House, London Road
Ware, Herts SG12 9QU
e-mail: tgou104885@aol.com
Fax: 01920 461044   Tel: 01920 460335

BABOO William
(Theatrical Tailor)
46 Berwick Street
London W1F 8SG   Tel: 020-7434 1680

BAHADLY R
(Hair & Make-Up Specialist, Cheshire Area)
48 Ivy Meade Road
Macclesfield, Cheshire
Mobile: 07973 553073   Tel/Fax: 01625 869712

COSPROP

COSTUMES 1640-1970

with accessories

26-28 Rochester Place, London NW1 9JR
Tel: 020-7485 6731 Fax: 020-7485 5942
enquiries@cosprop.com

Dr. Richard Casson
D E N T A L   C A R E

I provide a complete range of cosmetic and stage dentistry effects for those wishing to add a bit more bite to their big performance.

Free consultation for:

- fangs
- witches teeth
- goofy teeth
- crooked teeth
- replacement of children's missing teeth for stage, television & films

For further information phone or write to
Dr. Richard Casson BDS (GLAS)
on **020 7935 6511/020 7935 8854**

6 Milford House, 7 Queen Anne Street, London W1G 9HN
Website: www.richardcasson.com

BBC COSTUME & WIGS
172-178 Victoria Road
North Acton
London W3 6UL
Fax: 020-8993 7040   Tel: 020-8576 7885

BERTRAND Henry
(London Stockhouse for Silk)
11 Melton Street
London NW1 2EA
Fax: 020-7383 4797   Tel: 020-7383 3868

BIRMINGHAM COSTUME HIRE
Suites 209-210, Jubilee Centre
130 Pershore Street
Birmingham B5 6ND
Fax: 0121-622 2758   Tel: 0121-622 3158

BOSANQUET Pamela COSTUME SERVICES
e-mail: lily.jones@virgin.net
Fax: 020-8891 6259   Tel: 020-8891 4346

BRISTOL COSTUME SERVICES Ltd
(Costume Hire)
Unit 4/5, Whitby Road
St Philips, Bristol BS4 3QF
Fax: 0117-940 5751   Tel: 0117-940 5750

BROE Bert
(Make-Up Artist, Consultant, Lecturer)
38A The Avenue
Hatch End
Middlesex HA5 4EY   Tel: 020-8428 5706

BRYAN PHILIP DAVIES ENTERPRISES
(Lavish Pantomime Costumes/Revue Costumes)
68 Court Road, Lewes
East Sussex BN7 2SA
e-mail: bryan.davies4@btinternet.com
Mobile: 07931 249097   Tel/Fax: 01273 481004

BUTTERFIELD 8
(Formerly Jo Dalby,
Vintage Costume 1910-1980's)
Top Floor, Herbert House
Bristol Temple Meads Station
Bristol   Tel: 01432 840765

CALICO
(Suppliers of Unbleached Calico for Stage
Costumes, Backdrops etc)
3 Ram Passage
High Street
Kingston-upon-Thames KT1 1HH
e-mail: sales@calicofabrics.co.uk
Fax: 020-8546 7755   Tel: 020-8541 5274

CATCO MILLINERY
134 Mercers Road
London N19 4PV   Tel: 020-7272 4833

CAVALCADE COSTUMES
(Period & Light Entertainment Costumes,
Single Outfits to Full Productions)
57 Pelham Road
London SW19 1NW
Fax: 020-8540 2243   Tel: 020-8540 3513

CHANGING FACES
(Theatrical and Media Make-Up Artist)
e-mail: changingfaces@tinyworld.co.uk
Mobile: 07956 817828   Tel: 020-7226 5623

CHRISANNE Ltd
(Specialist Fabrics & Accessories)
Chrisanne House, 14 Locks Lane
Mitcham, Surrey CR4 2JX
e-mail: sales@chrisanne.co.uk
Fax: 020-8640 2106   Tel: 020-8640 5921

COLTMAN Mike
(See COSTUME CONSTRUCTION)

COOK Sheila
(Period Jewellery, Textiles, Costumes and
Accessories for Hire/Sale)
283 Westbourne Grove
London W11 2QA
e-mail: sheilacook@sheilacook.co.uk
Fax: 020-7229 3855   Tel: 020-7792 8001

COSPROP Ltd
(Costumes & Accessories)
26-28 Rochester Place, London NW1 9JR
e-mail: enquiries@cosprop.com
Fax: 020-7485 5942   Tel: 020-7485 6731

COSTUME CONSTRUCTION
(Costumes, Masks, Props, Puppets)
21A Silchester Road
London W10 6SF   Tel/Fax: 020-8968 9136

COSTUME REPRODUCTIONS
(Costumiers)
200 Main Road, Goostrey, Cheshire CW4 8PD
e-mail: lesleyedwards@replicawarehouse.co.uk
          Tel/Fax: 01477 534075

COSTUME STUDIO Ltd
(Costumes & Wigs)
Montgomery House
159-161 Balls Pond Road
London N1 4BG
e-mail: costume.studio@easynet.co.uk
Tel/Fax: 020-7837 6576   Tel: 020-7275 9614

COUNTY DRAMA WARDROBE
(Costume Hire)
25 Gwydir Street
Cambridge CB1 2LG   Tel: 01223 313423

CRAZY CLOTHES CONNECTION
(1920's-1970's for Sale or Hire)
134 Lancaster Road
Ladbroke Grove
London W11 1QU   Tel: 020-7221 3989

DARBY Kevin COSTUMES
(Costumes, Hats, Headdresses & Feathers
Designed, Supplied & Hired)
Unit 10, Douglas Buildings
Royal Stuart Lane
Cardiff CF10 5EL
Fax: 029-2045 1628   Tel: 029-2045 1646

DELANEY Catherine
(Hats/Millinery)
Studio 5, Waterside
99 Rotherhithe Street
London SE16 4NF
e-mail: c.delaney@btconnect.com
Fax: 020-7231 9051   Tel: 020-7231 7173

DESIGNER ALTERATIONS
(Restyling & Remodelling of
Clothes & Costumes)
2 Queenstown Mews
Battersea, London SW8 3QG
Fax: 020-7720 3675   Tel: 020-7498 4360

D'OYLY CARTE OPERA COMPANY
(Wardrobe Services)
The Powerhouse
6 Sancroft Street
London SE11 5UD
Fax: 020-7793 7205   Tel: 020-7793 7100

EASTON Derek
(Wigs For Theatre, Film & TV)
Studio on 2nd Avenue, Kingsway Court
Second Avenue, Hove
East Sussex BN3 2LR
Mobile: 07768 166733   Tel/Fax: 01273 770069

EDA ROSE MILLINERY
(Ladies' Model Hat Design & Manufacture)
Lalique, Mongewell, Wallingford
Oxon OX10 8BP   Tel/Fax: 01491 837174

FOON Kim Yee
(Professional Make-Up Artist for Hire,
Certified & Experienced in Theatre, Film, TV,
Stage, Special Fx, Cosmetic).
                           Mobile: 07779 552612

FOSTER Pam ASSOCIATES
(Wig Makers)
Unit 009, The Chandlery
50 Westminster Bridge Road
London SE1 7QY
e-mail: pam@pfosterassoc.demon.co.uk
Fax: 020-7721 7409   Tel: 020-7721 7641

FOX Charles H. Ltd
(Professional Make-Uup & Wigs)
22 Tavistock Street
London WC2E 7PY
Fax: 0870 2001 369   Tel: 0870 2000 369

FREED OF LONDON
(Dancewear & Danceshoes)
94 St Martin's Lane
London WC2N 4AT
e-mail: shop@freed.co.uk
Fax: 020-7240 3061   Tel: 020-7240 0432

FROCKS
(Dina Hall) (Costume Supervisor & Maker)
Lower Wrescombe Farm Cottage, Yealmpton
Nr Plymouth PL8 2NL   Tel: 01752 881443

FUNN Ltd
(Silk, Cotton Wool Stockings, Opaque Opera
Tights & 40's Rayon Stockings)
PO Box 102 Steyning
West Sussex BN44 3DS
e-mail: funnltd@bigfoot.com
                           Tel/Fax: 01903 892841

GAV NICOLA THEATRICAL SHOES
1A Suttons Lane, Hornchurch
Essex RM12 6RD
e-mail: sales@gavnicola.freeserve.co.uk
Mobile: 07961 974278   Tel/Fax: 01708 438584

GILLHAM Felicite
(Wigs)
10 Newland, Sherborne
Dorset DT9 3JQ
e-mail: f.gillham.wigs@gmx.net
Fax: 0870 0557660   Tel: 01935 814328

HAIRAISERS
(Wigs)
9-11 Sunbeam Road
Park Royal, London NW10 6JP
Fax: 020-8963 1600   Tel: 020-8965 2500

HARVEYS OF HOVE
(Theatrical Costumes & Military Specialists)
110 Trafalgar Road, Portslade
Sussex BN41 1GS
Fax: 01273 708699   Tel: 01273 430323

HERALD & HEART HATTERS
(Men's & Women's Hats &
Head Dresses - Period & Modern)
131 St Philip Street
London SW8 3SS   Tel: 020-7627 2414

HIREARCHY
(Classic & Contemporary Costume)
45-47 Palmerston Road
Boscombe, Bournemouth
Dorset BH1 4HW   Tel: 01202 394465

HIYA COSTUME
(Hire of Theatre Costumes for Adults & Children)
1 Ham Road, Shoreham-by-Sea
Sussex BN43 6PA   Tel: 01273 453421

HODIN Annabel
(Costume Designer/Stylist)
12 Eton Avenue
London NW3 3EH
e-mail: annabelhodin@aol.com
Mobile: 07836 754079   Tel: 020-7431 8761

JULIETTE DESIGNS
(Diamante Jewellery Manufacturers)
90 Yerbury Road
London N19 4RS
Fax: 020-7281 7326   Tel: 020-7263 7878

K & D Ltd
(Footwear)
Unit 7A, Thames Road Industrial Estate
Thames Road, Silvertown
London E16 2EZ
e-mail: k&d@shoemaking.co.uk
Fax: 020-7476 5220   Tel: 020-7474 0500

KING Shelley J
(Make-up Artist/Wigdresser)
4 Church Walk
Bletchingley
Surrey RH1 4PD
Mobile: 07973 249998   Tel: 01883 743593

LANDSFIELD Warren
(Period Legal Wigs)
47 Glenmore Road
London NW3 4DA   Tel: 020-7722 4581

LAURENCE CORNER THEATRICALS
(Theatrical Costumiers - Militaria,
Uniforms - Hire & Sale)
62-64 Hampstead Road
London NW1 2NU
Fax: 020-7813 1413   Tel: 020-7813 1010

LEWIS HENRY Ltd
(Dress Makers)
3rd Floor, 42 Great Titchfield Street
London W1P 7AE   Tel: 020-7636 6683

LONDON HAT HOUSE The
(Hatmakers, Masks, Head Dresses
& Specialist Dyers)
7 Kensington Mall, Kensington
London W8 4EB   Tel: 020-7727 3859

MADDERMARKET THEATRE
(Period Clothing, Costume Hire & Wig Hire)
St John's Alley
Norwich NR2 1DR
e-mail: theatre@maddermarket.freeserve.co.uk
Fax: 01603 661357   Tel: 01603 626292

MAKEUP CENTRE The
(Make-Up Lessons & Supplies)
52A Walham Grove
London SW6 1QR
e-mail: info@themake-upcentre.co.uk
          Tel: 020-7381 0213

MARGARITA
(Film Wardrobe, Costume Designer)
178 Lichfield Court
Sheen Road, Richmond
Surrey TW9 1AZ
e-mail: margaret101uk@yahoo.co.uk
          Tel: 020-8940 4603

MASTER CLEANERS The
(Specialist Dry Cleaners)
189 Haverstock Hill
London NW3 4QG   Tel: 020-7431 3725

MBA COSTUMES
Goodyear House, 52-56 Osnaburgh Street
London NW1 3ND
e-mail: mbacostumes@btinternet.com
Fax: 020-7383 2038   Tel: 020-7388 4994

Cutting Room	**DC**	*The Powerhouse*
Sewing Machines	**DOYLY**	*6 Sancroft Street*
Fitting Room	**CARTE**	*London*
Office		*SE11 5UD*
Convenient for	*Opera Company* **WARDROBE SERVICES**	*Contact:*
South London	**A Fully Equipped Production Wardrobe Available For Hire**	*Marian Padina*
Rehearsal Halls	*Daily * Weekly * Monthly * By The Show * Staffing Available * Competitive Rates*	*020 7793 7100*

McKAY Glynn MASKS
(Specialists in Special Effect Make-Up)
11 Mount Pleasant, Framlingham
Suffolk IP13 9HQ
Mobile: 07780 865073   Tel/Fax: 01728 723865

MIDNIGHT
(Costume Design & Wardrobe,
Film, Music, Theatre)
e-mail: midnight.costumedesign@virgin.net
Mobile: 07941 313223

MUMFORD Jean
(Costume Maker)
92B Fortess Road
London NW5 2HJ   Tel: 020-7267 5829

NICOLERENEE
(Wedding & Evening Dresses/Ballgowns)
4 Puma Court, Spitalfields
City, London EC1 6QG
e-mail: info@nicolerenee.co.uk
Fax: 020-7247 9276   Mobile: 07961 180949

ORIGINAL KNITWEAR
(Inc. Fake Fur)
Waterside, 99 Rotherhithe Street
London SE16 4NF
Fax: 020-7231 9051   Tel: 020-7231 9020

PANTO BOX
(Animal Costume Specialists)
51 Chapel Road, Dersingham
Norfolk PE31 6PJ   Tel/Fax: 01485 544844

PERMODE
(Costume)
46 Berwick Street
London W1F 8SG   Tel: 020-7434 1680

PINK POINTES DANCEWEAR
1A Suttons Lane, Hornchurch
Essex RM12 6RD
e-mail: sales@gavnicola.freeserve.co.uk
Tel/Fax: 01708 438584

POLAND DENTAL STUDIO
(Film/Stage Dentistry)
1 Devonshire Place
London W1N 1PA
Fax: 020-7486 3952   Tel: 020-7935 6919

PROBLOOD
11 Mount Pleasant
Framlingham
Suffolk IP13 9HQ   Tel/Fax: 01728 723865

PULLON PRODUCTIONS
(Costumiers)
St George's Studio
Wood End Lane
Fillongley, Coventry CV7 8DF
e-mail: junepullon@faxvia.net
Tel/Fax: 01676 541390

RAINBOW PRODUCTIONS Ltd
(Manufacture and Handling of Costume
Characters)
Rainbow House
56 Windsor Avenue
London SW19 2RR
e-mail: info@rainbowproductions.co.uk
Fax: 020-8545 0777   Tel: 020-8545 0700

ROBBINS Sheila
(Costumes & Wigs)
60 Hurst Street
Oxford OX4 1HA   Tel: 01865 240268

ROYAL EXCHANGE THEATRE COSTUME HIRE
(Period Costumes, Wigs & Accessories)
47-53 Swan Street
Manchester M4 4JY
e-mail: costume.hire@royalexchange.co.uk
Tel/Fax: 0161-932 6800   Tel: 0161-833 9333

ROYAL LYCEUM THEATRE COMPANY
(Theatrical Costume Hire)
29 Roseburn Street
Edinburgh EH12 5PE
Fax: 0131-346 8072   Tel: 0131-337 1997

ROYAL NATIONAL THEATRE
(Costume & Furniture Hire)
Chichester House
Kennington Park Estate
1-3 Brixton Road
London SW9 6DE
e-mail: costume-hire@nationaltheatre.org.uk
Tel: 020-7735 4774 (Costume)
Tel: 020-7820 1358 (Props)

RUMBLE Jane
(Masks, Millinery, Helmets Made to Order)
121 Elmstead Avenue
Wembley
Middlesex HA9 8NT   Tel: 020-8904 6462

SABAH
(Stylist - Wardrobe, Fashion, Sets & Props)
155 Cholmley Gardens, Mill Lane
London NW6 1AB
e-mail: sabah.saoud@lineone.net
Mobile: 07956 244664   Tel: 020-7794 3213

SCOTT Allan COSTUMES
(Costume Hire, Stage, Film & TV)
Offley Works, Unit F
Prima Road
London SW9 0NA   Tel: 020-7793 1197

SEXTON Sally Ann
(Hair & Make-Up Stylist)
31 Sylvester Road
East Finchley
London N2 8HN
Mobile: 07973 802842   Tel: 020-8346 2745

SHOWBIZ WIGMASTERS
(Theatrical Wigmakers & Hire)
7 Tumulus Close
Southampton SO19 6RL   Tel/Fax: 023-8040 6699

SIDE EFFECTS
(Custom-made Character/FX Costumes)
Unit 4, Camberwell Trading Estate
117 Denmark Road, London SE5 9LB
e-mail: sfx@lineone.net
Fax: 020-7738 5198   Tel: 020-7738 5199

SINGER Sandra ASSOCIATES
21 Cotswold Road
Westcliff on Sea, Essex SS0 8AA
e-mail: sandra.singer@virgin.net
Fax: 01702 339393   Tel: 01702 331616

SKINNER Rachel MILLINERY
13 Princess Road, London NW1 8JR
e-mail: rachel@rachelskinner.co.uk
                          Tel/Fax: 020-7209 0066

SHOWBIZ!

WIGMAKERS / HIRE FOR THEATRE, TV, FILMS,   TEL / FAX 023 8040 6699

SLEIMAN Hilary
(Specialist & Period Knitwear)
72 Godwin Road, London E7 0LG
e-mail: hilarysl@aol.com
Mobile: 07940 555663   Tel: 020-8555 6176

S & M ANDREWS (NORTHERN) Ltd
(Melton, Crepe, Suiting, Barathea, Cut Lengths)
Wira Business Park, West Park Ring Road
Leeds LS16 6EB
e-mail: info@stroud-brothers.demon.co.uk
Fax: 0113-275 3591   Tel: 0113-230 4143

STEP BACK IN TIME
(Decade by Decade Collection of Costume,
Props etc 1890's to present, 1940's Specialist)
Walkers Industrial Park, Ollerton Road
Tuxford Notts NG22 0PQ
Fax: 01777 870033   Tel: 01777 870044

STUDIO FOUR COSTUMES
(Childrenswear for Hire to Film & TV)
4 Warple Mews, Warple Way
Acton, London W3 0RF   Tel/Fax: 020-8749 6569

SWINFIELD Rosemarie
(Make-Up Design & Training)
Rosie's Make-Up Box
6 Brewer Street, Soho
London W1R 3FS
e-mail: rosemarie@rosiesmake-up.co.uk
Fax: 020-8390 7773   Mobile: 07976 965520

TRENDS CREATIVE COSTUMES Ltd
(Theatrical Costume Hire, Design & Making)
54 Lisson Street
London NW1 5DF
e-mail: info@trendsgroup.co.uk
Fax: 020-7258 3591   Tel: 020-7723 8001

VICKERS Jean
(Costumes made for Stage, TV & Film)
40 Abingdon Road
London W8 6AR   Tel: 020-7937 2870

VIVAS INTERNATIONAL
(Dance & Costume Hire)
L'Apache, Woodgate, Chichester
West Sussex PO20 6SS
e-mail: vivas@vivas.demon.co.uk
Fax: 01243 543844   Tel: 01243 542020

WAIN SHIELL & SON Ltd
(High Quality Cloth Merchants)
Savile House
7 Sheffield Road
New Mill
Huddersfield HD7 7EL
Fax: 01484 688796   Tel: 01484 688848

12 Savile Row
London W1X 1AE
e-mail: wainshiell@compuserve.com
Fax: 020-7437 3600   Tel: 020-7734 7114

WASHTELL Susan TIARAS
(Bridal and Theatrical Headdresses. Original
Designs - New Age, Period and Modern)
Tel: 023-9257 1434

WIG ROOM The
315 The Custard Factory
Digbeth
Birmingham B9 4AA
e-mail: wigroom@fsbdial.co.uk
Tel/Fax: 0121-773 4668

WIG SPECIALITIES Ltd
(Wigs and Facial Hair, Hair Extensions etc)
173 Seymour Place
London W1H 4PW
e-mail: wigspecialities@btconnect.com
Fax: 020-7723 1566   Tel: 020-7262 6565

WILLIAMS Emma
(Costume Designer,
Supervisor & Stylist - Film, TV & Theatre)
3-4 Nelson Place West
Bath BA1 2BA
e-mail: emmaw@costume.fsnet.co.uk
Mobile: 07710 130345   Tel/Fax: 01225 447169

WILSON Marian WIGS
(Theatrical & Film Wigmaker)
59 Gloucester Street
Faringdon
Oxon SN7 7JA
e-mail: wigmaker@wigmaker.screaming.net
Fax: 01367 242438   Tel: 01367 241696

WORLD OF FANTASY
(Costumes & Props)
Swansnest
Rear of 2 Windmill Road
Hampton Hill
Middlesex TW12 1RH
e-mail: info@world-of-fantasy.co.uk
Fax: 020-8783 1366   Tel: 020-8941 1595

DAILY EXPRESS   Tel: 020-7928 8000
Theatre: Robert Gore-Langton
Films: Ryan Gilbey, Alan Hunter
Television: Tim Hulse
Jeremy Novick
Saturday Magazine/
Programmes: Pat Stoddart

DAILY MAIL   Tel: 020-7938 6000
Theatre: Michael Coveney
Films: Chris Tookey
Television: Peter Paterson
Christopher Matthew

DAILY STAR   Tel: 020-7928 8000
Show Business & Television: Nigel Pauley
Debbie Pogue
Gareth Morgan
Ben Todd
Simon Wheeler
Niki Waldegrave
Films & Video: Alan Frank
Rachel Dobson

DAILY TELEGRAPH   Tel: 020-7538 5000
Theatre: Charles Spencer
Films: Andrew O'Hagan
Radio: Gillian Reynolds
Art: Richard Dorment
Dance: Ismene Brown
Music: Geoffrey Norris

FINANCIAL TIMES   Tel: 020-7873 3000
Theatre: Alastair MacAulay
Films: Nigel Andrews
Television: Chris Dunkley

GUARDIAN   Tel: 020-7278 2332
Theatre: Michael Billington
Films: Peter Bradshaw
Television: Nancy Banks-Smith
Radio: Ann Karpf

INDEPENDENT   Tel: 020-7249 8229
Television: Robert Hanks

LONDON EVENING STANDARD
    Tel: 020-7938 6000
Theatre: Nicholas de Jongh
Fringe Theatre: Patrick Marmion
Films: Alexander Walker
Television: Victor Lewis-Smith
Terry Ramsay
Radio: Terry Ramsay

MAIL ON SUNDAY
(Review Section)   Tel: 020-7938 6000
Theatre: Georgina Brown
Films: Jason Solomons
Television: Jaci Stephen
Radio: Simon Garfield

MIRROR   Tel: 020-7510 3000
Films: Jonathan Ross
Television: Tony Purnell

MORNING STAR   Tel: 020-7538 5181
Theatre, Film, Arts: Bunmi Daramola
Television: Kevin Russelll
Alex Reid

NEWS OF THE WORLD   Tel: 020-7782 4000
Show Business/Films: Rav Singh
Paul Ross
Shebah Ronayh

OBSERVER   Tel: 020-7278 2332
Theatre: Susannah Clapp
Films: Philip French
Akin Ofumu
Radio: Sue Arnold
Stephanie Billu

SPORT   Tel: 0161-238 8151
Show Business/Features: Sarah Stephens

SUN   Tel: 020-7782 4000
Television: Gary Bushell

SUNDAY EXPRESS   Tel: 020-7928 8000
Theatre: Robert Gore-Langton
Films: Henry Fitzherbert
Television: Tim Hulse
Jeremy Novick
Glyn George
Radio: Ken Garner

SUNDAY MIRROR   Tel: 020-7510 3000
Theatre & Television: Ian Hyland
Films: Quentin Falk

SUNDAY PEOPLE   Tel: 020-7510 3000
Television & Radio: Sharon Marshall
Films: Jane Simon
Show Business: Sean O'Brien
Features: Alison Phillips

SUNDAY TELEGRAPH   Tel: 020-7538 5000
Theatre: John Gross
Films: Jenny McCartney
Television: John Preston
Radio: David Sexton

SUNDAY TIMES   Tel: 020-7782 5000
Theatre: John Peter
Films: Cosmo Landesman
Television: A.A. Gill
Radio: Paul Donovan

TIMES   Tel: 020-7782 5000
Theatre: Benedict Nightingale
Film: Barbara Ellen
Television: Joe Joseph
Radio: Peter Barnard
Video: Geoff Brown

**ADVENTURES IN MOTION PICTURES &
KATHARINE DORÉ MANAGEMENT Ltd**
Suite 3
140A Gloucester Mansions
Cambridge Circus
London WC2H 8HD
e-mail: fiona@amplimited.co.uk
Fax: 020-7836 8717   Tel: 020-7836 8716

ADZIDO
Canonbury Business Centre
202 New North Road
London N1 7BL
e-mail: info@adzido.co.uk
Fax: 020-7704 0300   Tel: 020-7359 7453

AKADEMI
(South Asian Dance in the UK)
Hampstead Town Hall
Haverstock Hill
London NW3 4QP
e-mail: admin@akademi.co.uk
Fax: 020-7691 3211   Tel: 020-7691 3210

AKSHAYA DANCE THEATRE
Formerly Pushkala Gopal Unnikrishnan & Co
(Classical Indian Dance-Theatre)
20 Brisbane Road
Ilford Essex IG1 4SR   Tel/Fax: 020-8554 4054

ALEXANDER ROY LONDON BALLET THEATRE
North House
69 Eton Avenue
London NW3 3EU
Fax: 020-7722 9942   Tel: 020-7586 2498

The UK Choreographers' Directory

Are you looking for a Choreographer, Movement Director or dance coach?

Tel: 020 7228 4990

www.danceuk.org

Dance UK

Funded by
THE
ARTS
COUNCIL
OF ENGLAND

Created by ATP Europe Ltd. See back cover for details

ALSTON Richard DANCE COMPANY
The Place
17 Duke's Road, London WC1H 9PY
e-mail: radc@theplace.org.uk
Fax: 020-7383 4851   Tel: 020-7387 0324

BABE
(Artistic Director - Claire Missingham)
4 Glyn Road
London E5 0JD
e-mail: claire.missingham@virgin.net
Tel: 020-7682 0865

BALLET CREATIONS
3 Blackbird Way
Bransgore
Nr Christchurch
Hants BH23 8LG
e-mail: info@ballet-creations.co.uk
Tel/Fax: 01425 674163

BALLROOM - LONDON THEATRE OF
(Artistic Director - Paul Harris)
24 Ovett Close, Upper Norwood
London SE19 3RX
e-mail: paulharrisdance@hotmail.com
Mobile: 07958 784462   Tel/Fax: 020-8771 4274

BIRMINGHAM ROYAL BALLET
Thorp Street
Birmingham B5 4AU
e-mail: administrator@brb.org.uk
Fax: 0121-689 3070   Tel: 0121-622 2555

B.O.P. PRODUCTIONS Ltd
(Theatre, Music & Dance Company)
10 Stayton Road
Sutton
Surrey SM1 1RB
e-mail: info@bop.demon.co.uk
Tel: 020-8641 6959

CAPITAL ARTS THEATRE SCHOOL
(Kathleen Shanks)
Wyllyotts Centre, Darkes Lane
Potters Bar, Herts EN6 2HN
e-mail: capitalartstheatre@genie.co.uk
Mobile: 07885 232414   Tel/Fax: 020-8449 2342

CHOLMONDELEYS The
LFI .1
Lafone House
The Leathermarket
11-13 Leathermarket Street
London SE1 3HN
e-mail: admin@cholmondeleys.freeserve.co.uk
Tel: 020-7378 8800

COMPANY OF CRANKS
1st Floor, 62 Northfield House, Frensham Street
London SE15 6TN   Tel: 020-7358 0571

CREATIVE DANCE ARTISTS TRUST
15B Lauriston Road
London SW19 4TJ   Tel: 020-8946 3444

DANCE FOR EVERYONE Ltd
30 Sevington Road
London NW4 3RX
e-mail: orders@dfe.org.uk   Tel: 020-8202 7863

DANCE UK
(Including the Healthier Dancer Programme)
Battersea Arts Centre, Lavender Hill
London SW11 5TN
e-mail: danceuk@easynet.co.uk
Fax: 020-7223 0074   Tel: 020-7228 4990

Dance Companies & Organisations

DANCE UMBRELLA
20 Chancellors Street
London W6 9RN
e-mail: mail@danceumbrella.co.uk
Fax: 020-8741 7902   Tel: 020-8741 4040

DIVERSIONS DANCE COMPANY
Ebenezer Studio
Charles Street
Cardiff CF10 2GA
Fax: 029-2022 7176   Tel: 029-2022 8855

ENGLISH NATIONAL BALLET Ltd
Markova House
39 Jay Mews
London SW7 2ES
e-mail: info@ballet.org.uk   Tel: 020-7581 1245

FEATHERSTONEHAUGHS The
LFI .1
Lafone House, The Leathermarket
11-13 Leathermarket
London SE1 3HN
e-mail: admin@cholmondeleys.freeserve.co.uk
                              Tel: 020-7378 8800

IDTA (INTERNATIONAL DANCE TEACHERS' ASSOCIATION)
International House, 76 Bennett Road
Brighton, East Sussex BN2 5JL
e-mail: info@idta.co.uk
Fax: 01273 674388   Tel: 01273 685652

IRISH FOLK-BALLET COMPANY
c/o Victor House
Marlborough Gardens, Whetstone
London N20 0SH
e-mail: rosemaryifbco@aol.com
Tel/Fax: 020-8361 0678   Tel: 020-8361 0549

KOSH The
(Physical Theatre)
59 Stapleton Hall Road
London N4 3QF
e-mail: the-kosh@dircon.co.uk
Fax: 020-8374 5661   Tel: 020-8374 0407

LONDON CONTEMPORARY DANCE SCHOOL
The Place, 17 Duke's Road
London WC1H 9PY
e-mail: lcds@theplace.org.uk
Fax: 020-7387 3976   Tel: 020-7387 0152

LUDUS DANCE AGENCY
Assembly Rooms
King Street
Lancaster LA1 1RE
e-mail: ludus@easynet.co.uk
Fax: 01524 847744   Tel: 01524 35936

NATIONAL RESOURCE CENTRE FOR DANCE
University of Surrey
Guildford GU2 7XH
e-mail: nrcd@surrey.ac.uk   Tel: 01483 689316

NORTHERN BALLET THEATRE
West Park Centre
Spen Lane
Leeds LS16 5BE
e-mail: directors@nbtdance.demon.co.uk
Fax: 0113-274 5381   Tel: 0113-274 5355

PHOENIX DANCE COMPANY
3 St Peter's Building, St Peter's Square
Leeds LS9 8AH
e-mail: phoenx@phoenx.dircon.co.uk
Fax: 0113-244 4736   Tel: 0113-242 3486

RAMBERT DANCE COMPANY
94 Chiswick High Road
London W4 1SH
e-mail: rdc@rambert.org.uk
Fax: 020-8747 8323   Tel: 020-8630 0600

RE.ANIMATOR
Wimbledon Theatre, The Broadway
London SW19 1QG
e-mail: re.animator@virgin.net
Fax: 020-8542 8081   Tel: 020-8543 8360

ROYAL BALLET The
Royal Opera House
Covent Garden
London WC2E 9DD
Fax: 020-7212 9121   Tel: 020-7240 1200

SCOTTISH BALLET
261 West Princes Street
Glasgow G4 9EE
e-mail: sb@scottishballet.co.uk
Fax: 0141-331 2629   Tel: 0141-331 2931

SCOTTISH DANCE THEATRE
Dundee Repertory Theatre
Tay Square, Dundee DD1 1PB
e-mail: achinn@dundeereptheatre.co.uk
Fax: 01382 228609   Tel: 01382 342600

SOLE ARMY The
151A Field End Road
Eastcote
Middlesex HA5 1QL
e-mail: sole.file@virgin.net   Tel: 020-8868 7960

SOUTH EAST DANCE - NATIONAL DANCE AGENCY
5 Palace Place, Castle Square
Brighton, East Sussex BN1 1EF
e-mail: southeast.dance@virgin.net
Tel/Fax: 01273 205540   Tel: 01273 202032

UNION DANCE COMPANY
c/o Marylebone Dance Studio
12 Lisson Grove, London NW1 6TS
e-mail: danceunion@aol.com
Fax: 020-7224 8911   Tel: 020-7724 5765

YORKSHIRE DANCE CENTRE NATIONAL DANCE AGENCY
3 St Peter's Buildings, St Peter's Square
Leeds LS9 8AH
e-mail: admin@yorkshiredance.org.uk
                              Tel: 0113-243 9867

ASH SCHOOL OF DANCE AND DRAMA The
50 Craneford Way
Twickenham
Middlesex TW2 7SE
e-mail: ashschool@hotnmail.com
Tel: 020-8892 6554

BALLROOM - LONDON THEATRE OF
(Artistic Director - Paul Harris)
24 Ovett Close
Upper Norwood
London SE19 3RX
e-mail: paulharrisdance@hotmail.com
Mobile: 07958 784462   Tel/Fax: 020-8771 4274

BELLYDANCE CENTRE The
(Private Lessons, Consultancy, Choreography)
Mayfield, 5 Rother Road
Seaford, East Sussex BN25 4HT
e-mail: annrusty@hotmail.com
Tel: 01323 899083

BIRD COLLEGE OF PERFORMING ARTS
(Dance & Theatre Performance
Diploma/BA (Hons) Degree Course)
Birkbeck Centre, Birkbeck Road
Sidcup, Kent DA14 4DE
Fax: 020-8308 1370   Tel: 020-8300 6004

BODEN STUDIOS
(Part-time Performing Arts Classes)
6-12 Windmill Hill, Enfield
Middlesex EN2 6SL
e-mail: bodens2692@aol.com
Fax: 020-8367 1836   Tel: 020-8367 2692

BRITISH BALLET ORGANIZATION The
(Dance Examining Society & Teacher Training)
Woolborough House
39 Lonsdale Road
Barnes
London SW13 9JP
e-mail: info@bbo.org.uk   Tel: 020-8748 1241

CAPITAL ARTS THEATRE SCHOOL
Wyllyotts Centre, Darkes Lane
Potters Bar, Herts EN6 2HN
e-mail: capitalartstheatre@genie.co.uk
Mobile: 07885 232414   Tel/Fax: 020-8449 2342

CENTRAL SCHOOL OF BALLET
10 Herbal Hill, Clerkenwell Road
London EC1R 5EG
e-mail: central@centralschoolofballet.fsnet.co.uk
Fax: 020-7833 5571   Tel: 020-7837 6332

CENTRE OF PERFORMING ARTS The
c/o 152 Earshall Road
Eltham Park
London SE9 1PN
e-mail: dance@thecentrese9.freeserve.co.uk
Tel/Fax: 020-8859 6918

COLIN'S PERFORMING ARTS Ltd
The Studios, 219B North Street
Romford RM1 4QA
e-mail: admin@colinsperformingarts.co.uk
Fax: 01708 766077   Tel: 01708 766007

COLLECTIVE DANCE & DRAMA
The Studio Rectory Lane
Rickmansworth, Herts WD3 2AD
Tel/Fax: 020-8428 0037

CONTI Italia ACADEMY
Italia Conti House, 23 Goswell Road
London EC1M 7AJ
e-mail: sca@italiaconti36.freeserve.co.uk
Fax: 020-7253 1430   Tel: 020-7608 0047

CUSTARD FACTORY
Gibb Street, Digbeth
Birmingham B9 4AA
e-mail: custardfactory@clara.net
Fax: 0121-604 8888   Tel: 0121-693 7777

DANCEWORKS
(Also Fitness, Yoga & Martial Art Classes,
Studio/Rehearsal Rooms for Hire)
16 Balderton Street
London W1Y 1TF   Tel: 020-7629 6183

ELMHURST - SCHOOL FOR DANCE & PERFORMING ARTS
Heathcote Road, Camberley
Surrey GU15 2EU
e-mail: elmhurst@cableol.co.uk
Fax: 01276 670320   Tel: 01276 65301

GIELGUD FOUNDATION The
(Programme of classes for professional dancers)
Wimbledon Theatre
The Broadway
London SW19 1QG
e-mail: foundation@gielgud.com
Fax: 020-8542 8081   Tel: 020-8542 9721

GREASEPAINT ANONYMOUS
4 Gallus Close, Winchmore Hill
London N21 1JR
e-mail: info@greasepaintanonymous.co.uk
Fax: 020-8882 9189   Tel: 020-8886 2263

HAMPSTEAD DANCE THEATRE GROUP
(Creative Dance Part-Time 4-25 year olds)
14 Mount Drive, Wembley
Middlesex HA9 9ED   Tel: 020-8908 0505

HARRIS Paul
(Movement for Actors, Choreography and
Coaching in Social Dance)
24 Ovett Close
Upper Norwood
London SE19 3RX
Mobile: 07958 784462   Tel: 020-8771 4274

ISLINGTON ARTS FACTORY
2 Parkhurst Road
London N7 0SF
e-mail: islington@artsfactory.fsnet.co.uk
Fax: 020-7700 7229   Tel: 020-7607 0561

LEE STAGE SCHOOL The
(Office)
38 The Chase, Rayleigh, Essex SS6 8QN
e-mail: lynn@leetheatre.fsnet.co.uk
Tel: 01268 773204

LONDON CONTEMPORARY DANCE SCHOOL
(Full-time Contemporary Training at Degree,
Certificate & Postgraduate Level)
The Place, 17 Duke's Road
London WC1H 9PY
e-mail: lcds@theplace.org.uk
Fax: 020-7387 3976   Tel: 020-7387 0152

LONDON STUDIO CENTRE
42-50 York Way, London N1 9AB
e-mail: enquire@london-studio-centre.co.uk
Fax: 020-7837 3248   Tel: 020-7837 7741

MANN Stella COLLEGE
(Professional Dance
Performers & Teachers Course)
343A Finchley Road, Hampstead
London NW3 6ET   Tel: 020-7435 9317

NORTH LONDON PERFORMING ARTS CENTRE
(Performing Arts Classes 3-19 yrs/All Dance
Forms)
76 St James Lane
Muswell Hill, London N10 3DF
e-mail: nlpac@compuserve.com
Fax: 020-8444 4040   Tel: 020-8444 4544

PAUL'S THEATRE SCHOOL
Fairkytes Arts Centre
51 Billet Lane, Hornchurch
Essex RM11 1AX   Tel: 01708 447123

PERFORMERS COLLEGE
2-4 Chase Road, Corringham, Essex SS17 7QH
e-mail: pdc@dircon.co.uk
Fax: 01375 672353   Tel: 01375 672053

PINEAPPLE DANCE STUDIOS
7 Langley Street
London WC2H 9JA   Tel: 020-7836 4004

PULLEY Rosina SCHOOL OF STAGE DANCING
5 Lancaster Road
London E11 3EH   Tel: 020-8539 7740

ROEBUCK Gavin
(Classical Ballet)
51 Earls Court Square, London SW5 9DG
e-mail: grads@fsmail.net
Fax: 020-7370 5456   Tel: 020-7370 7324

RUSS Claire
(Choreography, Private Movement Tuition for
Actors)
59 Kenley Road, Twickenham TW1 1JT
Mobile: 07932 680224   Tel/Fax: 020-8892 9281

SOLE THEATRE SCHOOL
151A Field End Road
Eastcote
Middlesex HA5 1QL
e-mail: sole.file@virgin.net   Tel: 020-8868 7960

STEP ONE DANCE AND DRAMA SCHOOL
Rear of 24 Penrhyn Road
Colwyn Bay
Conwy LL29 8LG   Tel: 01492 534424

URDANG ACADEMY The
20-22 Shelton Street
Covent Garden
London WC2H 9JJ
e-mail: info@theurdangacademy.com
Fax: 020-7836 7010   Tel: 020-7836 5709

**VALLE ACADEMY OF PERFORMING
ARTS Ltd The**
The Rosedale Old Cestrians Club
Andrews Lane
Cheshunt, Herts EN7 6TB
e-mail: enquiries@valleacademy.co.uk
Fax: 01992 622868   Tel: 01992 622862

WHITEHALL PERFORMING ARTS CENTRE
Rayleigh Road
Leigh-on-Sea
Essex SS9 5UU   Tel/Fax: 01702 529290

YOUNG Sylvia THEATRE SCHOOL
Rossmore Road
London NW1 6NJ
Fax: 020-7723 1040   Tel: 020-7402 0673

**:MY OF LIVE
:D ARTS)**
ia Building, Fitzhugh Grove
~on SW18 3SX
g@alra.demon.co.uk
~-8875 0789   Tel: 020-8870 6475

ARTS EDUCATIONAL SCHOOLS LONDON
14 Bath Road
London W4 1LY
e-mail: drama@artsed.co.uk
Fax: 020-8987 6699   Tel: 020-8987 6666

BIRMINGHAM SCHOOL OF SPEECH & DRAMA
The Link Building
Paradise Place
Birmingham B3 3HJ
e-mail: bssd@bssd.ac.uk
Fax: 0121-262 6801   Tel: 0121-262 6800

BRISTOL OLD VIC THEATRE SCHOOL
2 Downside Road
Clifton
Bristol BS8 2XF
e-mail: enquiries@oldvic.drama.ac.uk
Fax: 0117-923 9371   Tel: 0117-973 3535

CENTRAL SCHOOL OF SPEECH & DRAMA
Embassy Theatre
64 Eton Avenue
Swiss Cottage
London NW3 3HY   Tel: 020-7722 8183

CONTI Italia ACADEMY OF THEATRE ARTS
Avondale
72 Landor Road
London SW9 9PH
e-mail: baacting.italiaconti@btinternet.com
Fax: 020-7737 2728   Tel: 020-7733 3210

CYGNET TRAINING THEATRE
New Theatre, Friars Gate
Exeter, Devon EX2 4AZ
e-mail: cygnetarts@btinternet.com
                          Tel/Fax: 01392 277189

DRAMA CENTRE LONDON
176 Prince of Wales Road
London NW5 3PT
e-mail: drama@linst.ac.uk
Fax: 020-7485 7129   Tel: 020-7267 1177

EAST 15 ACTING SCHOOL
The University of Essex
Hatfields & Corbett Theatre
Rectory Lane
Loughton
Essex IG10 3RY
e-mail: east15.acting@ukonline.co.uk
Fax: 020-8508 7521   Tel: 020-8508 5983

GSA GUILDFORD SCHOOL OF ACTING
Millmead Terrace
Guildford
Surrey GU2 4YT
e-mail: enquiries@gsa.drama.ac.uk
                          Tel: 01483 560701

GUILDHALL SCHOOL OF MUSIC & DRAMA
Silk Street, Barbican
London EC2Y 8DT
e-mail: info@gsmd.ac.uk
Fax: 020-7256 9438   Tel: 020-7382 7192

LAMDA
Tower House
226 Cromwell Road
London SW5 0SR
e-mail: enquiries@lamda.org.uk
Fax: 020-7370 4739   Tel: 020-7373 9883

MANCHESTER METROPOLITAN UNIVERSITY SCHOOL OF THEATRE
The Mabel Tylecote Building
Cavendish Street
Manchester M15 6BG   Tel: 0161-247 1305

MOUNTVIEW
Academy of Theatre Arts
104 Crouch Hill
London N8 9EA
e-mail: enquiries@mountview.ac.uk
Fax: 020-8348 1727   Tel: 020-8347 3602

OXFORD SCHOOL OF DRAMA The
Sansomes Farm Studios
Woodstock
Oxford OX20 1ER
e-mail: info@oxford.drama.ac.uk
Fax: 01993 811220   Tel: 01993 812883

QUEEN MARGARET UNIVERSITY COLLEGE
The Gateway Theatre
Elm Row
Edinburgh EH7 4AH
e-mail: admissions@qmuc.ac.uk
Fax: 0131-317 3902   Tel: 0131-317 3900

ROSE BRUFORD COLLEGE
Lamorbey Park
Burnt Oak Lane
Sidcup
Kent DA15 9DF
e-mail: admiss@bruford.ac.uk
Fax: 020-8308 0542   Tel: 020-8300 3024

ROYAL ACADEMY OF DRAMATIC ART
62-64 Gower Street
London WC1E 76ED
e-mail: enquiries@rada.ac.uk
Fax: 020-7323 3865   Tel: 020-7636 7076

ROYAL SCOTTISH ACADEMY OF MUSIC AND DRAMA
100 Renfrew Street
Glasgow G2 3DB
e-mail: registry@rsamd.ac.uk
                          Tel: 0141-332 4101

WEBBER DOUGLAS ACADEMY OF DRAMATIC ART
30 Clareville Street
London SW7 5AP
Fax: 020-7373 5639   Tel: 020-7370 4154

WELSH COLLEGE OF MUSIC AND DRAMA
Drama Department
Castle Grounds
Cathays Park
Cardiff CF10 3ER
e-mail: drama.admissions@wcmd.ac.uk
Fax: 029-2039 1302   Tel: 029-2039 1327

CONFERENCE OF DRAMA SCHOOLS

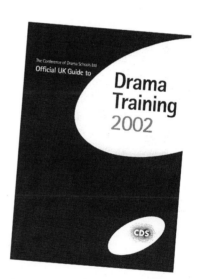

The Conference of Drama Schools was founded in 1969. The member schools of the CDS offer courses in Acting, Musical Theatre, Stage Management and Technical Courses. The CDS exists to:

- Contribute to maintaining and developing standards of vocational drama training and education within its member institutions.
- Encourage good practice with its member institutions
- Represent the interests of its member institutions at regional, national, European and International levels.
- Advise on matters relating to the interest of students and staff within its member institutions
- Encourage diversity of provision and/or qualifications within the vocational drama training sector as a whole.

CDS Member Schools

ALRA Academy of Live and Recorded Arts

The Arts Educational Schools London

Birmingham School of Speech and Drama

The Bristol Old Vic Theatre School

The Central School of Speech and Drama

Cygnet Training Theatre

Drama Centre London

East 15 Acting School

GSA Guildford School of Acting

Guildhall School of Music and Drama

The Italia Conti Academy of Theatre Arts

LAMDA The London Academy of Music and Dramatic Art

Manchester Metropolitan University School of Theatre

Mountview Academy of Theatre Arts

The Oxford School of Drama

Queen Margaret University College - Department of Drama

Rose Bruford College

RADA The Royal Academy of Dramatic Art

The Royal Scottish Academy of Music and Drama

The Webber Douglas Academy of Dramatic Art

Welsh College of Music and Drama

Further information on careers and the courses offered by our member schools can be found in the **CDS Official UK Guide to Drama Training.**
For a free copy, please write
(including a C5 SAE for 44p postage per Guide) to:

The President
CDS Ltd.
c/o 11 Bates Close
Market Harborough
Leicestershire LE16 7NT

For information on the CDS:

The Secretary CDS
1 Stanley Avenue
Thorpe
Norwich NR7 0BE

Tel/Fax: 01603 702021
e-mail: enquiries@cds.drama.ac.uk
or see our website on:
http://www.drama.ac.uk

Abbreviations: SS Stage School for Children **D** Dramatic Art (incl Coaching. Audition Technique etc) **DS** Full time Drama Training **E** Elocution Coaching (incl Correction of Accents. Speech Therapy, Dialects etc) **S** Singing **Md** Modelling **Sp** Specialised Training

A B CENTRE OF PERFORMING ARTS
22 Greek Street
Stockport
Cheshire SK3 8AB   Tel/Fax: 0161-429 7413

ACADEMY DRAMA SCHOOL The
DS (2 year F/T Evening Course &
Day Time Preparatory)
189 Whitechapel Road
London E1 1DN
e-mail: academy@eada.demon.co.uk
                         Tel: 020-7377 8735

ACE ACCOMPANIST
S (Accompanist and
Bands for Rehearsal & Recordings)
165 Gunnersbury Lane
London W3 8LJ   Tel: 020-8993 2111

ACKERLEY STUDIOS OF SPEECH, DRAMA & PUBLIC SPEAKING
SP D Margaret Christina Parsons (Principal)
5th Floor
Hanover House
Hanover Street
Liverpool L1 3DZ   Tel: 0151-709 5995

ACT ACADEMY OF CHILDREN'S THEATRE
(Part-time Children's Theatre School)
373 Lower Addiscombe Road
Croydon CR0 6RJ   Tel: 020-8655 3438

ACT ONE DRAMA STUDIO & AGENCY
31 Dobbin Hill
Sheffield S11 7JA
e-mail: casting@actonedrama.co.uk
Fax: 07971 112153   Tel: 0114-266 7209

ACT UP
(Acting Classes for Everyone)
Unit 88, Battersea Business Centre
99-109 Lavender Hill
London SW11 5QL
e-mail: info@act-up.co.uk
Fax: 020-7924 6606   Tel: 020-7924 7701

ACTING & AUDITION SUCCESS
(Philip Rosch LALAM (Distinction); BA Drama
(Hons) (Associate Guildhall & Lamda Teacher)
Flat C
26 Rotherwick Road, Golders Green
London NW11 7DA
e-mail: phil.rosch@virgin.net
                         Tel: 020-8455 5126

ACTORS' THEATRE SCHOOL
DS
32 Exeter Road
London NW2 4SB
e-mail: ats@mywebaddress.net
Fax: 020-8450 1057   Tel: 020-8450 0371

A & J THEATRE WORKSHOP
The Open Door Community Centre
Beaumont Road, London SW19
Fax: 020-8882 5983   Tel: 020-8882 7716

ALEXANDER ALLIANCE
(Alexander Technique, Voice and Audition
Coaching)
3 Hazelwood Drive
St Albans, Herts   Tel: 01727 843633

ALEXANDER CENTRE The Bloomsbury
(Alexander Technique)
Bristol House
80A Southampton Row
London WC1B 4BB
e-mail: bloomsbury.alexandercentre@btinternet.com
Tel: 020-7404 5348

ALEXANDER Helen
(Audition Technique/Drama School Entry)
14 Chestnut Road
Raynes Park
London SW20 8EB   Tel: 020-8543 4085

ALEXANDER TECHNIQUE
Jackie Coote MSTAT
27 Brittannia Road
London SW6 2HJ   Tel: 020-7731 1061

ALL EXPRESSIONS
(Children & Teenagers)
5 Osterley Avenue, Osterley, Middlesex TW7 4QF
Fax: 020-8560 3562   Tel: 020-8560 8857

ALRA, ACADEMY OF LIVE & RECORDED ARTS
See DRAMA SCHOOLS (Conference Of)

ALLSORTS - DRAMA FOR CHILDREN
2 Pember Road, London NW10 5LP
e-mail: enquiries@allsorts.ltd.uk
Tel/Fax: 020-8969 3249

AND ALL THAT JAZZ
(Eileen Hughes - Accompanist and Vocal Coaching)
165 Gunnersbury Lane, Acton Town
London W3 8LJ   Tel: 020-8993 2111

ARDEN SCHOOL OF THEATRE The
Sale Road, Northenden
Manchester M23 0DD
e-mail: ast@ccm.ac.uk
Tel/Fax: 0161-957 1715

ARMSTRONG ARTS ACADEMY
9 Greville Hall, Greville Place
London NW6 5JS
e-mail: academy@armstrongarts.com
Fax: 020-7625 2213   Tel: 020-7372 7110

ARTS EDUCATIONAL LONDON SCHOOLS
See DRAMA SCHOOLS (Conference of)

ARTS EDUCATIONAL SCHOOL
(Performing Arts School)
Tring Park, Tring, Herts HP23 5LX
e-mail: info@aes-tring.com   Tel: 01442 824255

ARTTS INTERNATIONAL
Highfield Grange, Bubwith
North Yorks YO8 6DP
e-mail: admin@artts.co.uk
Fax: 01757 288253   Tel: 01757 288088

ASH SCHOOL OF DANCE AND DRAMA The
50 Craneford Way, Twickenham
Middlesex TW2 7SE
e-mail: ashschool@hotmail.com
Tel: 020-8892 6554

ASHCROFT ACADEMY OF DRAMATIC ART The
(Drama LAMDA, Dance ISTD, Singing,
Age 4-18 yrs, Students 19+)
Bellenden Old School
Bellenden Road
London SE15 4DG   Tel/Fax: 020-8693 8088

BAC
(Children's Drama Classes, Age 2-25)
Lavender Hill
London SW11 5TN
e-mail: mailbox@bac.org.uk
Fax: 020-7978 5207   Tel: 020-7223 6557

BARNES Bi Bi
(Feldenkrais Practitioner & Voice Coach)
40 Russell Street, Woburn Sands
Bucks MK17 8NX
e-mail: bibibarnes@aol.com
Mobile: 07770 375 339   Tel: 01908 585166

BARNES Joan THEATRE SCHOOL
SS D E
20 Green Street, Hazlemere
High Wycombe
Bucks HP15 7RB   Tel: 01494 523193

BATE Richard LGSM (TD) PGCE (FE) Equity
D E
26 Applecross Close
The Esplanade
Rochester, Kent ME1 1PJ
Mobile: 07944 982193   Tel: 01634 830304

BECK Eirene
D E
Flat 4, 57 Knightsbridge
London SW1X 7RA   Tel: 020-7235 4659

**BENCH Paul MEd LGSM ALAM FRSA LJBA
MASCC MIFA (Reg)**
D E
1 Whitehall Terrace, Shrewsbury
Shropshire SY2 5AA
e-mail: paulbench@compuserve.com
Tel/Fax: 01743 233164

• ArtsEd •
London

SCHOOL OF MUSICAL THEATRE
Director: Ian Watt-Smith

Tel: 020 8987 6677 **Fax:** 020 8987 6680
e-mail: mts@artsed.co.uk **web:** www.artsed.co.uk

SCHOOL OF ACTING
Director: Jane Harrison
Associate Director: Adrian James

Tel: 020 8987 6655 **Fax:** 020 8987 6656
e-mail: drama@artsed.co.uk **web:** www.artsed.co.uk

3 Year Acting Course
National Diploma in Professional Acting
An NCDT Accredited Course

A 3-year course offering the full range of acting skills to
Adult students aged 18 or over. The emphasis is on the actor in performance and
the relationship with an audience. Classes and tutorial work include: a range of
textual, psychological and physical acting techniques, screen acting and
broadcasting, voice and speech, movement and dance, mask and theatre history.

The Acting Company
1 Year National Advanced Certificate in Professional Acting
An NCDT Accredited Course

An intensive one year post-graduate acting course offering a fully integrated
ensemble training for mature students with a degree or equivalent professional
experience. Emphasis is on the pro-active contemporary performer.

3 Year Musical Theatre Course
National Diploma in Professional Dance (Musical Theatre)
A CDET Accredited Course

A full time course (18+). A flexible approach providing outstanding training in
dance, acting and singing by leading professionals. Training the Complete
Performer with excellent employment opportunities for graduates.

Government 2001 Inspection praised the high standard of student
achievement, quality of teaching, well balanced training, effective
links with the industry, good graduate employment record.

ArtsEd, London
14 Bath Rd, Chiswick, London W4 1LY

BENSKIN Eileen
(Dialect Coach)   Tel: 020-8455 9750

BERKERY Barbara
(Dialogue/Dialect Coach for Film & Television)
ICM, The Barracks
76 Irishtown Road, Dublin 4
e-mail: ciara-icm@oceanfree.net
Fax: + 353 1 667 6474   Tel: + 353 1 667 6455

BEST SHOT YOUTH THEATRE COMPANY
(Weekly Drama Classes and Theatre Based
Holiday Courses)
1 Queensland Avenue
Wimbledon SW19 3AD
e-mail: enquiries@bestshot.org.uk
                        Tel/Fax: 020-8540 1238

BEST THEATRE ARTS
61 Marshalswick Lane, St Albans
Herts AL1 4UT
e-mail: bestarts@aol.com   Tel: 01727 759634

BILLINGS Una
(Dance Training)
Methodist Church, Askew Road
London W12   Tel: 020-7603 8156

BIRMINGHAM SCHOOL OF SPEECH & DRAMA
See DRAMA SCHOOLS (Conference of)

BIRMINGHAM THEATRE SCHOOL
The Old Rep Theatre
Station Street
Birmingham B5 4DY   Tel/Fax: 0121-643 3300

B.L.A. THEATRE SCHOOL
(Stage School & Agency)
Performance House
20 Passey Place, Eltham
London SE9 5DQ
e-mail: bla@dircon.co.uk
Fax: 020-8850 9944   Tel: 020-8850 9888

BODEN STUDIOS
D S E SS
6-12 Windmill Hill, Enfield
Middlesex EN2 6SA
e-mail: bodens2692@aol.com
Fax: 020-8367 1836   Tel: 020-8367 2692

BORLAND Denise LRAM
(Singing and Acting Coach)
25 Frogston Road West
Edinburgh EH10 7AB
e-mail: deniseborland@hotmail.com
Fax: 0131-445 7492   Tel: 0131-445 7491

BOURNEMOUTH YOUTH THEATRE The (BYT)
(Klair/Lucinda Spencer)
14 Cooper Dean Drive
Bournemouth BH8 9LN
e-mail: klair@thebyt.co.uk
Fax: 01202 255826   Tel: 01202 780210

BOYD Beth
D S
10 Prospect Road, Long Ditton
Surbiton, Surrey KT6 5PY   Tel: 020-8398 6768

BRAITHWAITE'S ACROBATIC SCHOOL
8 Brookshill Avenue, Harrow Weald
Middlesex   Tel: 020-8954 5638

BRIDGE THEATRE TRAINING CO The
19 Parkfield Road, Harrow
Middlesex HA2 8LA   Tel: 020-8864 8790

BRIGHTON DRAMA CENTRE
(Independent Part-time Acting School for
Brighton & Hove Area)
Office: 79 Sherwood Road, Seaford
East Sussex BN25 3ED   Tel: 01323 897949

BRIGHTON SCHOOL OF MUSIC & DRAMA
96 Claremont Road, Seaford
East Sussex BN25 2QA   Tel: 01323 492918

BRIGHT SPARKS THEATRE SCHOOL
SS
16 Wellfield Road, Streatham
London SW16 2BP
Fax: 020-8677 8659   Tel: 020-8769 3500

BRISTOL OLD VIC THEATRE SCHOOL
See DRAMA SCHOOLS (Conference of)

BRITISH AMERICAN DRAMA ACADEMY
14 Gloucester Gate, Regent's Park
London NW1 4HG
Fax: 020-7487 0731   Tel: 020-7487 0730

The Actors Company is a one-year intensive, affordable and accessible full-time training, exclusively for mature students and post-graduates (21+), held on one site in superb studios in fashionable Hoxton.

Agents, Casting Directors, Producers and the theatre-going public attend The Actors Company six week Repertory Season at The Jermyn Street Theatre in London's West End at the conclusion of the fourth, final term.

Auditioning now for 2002

The first three twelve week terms comprise the highest quality training by established and highly experienced professionals. The lack of government funding for one-year courses precipitated LCTS to create this uniquely presented and very successful course run forty hours per week on Thursday evenings and all day Friday, Saturdays and Sundays thus enabling professional people to support themselves during training.

Excellence is achieved by offering a clear philosophy and approach to acting as a craft, creating ensemble playing in productions, where 'the play is the star'.

For a prospectus contact:
The London Centre for Theatre Studies
12–18 Hoxton Street London N1 6NG

T/F 020 7739 5866
E ldncts@aol.com
www.lcts.co.uk

THE ACTORS COMPANY

B.R.I.T. SCHOOL FOR PERFORMING ARTS & TECHNOLOGY The
60 The Crescent
Croydon CR0 2HN
Fax: 020-8665 8676   Tel: 020-8665 5242

C.A.L.S. THEATRE SCHOOL
Unit E2, Bellevale Shopping Centre
Liverpool L25 2RG   Tel/Fax: 0151-487 8500

CAMERON BROWN Jo PGDVS
(Dialect and Voice)
6 The Bow Brook, Gathorne Street
London E2 0PW
e-mail: jocameronbrown@hotmail.com
Mobile: 07970 026621   Tel: 020-8981 1005

CAMPBELL Kenneth
S E D
Parkhills, 6 Clevelands Park, Northam
Bideford, North Devon EX39 3QH
e-mail: kencam@tinyworld.co.uk
                         Tel: 01237 425217

CAMPBELL Ross ARCM DIP RCM (Perf)
(Singing Coach, Accompanist & Music Director)
17 Oldwood Chase, Farnborough
Hants GU14 0QS
e-mail: rosscampbell@ntlworld.com
                         Tel: 01252 510228

CAPITAL ARTS THEATRE SCHOOL
(Kathleen Shanks)
Wyllyotts Centre, Darkes Lane, Potters Bar
Herts EN6 2HN
e-mail: capitalartstheatre@genie.co.uk
Mobile: 07885 232414   Tel/Fax: 020-8449 2342

CARR Norrie AGENCY & DRAMA SCHOOL
(4-16 year olds) (Principal: Emma Taylor)
Holborn Studios, Eagle Wharf Road
London N1 8ND
e-mail: emma.rebaldi@btinternet.com
Mobile: 07961 303449   Tel: 020-7253 1774

CARTEURS THEATRICAL AGENCY
170A Church Road, Hove
East Sussex BN3 2DJ
e-mail: dianacarteur@stonelandsschool.co.uk
Fax: 01273 770444   Tel: 01273 770445

CASE, Sarah BA Hons PGDVS
D E (Voice, Text, Auditions)
14 Northern Heights
Crescent Road, Crouch End
London N8 8AS   Tel: 020-8347 6784

CELEBRATION THEATRE COMPANY FOR THE YOUNG
S S D E S Sp
48 Chiswick Staithe
London W4 3TP   Tel: 020-8994 8886

CENTRAL SCHOOL OF SPEECH & DRAMA
See DRAMA SCHOOLS (Conference of)

CENTRESTAGE SCHOOL OF PERFORMING ARTS
(All Day Saturday Classes, Summer Courses,
Private Coaching for Professionals)
33 Margaret Street
London W1N 7LA
e-mail: vickiw@dircon.co.uk
Fax: 020-7372 2728   Tel: 020-7328 0788

CENTRE STAGE SCHOOL OF PERFORMING ARTS
The Croft, 7 Cannon Road
Southgate, London N14 7HJ
Fax: 020-8886 7555   Tel: 020-8886 4264

CHARLTON Catherine
8 Tudor Gates, Highfield Avenue
London NW9 0QE
e-mail: charlton@zoo.co.uk
                         Mobile: 07701 595744

CHARRINGTON Tim
E D
54 Topmast Point, Strafford Street
London E14 8SN
Mobile: 07967 418236   Tel: 020-7987 3028

CHEKHOV Michael CENTRE UK
1 St Paul's Road
London N1 2QH
e-mail: skane@chekhovcentre.freeserve.co.uk
                         Tel/Fax: 020-7226 4454

CHRISKA STAGE SCHOOL
37-39 Whitby Road, Ellesmere Port
Cheshire L64 8AA   Tel: 01928 739166

CHRYSTEL ARTS AGENCY & THEATRE SCHOOL
15 Churchill Road, Edgware
Middlesex HA8 6NX
e-mail: chrystelarts@talk21.com
Tel: 020-8952 1281

CHURCHER Mel MA
(Acting & Vocal Coach)
32 Denman Road, London SE15 5NP
e-mail: melchurcher@hotmail.com
Tel: 020-7701 4593

CITY LIT The
(Part-time Day & Evening)
16 Stukeley Street, Drury Lane
London WC2B 5LJ   Tel: 020-7430 0544

CITY LITES
PO Box 29673
London E8 3FH
e-mail: gulcan_ismail@yahoo.com
Mobile: 07773 353645   Tel/Fax: 020-7683 9016

CLASS ACT THEATRE SCHOOL
(Part-time weekend 5-16yrs)
(Principal: Alice Hyde)
47 St Margaret's Road, Twickenham
Middlesex TW1 2LL
Fax: 020-8395 2808   Tel: 020-8891 6663

CLEMENTS Anne MA, LGSM
(Drama/Speech/Auditions/Coaching)
293 Shakespeare Tower, Barbican
London EC2Y 8DR   Tel: 020-7374 2748

CLEVELAND COLLEGE OF ART & DESIGN
Green Lane Linthorpe
Middlesbrough TS5 7RJ
Fax: 01642 288828   Tel: 01642 288000

COLDIRON M. J.
(Private Coaching & Audition Preparation)
21 Chippendale Street
London E5 0BB
e-mail: jiggscol@aol.com
Fax: 020-8525 0687   Tel: 020-8533 1506

COLGAN Valerie
The Green, 17 Herbert Street
London NW5 4HA   Tel: 020-7267 2153

COLIN'S PERFORMING ARTS Ltd
(Full-time 3 year Performing Arts College)
The Studios, 219B North Street
Romford, Essex RM1 4QA
e-mail: admin@colinsperformingarts.co.uk
Fax: 01708 766077   Tel: 01708 766007

COLLIER Julia ADVS
(D E Voice)
5 Cancell Road
London SW9 6HR   Tel: 020-7735 5098

COMPAGNIE LIAN
(Voice, Accent & Speech Coaching)
2 Ravenscourt Park, London W6 0TH
e-mail: compagnielian9@hotmail.com
Tel: 020-8563 0220

CONSTRUCTIVE TEACHING CENTRE Ltd
(Alexander Technique Teacher Training)
18 Lansdowne Road
London W11 3LL
e-mail: info@alexandertek.com
Tel: 020-7727 7222

CONTI Dizi
D Sp E
4 Brentmead Place
London NW11 9LH   Tel: 020-8458 5535

CONTI Italia ACADEMY OF THEATRE ARTS
3 yr Acting Course (NCDT Accredited)
See DRAMA SCHOOLS (Conference of)

DEGREE BA (HONS) THEATRE
in **ACTING** and
MUSICAL THEATRE (3yrs)

ONE YEAR
ACTING COURSE
Pathways in **Acting**
and **Musical Theatre**
for **Graduates**
and **Mature Students** (1yr)

DIPLOMA HE (2yrs)
STAGE MANAGEMENT
and **TECHNICAL THEATRE**
Cert HE (1yr) for **Graduates**
and **Mature Students**

SUMMER SCHOOLS
JULY/AUGUST

All courses are accredited by
The National Council for Drama Training
GSA, Millmead Terrace, Guildford,
Surrey GU2 4YT

Phone: 01483 560701 Fax: 01483 535431
web-site: http.//gsa.drama.ac.uk
e-mail: enquiries@gsa.drama.ac.uk

A Registered Charity
providing quality training in the performing arts

GUILDFORD SCHOOL of ACTING

DIALECT COACH

LINDA JAMES
R.A.M. Dip. Ed., I.P.D. (Lon Univ), L.R.A.M.

FILMS, TV., STAGE & PRIVATE COACHING
ERADICATION OF ACCENT
020-8568 2390

CONTI Italia ACADEMY OF THEATRE ARTS Ltd
SS
Italia Conti House, 23 Goswell Road
London EC1M 7AJ
e-mail: sca@italiaconti36.freeserve.co.uk
Fax: 020-7253 1430   Tel: 020-7608 0047

CORNER Clive AGSM LRAM
(Qualified Teacher, Private Coaching and
Audition Training)
73 Gloucester Road, Hampton
Middlesex TW12 2UQ
e-mail: cornerco@cwcom.net
                         Tel: 020-8287 2726

COURT THEATRE TRAINING COMPANY
The Courtyard Theatre
10 York Way, King's Cross, London N1 9AA
e-mail: cttc@courtyardtheatre.freeserve.co.uk
                         Tel/Fax: 020-7833 0870

COURTENAY Julian
(NLP Master Practitioner, MANLP Mental
Fitness UK)
42 Langdon Park Road, London N6 5QG
e-mail: info@mentalfitness.uk.com
                         Tel: 020-8348 9033

CREATIVE THEATRE SCHOOL
Bretons Manor, 411 Rainham Road
Rainham, Essex RM12 7LP
e-mail: wildtm@lineone.net
                         Tel/Fax: 020-7071 0317

CRYER Charles STUDIO THEATRE
DS
39 High Street, Carshalton, Surrey SM5 3BB
e-mail: info@charlescryer.org.uk
Fax: 020-8770 4969   Tel: 020-8770 4950

CYGNET TRAINING THEATRE
See DRAMA SCHOOLS (Conference of)

D & B SCHOOL OF PERFORMING ARTS
Central Studios, 470 Bromley Road
Bromley BR1 4PN
Fax: 020-8697 8100   Tel: 020-8698 8880

DALLA VECCHIA Sara
(Italian Teacher)
117A Carr Road, Walthamstow
London E17   Mobile: 07774 703686

DAVIDSON Clare
D E
30 Highgate West Hill
London N6 6NP   Tel: 020-8348 0132

DE COURCY Bridget
S (Singing Teacher)
19 Muswell Road
London N10   Tel: 020-8883 8397

DIGNAN Tess PDVS
(Audition, Text & Voice Coach)
60 Mereton Mansions, Brookmill Road
London SE8 4HS
e-mail: tess.dignan@lineone.net
                         Tel: 020-8691 4275

DONNELLY Elaine
(Children's Acting Coach)
c/o Maggi Sangwin Management
                         Tel: 020-8994 7878

DRAGONDRAMA
(Drama for Children)
1B Station Road, Hampton Wick
Kingston KT1 4HG
e-mail: dragondrama@hotmail.com
                         Tel/Fax: 020-8943 1504

DRAMA ASSOCIATION OF WALES
(Summer Courses for Amateur
Actors & Directors)
The Old Library, Singleton Road
Splott Cardiff CF24 2ET
e-mail: aled.daw@virgin.net
Fax: 029-2045 2277   Tel: 029-2045 2200

DRAMA CENTRE LONDON
See DRAMA SCHOOLS (Conference of)

DRAMA CLUB
12 Hardy Close, Surrey Quays
London SE16 6RT
e-mail: samanthahgiblin@hotmail.com
Fax: 0870 1645895   Tel: 020-7231 6083

DRAMA STUDIO EDINBURGH The
(Children's weekly drama workshops)
19 Belmont Road
Edinburgh EH14 5DZ
e-mail: 106347.3507@compuserve.com
Fax: 0131-453 3108   Tel: 0131-453 3284

DRAMA STUDIO LONDON
DS
Grange Court, Grange Road
London W5 5QN
e-mail: admin@dramastudiolondon.co.uk
Fax: 020-8566 2035   Tel: 020-8579 3897

DRAMA ZONE
(Weekend Acting Classes)
3 Great Portland Street House
305 Great Portland Street, London W1W 5DA
e-mail: frankeymel@taxithi.freeserve.co.uk
                         Tel/Fax: 020-8455 8828

DRAMASCENE
(Speech and drama classes, 6 - late teens,
Lynda Gregory LTCL)
23 High Ash Avenue
Leeds LS17 8RS   Tel: 0113-268 4519

VOICE CONSULTANT & COACH
020-7359 7848
Basic technique. Acting & audition voice work.
Consultancy in all areas of voice use.

Jessica Higgs

THE SCHOOL OF THE
SCIENCE *of* ACTING®

FULL TIME ACTING COURSES

1-Year (4 term) Daytime Acting Course

2-Year (8 term) Daytime Acting Course

3-Year (12 term) Daytime Acting Course

3-Year Evening plus 1-Year Daytime (16 term) Acting Course

DIRECTING MODULES

7 term Daytime (in conjunction with the 3-Year Daytime Acting Course)

6 term Evening + 4 terms Daytime (in conjunction with 3-Year Evening plus 1-Year Daytime (16 term) Acting Course)

PART-TIME COURSES & WORKSHOPS

Intensive Course

Spring Workshop

Summer School

August Workshop

GUARANTEE

If, after a certain period at the School of the Science of Acting you do not believe that your course is the best way to learn to act or direct in the time given, we will return your money in full.

CONTACT

The School of the Science of Acting

Dept E, 67-83 Seven Sisters Road, London N7 6BU

Tel: 020 7272 0027 Fax: 020 7272 0026

E-mail: find@scienceofacting.org.uk

Website: www.scienceofacting.org.uk

A charity formed to advance standards in drama training.

Registered Charity No. 1014419

Recognised as Efficient by the British Accreditation Council for Independent Further and Higher Education

FS45916   BS EN ISO9001:1994

UKAS QUALITY MANAGEMENT

DUFFILL Drusilla THEATRE SCHOOL
Grove Lodge, Oakwood Road
Burgess Hill
West Sussex RH15 0HZ
e-mail: drusilladschool@btclick.com
Tel/Fax: 01444 232672

DUNMORE Simon
(Acting & Audition Tuition)
e-mail: simon.dunmore@btinternet.com

DURRENT Peter
(Audition & Rehearsal Pianist & Vocal Coach)
Blacksmiths Cottage, Bures Road
Little Cornard, Sudbury
Suffolk CO10 0NR
Tel: 01787 373483

EARNSHAW Susi THEATRE SCHOOL
SS
5 Brook Place
Barnet EN5 2DL
Fax: 020-8364 9618
Tel: 020-8441 5010

EAST 15 ACTING SCHOOL
See DRAMA SCHOOLS (Conference of)

EAST LONDON ALEXANDER CENTRE
(Alexander Technique)
Bodywise 119 Roman Road
London E2 0QN
e-mail: bodywise2@msn.com
Tel: 020-8981 6938

ECOLE INTERNATIONALE DE THEATRE JACQUES LECOQ
57 rue du Faubourg Saint-Denis
75010 Paris
e-mail: ecole-jacques-lecoq@wanadoo.fr
Fax: 00 331 45 234014
Tel: 00 331 47 704478

ELLIOTT CLARKE SCHOOL
(Saturday & Evening Classes in Dance & Drama)
75A Bold Street
Liverpool L1 4EZ
Tel: 0151-709 3323

FAITH Gordon BA IPA Dip REM Sp MCHC (UK)
Sp
1 Wavel Mews, Priory Road
London NW6 3AB
Tel: 020-7328 0446

FBI AGENCY Ltd
(Acting Classes for Everyone)
PO Box 250, Leeds LS1 2AZ
e-mail: j.spencer@fbi-agency.ltd.uk
Tel/Fax: 07050 222747

FELDENKRAIS CENTRE The
(Meir Pfeffer)
10 Fernside Court
London NW4 1JT
Tel: 020-8346 0258

FINBURGH Nina
D Sp
1 Buckingham Mansions
West End Lane
London NW6 1LR
Tel/Fax: 020-7435 9484

FITZ-PATRICK Belinda & ASSOCIATES
(Voice Coaching, Singing, Confidence)
West London
Tel: 01392 876774

FLYING DOG PRODUCTIONS
(TV Presenters Courses & Training)
29 Maiden Lane, Covent Garden
London WC2E 7JS
Tel: 020-7692 9203

FOOTSTEPS THEATRE SCHOOL
(Children's Drama, Dance, Singing Training)
Tunwell Street, Eccleshill, Bradford
West Yorkshire BD2 2BH
Tel: 01274 833681

FORD Carole Ann ADVS
E D Sp
The Ridge, Hendon Wood Lane
London NW7 4HR
Fax: 020-8906 4669　　　　Tel: 020-8959 8159

FORD Robert L
(Drama, LAMDA and Audition Coaching)
58 Holyhead Road
Oakengates, Telford
Shropshire TF2 6BN　　　　Tel: 01952 618569

FORREST Dee
(Voice/Dialects, Film & TV)
87 Pepys Road
London SE14 5SE
e-mail: dee_forrest@yahoo.com
Mobile: 07957 211065　　　　Tel: 020-7639 9031

FOX Betty STAGE SCHOOL
The Friends Institute, 220 Moseley Road,
Birmingham B12 0DG
e-mail: bettyfox.school@virgin.net
　　　　　　　　　　Tel/Fax: 0121-440 1635

FRANKLIN Michael
(Meisner Technique)
Correspondence: c/o The Spotlight
7 Leicester Place
London WC2H 7RJ　　　　Tel/Fax: 020-8979 9185

FRIEZE Sandra
D E Sp (English & Foreign Actors)
30 Canfield Gardens
London NW6 3LA　　　　Tel: 020-7624 7633

GEORGESON Rosalind BA
(Drama for Children)
(See DRAGONDRAMA)

GIELGUD FOUNDATION The
(Programme of Classes for ProfessionaAactors)
Wimbledon Theatre, The Broadway
London SW19 1QG
e-mail: foundation@gielgud.com
Fax: 020-8542 8081　　　　Tel: 020-8542 9721

GIRAUDON Olivier
(Alexander Technique Teacher)
26 Church Rise, Forest Hill
London SE23 2UD　　　　Tel: 020-8699 9080

GLYNNE Frances THEATRE STUDENTS
SS
11 High Ash Avenue
Leeds LS17 8RS
e-mail: franandmo@cwctv.net
Fax: 0113-295 9408　　　　Tel: 0113-266 4286

GO FOR IT THEATRE SCHOOL
47 North Lane, Teddington
Middlesex TW11 0HU
e-mail: info@goforittheatreschool.co.uk
Fax: 020-8287 9405　　　　Tel: 020-8943 1120

GRAYSON John
(Vocal Tuition)
14 Lile Crescent, Hanwell
London W7 1AH
e-mail: john@bizzybee.freeserve.co.uk
Mobile: 07702 188031　　　　Tel: 020-8578 3384

GREASEPAINT ANONYMOUS
Theatre Youth & Training Company
4 Gallus Close, Winchmore Hill
London N21 1JR
e-mail: info@greasepaintanonymous.co.uk
Fax: 020-8882 9189　　　　Tel: 020-8886 2263

GREGORY Paul
(Drama Coach)
133 Kenilworth Court
Lower Richmond Road, Putney
London SW15 1HB   Tel: 020-8789 5726

GREVILLE Jeannine THEATRE SCHOOL
Melody House, Gillott's Corner
Henley-on-Thames
Oxon RG9 1QU   Tel: 01491 572000

GROUT Philip
D
5 Dickenson Road, Crouch Hill
London N8 9EN   Tel: 020-8340 4559

GSA GUILDFORD SCHOOL OF ACTING
See DRAMA SCHOOLS (Conference of)

GUILDHALL SCHOOL OF MUSIC & DRAMA
See DRAMA SCHOOLS (Conference of)

HALEY Jennifer STAGE SCHOOL
(Dance RAD, ISTD, Drama LAMDA)
Toad Hall, 67 Poppleton Road
London E11 1LP   Tel: 020-8989 8364

HANCOCK Allison LLAM
D E (Dramatic Art, Acting, Voice, Audition, Coaching, Elocution, Speech Correction etc)
38 Eve Road, Isleworth
Middlesex TW7 7HS   Tel/Fax: 020-8891 1073

HARLEQUIN STUDIOS PERFORMING ARTS SCHOOL
(Drama & Dance Training)
223 Southcoast Road
Peacehaven
East Sussex BN10 8LB   Tel: 01273 581742

HARRIS Sharon NCSD LRAM IPA Dip DA
London Univ
Sharon Harris School of Speech & Drama
52 Forty Avenue, Wembley
Middlesex HA9 8LQ
e-mail: sharrisltd@aol.com
Fax: 020-8908 4455   Tel: 020-8908 4451

HARRISON Joy
(Coaching in Audition Technique, Confidence Building, Text Work and Drama School Entry)
Tel: 020-7226 8377

HAW - HOLLYWOOD ACTING WORKSHOP
The International Film Acting School
2400 W. Silverlake Drive
Los Angeles CA 90039
e-mail: info@actingtraining.com
Fax: 001 (323) 668-0853   Tel: 001 (323) 668-2685

HEIDELBACH Sabine MSTAT
(Alexander Technique)
50 Hillside Grove
London N14 6HE   Tel: 020-8882 8562

HERTFORDSHIRE THEATRE SCHOOL
Queen Street House, 40 Queen Street
Hitchin, Herts SG4 9TS   Tel: 01462 421416

HESTER John LLCM (TD)
D E (Member of The Society of Teachers of Speech & Drama)
105 Stoneleigh Park Road, Epsom
Surrey KT19 0RF
e-mail: hester92@hotmail.com
Tel: 020-8393 5705

HEWITT PERFORMING ARTS
160 London Road, Romford
Essex RM7 9QL
e-mail: hewittcontrol@aol.com
Tel: 01708 727784

HIGGS Jessica
(Voice)
41A Barnsbury Street
London N1 1PW   Tel/Fax: 020-7359 7848

HONEYBORNE Jack
S (Accompanist & Coach)
The Studio, 165 Gunnersbury Lane
London W3 8LJ   Tel: 020-8993 2111

HOPNER Ernest LLAM
E D Public Speaking
Bluecoat Chambers, School Lane
Liverpool L1 3BX   Tel: 0151-709 1966

HOUSEMAN Barbara
(Ex RSC Voice Dept, Voice/Text/Acting/Posture/Relaxation)
e-mail: barbarahouseman@hotmail.com
Tel/Fax: 020-8693 9898

HERTFORDSHIRE THEATRE SCHOOL
LIMITED

THREE YEAR ACTING & MUSICAL THEATRE COURSE & ONE YEAR COURSE FOR POSTGRADUATES & TEACHERS

Applications now being accepted for the academic year commencing Sept. 2002 from the U.K. and abroad. Please apply for prospectus and audition details from The Registrar, Hertfordshire Theatre School, Queen Street House, 40 Queen Street, Hitchin, Herts SG4 9TS or phone 01462 421416

HOUSTON Roxane LRAM
8 Hartington Road
Aldeburgh
Suffolk IP15 5HD   Tel: 01728 454048

HUGHES Elianne
S
(Accompanist & Coach for, Rehearsal &
Auditions)
165 Gunnersbury Lane
London W3 8LJ   Tel: 020-8993 2111

IDEAL SOLUTIONS
Pat O'Toole - Private Coaching, Presentation,
Audition Work, Acting, Corporate, Counselling)
e-mail: patideal@aol.com
Fax: 020-7564 3147   Tel: 020-7564 3384

IVES-CAMERON Elaine
(Private Coaching, Dialect, Drama School
Entrance/Auditions)
29 King Edward Walk
London SE1 7PR
Mobile: 07980 434513   Tel: 020-7928 3814

JACK Andrew
Vrouve Johanna
PO Box 412
Weybridge
Surrey KT13 8WL   Mobile: 07836 615839

JAMES Linda RAM Dip. Ed. IPD LRAM
(Dialect Coach)
25 Clifden Road, Brentford
Middlesex TW8 0PB   Tel: 020-8568 2390

JIGSAW PERFORMING ARTS SCHOOL
64-66 High Street, Barnet
Hertfordshire EN5 5SJ
e-mail: nicola@jigsaw-arts.co.uk
Tel: 020-8447 4530

JONES Desmond SCHOOL OF MIME AND PHYSICAL THEATRE The
20 Thornton Avenue
London W4 1QG
e-mail: enquiries@desmondjones.co.uk
Tel: 020-8747 3537

JUSTICE Herbert ACADEMY of THEATRE ARTS
SS
25 Ronald Close
Beckenham
Kent BR3 3HX   Tel: 020-8650 8878

K-BIS THEATRE SCHOOL
Clermont Hall, Cumberland Road
Brighton BN1 6SL
e-mail: k-bis@zoom.co.uk
Mobile: 07798 610010   Tel/Fax: 01273 564366

KENT YOUTH THEATRE & AGENCY
Pinks Hill House
Briton Road, Faversham
Kent ME13 8QH
e-mail: kentyouththeatre@aol.com
Tel/Fax: 01795 534395

KORDA Anna
(Dialogue Coach, Languages & Accents,
French, English, German, Italian, Spanish &
Russian)
Via Antonio, Chinotto 1
00195 Rome, Italy   Tel/Fax: 00 39 06 3612754

LAINE THEATRE ARTS
(Betty Laine)
The Studios, East Street
Epsom, Surrey KT17 1HH
Fax: 01372 723775   Tel: 01372 724648

LAMDA
See DRAMA SCHOOLS (Conference of)

LAMONT DRAMA SCHOOL AND CASTING AGENCY
94 Harington Road, Formby, Liverpool
e-mail: diane@lamontcasting.co.uk
Fax: 01704 872422   Tel: 01704 877024

LANG Margaret
18 Dalkeith Court, 45 Vincent Street
London SW1P 4HH   Tel: 020-7828 4297

LAURIE Rona
(Coach for Auditions and Voice & Speech
Technique)
21 New Quebec Street
London W1H 7SA   Tel: 020-7262 4909

LEAN David Lawson BA Hons
(Acting Tuition, LAMDA Exams, Licensed
Chaperone)
72 Shaw Drive, Walton-on-Thames
Surrey KT12 2LS   Tel: 01932 230273

LEE STAGE SCHOOL The
(office)
38 The Chase, Rayleigh, Essex SS6 8QN
e-mail: lynn@leetheatre.fsnet.co.uk
Tel/Fax: 01268 773204

LESLIE Maeve
(Singing, Voice Production, Presentation) .
60 Warwick Square
London SW1V 2AL   Tel: 020-7834 4912

LEVENTON Patricia BA Hons
D E Sp
113 Broadhurst Gardens, West Hampstead
London NW6 3BJ
e-mail: patricia.leventon@lites2000.com
Tel: 020-7624 5661

LINTON MANAGEMENT
Carol Godby Theatre Workshop
The Studios, Back Broad Street
Bury, Lancs BL9 0DA
Fax: 0161-761 1999   Tel: 0161-763 6420

LITTLE HEATH THEATRE WORKSHOP
67 Brookmans Avenue
Brookmans Park, Herts AL9 7QG
Tel: 01707 644276   Tel: 020-8886 4264

LIVERPOOL INSTITUTE FOR PERFORMING ARTS The
Mount Street, Liverpool L1 9HF
e-mail: reception@lipa.ac.uk
Fax: 0151-330 3131   Tel: 0151-330 3000

LIVINGSTON Dione LRAM FETC
Sp E D
7 St Luke's Street
Cambridge CB4 3DA   Tel: 01223 365970

LOCATION TUTORS NATIONWIDE
(Fully Qualified/Experienced Support Teachers
Covering all Key Stages in National Curriculum)
16 Poplar Walk
Herne Hill SE24 0BU
Fax: 020-7207 8794   Tel: 020-7978 8898

LONDON ACADEMY OF PERFORMING ARTS (LAPA)
St Matthews Church
St Petersburgh Place
London W2 4LA
e-mail: londonacademy.performingarts@btinternet.com
Fax: 020-7727 0330   Tel: 020-7727 0220

SCREEN ACTING
STEFAN GRYFF (DGGB) (LLB)

"I believe that for film and TV an actors quality is more important than their level of talent."

I will provide:

○ Individual or group tuition in camera acting
○ Preparation of show reels for Casting Directors and Agents
○ Special training for beginners and artists unused to camera acting
○ Rehearsal & workshops for experienced actors currently employed in TV or film

MARBLE ARCH STUDIO TEL: 020 7723-8181

LONDON DRAMA SCHOOL
(Drama & Speech Training Courses)
30 Brondesbury Park
London NW6 7DN
e-mail: enquiries@startek-uk.com
Fax: 020-8830 4992   Tel: 020-8830 0074

LONDON FILMMAKERS STUDIO The
10 Brunswick Centre, Bernard Street
London WC1N 1AE
e-mail: business@skoob.com
Mobile: 07712 880909   Tel: 020-7278 8760

LONDON SCHOOL OF MUSICAL THEATRE
83 Borough Road
London SE1 1DN
e-mail: enquiries@lsmt.co.uk
                        Tel/Fax: 020-7407 4419

LONDON STUDIO CENTRE
42-50 York Way
London N1 9AB
e-mail: enquire@london-studio-centre.co.uk
Fax: 020-7837 3248   Tel: 020-7837 7741

LYTTON Gloria
E D
22 Green Road, Oakwood, Southgate
London N14 4AU   Tel: 020-8441 3118

MACKEY Beatrix LGSM
E D (Coaching For Drama, Speech &
Communication)
3 The Valley, Stanmore, Winchester
Hants SO22 4DG   Tel: 01962 855533

MACKINNON Alison
(Voice, Dialects & Auditions)
e-mail: alinaji@lineone.net
                        Mobile: 07855 061401

MACKINTOSH Stewart ARCM ABSM
S
106 Boundaries Road, London SW12 8HQ
e-mail: stewartmackintosh@email.com
Mobile: 07970 448109   Tel: 020-8672 6179

MADDERMARKET THEATRE
D (Training for Adults & Youths)
St John's Alley, Norwich NR2 1DR
e-mail: theatre@maddermarket.freeserve.co.uk
Fax: 01603 661357   Tel: 01603 626560

MALLETT Chuck
35 Lancaster Mews
London W2 3QF
e-mail: chucko21@btinternet.com
Fax: 020-7402 6672   Tel: 020-7262 1575

**MANCHESTER METROPOLITAN UNIVERSITY
SCHOOL OF THEATRE**
See DRAMA SCHOOLS (Conference of)

MANN Stella COLLEGE
343A Finchley Road, Hampstead
London NW3 6ET
Fax: 020-7435 3782   Tel: 020-7435 9317

MARLOW Jean LGSM
D E
32 Exeter Road
London NW2 4SB   Tel: 020-8450 0371

**MARSHALL Elizabeth Tracey LGSM GSMD
LGSMD**
(Dialects, Speech Faults, Drama for Stage
Film & Modelling, Training for Corporates eg.
Presentation Skills)
5 Mount Street, Cromer, Norfolk NR27 9DB
e-mail: marshall@grenedan.demon.co.uk
                        Tel: 01263 515769

HOLLY WILSON

LLAM. Actor. Teacher-London Drama Schools.
Voice, Speech & Drama, Audition coaching. Private tuition.

Tel: 020-8878 0015

MARTIN Liza GRSM ARMCM (Singing) ARMCM (Piano)
(Singing Tuition, Sounds Sensational)
Tel: 020-8348 0346

MASTERS PERFORMING ARTS COLLEGE
(Dance, Musical Theatre Course)
Arterial Road, Rayleigh
Essex SS6 7UQ   Tel: 01268 777351

McCALLION Anna
(Alexander Technique)
Flat 2, 11 Sinclair Gardens
London W14 0AU   Tel: 020-7602 5599

McCALLION Michael
D E
Flat 2, 11 Sinclair Gardens
London W14 0AU   Tel: 020-7602 5599

McCRACKEN Jenny
2 Stamford Court, Goldhawk Road
London W6 0XB   Tel: 020-8748 7638

McCULLOUGH Jill
Sp
89 Montagu Mansions, London W1H 6LF
e-mail: dialectjillmcc@compuserve.com
Mobile: 07976 799739   Tel: 020-7486 8445

METHOD STUDIO, LONDON The
Conway Hall, 25 Red Lion Square
London WC1R 4RL
e-mail: info@themethodstudio.com
Fax: 020-7831 8319   Tel: 020-7831 7335

MICHEL Hilary ARCM
(Singing, Piano, Recorders)
82 Greenway, Totteridge
London N20 8EJ
Mobile: 07775 780182   Tel: 020-8343 7243

MIDDLESEX UNIVERSITY
Bramley Road, Oakwood
London N14 4YZ
Fax: 020-8441 4672   Tel: 020-8362 5000

MILNER Jack COMEDY WORKSHOPS
88 Pearcroft Road, London E11 4DR
e-mail: jack@jackmilner.com
Tel: 020-8556 9768

MONTAGE THEATRE
(Dance, Drama, Singing - Children & Adults)
45 Chalsey Road, London SE4 1YN
e-mail: info@montagetheatre.com
Tel: 020-8694 9497

MONTFORD DANCE AND STAGE ACADEMY
96 Surbiton Court, St Andrews Square
Surbiton, Surrey KT6 4EE
Fax: 020-8287 6015   Tel: 020-8399 9065

MORLEY COLLEGE THEATRE SCHOOL
(LOCN Accredited Part-time Evening Drama Training)
61 Westminster Bridge Road
London SE1 7HT
e-mail: nina.anderson@morleycollege.ac.uk
Fax: 020-7928 4074   Tel: 020-7450 9232

MOUNTVIEW
See DRAMA SCHOOLS (Conference of)

MRS WORTHINGTON'S WORKSHOPS
SS S Md (Part-time Performing Arts for Children)
16 Ouseley Road
London SW12 8EF   Tel: 020-8767 6944

MURRAY Barbara LGSM LALAM
129 Northwood Way, Northwood
Middlesex HA6 1RF   Tel: 01923 823182

NATIONAL PERFORMING ARTS SCHOOL & AGENCY The
The Factory Rehearsal Studios
35A Barrow Street, Dublin 4
e-mail: info@npas.ie
Fax: 00 353 1 668405   Tel: 00 353 1 6684035

NEIL Andrew
2 Howley Place
London W2 1XA
e-mail: andrewneil@annabar.globalnet.co.uk
Tel/Fax: 020-7262 9521

NEW ERA ACADEMY (Speech & Drama)
E D Examination Board
137B Streatham High Road
London SW16 1HJ
e-mail: neweraacademy@aol.com
Tel/Fax: 020-8769 0384

NEWNHAM Caryll
(Singing Teacher)
35 Selwyn Crescent, Hatfield
Herts AL10 9NL
e-mail: caryll@ntlworld.com
Mobile: 07976 635745   Tel: 01707 267700

NORTHERN ACADEMY TELEVISION AND THEATRE WORKSHOPS FOR YOUNG PEOPLE The
(Oldham, Bolton & Worsley)
(Students aged 8-18)
c/o 1 Dunwood Bridge, Bridge Street
Shaw OL2 8BG   Tel/Fax: 01706 882442

NORTHERN FILM & DRAMA
PO Box 27, Tadcaster
North Yorks LS24 9XS
e-mail: alyson@connew.com
Tel/Fax: 01937 530600

NORTHERN FILM SCHOOL
Leeds Metropolitan University
2 Queen Square, Leeds LS2 8AF
e-mail: nfs@lmu.ac.uk
Tel: 0113-283 1900   Fax: 0113-283 1901

NORTHERN THEATRE SCHOOL OF PERFORMING ARTS
The Studios, Madeley Street
Hull, East Yorkshire HU3 2AH
e-mail: northco75@aol.com
Fax: 01482 212280   Tel: 01482 328627

NORTH LONDON PERFORMING ARTS CENTRE
(Performing Arts Classes 3-19 yrs, GCSE
Drama & LAMDA Exams)
76 St James Lane, Muswell Hill
London N10 3DF
e-mail: nlpac@compuserve.com
Fax: 020-8444 4040   Tel: 020-8444 4544

NUTOPIA ACTORS STUDIO LONDON
(Camera Acting and Presenting Courses)
8, 132 Charing Cross Road
London WC2H 0LA   Tel/Fax: 020-8882 6299

O'FARRELL STAGE SCHOOL & AGENCY
SS
36 Shirley Street, Canning Town
London E16 1HU
Fax: 020-7476 0010   Tel: 020-7511 9444

OLLERENSHAW Maggie BA (Hons) Dip Ed.
D Sp (TV & Theatre Coaching,
Career Guidance)
151D Shirland Road
London W9 2EP
e-mail: maggieoll@aol.com   Tel: 020-7286 1126

OLSON Lise
(American Accents, Voice & Text)
17A Park Road, West Kirby
Wirral CH48 4DN
e-mail: l.olson@lipa.ac.uk
Tel: 0151-625 5667   Tel: 0151-330 3032

OMOBONI Lino
Sp
2nd Floor, 12 Weltje Road
London W6 9TG
e-mail: lino@bluewand.co.uk
Mobile: 07885 528743   Tel/Fax: 020-8741 2038

OPEN VOICE
(Consultancy, Auditions, Personal
Presentation - Catherine Owen)
9 Bellsmains, Gorebridge
Near Edinburgh EH23 4QD   Tel: 01875 820175

ORTON Leslie LRAM ALAM ANEA
E D Sp
141 Ladybrook Lane, Mansfield
Notts NG18 5JH   Tel: 01623 626082

OSBORNE HUGHES John
(Art & Craft of Acting)
Venus Productions Training Department
51 Church Road, London SE19 2TE
                        Tel: 020-8653 7735

OXFORD SCHOOL OF DRAMA
See DRAMA SCHOOLS (Conference of)

OXYGENESIS
(Maurice Rowdon, Breath Initiation)
Hale Clinic, Regent's Park
London W1B 1PF
Tel: 01202 744747   Tel: 020-8874 5361

PALMER Jackie STAGE SCHOOL
30 Daws Hill Lane, High Wycombe
Bucks HP11 1PW
e-mail: jackie.palmer@btinternet.com
Fax: 01494 510479   Tel: 01494 520978

PALMER Marie LLAM FRSA
SS E Sp (Speechcraft Consultancy)
Church Studios, Common Road
Stafford ST16 3EQ
e-mail: enquiries@speechcraft.co.uk
Tel: 01785 226326   Fax: 01785 220460

PAUL'S THEATRE SCHOOL
Fairkytes Arts Centre
51 Billet Lane, Hornchurch
Essex RM11 1AX   Tel: 01708 447123

PERFORMERS COLLEGE
(Brian Rogers - Susan Stephens)
2-4 Chase Road, Corringham, Essex SS17 7QH
e-mail: pdc@dircon.co.uk
Fax: 01375 672353   Tel: 01375 672053

PETHICK Fiona & Claire BA Hons ADB LRAM LGSM
D Sp (Musical Theatre: 12 week courses - weekends only)
e-mail: ata-productions@hotmail.com
                              Tel: 01932 702174

PHELPS Neil
D Sp
61 Parkview Court, London SW6 3LL
e-mail: nphelps@ondigital.com
                              Tel: 020-7731 3419

PHILLIPS Penny AGSM Dip. Ed LLAM GODA
'Shiraz' at Willow Tree Marina
West Quay Drive
Yeading in Hayes UB4 9TA
e-mail: penny@speak.free-online.co.uk
Mobile: 07976 365134   Tel/Fax: 020-8241 9287

PILATES INTERNATIONAL Ltd
(Physical Coaching, Stage, Film & Dance)
Unit 1, Broadbent Close
20-22 Highgate High Street
London N6 5JG   Tel/Fax: 020-8348 1442

POLLYANNA CHILDRENS TRAINING THEATRE
PO Box 30661, London E1W 3GG
e-mail: pollyanna-mgmt@yahoo.co.uk
Fax: 020-7480 6761   Tel: 020-7702 1937

POOR SCHOOL
242 Pentonville Road
London N1 9JY   Tel: 020-7837 6030

PRESENT YOURSELF
(Television Presenting Courses)
                              Tel: 020-8255 2361

QUEEN MARGARET COLLEGE
See DRAMA SCHOOLS (Conference of)

QUESTORS THEATRE EALING The
12 Mattock Lane, London W5 5BQ
e-mail: paul@questors.org.uk
Fax: 020-8567 8736   Admin: 020-8567 0011

RAVENSCOURT THEATRE SCHOOL Ltd
Tandy House, 30-40 Dalling Road
London W6 0JB
e-mail: ravenscourt@hotmail.com
Fax: 020-8741 1786   Tel: 020-8741 0707

RE:ACTORS
15 Montrose Walk, Weybridge
Surrey KT13 8JN
e-mail: michael@reactors.co.uk
Fax: 01932 830248   Tel: 01932 888885

REDROOFS THEATRE SCHOOL
DS SS D E S Sp
Littlewick Green
Maidenhead
Berks SL6 3QY   Tel: 01628 822982

REP COLLEGE The
17 St Mary's Avenue
Purley on Thames
Berks RG8 8BJ
e-mail: tudor@repcollege.freeserve.co.uk
                              Tel/Fax: 0118-942 1144

REYNOLDS Sandra COLLEGE
(Model Grooming School)
35 St Georges Street
Norwich NR3 1DA
e-mail: tessa@sandrareynolds.co.uk
Fax: 01603 219825   Tel: 01603 623842

REYNOLDS THEATRE ARTS ACADEMY
(Children/Teenagers)
Westgate House, Spital Street
Dartford, Kent DA1 2EH
e-mail: info@reynoldsgroup.co.uk
Fax: 01634 329079   Tel: 01322 277200

RICHMOND DRAMA SCHOOL
DS (One Year Course)
Parkshot Centre, Parkshot, Richmond
Surrey TW9 2RE
e-mail: drwhitters@aol.com
                              Tel: 020-8940 0170 Ext 325

RIDGEWAY STUDIOS PERFORMING ARTS COLLEGE
Fairley House, Andrews Lane
Cheshunt, Herts EN7 6LB
e-mail: info@ridgewaystudios.co.uk
Fax: 01992 633844   Tel: 01992 633775

ROSE BRUFORD COLLEGE
See DRAMA SCHOOLS (Conference of)

ROWE James Dip GSA STSD
(Audition Coaching & Drama Courses)
Kinfauns 11 New Road
Higher Brea, Camborne
Cornwall TR14 9DD   Tel: 01209 710672

ROYAL ACADEMY OF DRAMATIC ART
See DRAMA SCHOOLS (Conference of)

ROYAL SCOTTISH ACADEMY OF MUSIC AND DRAMA
See DRAMA SCHOOLS (Conference of)

SCHER Anna THEATRE The
70-72 Barnsbury Road, London N1 0ES
e-mail: theagency@annaschermanagement.fsnet.co.uk
Fax: 020-7833 9467   Tel: 020-7278 2101

SCHOOL OF THE SCIENCE OF ACTING The
Dept E
67-83 Seven Sisters Road, London N7 6BU
e-mail: find@scienceofacting.org.uk
Fax: 020-7272 0026   Tel: 020-7272 0027

SCREENWRITERS' WORKSHOP
Screenwriters' Centre, Suffolk House
1-8 Whitfield Place, London W1T 5JU
e-mail: screenoffice@cwcom.net
                         Tel/Fax: 020-7387 5511

SETTELEN Peter
181 Jersey Road, Osterley
Middlesex TW7 4QJ
e-mail: peter@settelen.net
Fax: 020-8737 2987   Tel: 020-8737 1616

SHAND Mary PGDVS
D E (Voice Coach)
48 Peacock Street
London SE17 3LF
e-mail: voicehelp@cwcom.net
Mobile: 07802 167342   Tel: 020-7735 6216

SHARONA STAGE SCHOOL AGENCY & MANAGEMENT
82 Grennell Road, Sutton
Surrey SM1 3DN
Fax: 020-8395 0009   Tel: 020-8642 9396

SHAW Philip
(Actors Consultancy Service,
Voice/Audition Coaching)
Suite 476, 2 Old Brompton Road
South Kensington, London SW7 3DQ
e-mail: hadespluto@aol.com
Fax: 020-8408 1193   Tel: 020-8715 8943

SHENEL Helena
(Singing Teacher)
80 Falkirk House, 165 Maida Vale
London W9 1QX   Tel: 020-7328 2921

SHERRIFF David
(Vocal Coaching, Accompanist,
Act Preparation, Video Showreels)
Musical Services
106 Mansfield Drive
Merstham
Surrey RH1 3JN
Fax: 01737 271231   Tel: 01737 642829

SINGER Sandra ASSOCIATES
21 Cotswold Road, Westcliff on Sea
Essex SS0 8AA
e-mail: sandra.singer@virgin.net
Fax: 01702 339393   Tel: 01702 331616

SMITH Susan Graham MA ARCM
(Piano Accompanist & Coach)
Hertfordshire
Westcliff-on-Sea   Tel: 01992 503896

SOCIETY OF TEACHERS OF SPEECH AND DRAMA The
73 Berry Hill Road, Mansfield
Notts NG18 4RU
e-mail: ann.p.jones@btinternet.com
          Tel: 01623 627636

SPEAKE Barbara STAGE SCHOOL
East Acton Lane
London W3 7EG
e-mail: speakekids1@aol.com
          Tel/Fax: 020-8743 1306

SPEED Anne-Marie Hon ARAM MA (Voice Studies) CSSD ADVS BA
(Vocal Technique, Coaching,
Auditions, Accents)
61 Donaldson Road
London NW6 6NE
e-mail: anne-marie.speed@virgin.net
Mobile: 07957 272554   Tel/Fax: 020-7328 2582

SPENCER Jay
(Acting and Audition Tuition)
e-mail: j.spencer@fbi-agency.ltd.uk
          Tel/Fax: 07050 321654

STAGE 01 THEATRE PRODUCTION SCHOOL
32 Westbury Lane, Buckhurst Hill
Essex IG9 5PL
e-mail: stage01@lineone.net
Mobile: 07939 121154   Tel/Fax: 020-8506 0949

STAGE 84 YORKSHIRE SCHOOL OF PERFORMING ARTS
(Evening Classes only)
Old Bell Chapel, Town Lane
Bradford, West Yorks BD10 8PR
Mobile: 07785 244984   Tel: 01274 569197

STAGECOACH TRAINING CENTRES FOR THE PERFORMING ARTS
The Courthouse, Elm Grove
Walton-on-Thames
Surrey KT12 1LZ
e-mail: mail@stagecoach.co.uk
Fax: 01932 222894   Tel: 01932 254333

STARLINGS THEATRICAL AGENCY
45 Viola Close, South Ockendon
Essex RM15 6JF
e-mail: juliecartercar24w@supanet.com
Mobile: 07941 653463   Tel: 01708 859109

STAT (The Society of Teachers of the Alexander Technique)
129 Camden Mews, London NW1 9AH
e-mail: enquiries@stat.org.uk
Fax: 020-7482 5435   Tel: 020-7284 3338

STEP ONE DANCE AND DRAMA SCHOOL
Rear of 24 Penrhyn Road, Colwyn Bay
Conwy LL29 8LG   Tel: 01492 534424

STEVENS Dacia STAGE SCHOOL
SS E D Md Sp
Glenavon Lodge, Lansdowne Road
South Woodford
London E18 2BE   Tel: 020-8989 0166

STOCKTON & BILLINGHAM COLLEGE OF FURTHER EDUCATION
(Education & Training)
The Causeway
Billingham TS23 2DB   Tel: 01642 865566

STONELANDS SCHOOL
(Full-time Training in Ballet & Theatre Arts)
170A Church Road
Hove BN3 2DJ
e-mail: dianacarteur@stonelandsschool.co.uk
Fax: 01273 770444   Tel: 01273 770445

www.ukspeech.co.uk
william trotter

ST. RAPH'S COMMUNITY THEATRE
(TIE/Workshops, Children 5-11 Part-time)
20 Pembroke Road
North Wembley
Middlesex HA9 7PD
e-mail: jennymayers@totalise.co.uk
Tel/Fax: 020-8908 0502

STREETON Jane
(Singing Teacher - RADA)
24 Richmond Road, Leytonstone
London E11 4BA   Tel: 020-8556 9297

SWAIN Neil BA (Hons) PGDVS CSSD
34 Saltash Road, Welling
Kent DA16 1HB
Fax: 020-8306 2934   Tel: 020-8306 2936

SWINFIELD Rosemarie
(Make-Up)
Rosie's Make-Up Box
6 Brewer Street, Soho
London W1R 3FS
e-mail: rosemarie@rosiesmake-up.co.uk
Fax: 020-8390 7773   Mobile: 07976 965520

TANWOOD in association with The Young Actors' File
SS
46 Bath Road, Swindon
Wilts SN1 4AY
Fax: 01793 643219   Tel: 01793 523895

THEATRE ARTS (WEST LONDON)
(Agency & Part-time Classes in Drama,
Dance & Singing)
18 Kingsdale Gardens, Notting Hill
London W11 4TZ
e-mail: theatreartswestlondon@hotmail.com
Tel/Fax: 020-7603 3471

THEATRETRAIN
(6 -18 years, Annual West End Productions
involving all Pupils)
PO Box 117, Ilford, Essex IG3 8PN
e-mail: theatretrain@talk21.com
Fax: 01992 522657   Tel: 01992 524607

THOMPSON Guy BA (Hons) ALAM MTS Dip
(Professional Vocal Coaching, Audition Speech
Direction & LAMDA examinations)
No 1, Earlham Grove
London N22 5HJ
e-mail: info@stateofplaytheatre.co.uk
Mobile: 07973 445328

THORN Barbara
D Sp (TV & Theatre Coaching,
Career Guidance)
51 Parkside, Vanbrugh Park, Blackheath
London SE3 7QF   Tel: 020-8305 0094

TO BE OR NOT TO BE
(TV/Film Acting Techniques using pro 'equip'
Theatre/Audition pieces) (Anthony Barnett)
32 Green Lane, Kettering
Northants NN16 0DA
e-mail: tobeornottobeacting@hotmail.com
Mobile: 07958 996227   Tel/Fax: 01536 481554

TOTAL ACTOR The
(Graded, Progressive Acting Workshop, taught
by Working Actors and Directors)
66 Shaftesbury Road
London N19 4QN   Tel/Fax: 020-7281 3686

TOTS-TWENTIES THEATRE SCHOOL
SS
Unit 3, Ground Floor, Clements Court
Clements Lane, Ilford
Essex IG1 2QY
e-mail: sara@tots-twenties.co.uk
Fax: 020-8553 1880   Tel: 020-8478 1848

TRAPEZE AND AERIAL SKILL COACHING
(Denise and Raven Wolf)
26 Fairfield, Arlington Road
London NW1 7LE
Mobile: 07944 835639   Tel: 020-7388 3824

TROTTER William BA MA PGDVS
D E Sp
25 Thanet Lodge, Mapesbury Road
London NW2 4JA
e-mail: william.trotter@ukgateway.net
Tel/Fax: 020-8459 7594

TURNBULL-ENTERTRAIN Terry UK Ltd
18 Runnymede House, Courtlands
Sheen Road
Richmond TW10 5AY
Mobile: 07740 802602   Tel: 020-8241 0207

TV ACTING CLASSES
(Elisabeth Charbonneau)
9 Alderton Road, Herne Hill
London SE24 0HS
Mobile: 07885 621061   Tel: 020-7326 3967

TWICKENHAM THEATRE WORKSHOP FOR CHILDREN
22 Butts Crescent
Hanworth
Middlesex TW13 6HQ   Tel:, 020-8898 5882

URQUHART Moray
61 Parkview Court
London SW6 3LL
e-mail: nphelps@ondigital.com
Tel: 020-7731 3419

VALLE ACADEMY OF PERFORMING ARTS Ltd The
D S E SS
The Rosedale Old Cestrians Club
Andrews Lane
Cheshunt, Herts EN7 6TB
e-mail: enquiries@valleacademy.co.uk
Fax: 01992 622868   Tel: 01992 622862

VERRALL Charles
D
19 Matilda Street, London N1 0LA
e-mail: charles.verrall@virgin.net
                          Tel: 020-7833 1971

VOICE BODY COMMUNICATION
(Patricia Perry)
65 Castelnau, Barnes SW13 9RT
                          Tel/Fax: 020-8748 9699

VOICE CASTER
(Specialised Training for Voice Overs &
TV Presenters)
Fax: 020-8455 2344   Tel: 020-8455 2211

VOICE TAPE SERVICES INT Ltd
(Professional Voice Over Direction & CDs)
80 Netherlands Road, New Barnet
Herts EN5 1BS
e-mail: info@vtsint.co.uk
Fax: 020-8441 4828   Tel: 020-8440 4848

VOICEHELP
48 Peacock Street
London SE17 3LF
e-mail: voicehelp@cwcom.net
                          Tel: 020-7735 6216

WALLACE Elaine BA
D Sp Voice
249 Goldhurst Terrace
London NW6 3EP
e-mail: elainewallace33@hotmail.com
                          Tel: 020-7625 4049

WALTZER Jack
5 Minetta Street Apt 2B
New York NY 10012
Tel: 001 (212) 840-1234   Tel: 020-7207 1318

WEBB BRUCE
S
Abbots Manor, Kirby Cane, Bungay
Suffolk NR35 2HP   Tel: 01508 518703

WEBBER DOUGLAS ACADEMY OF DRAMATIC ART
See DRAMA SCHOOLS (Conference of)

WELSH COLLEGE OF MUSIC & DRAMA
See DRAMA SCHOOLS (Conference of)

WESTMINSTER KINGSWAY COLLEGE
(Performing Arts)
Regent's Park Centre
Longford Street
London NW1 3HB
e-mail: courseinfo@westking.ac.uk
Fax: 020-7306 5950 Tel: 020-7306 5954

WHITEHALL PERFORMING ARTS CENTRE
Rayleigh Road, Leigh-on-Sea
Essex SS9 5UU Tel: 01702 529290

WHITWORTH Geoffrey LRAM MA
S (Piano Accompanist)
789 Finchley Road
London NW11 8DP Tel: 020-8458 4281

WILDER Andrea
D E
23 Cambrian Drive
Colwyn Bay
Conwy LL28 4SL
e-mail: andrea@awagency.co.uk
Fax: 07092 249314 Tel: 01492 547542

WILMER Elizabeth J
E D
34 Campden Street
London W8 7ET Tel: 020-7727 6624

WILSON Holly
3 Worple Street
Mortlake
London SW14 8HE Tel: 020-8878 0015

WIMBUSH Martin Dip GSMD
D E Sp (Audition Coaching)
Flat 4, 289 Trinity Road
Wandsworth Common
London SW18 3SN
e-mail: mtnwimbush@netscapeonline.co.uk
Tel: 020-8877 0086

WINDSOR Judith MA
(American Accents/Dialects)
Woodbine
Victoria Road, Deal
Kent CT14 7AS
e-mail: joyce.edwards@virgin.net
Fax: 020-7820 1845 Tel: 020-7735 5736

WOOD Tessa, Teach Cert AGSM, CSSD, PGVDS
(Voice Coach)
Ground Floor
11 Chaucer Road, Poet's Corner
London W3 6DR Tel: 020-8896 2659

WOODHOUSE Alan AGSM ADVS
(Voice & Acting Coach)
33 Burton Road
Kingston
Surrey KT2 5TG
e-mail: alanwoodhouse50@hotmail.com
Tel/Fax: 020-8549 1374

WOODHOUSE Nan
(Playwright & LAMDA Examiner)
LGSM (Hons medal) LLAM LLCM (TD) ALCM
Write, 2 New Street
Morecambe
Lancashire LA4 4BW

WOOSTER Margaret LRAM Bar
D E
97 Hughenden Road
High Wycombe
Bucks HP13 5HT Tel: 01494 530756

WORTMAN Neville
E (Dialogue Coach)
48 Chiswick Staithe
London W4 3TP
e-mail: nevillewortman@beeb.net
Mobile: 07976 805976 Tel: 020-8994 8886

WRIGG Ann ALAM
E D
The Little House
6 Frith Lane
London NW7 1JA Tel: 020-8346 6745

WYNN Madeleine
(Director & Acting Coach)
40 Barrie House
Hawksley Court
Albion Road
London N16 0TX
e-mail: madeleine@onetel.net.uk
Tel: 020-7249 4487

YOUNG Sylvia THEATRE SCHOOL
SS
Rossmore Road
London NW1 6NJ
e-mail: younguns@freeuk.com
Fax: 020-7723 1040 Tel: 020-7402 0673

ZANDER Peter
D E SP (German)
22 Romilly Street
London W1D 5AG
e-mail: peterzan.berlin@virgin.net
Tel: 020-7437 4767

For information on the FIA please contact
International Federation of Actors
Guild House, Upper St Martin's Lane
London WC2H GEG
Tel: 020-7379 0900   Fax: 020-7379 8260
e-mail: office@fia-actors.com

■ Belgium
ACV - Transcom
Galerie Agora
Rue du Marche aux Herbes
105, Bte 40, B-1000 Brussels
Fax: 00 32 2 5128591   Tel: 00 32 2 549 0769

■ Belgium
C.G.S.P.
Place Fontainas 9-11, B-1000 Brussels
Fax: 00 32 2 508 5902   Tel: 00 32 2 508 5811

■ Denmark
DANSK ARTIST FORBUND
Vendersgade 24, DK-1363 Copenhagen K
e-mail: artisten@artisten.dk
Fax: 00 45 33 33 73 30   Tel: 00 45 33 32 66 77

■ Denmark
DANSK SKUESPILLERFORBUND
Sankt Knuds vej 26, DK-1903, Frederiksberg C
e-mail: dsf@skuespillerforbundet.dk
Fax: 00 45 33 24 81 59   Tel: 00 45 33 24 22 00

■ Finland
SUOMENNAAYTTELIJALITTO - SNL
Temppelikatu 3-5 A 11, SF-00100 Helsinki
e-mail: suomen.nayttelijalitto@coinet.fi
Fax: 00 358 9 4372 7350   Tel: 00 358 9 4342 730

■ France
S.F.A.
21 bis Rue Victor Masse, F-75009 Paris
e-mail: sfa75@aol.com
Fax: 00 33 1 53 25 09 01   Tel: 00 33 1 53 25 09 09

■ Germany
G.D.B.A.
Feldbrunnenstrasse 74, D-20148 Hamburg
e-mail: gdba@buehnengenossenschaft.de
Fax: 00 49 40 45 93 52   Tel: 00 49 40 44 51 85

■ Greece
HELLENIC ACTORS' UNION - HAU
33 Kaniggos Street, GR-106 82 Athens
e-mail: sei@greektour.com
Fax: 00 30 1 380 8651   Tel: 00 30 1 383 3742

■ Greece
UNION OF GREEK SINGERS
130 Patission Street, GR-112 57 Athens
Fax: 00 30 1 823 8321   Tel: 00 30 1 823 8335

■ Ireland
IRISH ACTORS' EQUITY GROUP
S I P T U - Liberty Hall, Dublin 1
e-mail: equity@siptu.ie
Fax: 00 353 1 874 9731   Tel: 00 353 1 874 3691 Ext 2301

■ Italy
SAI
Via Ofanto 18, I-00198 Rome
e-mail: crc@corelli.nexus.it
Fax: 00 39 06 854 6780   Tel: 00 39 06 841 7303

■ Luxembourg
OGB-L
19 rue d'Epernay, B.P. 2031, L-1010 Luxembourg
e-mail: nick.clesen@ogb-l.lu
Fax: 00 352 486 925   Tel: 00 352 540 005 Ext 210

■ Netherlands
FNV Kiem
Postbus 9354, NL-1006 AJ Amsterdam
e-mail: ivan.westerlaake@fnv-klem.nl
Fax: 00 31 20 355 37 37   Tel: 00 31 20 355 36 36

■ Norway
NORSK SKVESPILLERFORBUND
Welhavensgate 3, N-0166 Oslo
e-mail: agnete@skuespillerforbund.no
Fax: 00 47 2102 7191   Tel: 00 47 2102 7190

■ Portugal
**SINDICATO DOS TRABALHADORES DE
ESPECTACULOS**
Rua Da Fe 23, 2 do Piso, 1050-149 Lisbon
e-mail: sind.trab.espect@mail.telepac.pt
Fax: 00 351 1 8853787   Tel: 00 351 1 8852728

■ Spain
ACTORES DEL ESTADO ESPANOL
c/Montera 34, 1ro Piso, E-28013 Madrid
e-mail: fedactors@mx2.redestb.es
Fax: 00 34 91 522 6055   Tel: 00 34 91 522 2804

■ Spain
CC.OO.
Plaza Cristino Martos 4, 6a Planta, E-28015,
Madrid
e-mail: international.fct@fct.ccoo.es
Fax: 00 34 91 548 1613   Tel: 00 34 91 540 9295

■ Sweden
**SWEDISH UNION FOR THEATRE, ARTISTS AND
MEDIA**
Box 12 710, S-112 94 Stockholm
e-mail: tomas.bolme@telia.com
Fax: 00 46 8 653 9507   Tel: 00 46 8 441 1300

■ UK
EQUITY
Guild House, Upper St Martin's Lane
London WC2H 9EG
info@equity.org.uk
Fax: 020-7379 7001   Tel: 020-7379 6000

ALDEBURGH FESTIVAL OF MUSIC AND THE ARTS
(7 - 23 June 2002)
Aldeburgh Productions
Snape Maltings Concert Hall, Snape Bridge
Nr Saxmundham, Suffolk IP17 1SP
e-mail: enquiries@aldeburghfestivals.org
Fax: 01728 687120   Admin: 01728 687100
BO: 01728 687110

ALMEIDA OPERA
(July 2002)
Almeida Street, Islington, London N1 1TA
e-mail: pdickie@almeidatheatre.demon.co.uk
Fax: 020-7704 9581   Tel: 020-7226 7432

BARBICAN INTERNATIONAL THEATRE EVENT (BITE)
(Annually May to October)
Barbican Theatre, Silk St, London EC2Y 8DS
e-mail: gyorke@barbican.org.uk
Fax: 020-7382 7377   Tel: 020-7382 7315

BATH INTERNATIONAL MUSIC FESTIVAL
(17 May - 2 June 2002)
Bath Festivals Trust, 5 Broad Street
Bath BA1 5LJ
e-mail: info@bathfestivals.org.uk
Fax: 01225 445551   Tel: 01225 462231

BATH LITERATURE FESTIVAL
(2 - 10 March 2002)
Bath Festivals Trust, 5 Broad Street
Bath BA1 5LJ
e-mail: info@bathfestivals.org.uk
Fax: 01225 445551   Tel: 01225 462231

BELFAST FESTIVAL AT QUEEN'S
(26 Oct - 11 Nov 2001) (25 Oct - 10 Nov 2002)
25 College Gardens, Belfast BT9 6BS
e-mail: festival@qub.ac.uk
Fax: 028-9066 3733   Tel: 028-9066 7687

BRIGHTON FESTIVAL
(4 - 26 May 2002)
12A Pavilion Buildings, Castle Square
Brighton BN1 1EE
General Manager: Jane McMorrow
BO: 01273 709709   Admin: 01273 700747

BUXTON FESTIVAL
(11 - 21 July 2002)
5 The Square, Buxton, Derbyshire SK17 6AZ
e-mail: info@buxtonfestival.co.uk
Admin: 01298 70395   BO: 01298 72190

CHESTER SUMMER MUSIC FESTIVAL
(July 2002)
8 Abbey Square, Chester CH1 2HU
Contact: Patti Dawson
BO: 01244 341200   BO: 01244 320700

CHICHESTER FESTIVITIES
(Not Chichester Festival Theatre)
(July 2002)
Canon Gate House, South Street
Chichester West, Sussex PO19 1PU
Fax: 01243 528356   Tel: 01243 785718

DANCE UMBRELLA
(Oct - Nov 2002)
Annual Contemporary Dance Festival
20 Chancellor's Street, London W6 9RN
e-mail: mail@danceumbrella.co.uk
Fax: 020-8741 7902   Tel: 020-8741 4040

DUBLIN THEATRE FESTIVAL
(Oct 2002)
44 East Essex Street, Temple Bar, Dublin 2, Ireland
Contact: Fergus D. Linehan
e-mail: info@dublintheatrefestival.com
Fax: 00 353 1 6797709   Tel: 00 353 1 6778439

EDINBURGH FESTIVAL FRINGE
(6 - 28 Aug 2002)
Festival Fringe Society Ltd, 180 High Street
Edinburgh EH1 1QS
e-mail: admin@edfringe.com
Fax: 0131-220 4205   Tel: 0131-226 5257

EDINBURGH INTERNATIONAL FESTIVAL
(11 Aug - 31 Aug 2002)
The Hub, Castlehill
Edinburgh EH1 2NE
e-mail: eif@eif.co.uk
Admin: 0131-437 2099   Tickets: 0131-473 2000

GLYNDEBOURNE FESTIVAL OPERA
(End May - End Aug 2002)
Lewes, East Sussex BN8 5UU
e-mail: info@glyndebourne.com
Manager: 01273 812321
Information: 01273 815000   Fax: 01273 812783

GREENWICH & DOCKLANDS INTERNATIONAL FESTIVAL
(6 - 15 July 2002)
Festival Office, 6 College Approach,
Greenwich, London SE10 9HY
e-mail: info@festival.org.uk
Fax: 020-8305 1188   Tel: 020-8305 1818

HARROGATE INTERNATIONAL FESTIVAL
(18 July - 3 August 2002)
1 Victoria Avenue, Harrogate
North Yorkshire HG1 1EQ
e-mail: info@harrogate-festival.org.uk
Fax: 01423 521264   Tel: 01423 562303

INTERNATIONAL FESTIVAL OF MUSICAL THEATRE IN CARDIFF The
St David's House, Wood Street
Cardiff CF10 1ES
e-mail: enquiries@cardiffmusicals.com
Fax: 029-2040 4216   Tel: 029-2090 1111

KING'S LYNN FESTIVAL
(25 July - 3 August 2002)
5 Thoresby College, Queen Street
King's Lynn, Norfolk PE30 1HX
Fax: 01553 767688   Tel: 01553 767557

LIFT - LONDON INTERNATIONAL FESTIVAL OF THEATRE
(Throughout Year)
19-20 Great Sutton Street
London EC1V 0DR
e-mail: info@liftfest.org.uk
Fax: 020-7490 3976   Tel: 020-7490 3964

LLANDOVERY ARTS FESTIVAL
(July 2002)
Llandovery Theatre, Stone Street, Llandovery
Carmarthenshire SA20 0DQ
Artistic Directors: Simon Barnes,
Jaqueline Harrison   Tel: 01550 720113

LONDON NEW PLAY FESTIVAL
(April - May 2002)
45 Lakeside Road, London W1Y 0DX
Administrator: Chris Cooke
Mobile: 07973 337642

LUDLOW FESTIVAL SOCIETY Ltd
(22 June - 7 July 2002)
Festival Office, Castle Square, Ludlow
Shrops SY8 1AY
Fax: 01584 877673   BO: 01584 872150

NATIONAL STUDENT DRAMA FESTIVAL
(23-30 March 2002, Scarborough)
Information Office, University of Hull Campus,
Filey Road, Scarborough YO11 3AZ
Artistic Director: Nick Stimson
e-mail: info@nsdf.org.uk
Fax: 01723 370815   Tel: 01723 501106

VISIONS - FESTIVAL OF INTERNATIONAL ANIMATED THEATRE
(October 2002)
University of Brighton Gallery, & Sallis Benney
Theatre, University of Brighton, Grand Parade
Brighton BN2 2JY
Executive Producer: Colin Matthews
e-mail: visions.fest@bton.ac.uk
Fax: 01273 643038   Tel: 01273 643012

Film & Television Distributors

ASIAN PICTURES INTERNATIONAL Ltd
1st Floor, 787 High Road
London E11 4QS
e-mail: asianpics@bizmane.com
Fax: 020-8558 9891   Tel: 020-8539 6529

BLUE DOLPHIN FILM AND VIDEO
(Film Production/Video Distribution)
40 Langham Street
London W1N 5RG
Fax: 020-7580 7670   Tel: 020-7255 2494

CONTEMPORARY FILMS
24 Southwood Lawn Road
London N6 5SF
e-mail: inquiries@contemporaryfilms.com
Fax: 020-8348 1238   Tel: 020-8340 5715

FILM COMPANY The
(International Sales)
25 Elizabeth Mews
London NW3 4UH
e-mail: sales@highpoint-thefilmcompany.co.uk
Fax: 020-7586 3117   Tel: 020-7586 3686

FRAME BAR FRAME
1st Floor, 7-11 French Place
Shoreditch
London E1 6JB   Tel/Fax: 020-7729 1736

GUERILLA FILMS Ltd
35 Thornbury Road
Isleworth
Middlesex TW7 4LQ
e-mail: david@guerilla-films.com
Fax: 020-8758 9364   Tel: 020-8758 1716

HIGH POINT FILMS & TV
25 Elizabeth Mews
London NW3 4UH
Fax: 020-7586 3117   Tel: 020-7586 3686

JACKSON Brian FILMS Ltd
39 Hanover Steps
St George's Fields
Albion Street
London W2 2YG
e-mail: brianjfilm@aol.com
Fax: 020-7262 5736   Tel: 020-7402 7543

MAINLINE PICTURES
37 Museum Street
London WC1A 1LP
Fax: 020-7430 0170   Tel: 020-7242 5523

PAN EUROPEAN FILMS
110 Trafalgar Road
Portslade, Sussex BN41 1GS
e-mail: filmangels@freenetname.co.uk
Fax: 01273 705451   Tel: 01273 277333

PATHE DISTRIBUTION Ltd
Kent House, 14-17 Market Place
Great Titchfield Street, London W1W 8AR
Fax: 020-7631 3568   Tel: 020-7323 5151

SONY PICTURES EUROPE HOUSE
25 Golden Square, London W1F 9LU
Fax: 020-7533 1015   Tel: 020-7533 1000

SOUTHERN STAR SALES
45-49 Mortimer Street, London W1W 8HX
Fax: 020-7436 7426   Tel: 020-7636 9421

SQUIRREL FILMS DISTRIBUTION Ltd
Grice's Wharf, 119 Rotherhithe Street
London SE16 4NF
Fax: 020-7231 2119   Tel: 020-7231 2209

UIP (UK)
12 Golden Square, London W1A 2JL
Fax: 020-7534 5202   Tel: 020-7534 5200

UNIVERSAL INTERNATIONAL TELEVISION
5-7 Mandeville Place
London W1M 5LB   Tel: 020-7535 3700

UNIVERSAL PICTURES INTERNATIONAL
Oxford House, 76 Oxford Street
London W1D 1BS
Fax: 020-7307 1301   Tel: 020-7307 1300

WARNER BROS PICTURES
Warner House, 98 Theobald's Road
London WC1X 8WB
Fax: 020-7984 5001   Tel: 020-7984 5200

Film Preview Theatres

ACCESS STUDIOS
8-10 Creekside
London SE8 3DX
e-mail: info@accessstudios.com
Fax: 0870 1205658   Tel: 020-7231 6185

BRITISH ACADEMY OF FILM & TELEVISION ARTS The
195 Piccadilly
London W1J 9LN
Fax: 020-7734 1792   Tel: 020-7734 0022

BRITISH FILM INSTITUTE
21 Stephen Street
London W1P 2LN
e-mail: roger.young@bfi.org.uk
Fax: 020-7436 7950   Tel: 020-7957 8976

CENTURY THEATRE
(Twentieth Century Fox)
31 Soho Square
e-mail: projection@foxinc.com
London W1D 3AP   Tel: 020-7437 7766

COLUMBIA TRI STAR FILMS (UK)
25 Golden Square
London W1F 9LU
Fax: 020-7533 1015   Tel: 020-7533 1111

DE LANE LEA
75 Dean Street, London W1D 3PU
e-mail: dll@delanelea.com
Fax: 020-7432 3838   Tel: 020-7432 3800

EXECUTIVE THEATRE
(Twentieth Century Fox)
31 Soho Square
e-mail: projection@foxinc.com
London W1D 3AP   Tel: 020-7437 7766

MR YOUNG'S PREVIEW THEATRE
14 D'Arblay Street, London W1F 8DY
Fax: 020-7734 4520   Tel: 020-7437 1771

RIVERSIDE STUDIOS
Crisp Road
London W6 9RL   Tel: 020-8237 1000

RSA
(Royal Society of Arts)
8 John Adam Street, London WC2N 6EZ
e-mail: conference@rsa-uk.demon.co.uk
Fax: 020-7321 0271   Tel: 020-7839 5049

TRICYCLE CINEMA
269 Kilburn High Road
e-mail: admin@tricycle.co.uk
London NW6 7JR   Tel: 020-7328 1000

4MC Ltd
(Post Production Facilities)
Film House 142 Wardour Street
London W1V 3AU
Fax: 020-7878 7800   Tel: 020-7878 0000

A1 VOX Ltd
(Specialising in Voices, Audio Editing,
Voice Over Training and Demo CDs)
20 Old Compton Street, London W1D 4TW
e-mail: info@a1vox.com
Fax: 020-7434 4414   Tel: 020-7434 4404

ACCESS STUDIOS
8-10 Creekside, London SE8 3DX
e-mail: info@accessstudios.com
Fax: 0870 120 5658   Tel: 020-7231 6185

ACTOR'S 'ONE-STOP' SHOP The
(Showreels, Photographs & CVs)
54 Belsize Avenue, London N13 4TJ
e-mail: info@actorsone-stopshop.com
Fax: 020-8482 7723   Tel: 020-8888 7006

ANVIL POST PRODUCTION
(Studio Manager - Mike Anscombe)
Denham Studios, North Orbital Road
Uxbridge, Middlesex UB9 5HL
Fax: 01895 835006   Tel: 01895 833522

ARK STUDIO Ltd
(Stills - Studio & Location)
Unit 5, 9 Park Hill, London SW4 9NS
e-mail: arkstudio@aol.com
Fax: 020-7498 9497   Tel: 020-7622 4000

ARRI MEDIA
4-5 Airlinks, Spitfire Way, Heston
Middlesex TW5 9NR
e-mail: info@arrimedia.com
Fax: 020-8756 0592   Tel: 020-8573 2255

AUTOMATIVE ACTION STUNTS
(Stunt Rigging & Supplies/Camera Tracking
Vehicles)
2 Sheffield House, Park Road
Hampton Hill, Middlesex TW12 1HA
Mobile: 07974 919589   Tel: 020-8977 6186

AXIS FILMS
(Film Equipment Rental)
Shepperton Studios, Studios Road
Middlesex TW17 0QD
e-mail: info@axisfilms.co.uk
Fax: 01932 572246   Tel: 01932 572244

CHANNEL 20/20 Ltd
20/20 House, 26-28 Talbot Lane
Leicester LE1 4LR
Fax: 0116-222 1113   Tel: 0116-233 2220

**CINE TO VIDEO & FOREIGN TAPE
CONVERSION & DUPLICATING**
(Peter J Snell Enterprises)
Amp House, Grove Road
Rochester, Kent ME2 4BX
e-mail: pjs-ent@dircon.co.uk
Fax: 01634 726000   Tel: 01634 723838

CLEAR CUT VIDEO EDITING & FILMING
(Peter J. Snell Enterprises)
Amp House, Grove Road
Rochester, Kent ME2 4BX
e-mail: pjs-ent@dircon.co.uk
Fax: 01634 726000   Tel: 01634 723838

CONTACT GROUP Ltd
(Conference, Computer Graphic & Video
Producers)
Oakridge, Weston Road, Stafford ST16 3RS
e-mail: mail@contactgroup.co.uk
Fax: 01785 610955   Tel: 01785 610966

CREATIVE FILM MAKERS Ltd
(Studio & Video Editing)
Pottery Lane House
34A Pottery Lane, London W11 4LZ
e-mail: nseligman@compuserve.com
Fax: 020-7229 4999   Tel: 020-7229 5131

CURIOUS YELLOW
33-37 Hatherley Mews, London E17 4QP
e-mail: info@curiousyellow.co.uk
Fax: 020-8521 6363   Tel: 020-8521 9595

DE LANE LEA
(Film & TV Sound Dubbing & Editing Suite)
75 Dean Street, London W1D 3PU
e-mail: dll@delanelea.com
Fax: 020-7432 3838   Tel: 020-7432 3800

DENMAN PRODUCTIONS
(3D Computer Animation, Film/Video
Equipment & Crew Hire)
5 Holly Road, Twickenham
Middlesex TW1 4EA   Tel: 020-8891 3461

DIVERSE PRODUCTIONS
(Facilities & Design)
6 Gorleston Street, London W14 8XS
Fax: 020-7603 2148   Tel: 020-7603 4567

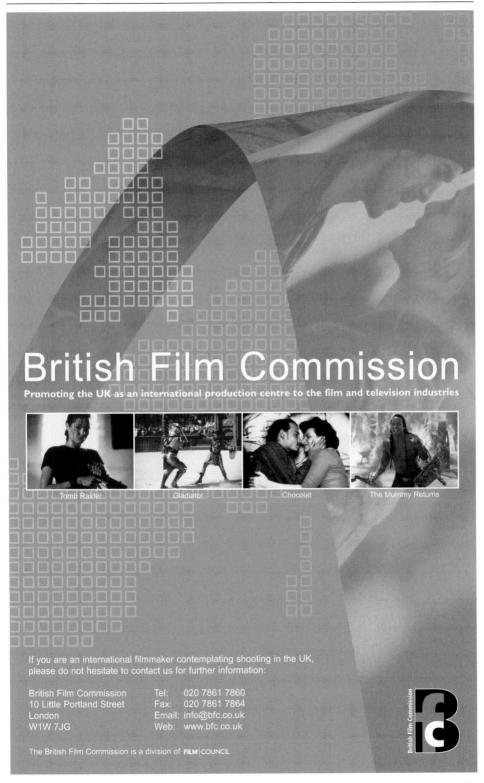

British Film Commission

Promoting the UK as an international production centre to the film and television industries

Tomb Raider Gladiator Chocolat The Mummy Returns

If you are an international filmmaker contemplating shooting in the UK, please do not hesitate to contact us for further information:

British Film Commission Tel: 020 7861 7860
10 Little Portland Street Fax: 020 7861 7864
London Email: info@bfc.co.uk
W1W 7JG Web: www.bfc.co.uk

The British Film Commission is a division of **FILM** COUNCIL

British Film Commission

EXECUTIVE AUDIO VISUAL
(Showreels for Actors & TV Presenters)
80 York Street
London W1H 1DP   Tel: 020-7723 4488

FOUR WHEEL FILMS
(Crews & Equipment, Full Beta SP Kit)
PO Box 1054, Kingston-upon-Thames
Surrey KT2 5YR
e-mail: david@fwfilms.freeserve.co.uk
Fax: 020-8715 5014   Tel: 020-8715 4861

GREENPARK PRODUCTIONS Ltd
(Film Archives)
Illand, Launceston, Cornwall PL15 7LS
e-mail: archives@clips.net
Fax: 01566 782127   Tel: 01566 782107

HUNKY DORY PRODUCTIONS Ltd
(Facilities & Crew)
Cambridge House
135 High Street
Teddington, Middlesex TW11 8HH
Fax: 020-8977 4464   Tel: 020-8943 3006

INTERACTIVE SHOWREELS
(Showreels & Production)
410 Crown House
North Circular Road
London NW10 7PN
e-mail: interactiveshowreels@btinternet.com
Mobile: 07966 460235   Tel: 020-8838 6800

KINGSTON INMEDIA
Studio K, PO Box 2287, Gerrards Cross
Bucks SL9 8BF
Fax: 01494 876006   Tel: 01494 878297

LENIHAN Sean ASSOCIATES
The Old Chapel, Abbey Hill
Lelant, St Ives Cornwall TR26 3EB
                                 Tel/Fax: 01736 757557

MAGPIE FILM PRODUCTIONS
31-32 Cheapside
Birmingham B5 6AY
Fax: 0121-666 6077   Tel: 0121-622 5884

MINAMON PRODUCTIONS
(Specialist in Showreels)
117 Downton Avenue, London SW2 3TX
e-mail: minamon.film@virgin.net
Fax: 020-8674 1779   Tel: 020-8674 3957

MOVING PICTURE COMPANY The
(Post-Production)
127-133 Wardour Street
London W1F 0NL
e-mail: mailbox@moving-picture.com
Fax: 020-7287 5187   Tel: 020-7434 3100

PANAVISION UK
Bristol Road, Greenford
Middlesex UB6 8GD
Fax: 020-8839 7300   Tel: 020-8839 7333

PANTECHNICON
(Audio Visual, Video, Conference Production,
Design for Print)
90 Lots Road, London SW10 0QD
e-mail: info@pantechnicon.co.uk
Fax: 020-7351 0667   Tel: 020-7351 7579

PEAK WHITE VIDEO
1 Latimer Road, Teddington
Middlesex TW11 8QA
Fax: 020-8977 8357   Tel: 020-8943 1922

PEDIGREE PUNKS
(Specialist Showreel Production Service)
49 Woolstone Road, Forest Hill, London SE23 2TR
e-mail: info@pedigree-punks.com
                                 Tel/Fax: 020-8291 5801

PHA CASTING STUDIO
Tanzaro House, Ardwick Green North
Manchester M12 6FZ
e-mail: studio@pha-agency.co.uk
Fax: 0161-273 4567   Tel: 0161-273 4444

PRO-LINK RADIO SYSTEMS Ltd
4 Woden Court, Saxon Business Park
Hanbury Road, Bromsgrove
Worcestershire B60 4AD
Fax: 01527 577757   Tel: 01527 577788

QUADRANT TELEVISION Ltd
17 West Hill, London SW18 1RB
e-mail: quadranttv@aol.com   Tel: 020-8870 9933

REPLAY Ltd
(Showreels & Performance Recording)
20 Greek Street
London W1D 4DU
e-mail: sales@replayfilms.co.uk
Fax: 020-7287 5348   Tel: 020-7287 5334

REYNOLDS George F
(Videographer & Editor, Video Production)
12 Mead Close, Grays, Essex RM16 2TR
e-mail: g.f.reynolds@talk21.com
                                 Tel: 01375 373886

RIVERSIDE STUDIOS
Crisp Road, London W6 9RL
e-mail: info@riversidestudios.co.uk
Fax: 020-8237 1001   Tel: 020-8237 1000

SALON Ltd
(Post Production Facilities)
12 Swainson Road, London W3 7XB
e-mail: hire@salonrentals.com
                                 Tel: 020-8746 7611

SAVOY HILL STUDIO CASTING SUITE
Adam House, 7-10 Adam Street
London WC2N 6AA
e-mail: savoyhillstudio@tabard.u-net.com
Fax: 020-7497 0830   Tel: 020-7497 0850

SHOWREEL COMPANY The
Suite 700, 2 Old Brompton Road
London SW7 3DQ
e-mail: the.showreelcompany@virgin.net
                                 Tel: 020-8525 0058

SHOWREEL SERVICES
35 Bedfordbury, Covent Garden
London WC2N 4DU
Fax: 020-7379 5210   Tel: 020-7379 6082

SILVER-TONGUED PRODUCTONS
(Specialising in Voice Reels, Tim Stockwell)
e-mail: silver-tongued@talk21.com
                                 Tel: 020-8309 0659

STAR PRODUCTIONS
(Facilities)
Star Studios
38A Lea Bridge Road
London E5 9QD   Tel: 020-8986 4470

TAKE FIVE
(Showreels)
25 Ganton Street
London W1F 9BP
Fax: 020-7287 3035   Tel: 020-7287 2120

TELE-CINE Ltd
(Post Production)
Video House, 48 Charlotte Street
London W1T 2NS
Fax: 020-7208 2250   Tel: 020-7208 2200

TO BE OR NOT TO BE
(Showreels) (Anthony Barnett)
32 Green Lane, Kettering, Northants NN16 0DA
Fax: 01536 481554   Mobile: 07958 996227

TODD AO UK
13 Hawley Crescent
London NW1 8NP
Fax: 020-7485 3667   Tel: 020-7284 7900

TV MEDIA SERVICES Ltd
(Video and Broadcast Facilities)
3rd Floor, 420 Sauchiehall Street
Glasgow G2 3JD
e-mail: tvmsmail@aol.com
Fax: 0141-332 9040   Tel: 0141-331 1993

VFG
(Film & TV Equipment Hire)
8 Beresford Avenue, Wembley
Middlesex HA0 1QD
e-mail: info@vfg.co.uk
Fax: 020-8795 3366   Tel: 020-8795 7000

VIDEO CASTING DIRECTORY Ltd
(Production of Peformers' Showreels)
1 Triangle House, 2 Broomhill Road
London SW18 4HX
Fax: 020-8874 8590   Tel: 020-8874 3314

VIDEO INN PRODUCTION
(AV Equipment Hire)
Glebe Farm, Wooton Road, Quinton
Northampton NN7 2EE
e-mail: andy@videoinn.co.uk
Tel: 01604 864868

VIDEOSONICS CINEMA SOUND
(Film & Television Dubbing Facilities)
68A Delancey Street
London NW1 7RY
e-mail: info@videosonics.com
Fax: 020-7419 4470   Tel: 020-7209 0209

VOICE CASTER
(Digital Studio & Video Editing)
Tel: 020-8455 2211

VOICE TAPE SERVICES INT Ltd
(Professional Voice-Over Direction & CDs)
80 Netherlands Road
New Barnet, Herst EN5 1BS
e-mail: info@vsint.co.uk
Fax: 020-8441 4828   Tel: 020-8440 4848

W6 STUDIO
(Video Production & Editing Facilities)
359 Lillie Road, London SW6 7PA
e-mail: ka2@w6studio.freeserve.co.uk
Fax: 020-7381 5252   Tel: 020-7385 2272

WILD IRIS FILMS
59 Brewer Street, London W1R 3FB
e-mail: joe@wildiris.co.uk
Fax: 020-7494 1764   Tel: 020-7494 9230

Key to areas of specialization:
F Films **FF** Feature Films **CV** Corporate Video
D Drama **Ch** Children's Entertainment
Co Comedy & Light Entertainment
Docs Documentaries

1/2 AND 1/2
44 Nelson Square, London SE1 0QA
Fax: 020-7803 0531   Tel: 020-7803 0530

30 BIRD PRODUCTIONS
Studio Voltaire, 1A Nelson's Row
London SW4 7JR
e-mail: thirtybird.productions@virgin.net
Fax: 020-7622 6707   Tel: 020-7622 6745

4MC
Film House, 142 Wardour Street
London W1V 3AU
Fax: 020-7878 7800   Tel: 020-7878 0000

ACADEMY COMMERCIALS Ltd
16 West Central Street, London WC1A 1JJ
Fax: 020-7240 0355   Tel: 020-7395 4155

ACTION TIME
Wrendal House, 2 Whitworth Street West
Manchester M1 5WX
Fax: 0161-236 8845   Tel: 0161-236 8999

ACTION TIME LONDON
1 Heathcock Court, 415 The Strand
London WC2R 0NS
Fax: 020-7836 1515   Tel: 020-7836 0505

AGE FILM & VIDEO
F CV
The Studio, 60 High Street, Guilden Morden
Near Royston, Herts SG8 0JS
e-mail: massey@cwcom.net
Fax: 01763 852927   Tel: 01763 852128

AGRAN BARTON TV Ltd
(See HARBOUR PICTURES)

ALEXANDER PRODUCTIONS
26 Bushy Park Gardens, Teddington
Middlesex TW11 0LQ
Fax: 020-8943 4912   Tel: 020-8943 1931

ALGERNON Ltd
15 Cleveland Mansions, Widley Road
London W9 2LA
e-mail: algernon_limited@hotmail.com
                    Tel/Fax: 020-7266 1582

ALIBI COMMUNICATIONS Plc
35 Long Acre
London WC2E 9JT
Fax: 020-7836 6919   Tel: 020-7845 0400

ALOMO PRODUCTIONS Ltd
1 Stephen Street, London W1T 1AL
Fax: 020-7691 6081   Tel: 020-7691 6531

AN ACQUIRED TASTE TV CORP
F TV D
51 Croham Road
South Croydon CR2 7HD
Fax: 020-8686 5928   Tel: 020-8686 1188

ANGLO-CARIBBEAN PRODUCTIONS
(Jason Young)
1A Gambole Road, Tooting Broadway
London SW17 0QJ
e-mail: jasonyoung72@yahoo.com
Fax: 020-8801 7592   Mobile: 07970 715080

ANTELOPE
29B Montague Street
London WC1B 5BH
e-mail: antelope@antelope.co.uk
Fax: 020-7209 0098   Tel: 020-7209 0099

APT FILM & TELEVISION Ltd
225A Brecknock Road
London N19 5AA
e-mail: admin@aptfilms.com
Fax: 020-7482 1587   Tel: 020-7284 1695

APTN
The Interchange, Oval Road
Camden Lock, London NW1 7DZ
Fax: 020-7413 8312   Tel: 020-7482 7400

ARENA FILMS Ltd
TV D
2 Pelham Road, London SW19 1SX
Fax: 020-8540 3992   Tel: 020-8543 3990

ARGYLE PRODUCTIONS
TV CV Radio, No unsolicited CV's
86 Goswell Road, London EC1V 7DB
Fax: 020-7608 1642   Tel: 020-7608 2095

ARLINGTON PRODUCTIONS Ltd
TV D Co
Pinewood Studios
Iver Heath, Bucks SL0 0NH
Fax: 01753 656050   Tel: 01753 651700

ARMSTRONG ARTS Ltd
9 Greville Hall, Greville Place, London NW6 5JS
e-mail: info@armstrongarts.com
Fax: 020-7625 2213   Tel: 020-7372 7110

ART BOX PRODUCTIONS
10 Heatherway
Crowthorne, Berks RG45 6HG
e-mail: artbox@nildram.co.uk
                    Tel/Fax: 01344 773638

ASHFORD ENTERTAINMENT CORPORATION Ltd The
182 Brighton Road
Coulsdon, Surrey CR5 2NF
e-mail: info@ashford-entertainment.co.uk
Fax: 020-8763 2558   Tel: 020-8645 0667

ATLANTIC SEVEN PRODUCTIONS Ltd
52 Lancaster Road, London N4 4PR
Fax: 020-7436 9233   Tel: 020-7263 4435

ATP Ltd
TV Ch Docs D
PO Box 24182, London SW18 2WY
e-mail: atpmedia@ukonline.co.uk
                    Tel/Fax: 020-7738 9886

ATTENBOROUGH Richard PRODUCTIONS Ltd
Twickenham Film Studios, St Margaret's
Twickenham, Middlesex TW1 2AW
Fax: 020-8744 2766   Tel: 020-8607 8873

ATTICUS TELEVISION Ltd
5 Clare Lawn
London SW14 8BH
e-mail: attwiz@aol.com
Fax: 020-8878 3821   Tel: 020-8876 0406

AVALON TELEVISION Ltd
4A Exmoor Street
London W10 6BD
Fax: 020-7598 7281   Tel: 020-7598 7280

AVIATOR
F TV D CV
3 Bourlet Close
London W1W 7BQ
e-mail: info@aviatortv.com
Fax: 020-7291 7841   Tel: 020-7436 5007

BAILEY Catherine Ltd
110 Gloucester Avenue, Primrose Hill
London NW1 8JA
Fax: 020-7483 4541   Tel: 020-7483 2681

BANANA PARK Ltd
(Animation Production Company)
Banana Park, 6 Cranleigh Mews
London SW11 2QL
Fax: 020-7738 1887　　　Tel: 020-7228 7136

BARFORD FILM COMPANY The
35 Bedfordbury
London WC2N 4DU
e-mail: info@barford.co.uk
Fax: 020-7379 5210　　　Tel: 020-7836 1365

BARRATT Michael
Field House, Ascot Road
Maidenhead, Berks SL6 3LD
e-mail: mbarratt@compuserve
Fax: 01628 627737　　　Tel: 01628 770800

BAZAL PRODUCTIONS Ltd
Shepherds Building Central, Charecroft,
Shepherds Bush, London W14 0EH
Fax: 0870 3331800　　　Tel: 0870 3331700

BBC WORLDWIDE Ltd
Woodlands, 80 Wood Lane
London W12 0TT
Fax: 020-8749 0538　　　Tel: 020-8433 2000

BBS PRODUCTIONS
26 Portland Square
Bristol BS2 8RZ
e-mail: enquiries@bbsprods.co.uk
Fax: 0117-942 6112　　　Tel: 0117-942 9411

BETTAVISION TV
1 Mount Parade
Cockfosters, Herts EN4 9DD
Fax: 020-8449 8259　　　Tel: 020-8449 4898

BFCS Ltd
59 North Wharf Road, London W2 1LA
e-mail: enquiries@bfcs.ltd.uk
Fax: 020-7402 7738　　　Tel: 020-7402 5561

BIG CHIEF PRODUCTIONS
16A Powis Terrace
London W11 1JD　　　Tel: 020-7792 5551

BIRD Martin PRODUCTIONS
TV
Saucelands Barn, Coolham, Horsham
West Sussex RH13 8QG
Fax: 01403 741647　　　Tel: 01403 741620

BIRDBOX PRODUCTIONS
67A Lane End, Corsley, Warminster
Wiltshire BA12 7PG
e-mail: brian.freeston@virgin.net
Mobile: 07979 280309　　　Tel: 01373 832267

BIZMANE ENTERTAINMENT Ltd
1st Floor, 787 High Road
London E11 4QS
e-mail: enquiries@bizmane.com
Fax: 020-8558 9891　　　Tel: 020-8558 4488

BLACK & WHITE PICTURES
Teddington Studios, Teddington
Middlesex TW11 9NT
e-mail: production@blackandwhitepictures.co.uk
Fax: 020-8614 2500　　　Tel: 020 8614 2344

BLACKBIRD PRODUCTIONS
6 Molasses Row, Plantation Wharf
Battersea, London SW11 3TW
Fax: 020-7924 4778　　　Tel: 020-7924 6440

BLUE FISH MEDIA
39 Ratby Close
Lower Earley, Reading RG6 4ER
e-mail: ideas@bfmedia.co.uk
Fax: 0118-975 0748　　　Tel: 0118-975 0272

BLUE HEAVEN PRODUCTIONS Ltd
TV D F
116 Great Portland Street, London W1W 6PG
graham@blueheavenproductions.freeserve.co.uk
Fax: 020-7436 0888　　　Tel: 020-7436 5552

BLUE ORANGE FILMS Ltd
88 Park Avenue South, London N8 8LS
e-mail: ruth@blueorangeltd.demon.co.uk
Fax: 020-8340 9889　　　Tel: 020-8341 9977

BLUE WAND PRODUCTIONS Ltd
2nd Floor, 12 Weltje Road, London W6 9TG
e-mail: lino@bluewand.co.uk
Mobile: 07885 528743　　　Tel/Fax: 020-8741 2038

BOWE TENNANT PRODUCTIONS
(Specialists Animal Pet Productions)
Applewood House Studio, Ringshall Road
Dagnall, Berkhamsted, Herts HP4 1RN
Fax: 01442 842453　　　Tel: 01442 842374

BOXCLEVER PRODUCTIONS Ltd
13 Great James Street, London WC1N 3DP
e-mail: chevron@dircon.co.uk
Fax: 020-7831 6606　　　Tel: 020-7831 1811

BRITISH LION
Pinewood Studios, Pinewood Road
Iver Heath, Bucks SL0 0NH
Fax: 01753 656391　　　Tel: 01753 651279

BRONCO FILMS
F TV D
61 Holland Street, Glasgow G2 4NJ
e-mail: broncofilm@btinternet.com
Fax: 0141-287 6815　　　Tel: 0141-287 6817

BROOKSIDE PRODUCTIONS Ltd
TV
Campus Manor, Childwall, Abbey Road
Liverpool L16 0JP
Fax: 0151-722 6839　　　Tel: 0151-722 9122

BRUNSWICK FILMS Ltd
(Formula One Grand Prix Film Library)
26 Macroom Road
Maida Vale, London W9 3HY
e-mail: brunswick.films@virgin.net
Fax: 020-8960 4997　　　Tel: 020-8960 0066

BUCKMARK PRODUCTIONS
Commer House, Station Road, Tadcaster
North Yorks LS24 9JF
e-mail: ed@buckmark.co.uk
Fax: 01937 835900　　　Tel: 01937 835901

BUENA VISTA PRODUCTIONS
3 Queen Caroline Street, Hammersmith
London W6 9PE
Fax: 020-8222 2795　　　Tel: 020-8222 1000

BURDER FILMS
7 Saltcoats Road, London W4 1AR
e-mail: jburder@aol.com
Fax: 020-8995 3376　　　Tel: 020-8995 0547

CALDERDALE TELEVISION
Dean Clough, Halifax HX3 5AX
e-mail: ctv@calderdaletv.co.uk
Fax: 01422 253101　　　Tel: 01422 253100

CAN TELEVISION
Smitham House, 127 Brighton Road
Coulsdon, Surrey CR5 2NJ
e-mail: cantv@talk21.com
Fax: 020-8668 0130　　　Tel: 020-8763 9444

CARAVEL FILM TECHNIQUES Ltd
The Great Barn Studios, Cippenham Lane
Slough, Berks SL1 5AU
e-mail: ajjcaraveltv@aol.com
Fax: 01753 571383　　　Tel: 01753 534828

CARDINAL BROADCAST
Bishops Lodge, Oakley Green Road
Windsor, Berks SL4 5UL
Fax: 01753 623304   Tel: 01753 623300

CARLTON TELEVISION Ltd
35-38 Portman Square, London W1H 6NU
Fax: 020-7486 1132   Tel: 020-7486 6688

CARNIVAL (FILMS & THEATRE) Ltd
12 Raddington Road, London W10 5TG
Fax: 020-8968 0155   Tel: 020-8968 0968

CASE TV.COM
209 Rivington House
82 Great Easton Street, London EC2A 3JF
e-mail: case@casetv.com
Fax: 020-7296 0011   Tel: 020-7296 0010

CASPIAN PRODUCTIONS
15 Ogilvie Terrace
Edinburgh EH11 1NS
e-mail: caspian@cableinet.co.uk
Fax: 0131-538 4666   Tel: 0131-346 0283

CELADOR PRODUCTIONS Ltd
39 Long Acre
London WC2E 9JT
Fax: 020-7836 1117   Tel: 020-7240 8101

CELTIC FILMS
Ground Floor, Government Buildings
Bromyard Avenue
London W3 7XH
e-mail: celticfilm@aol.com
Fax: 020-8740 9755   Tel: 020-8740 6880

CENTRELINE VIDEO PRODUCTIONS
138 Westwood Road, Tilehurst
Reading RG31 6LL   Tel: 0118-941 0033

CHAKRA PRODUCTIONS
181 Jersey Road, Osterley, Middlesex TW7 4QJ
e-mail: talk@chakra.co.uk
    Tel/Fax: 020-8737 1616

CHANNEL 20/20 Ltd
20/20 House, 26-28 Talbot Lane
Leicester LE1 4LR
Fax: 0116-222 1113   Tel: 0116-233 2220

CHATSWORTH TELEVISION Ltd
D Co
97-99 Dean Street, London W1D 3TE
e-mail: television@chatsworth-tv.co.uk
Fax: 020-7437 3301   Tel: 020-7734 4302

CHILDREN'S FILM & TELEVISION FOUNDATION Ltd
F TV Ch
Elstree Film & TV Studios, Borehamwood
Herts WD6 1JG
e-mail: annahome@cftf.onyxnet.co.uk
Fax: 020-8207 0860   Tel: 020-8953 0844

CINEMA VERITY PRODUCTIONS Ltd
F TV D Co
11 Addison Avenue, London W11 4QS
Fax: 020-7371 3329   Tel: 020-7460 2777

CLASSIC PICTURES ENTERTAINMENT Ltd
Shepperton Studios, Studios Road, Shepperton
Middlesex TW17 0QD
e-mail: lyn@classicpictures.co.uk
Fax: 01932 572046   Tel: 01932 572016

COLLINGWOOD O'HARE ENTERTAINMENT Ltd
10-14 Crown Street, Acton, London W3 8SB
e-mail: info@crownstreet.co.uk
Fax: 020-8993 9595   Tel: 020-8993 3666

COMEDY HOUSE The
6 Bayley Street, London WC1B 3HE
Fax: 020-7304 0048   Tel: 020-7304 0047

COMMUNICATOR Ltd
199 Upper Street, London N1 1RQ
e-mail: paul@communicator.ltd.uk
Fax: 020-7704 8444   Tel: 020-7704 8333

COMTEC Ltd
Unit 19, Tait Road, Croydon, Surrey CR0 2DP
e-mail: info@comtecav.co.uk
Fax: 020-8684 6947   Tel: 020-8684 6615

CONTACT GROUP Ltd
(Conference Production)
Oakridge, Weston Road, Staffs ST16 3RS
e-mail: mail@contactgroup.co.uk
Fax: 01785 610955   Tel: 01785 610966

CONVERGENCE PRODUCTIONS
10-14 Crown Street, Acton, London W3 8SB
e-mail: info@crownstreet.co.uk
Fax: 020-8993 9595   Tel: 020-8993 3666

CORKSCREW PRODUCTIONS
CV Pop Promos Commercials
5 Southwell Gardens
London SW7 4SB
Fax: 020-7373 7448   Tel: 020-7341 9752

COURTYARD PRODUCTIONS
TV Ch Co
Little Postlings Farmhouse, Four Elms
Kent TN8 6NA
Fax: 01732 700534   Tel: 01732 700324

C.P.S. Ltd
Fiord House, 10 Reservoir Road, Ruislip
Middlesex HA4 7TU
e-mail: david@bluelinecps.co.uk
Fax: 01895 635060   Tel: 01895 635100

CREATIVE CHANNEL Ltd
The Television Centre, La Pouquelaye
St Helier, Jersey JE1 3ZD
e-mail: creative@channeltv.co.uk
Fax: 01534 816889   Tel: 01534 816888

CREATIVE FILM MAKERS Ltd
Pottery Lane House, 34A Pottery Lane
London W11 4LZ
Fax: 020-7229 4999   Tel: 020-7229 5131

CREATIVE FILM PRODUCTIONS
68 Conway Road
London N14 7BE   Tel: 020-8447 8187

CREATIVE PARTNERSHIP The
13 Bateman Street, London W1V 5TB
Fax: 020-7437 1467   Tel: 020-7439 7762

CROFT TELEVISION & GRAPHICS
Croft House, Progress Business Centre
Whittle Parkway, Slough, Berks SL1 6DQ
Fax: 01628 668791   Tel: 01628 668735

CTVC
Hillside, Merry Hill Road
Bushey, Herts WD23 1DR
e-mail: ctvc@ctvc.co.uk
Fax: 020-8950 1437   Tel: 020-8950 7919

CUTHBERT Tony PRODUCTIONS
7A Langley Street
London WC2H 9JA
e-mail: info@tonycuthbert.com
Fax: 020-7734 6579   Tel: 020-7437 8884

DALTON FILMS Ltd
127 Hamilton Terrace
London NW8 9QR
Fax: 020-7624 4420   Tel: 020-7328 6169

DARLOW SMITHSON PRODUCTIONS Ltd
Fifth Floor, Highgate Business Centre
33 Greenwood Place, London NW5 1LB
e-mail: mail@darlowsmithson.com
Fax: 020-7482 7039   Tel: 020-7482 7027

DAWKINS ASSOCIATES Ltd
PO Box 615, Boughton Monchelsea
Kent ME17 4RN
e-mail: da@ccland.demon.co.uk
Fax: 01622 741731   Tel: 01622 741900

DIFFERENT FILMS
2 Searles Road, London SE1 4YU
e-mail: info@differentfilms.co.uk
Fax: 0845 4585791   Tel: 0845 4585790

DLT ENTERTAINMENT UK Ltd
10 Bedford Square, London WC1B 3RA
Fax: 020-7636 4571   Tel: 020-7631 1184

DRAMA HOUSE The
Coach Road Cottages, Little Saxham
Bury St Edmunds, Suffolk IP29 5LE
e-mail: jack@dramahouse.co.uk
Fax: 020-7586 1345   Tel: 020-7586 1000

DRUMBEAT PRODUCTIONS Ltd
17A Mercer Street, London WC2H 9QT
e-mail: tudorgates@compuserve.com
                        Tel: 020-7836 3710

DUCK LANE FILM COMPANY The
5 Carlisle Street, London W1V 5RG
Fax: 020-7437 2260   Tel: 020-7439 3912

EACH WORLD PRODUCTIONS
43 Moormead Road, St Margaret's
Twickenham TW1 1JS
Fax: 020-8744 0676   Tel: 020-8892 0908

ECLIPSE PRESENTATIONS Ltd
Presentations House
3 Croydon Road, Beckenham, Kent BR3 4AA
e-mail: info@eclipse-presentations.co.uk
Fax: 020-8249 6485   Tel: 020-8249 6473

ECLIPSE PRODUCTIONS
2 Cross Keys Close, London W1U 2DF
e-mail: firstname@eclipsefilms.co.uk
Fax: 020-7224 2882   Tel: 020-7224 1020

ECOSSE FILMS Ltd
12 Quayside Lodge, Watermeadow Lane
London SW6 2UZ
e-mail: info@ecossefilms.com
Fax: 020-7736 3436   Tel: 020-7371 0290

EDGE PICTURE COMPANY Ltd The
7 Langley Street, London WC2H 9JA
e-mail: ask.us@edgepicture.com
Fax: 020-7836 6949   Tel: 020-7836 6262

EDINBURGH FILM PRODUCTIONS
Keepers House, Traquair
Innerleithen EH44 6PP
Fax: 01896 831188   Tel: 01896 831199

EDUCATIONAL TRAINING FILMS
17 West Hill
London SW18 1RB   Tel: 020-8870 9933

ELEPHANT PRODUCTIONS
The Studio, 2 Rothamsted Avenue
Harpenden, Herts AL5 2DB
Fax: 01582 767532   Tel: 01582 621425

ELMGATE PRODUCTIONS
F TV D
Shepperton Studios, Studios Road
Shepperton, Middlesex
e-mail: elmgate@dial.pipex.com
Fax: 01932 569918   Tel: 01932 562611

ENGLISH & POCKETT (Broadcast)
F TV
Bridle House, 36 Bridle Lane, London W1R 3HJ
e-mail: cpowell@futurebrand.com
Fax: 020-7439 4203   Tel: 020-7287 1155

ENLIGHTENMENT PRODUCTIONS
CV
1 Briars Lane, Lathom, Ormskirk
Lancs L40 5TG   Tel: 01704 896655

EON PRODUCTIONS Ltd
Eon House, 138 Piccadilly
London W1V 9FH
Fax: 020-7408 1236   Tel: 020-7493 7953

EPA INTERNATIONAL MULTIMEDIA Ltd
31A Regent's Park Road, London NW1 7TL
Fax: 020-7267 8852   Tel: 020-7267 9198

EXCELSIOR GROUP PRODUCTIONS
Dorking Road, Tadworth
Surrey KT20 7TJ
Fax: 01737 813163   Tel: 01737 812673

FANTASY FILM COMPANY
74 Vivian Avenue
London NW4 3XG   Tel: 020-8202 4935

FARNHAM FILM COMPANY The
34 Burnt Hill Road, Lower Bourne
Farnham GU10 3LZ
e-mail: info@farnfilm.com
Fax: 01252 725855   Tel: 01252 710313

FEELGOOD FICTION Ltd
49 Goldhawk Road
London W12 8QP
e-mail: feelgood@feelgoodfiction.co.uk
Fax: 020-8740 6177   Tel: 020-8746 2535

FESTIVAL FILM AND TELEVISION Ltd
Festival House, Tranquil Passage
Blackheath Village, London SE3 0BJ
e-mail: info@festivalfilm.com
Fax: 020-8297 1155   Tel: 020-8297 9999

FILM AND GENERAL PRODUCTIONS Ltd
4 Bradbrook House, Studio Place
London SW1X 8EL
Fax: 020-7245 9853   Tel: 020-7235 4495

FILMS OF RECORD Ltd
2 Elgin Avenue, London W9 3QP
e-mail: rogerg@filmsofrecord.com
Fax: 020-7286 0444   Tel: 020-7286 0333

FIREDOG MOTION PICTURE CORPORATION Ltd The
182 Brighton Road
Coulsdon, Surrey CR5 2NF
e-mail: info@firedogfilms.co.uk
Fax: 020-8763 2558   Tel: 020-8660 8663

FIRST CHOICE
F TV D
5 Angler's Lane
London NW5 3DG
Fax: 020-7267 5441   Tel: 020-7485 5000

FIRST FREEDOM PRODUCTIONS Ltd
15 Rochester Square, London NW1 9SA
e-mail: firstfreedom@compuserve.com
Fax: 020-7485 4692   Tel: 020-7916 9355

FLASHBACK TELEVISION Ltd
11 Bowling Green Lane
London EC1R 0BD
e-mail: mailbox@flashbacktv.co.uk
Fax: 020-7490 5610   Tel: 020-7490 8996

FLICK MEDIA
15 Golden Square
London W1F 9JG
Fax: 020-7287 9495   Tel: 020-7734 7979

FLYING COLOURS FILM COMPANY The
11 Charlotte Mews, London W1T 4EQ
e-mail: fc@flyingc.co.uk
Fax: 020-7436 3055   Tel: 020-7436 2121

FLYING DOG PRODUCTIONS
29 Maiden Lane
Covent Garden
London WC2E 7JS   Tel: 020-7692 9203

FOCUS PRODUCTIONS Ltd
PO Box 173, Stratford-upon-Avon
Warwickshire CV37 7ZA
e-mail: maddern@focusproductions.co.uk
Fax: 01789 294845   Tel: 01789 298948

FORSTATER Mark PRODUCTIONS
27 Lonsdale Road
London NW6 6RA
Fax: 020-7624 1124   Tel: 020-7624 1123

FREEHAND PRODUCTIONS Ltd
33-37 Hatherley Mews
Hiltongrove Business Centre, London E17 4QP
e-mail: freehanduk@yahoo.com
Fax: 020-8520 7766   Tel: 020-8520 7777

FREEWAY FILMS
33A Pembroke Square
London W8 6PD   Tel: 020-7937 9114

FRONT PAGE & CHARISMA FILMS Ltd
Riverbank House
1 Putney Bridge, London SW6 3JD
Fax: 020-7610 6836   Tel: 020-7610 6830

FUJI INTERNATIONAL PRODUCTIONS (UK) Ltd
2nd Floor, 29 Princes Street, London W1B 2ND
Fax: 020-7734 1197   Tel: 020-7734 8888

FULL WORKS The
Suckling's Yard, Church Street
Ware
Herts SG12 9EN   Tel: 01920 486602

FULMAR TELEVISION & FILM Ltd
Pasoe House, 54 Bute Street, Cardiff Bay
Cardiff CF10 5AF
Fax: 029-2045 5111   Tel: 029-2045 5000

FUTUREMEDIA Plc
CV
Media House, Arundel Road, Walberton
Arundel, West Sussex BN18 0QP
Fax: 01243 555020   Tel: 01243 555000

GALA PRODUCTIONS Ltd
25 Stamford Brook Road, London W6 0XJ
e-mail: info@galaproductions.co.uk
Fax: 020-8741 2323   Tel: 020-8741 4200

GAMMOND Stephen ASSOCIATES
24 Telegraph Lane, Claygate, Surrey KT10 0DU
Fax: 01372 460032   Tel: 01372 470387

GARRETTS
F TV Commercials
8 Great Titchfield Street, London W1W 8JJ
e-mail: commercials@garretts.co.uk
Fax: 020-7580 6453   Tel: 020-7580 6452

GATES Martin PRODUCTIONS Ltd
Upper Farm House, Taynton, Nr Burford
Oxon OX18 4UH
Fax: 01993 822736   Tel: 01993 822718

GATEWAY TELEVISION PRODUCTIONS
Gemini House, 10 Bradgate
Cuffley, Herts EN6 4RL   Tel: 01707 872054

GAU John PRODUCTIONS
15 St Albans Mansions
Kensington Court Place, London W8 5QH
e-mail: johngau@hotmail.com
Fax: 020-7938 1429   Tel: 020-7938 1398

GAY Noel TELEVISION Ltd
TV D Ch Co
Shepperton Studios, Studios Road
Shepperton, Middlesex TW17 0QD
e-mail: charles.armitage@virgin.net
Fax: 01932 572172   Tel: 01932 572569

GHA GROUP
1 Great Chapel Street, London W1F 8FA
e-mail: sales@ghagroup.co.uk
Fax: 020-7437 5880   Tel: 020-7439 8705

GLASS PAGE
27-29 Millstone Lane, Leicester LE1 5JN
Fax: 0116-233 6566   Tel: 0116-233 6565

GLO & CO Ltd
5 Robertson Street, London SW8 3SH
Fax: 020-7498 1370   Tel: 020-7627 1982

GODMAN Colin PRODUCTIONS
TV D
41 Trelawney Road, Cotham
Bristol BS6 6DY   Tel: 0117-974 1058

GRADE COMPANY The
17 Albermarle Street
Mayfair, London W1S 4HP
Fax: 020-7408 2042   Tel: 020-7409 1925

GRANT NAYLOR PRODUCTIONS Ltd
Rooms 950-951 The David Lean Building
Shepperton Studios, Studios Road, Shepperton,
Middlesex TW17 0QD
Fax: 01932 572484   Tel: 01932 572175

GREAT GUNS Ltd
43-45 Camden Road
London NW1 9LR
e-mail: greatguns@greatguns.com
Fax: 020-7692 4422   Tel: 020-7692 4444

GREEDY PRODUCTIONS
F TV CV
109 St Paul's Road
London N1 2NA
e-mail: greedy@henandchickens.com
                         Tel/Fax: 020-8378 6001

GREENLIGHT PICTURE COMPANY The
Park West, Spiddal, Co. Galway, Ireland
e-mail: info@greenlightireland.com
                         Tel/Fax: 00 353 9155 8800

GREENPOINT FILMS
F TV D
Union Hall, 27-29 Union Street
London SE1 1SD
Fax: 020-7357 9920   Tel: 020-7357 9924

GROOVY MOVIES
(Video Production & Comedy Sketches)
The Dower House, Rocky Lane, Reigate
Surrey RH2 0TA   Tel/Fax: 01737 643731

GUERILLA FILMS Ltd
35 Thornbury Road, Isleworth
Middlesex TW7 4LQ
e-mail: david@guerilla-films.com
Fax: 020-8758 9364   Tel: 020-8758 1716

**HAMMERWOOD FILM PRODUCERS
& DISTRIBUTORS**
110 Trafalgar Road
Portslade, Sussex BN41 1GS
e-mail: ralph@hammerwood.fsnet.co.uk
Fax: 01273 705451   Tel: 01273 277333

david **fernandes**
photographer

Studio
252-254 Pentonville Rd **N1 9JY**.
M 07958 272 333
www.image2film.com

HARBOUR PICTURES
The Yacht Club, Chelsea Harbour
London SW10 0XA
e-mail: username@harbourpictures.com
Fax: 020-7352 3528   Tel: 020-7351 7070

HARTSWOOD FILMS
Twickenham Studios, The Barons, St Margaret's
Twickenham, Middlesex TW1 2AW
Fax: 020-8607 8744   Tel: 020-8607 8736

HASAN SHAH FILMS Ltd
153 Burnham Towers, Adelaide Road
London NW3 3JN
Fax: 020-7483 0662   Tel: 020-7722 2419

HAT TRICK PRODUCTIONS Ltd
TV Co
10 Livonia Street, London W1F 8AF
Fax: 020-7287 9791   Tel: 020-7434 2451

HAWK EYE FILMS
Twickenham Film Studios, The Barons
St Margarets, Twickenham, Middlesex TW1 2AW
Fax: 020-8241 1907   Tel: 020-8607 8871

HEAD Sally PRODUCTIONS
Twickenham Film Studios, The Barons
St Margaret's, Twickenham
Middlesex TW1 2AW
e-mail: admin@shpl.demon.co.uk
Fax: 020-8607 8964   Tel: 020-8607 8730

HEAVY ENTERTAINMENT Ltd
222 Kensal Road
London W10 5BN
e-mail: info@heavy-entertainment.com
Fax: 020-8960 9003   Tel: 020-8960 9001

HELIFILMS
The Cedars
Enborne Street, Enborne, Newbury
Berks RG20 0JS
e-mail: helifilms@msn.com
Fax: 01635 569298   Tel: 01635 569302

HENSON Jim ORGANISATION
30 Oval Road, Camden
London NW1 7DE
Fax: 020-7428 4001   Tel: 020-7428 4000

HEWETT Yvonne
Optimum Productions, 32 Thames Eyot
Cross Deep
Twickenham TW1 4QL   Tel: 020-8892 1403

HINCHLIFFE Barrie PRODUCTIONS Ltd
Boston House, 36-38 Fitzroy Square
London W1P 5LL
Fax: 020-7631 0255   Tel: 020-7631 1470

HIT ENTERTAINMENT Plc
5th Floor, Maple House
149 Tottenham Court Road, London W1T 7NF
e-mail: creative@hitentertainment.com
Fax: 020-7388 9321   Tel: 020-7554 2500

HOBBS Liz GROUP Ltd
Finsbury Business Centre
40 Bowling Green Lane
London EC1R 0NE
e-mail: info@lizhobbsgroup.com
Fax: 01636 703343   Tel: 020-7287 8870

68 Castlegate, Newark NG24 1BG
Fax: 01636 703343   Tel: 01636 703342

HOLMES ASSOCIATES & OPEN ROAD FILMS
F TV D
The Studio, 37 Reddington Rd, London NW3 7QY
e-mail: holmes@dial.pipex.com
Fax: 0870 124 5242   Tel: 020-7813 4333

HUDSON FILM Ltd
24 St Leonard's Terrace
London SW3   Tel/Fax: 020-7730 0002

HUMMINGBIRD FILMS
4 Rockleaze Avenue, Bristol BS9 1NG
Fax: 0117-907 6159   Tel: 0117-904 9446

HUNKY DORY PRODUCTIONS Ltd
TV D Co
Cambridge House, 135 High Street
Teddington, Middlesex TW11 8HH
Fax: 020-8977 4464   Tel: 020-8943 3006

HURLL Michael TELEVISION Ltd
Avon House, Kensington Village
Avonmore Road, London W14 8TS
e-mail: london@uniquegroup.co.uk
Fax: 020-7371 5355   Tel: 020-7371 5354

IAMBIC PRODUCTIONS Ltd
1st Floor, 31 Eastcastle Street, London W1W 8DL
e-mail: team@iambicproductions.com
Fax: 020-7637 7084   Tel: 020-7436 1400

ICON FILMS Ltd
4 West End, Somerset Street, Bristol BS2 8NE
Fax: 0117-942 0386   Tel: 0117-924 8535

ILLUSTRA PRODUCTIONS Ltd
14 Bateman Street
London W1V 6EB
Fax: 020-7734 7143   Tel: 020-7437 9611

IMMEDIA TELEVISION COMMUNICATIONS Ltd
Carlton Studios, Lenton Lane
Nottingham NG7 2NA
e-mail: info@immediagroup.co.uk
Fax: 0115-964 5502   Tel: 0115-964 5505

INFORMATION TRANSFER Ltd
CV (Training Video Packages)
Burleigh House, 15 Newmarket Road
Cambridge CB5 8EG
Fax: 01223 310200   Tel: 01223 312227

INITIAL
Shepherds Building Central, Charecroft Way
Shepherds Bush, London W14 0EH
Fax: 0870 3331800   Tel: 0870 3311700

INTERESTING TELEVISION Ltd
Oakslade Studios, Hatton
Warwick CV35 7LH
Fax: 01926 844045   Tel: 01926 844044

INVISION PRODUCTIONS
8 Barb Mews
London W6 7PA
Fax: 020-7371 2160   Tel: 020-7371 2123

ISIS PRODUCTIONS Ltd
106 Hammersmith Grove
London W6 7HB
e-mail: isis@isis-productions.com
Fax: 020-8748 3046   Tel: 020-8748 3042

ISSITT Erica ASSOCIATES Ltd
5 Elswick Street, London SW6 2QR
e-mail: eissitt@dialstart.net
Fax: 020-7287 3980   Tel: 020-7237 1080

JACKSON Brian FILMS Ltd
F TV Ch
39-41 Hanover Steps, St George's Fields
Albion Street, London W2 2YG
e-mail: brianjfilm@aol.com
Fax: 020-7262 5736   Tel: 020-7402 7543

JOLL Barrie ASSOCIATES Ltd
58 Frith Street
London W1V 5TA   Tel: 020-7437 9965

JUST TELEVISION
4 Northington Street
London WC1N 2JG
e-mail: info@justtv.co.uk
Fax: 020-7692 9080   Tel: 020-7916 6200

KAYE Tony & PARTNERS
33 Tottenham Street
London W1P 9PE
Fax: 020-7323 1711   Tel: 020-7323 1511

KICK SCREEN
13 D'Arblay Street
London W1F 8DX
e-mail: kick@thenet.demon.co.uk
Fax: 020-7437 0125   Tel: 020-7287 3757

KINGFISHER TELEVISION
Carlton Studios, Lenton Lane
Nottingham NG7 2NA
Fax: 0115-964 5263   Tel: 0115-964 5262

KNOWLES Dave FILMS
(Also Multimedia Interactive CD Roms)
34 Ashleigh Close, Hythe SO45 3QP
e-mail: mail@dkfilms.co.uk
Fax: 023-8084 1600   Tel: 023-8084 2190

LANDSEER FILM & TELEVISION PRODUCTIONS Ltd
140 Royal College Street
London NW1 0TA
e-mail: mail@landseefilms.com
Fax: 020-7485 7573   Tel: 020-7485 7333

LANGTON Jamie KELNAT PRODUCTIONS Ltd
9 Bushey Road
Ickenham Uxbridge
Middlesex UB10 8JP   Tel/Fax: 020-8582 1960

LARGE BEAST PRODUCTIONS Ltd
Unit 4B, The Coda Centre
189 Munster Road, London SW6 6AW
e-mail: e-mail@largebeastproductions.com
Fax: 020-7386 0356   Tel: 020-7381 8228

LE PARK TV Ltd
Windmill Studios, 49-51 York Road
Brentford, Middlesex TW8 0QP
Fax: 020-8568 4151   Tel: 020-8568 5855

LENIHAN Sean ASSOCIATES
The Old Chapel, Abbey Hill, Lerant
St Ives
Cornwall TR26 3EB   Tel/Fax: 01736 757557

LIGHT DIVISION Ltd
11 Christchurch Gardens, Reading
Berks RG2 7AH
Fax: 0118-931 2123   Tel: 0118-931 3859

LINK ENTERTAINMENT Ltd
7 Baron's Gate, 33-35 Rothschild Road
London W4 5HT
Fax: 020-8747 9452   Tel: 020-8996 4800

LITTLE BIRD COMPANY Ltd
9 Grafton Mews, London W1P 5LG
e-mail: info@littlebird.co.uk
Fax: 020-7380 3981   Tel: 020-7380 3980

LITTLE KING COMMUNICATIONS
The Studio, 2 Newport Road, Barnes
London SW13 9PE
Fax: 020-8653 2742   Tel: 020-8741 7658

LONDON COLLEGE OF PRINTING & DISTRIBUTIVE TRADES MEDIA SCHOOL
(Film & Video Division)
Media School, 10 Back Hill, Clerkenwell
London EC1R 5EN
Fax: 020-7514 6848   Tel: 020-7514 6500

LONDON FILMS
71 South Audley Street, London W1K 1JA
Fax: 020-7499 7994   Tel: 020-7499 7800

LONDON SCIENTIFIC FILMS
Suckling's Yard, Church Street, Ware
Herts SG12 9EN   Tel: 01920 486602

LOOKING GLASS FILMS Ltd
103 Brittany Point, Ethelred Estate
Kennington, London SE11 6UH
e-mail: lookingglassfilm@aol.com
          Tel/Fax: 020-7735 1363

LOYNES Geoff ANIMATION COMPANY
F TV Ch
Hornbrook Manor Farm House
Appledore Road, Woodchurch
Kent TN26 3TH   Tel: 01233 860252

MAGIC BOX MOTION PICTURES Ltd
Tan-y-Bryn, 51 Highdale Road, Clevedon
North Somerset BS21 7LR
e-mail: magicbox@blueyonder.co.uk
Fax: 01275 544913   Tel: 01275 544741

MAGPIE FILM PRODUCTIONS Ltd
31-32 Cheapside, Birmingham B5 6AY
Fax: 0121-666 6077   Tel: 0121-622 5884

MALLINSON TELEVISION PRODUCTIONS
(TV Commercials)
29 Lynedoch Street, Glasgow G3 6EF
e-mail: shoot@mtp.co.uk
Fax: 0141-332 6190   Tel: 0141-332 0589

MALONE GILL PRODUCTIONS Ltd
27 Campden Hill Road, London W8 7DX
e-mail: malonegill@cs.com
Fax: 020-7376 1727   Tel: 020-7937 0557

MANS Johnny PRODUCTIONS Ltd
The Maltings, Brewery Road, Hoddesdon
Herts EN11 8HF
Fax: 01992 470516   Tel: 01992 470907

MANSFIELD Mike TELEVISION Ltd
5th Floor, 41-42 Berners Street, London W1T 3NB
e-mail: mikemantv@aol.com
Fax: 020-7580 2582   Tel: 020-7580 2581

MANUEL Jo PRODUCTIONS Ltd
11 Keslake Road
London NW6 6DJ
e-mail: jomanuel@cwcom.net
Fax: 020-8933 5475   Tel: 020-8930 0777

MAP FILMS
3 Bourlet Close, London W1W 7BQ
e-mail: mail@mapfilms.com
Fax: 020-7291 7841   Tel: 020-7291 7840

MASON Bill FILMS Ltd
Orchard House, Dell Quay, Chichester
West Sussex PO20 7EE
e-mail: bill.mason@argonet.co.uk
                          Tel: 01243 783558

MAVERICK TELEVISION
The Custard Factory, Gibb Street
Birmingham B9 4AA
e-mail: maverick@mavericktv.co.uk
Fax: 0121-771 1550   Tel: 0121-771 1812

MAYA VISION INTERNATIONAL
43 New Oxford Street
London WC1A 1BH   Tel: 020-7836 1113

McLAREN ENTERTAINMENT
Setley Brake, Tile Barn Lane
Brockenhurst, Hants SO42 7UE
Fax: 01590 623968   Tel: 01590 622630

MELENDEZ FILMS
Suite 501, 189-191 Triumph House
Regent Street, London W1B 4JY
Fax: 020-7434 3131   Tel: 020-7434 0220

MENTORN BARRACLOUGH CAREY
43 Whitfield Street, London W1P 6TG
Fax: 020-7258 6888   Tel: 020-7258 6800

MERCHANT IVORY PRODUCTIONS
46 Lexington Street, London W1R 3LH
e-mail: miplondon@merchantivory.demon.co.uk
Fax: 020-7734 1579   Tel: 020-7437 1200

MERSEY TELEVISION COMPANY Ltd The
TV
Campus Manor, Childwall, Abbey Road
Liverpool L16 0JP
Fax: 0151-722 6839   Tel: 0151-722 9122

MIGHTY MOVIES (Mighty Media)
Long Boyds House, PO Box 73
Bourne End, Bucks SL8 5FJ
Fax: 01628 526530   Tel: 01628 522002

MINAMON PRODUCTIONS
117 Downton Avenue, London SW2 3TX
e-mail: minamon.film@virgin.net
Fax: 020-8674 1779   Tel: 020-8674 3957

MODUS OPERANDI FILMS
10 Soho Square, London W1V 6NT
Fax: 020-7287 6852   Tel: 020-7434 1440

MOGUL CORPORATION The
60 Aubert Park, London N5 1TS
Fax: 020-7242 2860   Tel: 020-7242 2850

MOGUL TV Ltd
High Pines, Westwood Road, Windlesham
Surrey GU20 6LS   Tel/Fax: 01344 622140

MOONLIGHT COMMUNICATIONS Ltd
48 Vyse Street, Hockley, Birmingham B18 6HF
e-mail: norman@moonlitt.demon.co.uk
Fax: 0121-551 6455   Tel: 0121-523 6221

MORE Alan FILMS
Pinewood Studios, Pinewood Road
Iver, Bucks SL0 0NH
e-mail: almorefilm@aol.com
Fax: 01753 650988   Tel: 01753 656789

MORNINGSIDE PRODUCTIONS INC.
8 Ilchester Place, London W14 8AA
Fax: 020-7602 1047   Tel: 020-7602 2382

MORRISON COMPANY The
302 Clive Court, Maida Vale
London W9 1SF
e-mail: don@morrisonco.com
                    Tel/Fax: 020-7289 7976

MOSAIC FILMS
The Old Butcher's Shop, St Briavels
Glos GL15 6TA
e-mail: info@mosaicfilms.com
Fax: 01594 530094   Tel: 01594 530708

MOUNTFORD John STUDIOS Ltd
(Radio Commercials & Video Production
Company)
3 Montagu Row, London W1U 6DY
e-mail: inbox@jmslondon.co.uk
Fax: 020-7224 4035   Tel: 020-7224 1031

Hethersett, Norwich, Norfolk NR9 3DL
e-mail: traffic@jmsradio.co.uk
Fax: 01603 812255   Tel: 01603 811855

MOVIT VIDEO PRODUCTIONS
(Video Production)
297 Glyn Road, London E5 0JP
e-mail: genevieve@movit.fsnet.co.uk
Mobile: 07711 863573   Tel/Fax: 020-8533 3877

MURPHY Patricia FILMS Ltd
40 Frith Street, London W1V 5TS
e-mail: patriciamurphyfilms@cwcom.net
Fax: 020-7434 0019   Tel: 020-7734 5462

MUSIC BOX Ltd
30 Sackville Street, London W1S 3DY
Fax: 020-7478 7403   Tel: 020-7478 7320

NEBRASKA PRODUCTIONS Ltd
12 Grove Avenue, London N10 2AR
e-mail: 101606.1467@compuserve.com
Fax: 020-8444 2113   Tel: 020-8444 5317

NEWGATE COMPANY
(Radio)
13 Dafford Street, Larkhall, Bath
Somerset BA1 6SW   Tel: 01225 318335

NEXUS PRODUCTIONS Ltd
(Animation for Commercials & Pop Promos)
113-114 Shoreditch High Street
London E1 6JN
e-mail: info@nexuslondon.com
Fax: 020-7749 7501   Tel: 020-7749 7500

NUTOPIA FILMS
8, 132 Charing Cross Road
London WC2H 0LA   Tel/Fax: 020-8882 6299

ON COMMUNICATIONS/ON TV
(Work across all Media in Business
Communications, Museum Prods
& Broadcast Docs)
5 East St Helen Street, Abingdon
Oxford OX14 5EG
e-mail: on@oncomms-tv.co.uk
Fax: 01235 530581   Tel: 01235 537400

ON SCREEN PRODUCTIONS Ltd
39 Cardiff Road, Llandaff
Cardiff CF5 2DT
e-mail: action@onscreenproductions.co.uk
Fax: 029-2057 8496   Tel: 029-2056 7593

OPEN MIND PRODUCTIONS
6 Newburgh Street, London W1F 7RQ
e-mail: imogen.robertson@openmind.co.uk
Fax: 020-7434 9256   Tel: 020-7437 0624

OPEN SHUTTER PRODUCTIONS Ltd
100 Kings Road, Windsor
Berks SL4 2AP   Tel/Fax: 01753 841309

**ORCHARD COMMUNICATIONS DESIGN
GROUP Ltd The**
(Interactive Multimedia Production)
Langler House, Market Place, Somerton,
Somerset TA11 7LZ
e-mail: lesle./@orchardcdg.co.uk
Fax: 01458 274590   Tel: 01458 274589

ORIGINAL FILM & VIDEO PRODUCTIONS Ltd
Greek Court, 14A Old Compton Street
London W1V 5PE
e-mail: original.films@btinternet.com
Fax: 020-7437 1782   Tel: 020-7734 9721

OSBORN Peter PRODUCTION Ltd
Square Red Studio, 249-251 Kensal Road
London W10 5DB
e-mail: peter.osborn@btinternet.com
Fax: 020-8960 7285   Tel: 020-8960 6069

OVATION PRODUCTIONS
1 Prince of Wales Passage, London NW1 3EF
e-mail: ovationgb@aol.com
Fax: 020-7380 0404   Tel: 020-7387 2342

OVC MEDIA Ltd
88 Berkeley Court, Baker Street
London NW1 5ND
e-mail: eliot@ovcmedia.uk
Fax: 020-7723 3064   Tel: 020-7402 9111

P4 FILMS
Cheltenham Film Studio, Hatherley Lane,
Cheltenham GL51 6PN
e-mail: info@p4films.com   Tel/Fax: 01453 872743

PALIN Barry ASSOCIATES
Unit 10, Princeton Court, 55 Felsham Road
London SW15 1AZ
e-mail: mail@barrypalinassociates.com
Fax: 020-8785 0440   Tel: 020-8394 5660

PANDER PICTURES Ltd
182 Brighton Road, Coulsdon
Surrey CR5 2NF
e-mail: info@panderpictures.com
Fax: 020-8763 2558   Tel: 020-8660 8663

PANTECHNICON
90 Lots Road, London SW10 0QD
e-mail: info@pantechnicon.co.uk
Fax: 020-7351 0667   Tel: 020-7351 7579

PAPER MOON PRODUCTIONS
Wychwood House, Burchetts Green Lane,
Littlewick Green, Maidenhead, Berks SL6 3QW
e-mail: david@paper-moon.co.uk
Fax: 01628 825949   Tel: 01628 829819

PARADINE David PRODUCTIONS Ltd
1st Floor, 5 St Mary Abbot's Place, Kensington
London W8 6LS
Fax: 020-7602 0411   Tel: 020-7371 3111

PARALLAX PICTURES Ltd
7 Denmark Street, London WC2H 8LZ
Fax: 020-7497 8062   Tel: 020-7836 1478

PARAMOUNT FILM SERVICES Ltd
UIP House, 45 Beadon Road, London W6 0EG
Fax: 020-8563 4266   Tel: 020-8563 4158

PARK VILLAGE Ltd
1 Park Village East, London NW1 7PX
e-mail: reception@parkvillage.co.uk
Fax: 020-7388 3051   Tel: 020-7387 8077

PARLIAMENTARY FILMS Ltd
11A Enterprise House
59-65 Upper Ground, London SE1 9PQ
Fax: 020-7827 9511   Tel: 020-7827 9514

PARTNERS IN PRODUCTION Ltd
Hillview, Hinders Lane
Huntley, Glos GL19 3EZ
Mobile: 07802 967369   Fax: 01452 830500

PASSION PICTURES Ltd
Animation
25-27 Riding House Street, London W1W 7DU
e-mail: info@passion-pictures.com
Fax: 020-7323 9030   Tel: 020-7323 9933

P.C.I. LIVE DESIGN
(Live Events, Live Design Exhibitions
Film & Video, 2D & 3D Design)
3/18 Harbour Yard, Chelsea Harbour
London SW10 0XD
Fax: 020-7352 7906   Tel: 020-7544 7500

PEAK WHITE VIDEO
1 Latimer Road, Teddington
Middlesex TW11 8QA
Fax: 020-8977 8357   Tel: 020-8943 1922

PEARSON TELEVISION
1 Stephen Street, London W1T 1AL
Fax: 020-7691 6100   Tel: 020-7691 6000

PERSONA FILMS Ltd
8 Plasturton Gardens, Cardiff,
South Glamorgan CF11 9HF
Fax: 029-2025 0488   Tel: 029-2025 0499

PICTURE PALACE FILMS Ltd
13 Egbert Street, London NW1 8LJ
e-mail: info@picturepalace.com
Fax: 020-7586 9048   Tel: 020-7586 8763

PIER PRODUCTIONS Ltd
Lower Ground Floor
1 Marlborough Place, Brighton BN1 1TU
e-mail: pieradmin@mistral.co.uk
Fax: 01273 693658   Tel: 01273 691401

PIEREND PRODUCTIONS
Unit 3, Rockware Business Centre
5 Rockware Avenue, Greenford
Middlesex UB6 0AA
e-mail: russell@pierend.fsnet.co.uk
Fax: 020-8575 1966   Tel: 020-8575 1606

POKER Ltd
143B Whitehall Court
London SW1A 2EL   Tel/Fax: 020-7839 6070

POSITIVE IMAGE HOUSE
25 Victoria Street, Windsor, Berks SL4 1HE
Fax: 01753 830878   Tel: 01753 842248

PRETTY CLEVER PICTURES
Post 59, Shepperton Studios, Studios Road
Shepperton, Middlesex TW17 0QD
e-mail: pcpics@globalnet.co.uk
Fax: 01932 572454   Tel: 01932 572047

PRINCIPAL PICTURES Ltd
Picture House, 65 Hopton Street
London SE1 9LR
e-mail: pictures@principalmedia.com
Fax: 020-7928 9886   Tel: 020-7928 9287

PRODUCERS The
8 Berners Mews, London W1T 3AW
Fax: 020-7636 4099   Tel: 020-7636 4226

PROFESSIONAL MEDICAL COMMUNICATIONS Ltd
Grosvenor House, 1 High Street
Edgware
Middlesex HA8 7TA   Tel: 020-8381 1819

PROMENADE PRODUCTIONS Ltd
6 Russell Grove, London SW9 6HS
e-mail: promenadeproductions@msn.com
Fax: 020-7564 3026   Tel: 020-7582 9354

P.S.A. Ltd
67 Ayres Road
Manchester M16 9NH
Fax: 0161-232 0949   Tel: 0161-226 7893

PURCHASE FX
46 St Dionis Road, London SW6 4TT
Fax: 020-7736 6830   Tel: 020-7731 1711

PURPLE FROG MEDIA Ltd
The Basement, 34 St Aubyns
Brighton BN3 2TD
e-mail: info@purplefrogmedia.com
Fax: 01273 775787   Tel: 01273 735475

PVA MANAGEMENT Ltd
Hallow Park, Hallow
Worcs WR2 6PG
e-mail: films@pva.co.uk
Fax: 01905 641842   Tel: 01905 640663

QUADRANT TELEVISION Ltd
17 West Hill
London SW18 1RB
e-mail: quadranttv@aol.com   Tel: 020-8870 9933

QUADRILLION
The Old Barn, Kings Lane
Cookham Dean, Berks SL6 9AY
e-mail: enq@quadrillion.net
Fax: 01628 487523   Tel: 01628 487522

RAW CHARM Ltd
Ty Cefn, Rectory Road, Cardiff CF5 1QL
e-mail: pam@rawcharm.co.uk
Fax: 029-2066 8220   Tel: 029-2064 1511

READ Rodney
45 Richmond Road, Twickenham
Middlesex TW1 3AW
e-mail: rodney_read@compuserve.com
Fax: 020-8744 9603   Tel: 020-8891 2875

RECORDED PICTURE COMPANY Ltd
24-26 Hanway Street, London W1T 1UH
Fax: 020-7636 2261   Tel: 020-7636 2251

RED ROSE CHAIN
1A Cauldwell Avenue, Ipswich IP4 4EB
e-mail: info@redrosechain.co.uk
                          Tel: 01473 723804

REEL EDITING COMPANY The
65 Goldhawk Road, London W12 8EH
Fax: 020-8743 2345   Tel: 020-8743 5100

REEL THING Ltd The
182 Brighton Road, Coulsdon, Surrey CR5 2NF
e-mail: info@reelthing.tv
Fax: 020-8763 2558   Tel: 020-8668 8188

REGENT PRODUCTIONS Ltd
1 Stephen Street, London W1P 1PJ
Fax: 020-7691 5098   Tel: 020-7691 6000

REPLAY Ltd
20 Greek Street, London W1D 4DU
e-mail: sales@replayfilms.co.uk
Fax: 020-7287 5348   Tel: 020-7287 5334

RESOURCE BASE
Television Centre, Southampton SO14 0PZ
e-mail: post@resource-base.co.uk
Fax: 023-8023 6816   Tel: 023-8023 6806

REUTERS TELEVISION
200 Gray's Inn Road, London WC1X 8XZ
Fax: 020-7542 5401   Tel: 020-7250 1122

RIVERSIDE STUDIOS
Crisp Road, London W6 9RL   Tel: 020-8237 1000

RM ASSOCIATES
46 Great Marlborough Street, London W1V 1DB
Fax: 020-7439 2316   Tel: 020-7439 2637

ROCLIFFE
12 Barnston Walk
Popham Street, London N1 8QP
e-mail: info@rocliffe.com Tel/Fax: 020-7688 0749

ROGERS Peter PRODUCTIONS Ltd
Pinewood Studios, Iver Heath
Bucks SL0 0NH   Tel: 01753 651700

ROOKE Laurence PRODUCTIONS
14 Aspinall House, 155 New Park Road
London SW2 4EY   Tel: 020-8674 3128

ROSE HACKNEY BARBER Ltd
5-6 Kingly Street, London W1B 5PF
Fax: 020-7434 4102   Tel: 020-7439 6697

R.S.A. FILMS
42-44 Beak Street, London W1F 9RH
Fax: 020-7734 4978   Tel: 020-7437 7426

RUSSO Denis ASSOCIATES
F TV Animation
161 Clapham Road, London SW9 0PU
Fax: 020-7582 2725   Tel: 020-7582 9664

SAMUELSON PRODUCTIONS Ltd
13 Manette Street, London W1D 4AW
e-mail: samuelsonp@aol.com
Fax: 020-7439 4901   Tel: 020-7439 4900

SANDS FILMS
Grice's Wharf, 119 Rotherhithe Street
London SE16 4NF
Fax: 020-7231 2119   Tel: 020-7231 2209

SCALA PRODUCTIONS Ltd
15 Frith Street, London W1D 4RE
e-mail: scalaprods@aol.com
Fax: 020-7437 3248   Tel: 020-7734 7060

SCIMITAR FILMS Ltd
219 Kensington High Street
London W8 6BD
e-mail: winner@ftech.co.uk
Fax: 020-7602 9217   Tel: 020-7734 8385

**SCOTTISH SCREEN PRODUCTION
& DEVELOPMENT**
249 West George Street
Glasgow G2 4QE
e-mail: info@scottishscreen.com
Fax: 0141-302 1711   Tel: 0141-302 1700

SCREEN FIRST Ltd
The Studios, Funnells Farm, Down Street
Nutley, East Sussex TN22 3LG
e-mail: info@screenfirst.co.uk
Fax: 01825 713511   Tel: 01825 712034

SCREEN VENTURES
49 Goodge Street, London W1T 1TE
Fax: 020-7631 1265   Tel: 020-7580 7448

SEDDON Julian FILMS Ltd
(Commercials)
51-53 Mount Pleasant
London WC1X 0AE
e-mail: julian.s@btconnect.com
Fax: 020-7405 3721   Tel: 020-7831 3033

SEPTEMBER FILMS Ltd
Glen House, 22 Glenthorne Road
Hammersmith, London W6 0NG
Fax: 020-8741 7214   Tel: 020-8563 9393

SHART BROS Ltd
52 Lancaster Road
London N4 4PR
Fax: 020-7436 9233   Tel: 020-7263 4435

SHELL FILM & VIDEO UNIT
F CV Docs
Shell Centre, York Road
London SE1 7NA
Fax: 020-7934 4095   Tel: 020-7934 3318

SHOOTS FILM & VIDEO Ltd
3 Lowndes Court, Newburgh Street
London W1V 1PP
Fax: 020-7439 8847   Tel: 020-7434 1912

SIGHTLINE
(Videos, Commercials, CD Rom, DVD, Websites)
Dylan House, Town End Street, Godalming
Surrey GU7 1BQ
e-mail: keith@sightline.co.uk
Fax: 01483 861516   Tel: 01483 861555

SILVER PRODUCTIONS Ltd
29 Castle Street
Salisbury, Wilts SP1 1TT
Fax: 01722 336227   Tel: 01722 336221

SIMAGE COMMUNICATIONS
Fulton House, Fulton Road, Wembley Park
Middlesex HA9 0TF
e-mail: simon@simage-comms.co.uk
Fax: 020-8584 0443   Tel: 020-8584 0444

SINDIBAD FILMS Ltd
5th Floor, 5 Princes Gate, London SW7 1QJ
e-mail: sindibad@lineone.net
Fax: 020-7823 9137   Tel: 020-7823 7488

SKREBA
27-29 Union Street, London SE1 1SD
Fax: 020-7357 9920   Tel: 020-7357 9924

SNEEZING TREE FILMS
C
1-2 Bromley Place, London W1T 6DA
e-mail: sneezingtree@compuserve.com
Fax: 020-7927 9909   Tel: 020-7927 9900

SOMERFILM Ltd
20 Stirling Street, Dundee DD3 6PH
e-mail: somerfilm@aol.com
Fax: 0800 4581901   Tel: 0800 4581900

SONY PICTURES EUROPE HOUSE
25 Golden Square, London W1F 9LU
Fax: 020-7533 1015   Tel: 020-7533 1000

SOREL STUDIOS
10 Palace Court, Palace Road, London SW2 3ED
e-mail: sorelstudios.co.uk
                    Tel/Fax: 020-8671 2168

SOUTHERN STAR
45-49 Mortimer Street
London W1N 7TD   Tel: 020-7636 9421

SPACE CITY PRODUCTIONS
77 Blythe Road, London W14 0HP
e-mail: info@spacecity.co.uk
Fax: 020-7371 4001   Tel: 020-7371 4000

SPAFAX
The Pump House
13-16 Jacobswell Mews
London W1U 3DY   Tel: 020-7906 2001

SPEAKEASY PRODUCTIONS Ltd
Wildwood House, Stanley
Perth PH1 4PX
e-mail: info@speak.co.uk
Fax: 01738 828419   Tel: 01738 828524

SPECIFIC FILMS Ltd
25 Rathbone Street, London W1T 1NQ
e-mail: specificfilms@compuserve.com
Fax: 020-7494 2676   Tel: 020-7580 7476

SPELLBOUND PRODUCTIONS Ltd
90 Cowdenbeath Path, Islington
London N1 0LG
e-mail: phspellbound@hotmail.com
                    Tel/Fax: 020-7713 8066

SPENCER Alan FILM COMPANY Ltd The
2 Teal Drive
Ducks Hill Road, Northwood
Middlesex HA6 2PT
e-mail: asfc2@excite.co.uk
Fax: 01923 823310   Tel: 01923 829410

SPIRAL PRODUCTIONS Ltd
Aberdeen Studios, 22 Highbury Grove
London N5 2EA
Fax: 020-7359 6123   Tel: 020-7354 5492

SPIRIT FILMS Ltd
1 Wedgwood Mews
12-13 Greek Street
London W1V 5LW
e-mail: spirit@spiritfilms.co.uk
Fax: 020-7734 9850   Tel: 020-7734 6642

STANDFAST FILMS
F TV D
The Studio, 14 College Road, Bromley
Kent BR1 3NS
Fax: 020-8313 0443   Tel: 020-8466 5580

STAR PRODUCTIONS
F CV D
Star Studios, 38 Lea Bridge Road
London E5 9QD
Fax: 020-8533 6597   Tel: 020-8986 4470

STONE PRODUCTIONS
Lakeside Studio, 62 Mill Street
St Osyth, Essex CO16 8EW
Fax: 01255 822160   Tel: 01255 822172

STRAWBERRY PRODUCTIONS Ltd
36 Priory Avenue, London W4 1TY
e-mail: strawprod1@aol.com
Fax: 020-8742 7675   Tel: 020-8994 4494

STREETWISE TV
11-15 Betterton Street
Covent Garden, London WC2H 9PB
e-mail: streetwise_tv@hotmail.com
Fax: 020-7470 8826   Tel: 020-7470 8825

STUDIO AKA
(Animation)
30 Berwick Street, London W1F 8RH
e-mail: info@studioaka.co.uk
Fax: 020-7437 2309   Tel: 020-7434 3581

SUN DANCE FILMS Ltd
6 Glamorgan Road, Hampton Wick
Kingston, Surrey KT1 4HP
Fax: 020-8977 9441   Tel: 020-8977 1791

SUNFLOWER PRODUCTIONS
(Docs TV)
106 Mansfield Drive, Merstham, Surrey RH1 3JN
Fax: 01737 271231   Tel: 01737 642829

SWIVEL FILMS
4th Floor, 23 Denmark Street
London WC2H 8NA
Fax: 020-7240 4486   Tel: 020-7240 4485

TABARD PRODUCTIONS
Adam House, 7-10 Adam Street
London WC2N 6AA
e-mail: johnherbert@tabard.u-net.com
Fax: 020-7497 0830   Tel: 020-7497 0850

TABLE TOP PRODUCTIONS
1 The Orchard, Bedford Park, Chiswick
London W4 1JZ
e-mail: berry@tabletopproductions.com
                    Tel/Fax: 020-8742 0507

TAKE 3 VIDEO & FILM PRODUCTIONS Ltd
72 Margaret Street, London W1W 8HA
e-mail: mail@take3.co.uk
Fax: 020-7637 4678   Tel: 020-7637 2694

TAKE FIVE PRODUCTIONS
CV Docs
25 Ganton Street, London W1F 9BP
Fax: 020-7287 3035   Tel: 020-7287 2120

TALISMAN FILMS Ltd
5 Addison Place, London W11 4RJ
e-mail: email@talismanfilms.com
Fax: 020-7602 7422   Tel: 020-7603 7474

TALKBACK PRODUCTIONS Ltd
20-21 Newman Street, London W1T 1PG
Fax: 020-7861 8001   Tel: 020-7861 8000

TALKING PICTURES
Swallowtiles, High Street, Drayton, St Leonard
Wallingford OX10 7BQ
e-mail: info@talkingpictures.co.uk
Fax: 01865 890504   Tel: 01865 890851

TANDEM TV & FILM Ltd
10 Bargrove Avenue, Hemel Hempstead
Herts HP1 1QP
e-mail: ttv@tandemtv.com
Fax: 01442 219250   Tel: 01442 261576

TAYLOR David ASSOCIATES Ltd
F CV D Ch
1 Lostock Avenue, Poynton
Cheshire SK12 1DR   Tel/Fax: 01625 850887

T.B. TV - TONY BASTABLE TELEVISION
The White House, Church Road, Lingfield
Surrey RH7 6AH
e-mail: tbtv@msn.com
Fax: 01342 834600   Tel: 01342 834588

TELEVISION BUSINESS The
3 Dovecote, Castle Donington
Derby DE74 2LH
Fax: 01332 814592   Tel: 01332 812592

TELEVISION & THEATRE PROJECTS
17 Lord Roberts Avenue, Leigh-on-Sea
Essex SS9 1ND
Fax: 01702 710733   Tel: 01702 480488

THIN MAN FILMS
9 Greek Street, London W1D 4DQ
e-mail: info@thinman.co.uk
Fax: 020-7287 5228   Tel: 020-7734 7372

TIMELESS PRODUCTIONS
Media Arts Workshops, 12 Mead Close
Grays, Essex RM16 2TR
e-mail: timeless.productions@talk21.com
                          Tel: 01375 373886

TKO COMMUNICATIONS Ltd
PO Box 130 Hove, Sussex BN3 6QU
e-mail: jskruger@tkogroup.com
Fax: 01273 540969   Tel: 01273 550088

TMB MARKETING COMMUNICATIONS
Milton Heath House, Westcott Road
Dorking, Surrey RH4 3NB
e-mail: www.mail@motivation.co.uk
Fax: 01306 877777   Tel: 01306 877000

TVE Ltd
(Broadcast Facilities, Non-Linear Editing)
99 Holdenhurst Road, Bournemouth
Dorset BH8 8EB
e-mail: avid@tvegroup.com
Fax: 01202 311502   Tel: 01202 311501

TVF
375 City Road
London EC1V 1NB
Fax: 020-7833 2185   Tel: 020-7837 3000

TV MEDIA SERVICES Ltd/TVMS
3rd Floor, 420 Sauchiehall Street
Glasgow G2 3JD
e-mail: tvmsmail@aol.com
Fax: 0141-332 9040   Tel: 0141-331 1993

T.V. PRODUCTION PARTNERSHIP Ltd
89 Andover Road, Ludgershall
Hants SP11 9LY
e-mail: dbj@dbji.demon.co.uk
Fax: 0870 1641755   Tel: 01264 791688

TWENTIETH CENTURY FOX TELEVISION Ltd
Twentieth Century House
31-32 Soho Square, London W1D 3AP
Fax: 020-7434 2170   Tel: 020-7437 7766

TWO FOUR PRODUCTIONS Ltd
Quay West Studios, Old Newnham
Plymouth PL7 5BH
e-mail: enq@twofour.co.uk
Fax: 01752 344224   Tel: 01752 345424

TWO SIDES TV Ltd
53A Brewer Street
London W1F 9UH
e-mail: twosidestv@clara.net
Fax: 020-7287 2289   Tel: 020-7439 9882

TYBURN FILM PRODUCTIONS Ltd
F
Pinewood Studios, Iver Heath
Buckinghamshire SL0 0NH
Fax: 01753 656050   Tel: 01753 651700

TYRO PRODUCTIONS
The Coach House
20A Park Road, Teddington
Middlesex TW11 0AQ
Fax: 020-8943 4901   Tel: 020-8943 4697

UNGER Kurt
112 Portsea Hall, Portsea Place
London W2 2BZ
Fax: 020-7584 1549   Tel: 020-7584 0542

UNIQUE TELEVISION
Avon House, Kensington Village
Avonmore Road, London W14 8TS
e-mail: london@uniquegroup.co.uk
Fax: 020-7371 5352   Tel: 020-7371 5353

UNITED PRODUCTIONS & LWT PRODUCTIONS
Drama Department, The London Television
Centre, London SE1 9LT   Tel: 020-7620 1620

UNIVERSAL PICTURES Ltd
UIP House, 45 Beadon Road
London W6 0EG
Fax: 020-8563 4331   Tel: 020-8563 4329

UNIVERSAL STUDIOS
UIP House, 45 Beadon Road
London W6 0EG
Fax: 020-8563 4331   Tel: 020-8563 4329

VAGABOND HEART
2 Grassmere Road, Hornchurch
Essex RM11 3DP
e-mail: vagabondheart@virgin.net
                          Tel: 01708 781994

VC MEDIA
Chalfont Grove, Narcot Lane, Chalfont St Peter
Nr Gerrards Cross
Bucks SL9 8TY   Tel: 01494 87825

VERA
3rd Floor, 66-68 Margaret Street
London W1W 8SR
e-mail: rachael@vera.co.uk
Fax: 020-7436 6117   Tel: 020-7436 6116

VERA MEDIA
(Video Production and Training Company)
30-38 Dock Street, Leeds LS10 1JF
e-mail: vera@vera-media.co.uk
Fax: 0113-242 8739   Tel: 0113-242 8646

VIDEO AND FILM PRODUCTION
Robin Hill, The Ridge, Lower Basildon
Reading, Berks
e-mail: david.fisher@videoandfilm.co.uk
Fax: 0118-984 4316   Mobile: 07836 544955

VIDEO ARTS
Dumbarton House, 68 Oxford Street
London W1N 0LH
e-mail: info@videoarts.co.uk
Fax: 020-7580 8103   Tel: 020-7637 7288

VIDEO COMMUNICATIONS
17 West Hill
London SW18 1RB
e-mail: nikcookson@aol.com Tel: 020-8870 9933

VIDEO ENTERPRISES
12 Barbers Wood Road, High Wycombe
Bucks HP12 4EP
e-mail: maurice@vident.u-net.com
Mobile: 07831 875216   Tel/Fax: 01494 534144

VIDEOTEL PRODUCTIONS
84 Newman Street, London W1P 3LD
Fax: 020-7299 1818   Tel: 020-7299 1800

VILLAGE PRODUCTIONS
4 Midas Business Centre, Wantz Road
Dagenham, Essex RM10 8PS
e-mail: village@btconnect.com
Fax: 020-8593 0198   Tel: 020-8984 0322

VISAGE TELEVISION Ltd
Pinewood Studios, Pinewood Road,
Iver Heath, Bucks SL0 0NH
e-mail: television@visagegroup.com
Fax: 01753 652505   Tel: 01753 783500

W3KTS Ltd
10 Portland Street, York YO31 7EH
e-mail: chris@w3kts.demon.co.uk
Fax: 0870 0554863   Tel: 01904 647822

W6 STUDIO
(The Complete Video Service)
359 Lillie Road
London SW6 7PA   Tel: 020-7385 2272

WALKOVERS VIDEO PRODUCTION
Brook Cottage, Silver Street, Kington Langley
Nr Chippenham Wiltshire SN15 5NU
e-mail: walkoversvideo@msn.com
Fax: 01249 750155   Tel: 01249 750428

WALNUT PARTNERSHIP The
Crown House, Armley Road, Leeds LS12 2EJ
e-mail: mail@walnutpartnership.co.uk
Fax: 08707 427080   Tel: 08707 427070

WALSH BROS. Ltd
24 Redding House, Harlinger Street
King Henry's Wharf, London SE18 5SR
e-mail: walshbros@lycosmail.com
Tel/Fax: 020-8854 5557   Tel/Fax: 020-8858 6870

WARK CLEMENTS & Co Ltd
Studio 7, The Tollgate, Marine Crescent,
Glasgow G51 1HD
e-mail: info@warkclements.co.uk
Fax: 0141-429 1751   Tel: 0141-429 1750

WARNER BROS PRODUCTIONS Ltd
FF
Warner Suite, Pinewood Studios
Iver Heath, Bucks SL0 0NH
Fax: 01753 655703   Tel: 01753 654545

WARNER SISTERS FILM AND TELEVISION Ltd
The Cottage, Pall Mall Deposit
124 Barlby Road, London W10 6BL
e-mail: sisters@warnercine.com
Fax: 020-8960 3880   Tel: 020-8960 3550

WEST ONE FILM PRODUCERS Ltd
c/o Richard Hatton Ltd
29 Roehampton Gate, London SW15 5JR
Fax: 020-8876 6218   Tel: 020-8876 6699

WESTERN EYE TELEVISION
Easton Business Centre
Felix Road
Easton, Bristol BS5 0HE
e-mail: westerneyetv@cs.com
Fax: 0117-941 5851   Tel: 0117-941 5854

WHITE Michael
48 Dean Street
London W1D 5BF
e-mail: contact@michaelwhite.co.uk
Fax: 020-7734 7727   Tel: 020-7734 7707

WHITEHALL FILMS Ltd
10 Lower Common South
London SW15 1BP
e-mail: mwhitehall@email.msn.com
Fax: 020-8788 2340   Tel: 020-8785 3737

WHITTINGHAM Ian TELEVISION UK
1 Barker Street, Chelsea
London SW10 9EN
e-mail: iwtlondon@hotmail.com
Fax: 020-7351 9385   Tel: 020-7823 3009

WICKES COMPANY The
F TV D
10 Abbey Orchard Street
London SW1P 2LD
e-mail: wickesco@aol.com
Fax: 020-7222 0822   Tel: 020-7222 0820

WILD IRIS FILMS
59 Brewer Street, London W1R 3FB
e-mail: joe@wildiris.co.uk
Fax: 020-7494 1764   Tel: 020-7494 9230

WINNER Michael Ltd
219 Kensington High Street
London W8 6BD
e-mail: winner@ftech.co.uk
Fax: 020-7602 9217   Tel: 020-7734 8385

WORKING TITLE FILMS Ltd
Oxford House, 76 Oxford Street
London W1D 1BS
Fax: 020-7307 3001   Tel: 020-7307 3000

WORLD FILM SERVICES Ltd
Norman House, 105-109 Strand
London WC2R 0AA
Fax: 020-7240 3740   Tel: 020-7240 1444

WORLD PRODUCTIONS Ltd
Norman House, 105-109 Strand
London WC2R 0AA
Fax: 020-7240 3740   Tel: 020-7240 1444

WORLDWIDE PICTURES Ltd
21-25 St Anne's Court
London W1F 0BJ
e-mail: info@worldwidegroup.ltd.uk
Fax: 020-7734 0619   Tel: 020-7434 1121

WOT IMAGES Ltd
45 Fitzroy Street
London W1T 6EB
jackie.wot@virgin.net
Fax: 020-7387 7303   Tel: 020-7387 4040

X FILMS
(Live Action for Commercials & Music Videos)
47 Poland Street
London W1V 3DF
Fax: 020-7437 3720   Tel: 020-7287 2862

XINGU FILMS
12 Cleveland Row
London SW1A 1DH
Fax: 020-7451 0601   Tel: 020-7451 0600

YOUNGER Greg ASSOCIATES
Baron's Croft, Hare Lane, Blindley Heath
Surrey RH7 6JA
Fax: 01342 833768   Tel: 01342 832515

ZAHRA & REMICK
186 Albert Road
London N22 7AH   Tel/Fax: 020-8889 6225

ZENITH ENTERTAINMENT Plc
43-45 Dorset Street
London W1U 7NA
Fax: 020-7224 3194   Tel: 020-7224 2440

ZEPHYR FILMS Ltd
24 Colville Road
London W11 2BS
e-mail: pippa@zephyrfilms.co.uk
Fax: 020-7221 9289   Tel: 020-7221 8318

ARTTS INTERNATIONAL
Highfield Grange, Bubwith
North Yorks YO8 6DP
e-mail: admin@artts.co.uk
Fax: 01757 288253   Tel: 01757 288088

BLACK CORAL FILM & TELEVISION TRAINING
2nd Floor
241 High Street
London E17 7BH
e-mail: bctraining@coralmedia.co.uk
Fax: 020-8520 2358   Tel: 020-8520 4569

BRIGHTON FILM SCHOOL
Member of the National Association for
Higher Education in the Moving Image.
Part-time Film Director's Courses in
Cinematography (Day and Evening
Courses plus Summer Schools).
Studio: Phoenix Arts Centre
Wellesley House
10-14 Waterloo Place
Brighton BN2 2NB
Senior Lecturer: Franz von Habsburg MBKS (BAFTA)
Admissions: Meryl von Habsburg BSc MSc Cert Ed
Admin Office: 13 Tudor Close
Dean Court Road
Rottingdean
East Sussex BN2 7DF
e-mail: brightonfilmschool@cwcom.net
Fax: 01273 302163   Tel: 01273 302166

LONDON INTERNATIONAL FILM SCHOOL The
(Two year, Full-time Diploma
Course in Film Making)
24 Shelton Street
London WC2H 9UB
e-mail: film.school@lifs.org.uk
Fax: 020-7497 3718   Tel: 020-7836 9642

MIDDLESEX UNIVERSITY
(School of Art, Design & Performing Arts)
Cat Hill, Barnet, Herts EN4 8HT
Fax: 020-8440 9541   Tel: 020-8411 5000

NATIONAL FILM & TELEVISION SCHOOL
(Full-time 2-year Courses in
Animation/Documentary or Fiction Direction;
Editing; Cinematography; Producing;
Screen Music; Sound; Screen Design; TV
Producing / Directing; One & Two-Year
Courses in Screenwriting. Also Short Courses
for Freelancers)
Beaconsfield Studios
Station Road
Beaconsfield
Bucks HP9 1LG
email: admin@nftsfilm-tv.ac.uk
Fax: 01494 674042   Tel: 01494 671234

RE:ACTORS
15 Montrose Walk
Weybridge
Surrey KT13 8JN
e-mail: michael@reactors.co.uk
Fax: 01932 830248   Tel: 01932 888885

**SURREY INSTITUTE OF ART & DESIGN
UNIVERSITY COLLEGE**
(3-year BA (Hons) Photography, Film & Video
& Production, Broadcast and New Media,
Animation)
Falkner Road
Farnham
Surrey GU9 7DS   Tel: 01252 722441

**UNIVERSITY OF WESTMINSTER SCHOOL OF
COMMUNICATION & CREATIVE INDUSTRIES**
(Degree courses in Film and
Television/Contemporary Media Practice)
Watford Road
Northwick Park
Harrow
Middlesex HA1 3TP   Tel: 020-7911 5000

M.V. DIXIE QUEEN

London's largest cruising/static Mississippi-style paddleboat. High 10' ceilings. 2500 sq. ft. of interior space. 2000 ft. exterior space. Additional restaurant deck. Available for Film/TV location work. Experienced personnel on board can assist with all aspects of waterside filming, permissions etc. Call Nigel Scandrett for a good deal and to discuss the potential of using a river venue.

Thames Luxury Charters 020 8780 1562 Website: www.thamesluxurycharters.co.uk

ACCESS STUDIOS
8-10 Creekside
London SE8 3DX
e-mail: info@accessstudios.com
Fax: 0870 1205658   Tel: 020-7231 6185

ARDMORE STUDIOS Ltd
Herbert Road
Bray, Co. Wicklow, Ireland
e-mail: film@ardmore.ie
Fax: 00 353 1 2861894   Tel: 00 353 1 2862971

BBC SOUTH (Elstree)
BBC Elstree Centre
Clarendon Road, Borehamwood
Herts WD6 1JF   Tel: 020-8953 6100

BBC TELEVISION
Television Centre
Wood Lane, Shepherds Bush
London W12 7RJ   Tel: 020-8743 8000

BRAY STUDIOS
Down Place, Water Oakley
Windsor Road, Windsor
Berks SL4 5UG
Fax: 01628 770381   Tel: 01628 622111

CAPITAL STUDIOS
13 Wandsworth Plain
London SW18 1ET
e-mail: info@capitalstudios.co.uk
Fax: 020-8877 0234   Tel: 020-8877 1234

C F S CHELTENHAM FILM STUDIOS
Arle Court, Hatherley Lane
Cheltenham, Glos GL51 6PN
e-mail: info@cheltstudio.com
Fax: 01242 542 701   Tel: 01242 542 700

CORINTHIAN TELEVISION FACILITIES
(TV Post Production, Studios, Transmission)
87 St John's Wood Terrace
London NW8 6PY
Fax: 020-7483 4264   Tel: 020-7483 6000

EALING STUDIOS OPERATIONS Ltd
Ealing Green, Ealing, London W5 5EP
e-mail: info@ealingstudios.com
Fax: 020-8758 8658   Tel: 020-8567 6655

ELSTREE STUDIOS
Shenley Road
Borehamwood
Herts WD6 1JG
e-mail: info@elstreefilmtv.com
Fax: 020-8905 1135   Tel: 020-8953 1600

HILLSIDE
Merry Hill Road, Bushey
Herts WD23 1DR
e-mail: enquiries@hillside-studios.co.uk
Fax: 020-8421 8085   Tel: 020-8950 7919

LONDON STUDIOS The
London Television Centre, Upper Ground
London SE1 9LT
Fax: 020-7928 8405   Tel: 020-7620 1620

PINEWOOD STUDIOS
Pinewood Road
Iver Heath
Bucks SL0 0NH
Fax: 01753 656844   Tel: 01753 651700

REUTERS TELEVISION
200 Gray's Inn Road
London WC1X 8YZ   Tel: 020-7250 1122

RIVERSIDE STUDIOS
Crisp Road
London W6 9RL
e-mail: info@riversidestudios.co.uk
Fax: 020-8237 1001   Tel: 020-8237 1000

ROTHERHITHE STUDIOS
119 Rotherhithe Street
London SE16 4NF
Fax: 020-7231 2119   Tel: 020-7231 2209

SANDS FILMS
119 Rotherhithe Street
London SE16 4NF
Fax: 020-7231 2119   Tel: 020-7231 2209

SAVOY HILL STUDIO
Adam House, 7-10 Adam Street
London WC2N 6AA
e-mail: savoyhillstudio@tabard.u-net.com
Fax: 020-7497 0830   Tel: 020-7497 0850

SHEPPERTON STUDIOS
Studios Road, Shepperton
Middlesex TW17 0QD
Fax: 01932 568989   Tel: 01932 562611

TEDDINGTON STUDIOS Ltd
Broom Road
Teddington
e-mail: sales@teddington.co.uk
Middlesex TW11 9NT   Tel: 020-8977 3252

TWICKENHAM FILM STUDIOS Ltd
The Barons St Margaret's, Twickenham
Middlesex TW1 2AW
Fax: 020-8607 8889   Tel: 020-8607 8888

Good Digs Guide

Compiled By JANICE CRAMER & DAVID BANKS

This is a list of digs recommended by those who have used them. To keep the list accurate please send recommendations for inclusion and suggestions for deletion to GOOD DIGS GUIDE at The Spotlight. Thanks to all who did so over the last year.

ABERDEEN
Mrs A Milne   5 Sunnyside Walk, Aberdeen AB2 3NZ   01224 638951

AYR
Sheila Dunn   The Dunn-Thing Guest House   01292 284531
13 Park Circus, Ayr KA7 2DJ   Mobile: 07887 928685

BATH
Andrew Ellis   32 Calton Walk, Bath BA2 4QQ   Tel/Fax: 01225 319904
Cecilia Hutton   **Bath Holiday Homes, 3 Frankley Buildings, Bath BA1 6EG**   **01225 332221**
e-mail: bhh@virgin.net
Mrs G Porter   95 Shakespeare Avenue, Bath, Avon BA2 4RQ   01225 420166
Jane Tapley   Camden Lodgings, 3 Upper Camden Place, Bath BA1 5HX   01225 446561

BELFAST
Mrs Cargill   Eglantine Guest House, 21 Eglantine Ave, Belfast BT9 6DW   028-9066 7585
Ms S McCully   28 Eglantine Ave, Belfast BT9 6DX 028-9068 2031   Mob: 07712 587706

BILLINGHAM
Audrey & Reg Bell   14 The Crescent, Linthorpe, Middlesbrough T55 6SQ   01642 822483
Pam & John Fanthorpe   Harker Hill Farm, Seamer, Stokesley, Middlesbrough TS9 5NF   01642 710431
Anna Farminer   168 Kennedy Gardens, Billingham, Cleveland TS23 3RJ   01642 530205
Mrs S Gibson   Northwood, 61 Tunstall Avenue, Billingham   01642 561071/553125
Mrs Edna Newton   97 Brendon Crescent, Billingham TS23 2QU   01642 647958
Mobile: 07946 237381

BIRMINGHAM
Mr N K Baker   41 King Edward Road, Mosley, Birmingham B13 8EL   0121-449 8220
John Eccles   18 Holly Road, Edgbaston, Birmingham B16 9NH   0121-454 4853
Ms B T Matusiak-Varley   **Red Gables, 69 Handsworth Wood Road, Handsworth Wood**
Birmingham B20 2DH   **Tel/Fax: 0121-686 5942 Mobile: 07711 751105**
Marlene P Mountain   **268 Monument Road, Edgbaston, Birmingham B16 8XF**   **0121-454 5900**
Mrs Wilson   17 Yew Tree Road, Edgbaston, Birmingham B15 2LX   0121-440 5182

BLACKPOOL
Jean Lees   Ascot Flats, 6 Hull Road, Central Blackpool FY1 4QB   01253 621059
Bob Priestley   Hollywood Apartments, 2-4 Wellington Rd, Blackpool FY1 6AR   01253 341633
The Proprietor   The Brooklyn Hotel, 7 Wilton Parade, Blackpool FY1 2HE   01253 627003

BOLTON
Mrs M Milton-White   20 Heywood Gardens, Great Lever, Bolton BL3 6RB   01204 531589

BOURNEMOUTH
Mrs Clarke   Yew Tree Guest House, 4 Upper Terrace Road
Bournemouth BH2 5NW   01202 554558

BRADFORD
Michael Calver   **33 Stockhill Fold, Greengates, Bradford BD10 9AY**   **01274 616990**
Theresa Smith   4 St Paul's Road, Shipley, Bradford BD18 3EP   01274 778568

BRIGHTON
Ms Carol Cleveland   13 Belgrave Street, Brighton BN2 2NS   01273 602607
Mrs Corinne Hamlin   Flat 6, Preston Lodge, Little Preston Street, Brighton BN1 2HQ   01273 321346
Zita Latham   Brighton House, 13 Powis Square, Brighton BN1 3HG   01273 326928
Kate Merrin   2a Exton House, 4 Second Avenue, Hove BN3 2LG   Mobile: 07714 672233

BRISTOL
Jinnie Blackburn   79 Stackpool Road, Southville, Bristol BS3 1NP   0117-983 3676
Jean Rozario   Manor Lodge, 21 Station Rd, Keynsham, N Somerset BS31 2BH   0117-986 2191

BROMLEY
Mrs S Greenwood   8 Sutherland Close, Chalk, Gravesend, Kent DA12 4XJ   01474 350819

PORTUGAL - ALGARVE Private, quiet, tasteful 2 bed apartment. 2nd floor elegant, 5 storey block, twin lift service and secure parking in basement. All mod.cons. 'home from home'. 7 mins walk to the biggest and best fine sandy beach, flanked by high red sandstone rocks. New Marina recently established 250m away. It is double glazed, heated so that it may be used off-season. Mild weather means golf of high standard is played in the Algarve all year round. Prices Low £300, Mid £400, £550 pw for the whole apartment. Not suitable for young children. Cleaner once a week. 50 mins away by car from Faro airport. No smoking. *Please call:* **01227 450064**

BURY ST EDMUNDS
| Mrs S Bird | 30 Crown Street, Bury St Edmunds, Suffolk IP33 1QU | 01284 754492 |
| Sue Harrington-Spier | 39 Well Street, Bury St Edmunds, Suffolk IP33 1EQ | 01284 768986 |

BUXTON
| Mrs M Kitchen | Flat 1, 17 Silverlands, Buxton, Derbyshire SK17 6QH | 01298 78898 |
| Anne & Colin Scruton | Griff Guest House, 2 Compton Road, Buxton SK17 9DN | 01298 23628 |

CANTERBURY
Mrs Jennifer J Butcher	5 Vernon Place, Canterbury, Kent CT1 3HG	01227 470712
Mrs A Dolan	**12 Leycroft Close, Canterbury, Kent CT2 7LD**	**01227 450064**
Nicola Ellen	Crockshard Farm House, Wingham Canterbury CT3 1NY	01227 720464 Fax: 01227 721929
Doris Stockbridge	Tudor House, 6 Best Lane, Canterbury, Kent CT1 2JB	01227 765650

CARDIFF
Anne Blade	25 Romilly Road, Canton, Cardiff CF5 1FH	029-2022 5860
Nigel Lewis	66 Donald St, Cardiff, South Glamorgan CF2 4TR	029-2049 4008
Michael Nelmes	12 Darran St, Cathays, Cardiff, South Glamorgan CF24 4JF	029-2034 2166
T Taylor & P Chichester	32 Kincraig St, Roath, Cardiff, South Glamorgan CF24 3HW	029-2048 6785

CHESTERFIELD
Linda & Chris Cook	27 Tennyson Avenue, Chesterfield, Derbyshire	01246 202631
Mr N Connell	Anis Louise Guest Hse, 34 Clarence Road, Chesterfield S40 1LN	01246 235412
Mr & Mrs Popplewell	23 Tennyson Avenue, Chesterfield, Derbyshire S40 4SN	01246 201738

CHICHESTER
Tricia & Richard Beeny	Hunston Mill Holiday Homes, Hunston, Nr Chichester PO20 6AU	01243 783375
Ann Drake	48 Cambrai Avenue, Chichester PO21 2JY	01243 778064
Joanna Green	Oakhurst Cottage, Carron Lane, Midhurst GU29 9LF	01730 813523

COVENTRY
| **Paddy & Bob Snelson** | **Banner Hill Farmhouse, Rouncil Lane, Kenilworth CV8 1NN** | **01926 852850** |

DARLINGTON
Mr E Barlow	George Hotel, Piercebridge, Darlington DL2 3SW	01325 374576
Mrs Bird	Gilling Old Mill, Gilling West, Richmond, N Yorks DL10 5JD	01748 822771
Mrs Jean Evans	26a Pierremont Crescent, Darlington DL3 9PB	01325 252032
Anne Graham	Holme House, Piercebridge, Darlington DL2 3SY	01325 374280

DUNDEE
| Mrs J Hill | Ash Villa, 216 Arbroth Road, Dundee DD4 7RZ | 01382 450831 |

EASTBOURNE
Peter Allen	Flat 1, 16 Enys Rd, Eastbourne BN21 2DN	01323 730235 Mobile: 07712 439289
S Awdry	31 Enys Road, Eastbourne BN21 2DH	01323 416147
David E J Chant	Hamdon, 49 King's Drive, Eastbourne BN21 2NY	01323 722544
Brent Chapman	13 Warrior Square, Eastbourne BN22 7DB	Tel/Fax: 01323 647007
Mrs J Dawson	14 New Upperton Road, Eastbourne	01323 729988
Summerfords	Holiday Flatlets, 5 Jevington Gardens, Eastbourne BN21 4HR	01323 638919
Mrs Weaver	Meads Holiday Flats, 1 Jevington Gardens, Eastbourne BN21 4HR	01323 724362

EDINBURGH
Edna Glen Miller	25 Bellevue Road, Edinburgh EH7 4DL	0131-556 4131
Mrs Helen Russell	**9 Lonsdale Terrace, Edinburgh EH3 9HN**	**0131-229 7219/527 8200**
Joyce Stobbart	25a Scotland Street, Edinburgh EH3 6PY	0131-226 6881/556 7546

GLASGOW
David W Baird	6 Beaton Road, Maxwell Park, Glasgow G41 4LA	0141-423 1340/570 5420
Simon Leslie-Carter	52 Charlotte Street, Glasgow G1 5DW e-mail: info@52charlottestreet.co.uk	01436 810264
David Lloyd Jones	3 Whittinghame Drive, Kelvinside, Glasgow G12 0XS	0141-339 3331
Lesley Robinson	28 Marywood Sq, Glasgow G41 2BJ	0141-423 6920 Mobile: 07957 188922

HULL
| The Arches Guesthouse | 38 Saner Street, Hull HU3 2TR | 01482 211558 |
| Sarah Gomme | 46 Marlborough Avenue, Hull | 01482 447440 |

Sheles Studios

Quality, comfortable clean serviced single studio bedrooms with own kitchenette £80 per week,
15 minutes Opera House/Palace Theatre. Metro station 3 minutes walk. Junction 17 M60 Motorway 1 mile.

Sheles Studios, 52 Ashtree Road, Higher Crumpsall, Manchester M8 5SA Phone: 0161 766 7542 Fax: 0161 766 2124

INVERNESS
Mrs Blair	McDonald Hse Hotel, 1 Ardross Terrace, Inverness IV3 5NQ	01463 232878
Jennifer Kerr-Smith	Ardkeen Tower, 5 Culduthel Road, Inverness	01463 233131
Mrs Paterson	Gowanlea, 11 Ballifeary Road, Inverness IV3 5PJ	01463 234906
Mrs Slaney	Abermar Guest House, 25 Fairfield Road, Inverness IV3 5QD Tel/Fax: 01463 239019

IPSWICH
Liz Bennett	Gayfers, Playford, Ipswich IP6 9DR	01473 623343
Anne Hyde-Johnson	64 Benton Street, Hadleigh, Ipswich, Suffolk IP7 5AT	01473 823110

ISLE OF MAN
Mr Holt	Mereside Private Hotel, 1 Empire Terrace, Douglas, Isle of Man	01624 676355

ISLE OF WIGHT
Miss Sue Ogston	Winward Hse, 69 Mill Hill Rd, Cowes, Isle of Wight PO31 7EQ Tel/Fax: 01983 280940

KIRKCALDY
Mrs Nicol	44 Glebe Park, Kirkcaldy, Fife KY1 1BL	01592 264531

LEEDS
Mrs M Baker	**2 Ridge Mount, (off Cliff Rd), Leeds LS6 2HD**	**0113-275 8735**
Mrs Kavanagh	Novello House, 2 Ladywood Rd, Roundhay, Leeds LS8 2QF	0113-265 8330
Bryan & Linda Littlewood	4 Oatland Green, Leeds LS7 1SN	0113-225 3281

LINCOLN
Andrew Carnell	Tennyson Court Cottages, 3 Tennyson Street, Lincoln LN1 1LZ	01522 533044
		0800 9805408
The Proprietor	Ye Old Crowne Inn (Theatre Pub), Clasketgate, Lincoln LN2 1JS	01522 542896
Mavis S Sharpe	Bight House, 17 East Bight, Lincoln LN2 1QH	01522 534477

LIVERPOOL
Kate Cowie	Flat 5, 2 Fulwood Park, Liverpool L17 5AG	0151-726 0061/709 9434
Ross Double	5 Percy Street, Liverpool L8 7LT	0151-708 8821
Anne Maloney	16 Sandown Lane, Wavertree, Liverpool L15 8HY	0151-734 4839/475 5522
Damian McGuinness	Seapark Apartments, (office) 51 Alexandra Road	
	Southport, Merseyside PR9 9HD	01704 500444
Sue Parry	7b Linnet Lane, Liverpool L17 3BE	0151-728 7733

LLANDUDNO
Alan Bell	Quinton Hotel, 36 Church Walks, Llandudno LL30 2HN	01492 876879

LONDON
Mrs I Allen	Flat 2, 9 Dorset Square, London NW1 6QB	020-7723 3979
Mrs P A Broughton	31 Ringstead Road, Catford, London SE6 2BU	020-8461 0146
Maggie Guess	36 Federal Road, Perivale, Middlesex UB6 7AW	020-8991 0918
Lindy Shaw	11 Baronsmede, Acton, London W5 4LS	020-8567 0877

MALVERN
Mrs Emuss	Priory Holme, 18 Avenue Road, Malvern WR14 3AR	01684 568455
Mr & Mrs McLeod	Sidney House, 40 Worcester Road, Malvern WR14 4AA	01684 574994

MANCHESTER
James & Risa Duff	40 Sunnybank Road, Bury, Lancs BL9 8HF	0161-796 7073
Lester Farber	**Sheles Studios, 169 Bury New Road, Manchester M45 6AB**	**0161-766 7542**
P M Jones	375 Bury New Road, Whitefield, Manchester M45 7SU	0161-766 9243
David Martin & Jez Dolan	86 Stanley Road, Old Trafford, Manchester M16 9DH	0161-848 9231
Fiona & John Prichard	45 Bamford Road, Didsbury, Manchester M20 2QP	0161-434 4877
Mr D Satterthwaite	Albany Hotel, 21 Albany Road, Chorton-cum-Hardy	
	Manchester M21 0AY	0161-881 6774
Susan Twist	45 Osborne Road, Levenshulme, Manchester M19 2DU	0161-225 1591

MILFORD HAVEN
Bruce & Diana Henricksen	**Belhaven Hse Hotel, 29 Hamilton Terrace, Milford Haven SA73 3JJ**	
	e-mail: hbruceh@aol.com	**01646 695983 Fax: 01646 690787**

MOLD
Mr & Mrs Major	The Mount, Higher Kinnerton, Chester CH4 9BQ	01244 660275

NEWARK-ON-TRENT
Anne Burns & Brien Chitty	69 Harcourt Street, Newark-on-Trent, Notts NG24 1RG	01636 702801

G

NEWCASTLE-UPON-TYNE

Miss Tot Charlton	Ryton Grange , Ryton, Tyne & Wear NE40 3UN	0191-413 3878
Thomas Guy	11 Rokeby Drive, Gosforth, Newcastle NE3 4JY	0191-285 7057
Mary Kalaugher	4 Tankerville Terrace, Jesmond, Newcastle upon Tyne NE2 3AH	0191-281 0475
Madaleine Moffatt	9 Curtis Road, Fenham NE4 9BH	0191-273 4744
Mrs P Stansfield	Rosebury Hotel, 2 Rosebury Cres, Jesmond, Newcastle NE2 1ET	0191-281 3363
Miss M E Steele	7 Stoneyhurst Road, S Gosforth, Newcastle NE3 1PR	0191-285 7771

NEWPORT

Mrs Dinah Price	'Great House', 16c Isca Road, Old Village, Caerleon Nr Newport, Gwent NP18 1QG e-mail: price.greathouse@tesco.net	01633 420216

NORWICH

Julia Edgeley	8 Chester Street, Norwich NR2 2AY	01603 598522 Mobile: 07713 367253
Maureen Moore	63 Surrey Street, Norwich NR1 3PG	01603 621979

NOTTINGHAM

Barbara Davis	3 Tattershall Drive, The Park, Nottingham NG7 1BX	0115-947 4179
Mrs J A Kniveton	22 Ingham Grove, Lenton Gardens, Nottingham NG7 2LQ	0115-978 7202
Mrs Offord	5 Tattershall Drive, The Park, Nottingham NG7 1BX	0115-947 6924
Mrs S Santos	Eastwood Farm, Hagg Ln, Epperstone, Nottingham NG14 6AX	0115-966 3018
Christine Walker	18a Cavendish Cresent North, The Park, Nottingham NG7 1BA	0115-947 2485

OXFORD

Susan Petty	74 Corn Street, Witney, Oxford	01993 703035

PLYMOUTH

Mr & Mrs Carson	6 Beech Cottages, Parsonage Rd, Newton Ferrers, Nr Plymouth	01752 872124
Mr & Mrs Curno	Russell Lodge, 9 Holyrood Place, The Hoe, Plymouth PL1 2QB	01628 670295
John & Sandra Humphreys	Lyttleton Guest House (Self Catering), 4 Crescent Avenue, Plymouth PL1 3AN	01752 220176
Julia Noble	Ashgrove Hotel, 218 Citadel Road, The Hoe, Plymouth PL1 3BB	01752 664046
Neta Pressland	1 Hollyrood Place, The Hoe, Plymouth PL1 2QB	01752 253965
Hugh & Eloise Spencer	10 Grand Parade, Plymouth PL1 3DF	01752 664066

POOLE

Mrs Burnett	63 Orchard Avenue, Parkstone, Poole, Dorset BH14 8AH	01202 743877
Sarah Moore	Harbour View, 11 Harbour View Road, Poole BH14 0PD	01202 734763
Mrs Saunders	1 Harbour Shallows, 15 Whitecliff Road, Poole BH14 8DU	01202 741637

READING

Estate Office	Mapledurham House and Watermill Mapledurham Estate, Reading RG4 7TR	0118-972 3350

SHEFFIELD

J Craig & B Rosen	59 Nether Edge Road, Sheffield S7 1RW	0114-258 1337
J Horton & L Cullumbine	223 Cemetery Road, Sheffield S11 8FQ	0114-255 6092
Carole Gillespie	251 Western Road, Crookes, Sheffield S10 1LE	0114-266 2666
Liz Godfrey	12 Victoria Road, Sheffield S10 2DL	0114-266 9389
Penny Slack	Rivelin Glen Quarry, Rivelin Valley Road, Sheffield S6 5SE e-mail: pennyslack@aol.com	0114-234 0382 Fax: 0114-234 7630

SOUTHSEA & PORTSMOUTH

Paddy & John Erskine	The Elms Guest Hse, 48 Victoria Rd South, Southsea PO5 2BT	023-9282 3924
Mrs Steward	81 Gains Road, Southsea PO4 0PJ	023-9283 3690
Wendy Tyrrell	Douglas Cottage, 27 Somerset Road, Southsea PO5 2NL	023-9282 1453

STOKE-ON-TRENT

Dorothy Griffiths	40 Princes Road, Hartshill, Stoke-on-Trent	01782 416198
Mrs Hindmoor	Verdon Guest Hse, 44 Charles St, Hanley, Stoke-on-Trent ST1 3JY	01782 264244
Mr & Mrs K Meredith	Bank End Farm Cottages, Hammond Ave, Brown Edge Stoke-on-Trent Staffs ST6 8QU	01782 502160

STRATFORD-UPON-AVON

The Proprietor	Caterham Hse, 58-59 Rother St, Stratford CV37 6LT	01789 297070/267309

SUNDERLAND

Hazel Clifford	Ravensbourne Guest House, 106 Beach Road South Shields, Tyne and Wear NE33	0191-456 5849
Mrs Henderson	22 Park Parade, Roker, Sunderland SR6 9LU	0191-565 6511
Pat Underwood	132 Fort Street, South Shields, Tyne and Wear NE33 2AZ	0191-422 5066

SWANSEA

Mr B Richards	152 Western Street, Swansea SA1	01792 464443

TAUNTON

Mike and Diana Jerrold	The Coach House, Pitminister, Taunton TA3 7AZ	01823 421571

TORQUAY

Frank & Irena Lovsey	Silverton Holiday Apts, 217 St Marychurch Rd, Torquay TQ1 3JT	Tel/Fax: 01803 327147
Mr William Peter	The Maisonette, 9 Ilsham Road, Wellswood, Torquay TQ1 2JG	01803 201782

Good Digs Guide

WESTCLIFF
Joy Hussey   42a Ceylon Road, Westcliff on Sea SS0 7HP   Mobile: 07946 413496
Nicola Swan   7 Old Leigh Road, Leigh, Essex   01702 471600

WESTON-SUPER-MARE
Mrs Jones   Marlborough Holiday Flats, (Sea Front), 41 Bimbeck Road
Weston-Super-Mare BS23 2EE   01934 636100

WINCHESTER
Mrs Fetherston-Dilke   85 Christchurch Road, Winchester SO23 9QY   Tel/Fax: 01962 868661
e-mail: fetherstondilke@x-stream.co.uk

WOLVERHAMPTON
Julia & Ron Bell   Treetops, The Hem, Shifnal, Shropshire TF11 9PS   01952 460566
Sonia Nixon   39 Stubbs Road, Pennfields, Wolverhampton WV3 7DJ   01902 339744
Peter A Riggs   'Bethesda', 56 Chapel Lane, Codsall, Nr Wolverhampton WV8 2EJ   01902 844068

WORCESTER
Mrs Chris Crossland   Greenlands, Uphampton, Ombersley, Worcester WR9 0JP   01905 620873

WORTHING
Mollie Stewart   School House, 11 Ambrose Place, Worthing BN11 1PZ   01903 206823

YORK
Abbey House Apts   7 St Mary's, Bootham, York YO30 7DD   01765 605133/01904 636154
Tom Blacklock   155 Lowther Street, York YO3 7LZ   01904 620487
Iris & Dennis Blower   Dalescroft Guest Hse, 10 Southlands Rd, York YO23 1NP   01904 626801
Mr & Mrs Harrand   Hedley House Hotel & Apts, 3 Bootham Terrace, York YO3 7DH   01904 637404

Opera Companies

BROOMHILL OPERA
Wilton's Music Hall
Graces Alley, Wellclose Square, London E1 8JB
e-mail: opera@broomhill.demon.co.uk
Fax: 020-7702 1414   Tel: 020-7702 9555

D'OYLY CARTE OPERA COMPANY
The Powerhouse
6 Sancroft Street, London SE11 5UD
e-mail: mail@doylycarte.org.uk
Fax: 020-7793 7300   Tel: 020-7793 7100

DUAL CONTROL INTERNATIONAL THEATRE
Historic Dockyard, Chatham, Kent ME4 4TE
e-mail: opera.international@virgin.net
Fax: 01634 819149   Tel: 01634 819141

ENGLISH FESTIVAL OPERA
27 Sea Avenue, Rustington
e-mail: info.efo@fastnet.co.uk
West Sussex BN16 2DQ   Tel: 01903 850432

ENGLISH NATIONAL OPERA
London Coliseum, St Martin's Lane
London WC2N 4ES
Fax: 020-7845 9277   Tel: 020-7836 0111

ENGLISH TOURING OPERA
250A Kennington Lane, London SE11 5RD
Fax: 020-7735 7008   Tel: 020-7820 1131

EUROPEAN CHAMBER OPERA
(Touring Opera)
60C Kyverdale Road, London N16 7AJ
e-mail: info@echopera.demon.co.uk
Fax: 020-8806 4465   Tel: 020-8806 4231

GLYNDEBOURNE FESTIVAL OPERA
Glyndebourne, Lewes
East Sussex BN8 5UU   Tel: 01273 812321

GRANGE PARK OPERA
5 Chancery Lane, London EC4 1BU
e-mail: info@grangeparkopera.co.uk
Fax: 020-7320 5429   Tel: 020-7320 5586

KENTISH OPERA
Watermede, Wickhurst Road
Sevenoaks, Weald,
Kent TN14 6LX   Tel: 01732 463284

LONDON OPERA PLAYERS
Broadmeade Copse
Westwood Lane, Wanborough, Surrey GU3 2JN
e-mail: operaplayers@gmx.net
Fax: 01483 811721   Tel: 01483 811004

MUSIC THEATRE LONDON
Chertsey Chambers
12 Mercer Street, London WC2H 9QD
e-mail: musictheatre.london@virgin.net
Fax: 020-7240 0805   Tel: 020-7240 0919

OPERA DELLA LUNA
7 Cotmore House
Fringford, Bicester, Oxon OX6 9RQ
e-mail: operadellaluna@aol.com
Fax: 01869 323533   Tel: 01869 325131

OPERA NORTH
Grand Theatre, 46 New Briggate, Leeds LS1 6NU
e-mail: ongendirectorpa@aol.com
Fax: 0113-244 0418   Tel: 0113-243 9999

OPERA PICCOLA
24-27 White Lion Street, London N1 9PD
e-mail: info@operapiccola.com
Fax: 020-7713 6070   Tel: 020-7713 6062

PEGASUS OPERA COMPANY Ltd
The Brix, St Matthew's
Brixton Hill
London SW2 1JF   Tel/Fax: 020-7501 9501

PIMLICO OPERA
5 Chancery Lane, London EC4A 1BU
e-mail: pimlico@grangeparkopera.co.uk
Fax: 020-7320 5429   Tel: 020-7320 5586

ROYAL OPERA The
Royal Opera House
Covent Garden
London WC2E 9DD   Tel: 020-7240 1200

SCOTTISH OPERA
39 Elmbank Crescent
Glasgow G2 4PT   Tel: 0141-248 4567

WELSH NATIONAL OPERA
John Street, Cardiff CF10 5SP
e-mail: marketing@wno.org.uk
Fax: 029-2048 3050   Tel: 029-2046 4666

ACTING POSITIVE
22 Chaldon Road, London SW6 7NJ
e-mail: ianflintoff@aol.com   Tel: 020-7385 3800

ACTORCLUB Ltd
17 Inkerman Road
London NW5 3BT   Tel: 020-7267 2759

ACTORS' ADVISORY SERVICE
29 Talbot Road, Twickenham
Middlesex TW2 6SJ   Tel: 020-8287 2839

ACTORS' BENEVOLENT FUND
6 Adam Street, London WC2N 6AD
e-mail: office@abf.org.uk
Fax: 020-7836 8978   Tel: 020-7836 6378

ACTORS CENTRE The (LONDON)
1A Tower Street, London WC2H 9NP
e-mail: act@actorscentre.co.uk
Fax: 020-7240 3896   Tel: 020-7240 3940

ACTORS CENTRE The (NORTHERN)
(See NORTHERN ACTORS CENTRE The)

ACTORS CENTRE NORTH - EAST The
1st Floor, 1 Black Swan Court, Westgate Road
Newcastle-upon-Tyne NE1 1SG
e-mail: actorscentrene@yahoo.com
                             Tel: 0191-221 0158

ACTORS' CHARITABLE TRUST
Suite 255-256, Africa House
64-78 Kingsway
London WC2B 6BD
e-mail: tact.actors@virgin.net
Fax: 020-7242 0234   Tel: 020-7242 0111

ACTORS' CHURCH UNION
St Paul's Church, Bedford Street
London WC2E 9ED   Tel: 020-7240 0344

ADVERTISING ASSOCIATION
Abford House, 15 Wilton Road
London SW1V 1NJ
e-mail: aa@adassoc.org.uk
Fax: 020-7931 0376   Tel: 020-7828 2771

AFTRA
(American Federation of TV & Radio Artists)
260 Madison Avenue
New York NY 10016
Fax: (212) 545 1238   Tel: (212) 532-0800

5757 Wilshire Boulevard, 9th Floor
Los Angeles CA 90036   Tel: (323) 634-8100

AGENTS' ASSOCIATION Ltd (Great Britain)
54 Keyes House, Dolphin Square
London SW1V 3NA
e-mail: association@agents-uk.com
Fax: 020-7821 0261   Tel: 020-7834 0515

AMATEUR DRAMATICS & OPERATICS DOTCOM
(Worldwide Directory of Amateur Theatre -
Jill Eccleston)
e-mail: editor@amateurdramatics.com
Fax: 0870 1694836   Tel: 01257 450386

**ARTS AND ENTERTAINMENT TECHNICAL
TRAINING INITIATIVE (AETTI)**
Lower Ground
14 Blenheim Terrace
London NW8 0EB
e-mail: aetti@sumack.freeserve.co.uk
Fax: 020-7328 5035   Tel: 020-7328 6174

ARTS & BUSINESS
Nutmeg House, 60 Gainsford Street
Butlers Wharf, London SE1 2NY
e-mail: head.office@aandb.org.uk
Fax: 020-7407 7527   Tel: 020-7378 8143

ARTS CENTRE GROUP The
The Courtyard, 59A Portobello Road
London W11 3DB
e-mail: info@artscentregroup.org.uk
Fax: 020-7221 7689   Tel: 020-7243 4550

ARTS COUNCIL OF ENGLAND
14 Great Peter Street, London SW1P 3NQ
e-mail: enquiries@artscouncil.org.uk
Fax: 020-7973 6590   Tel: 020-7973 6517

ARTS COUNCIL OF NORTHERN IRELAND
MacNeice House, 77 Malone Road
Belfast BT9 6AQ
Fax: 028-9066 1715   Tel: 028-9038 5200

ARTS COUNCIL OF WALES
9 Museum Place, Cardiff CF10 3NX
e-mail: information@ccc-acw.org.uk
Fax: 029-2022 1447   Tel: 029-2037 6500

ARTSLINE
(Disabled Actors Information)
54 Chalton Street, London NW1 1HS
e-mail: access@artsline.org.uk
Fax: 020-7383 2653   Tel: 020-7388 2474

**ASSOCIATION OF BRITISH THEATRE
TECHNICIANS**
47 Bermondsey Street
London SE1 3XT
Fax: 020-7378 6170   Tel: 020-7403 3778

ASSOCIATION OF LIGHTING DESIGNERS
PO Box 89, Welwyn Garden City AL7 1ZW
e-mail: office@ald.org.uk   Tel/Fax: 01707 891848

ASSOCIATION OF MODEL AGENTS
122 Brompton Road
London SW3 1JE
Info. Line: 0891 517644   Tel: 020-7584 6466

**ASSOCIATION OF PROFESSIONAL THEATRE
FOR CHILDREN & YOUNG PEOPLE (APT)**
c/o Brian Bishop, Warwick Arts Centre
University of Warwick
Coventry CV4 7AL
e-mail: b.c.bishop@warwick.ac.uk
Fax: 024-7652 3883   Tel: 024-7652 4252

BECTU
(See BROADCASTING ENTERTAINMENT
CINEMATOGRAPH & THEATRE UNION)

**BRITISH ACADEMY OF COMPOSERS &
SONGWRITERS The**
2nd Floor, British Music House
25-27 Berners Street
London W1T 3LR
e-mail: info@britishacademy.com
Fax: 020-7636 2212   Tel: 020-7636 2929

**BRITISH ACADEMY OF FILM &
TELEVISION ARTS The**
195 Piccadilly
London W1J 9LN
e-mail: membership@bafta.org
Fax: 020-7437 0473   Tel: 020-7734 0022

BRITISH ACADEMY OF FILM & TELEVISION ARTS (LOS ANGELES) The
930 South Robertson Boulevard, Los Angeles, California 90035 1626
e-mail: info@baftala.org
Fax: (310) 854-6002   Tel: (310) 652-4121

BRITISH ACADEMY OF STAGE AND SCREEN COMBAT
Suite 280, 37 Store Street
London WC1E 7QF
e-mail: info@bassc.org   Tel: 020-8352 0605

BRITISH ASSOCIATION OF DRAMA THERAPISTS The
41 Broomhouse Lane
London SW6 3DP
e-mail: gillian@badth.demon.co.uk
                              Tel/Fax: 020-7731 0160

BRITISH BOARD OF FILM CLASSIFICATION
3 Soho Square
London W1D 3HE
Fax: 020-7287 0141   Tel: 020-7440 1570

BRITISH COUNCIL The
(Drama & Dance Unit)
11 Portland Place, London W1B 1EJ
e-mail: theatredance@britishcouncil.org
Fax: 020-7389 3088   Tel: 020-7389 3097

BRITISH FILM COMMISSION
10 Little Portland Street, London W1W 7JG
e-mail: info@bfc.co.uk
Fax: 020-7861 7864   Tel: 020-7861 7860

BRITISH FILM INSTITUTE
21 Stephen Street, London W1T 1LN
e-mail: library@bfi.org.uk
Fax: 020-7436 2338   Tel: 020-7255 1444

BRITISH LIBRARY NATIONAL SOUND ARCHIVE
96 Euston Road
London NW1 2DB
e-mail: nsa@bl.uk
Fax: 020-7412 7441   Tel: 020-7412 7440

BRITISH MUSIC HALL SOCIETY
(Secretary: Daphne Masterton)
82 Fernlea Road
London SW12 9RW
Tel: 020-8673 2175   Tel: 01727 768878

BROADCASTING ENTERTAINMENT CINEMATOGRAPH & THEATRE UNION (BECTU) (Formerly BETA & ACTT)
111 Wardour Street, London W1V 4AY
e-mail: smacdonald@bectu.org.uk
Fax: 020-7437 8268   Tel: 020-7437 8506

CASTING DIRECTORS' GUILD
PO Box 34403
London W6 0YG   Tel/Fax: 020-8741 1951

CATHOLIC STAGE GUILD
(Write SAE)
Ms Molly Steele (Hon Secretary)
1 Maiden Lane
London WC2E 7NB   Tel: 020-7240 1221

CELEBRITY SERVICE Ltd
Room 203-209, 93-97 Regent Street
London W1R 7TA
e-mail: celebritylondon@aol.com
Fax: 020-7494 3500   Tel: 020-7439 9840

CHILDREN'S FILM & TELEVISION FOUNDATION Ltd
Elstree Film and Television Studios,
Borehamwood, Herts WD6 1JG
e-mail: annahome@cftf.onyxnet.co.uk
Fax: 020-8207 0860   Tel: 020-8953 0844

CINEMA EXHIBITORS' ASSOCIATION
22 Golden Square, London W1R 3PA
e-mail: cea@cinemauk.ftech.co.uk
Fax: 020-7734 6147   Tel: 020-7734 9551

CINEMA & TELEVISION BENEVOLENT FUND (CTBF)
22 Golden Square, London W1F 9AD
e-mail: charity@ctbf.co.uk
Fax: 020-7437 7186   Tel: 020-7437 6567

CLUB FOR ACTS & ACTORS
(Incorporating Concert Artistes Association)
20 Bedford Street
London WC2E 9HP
Office: 020-7836 3172   Members: 020-7836 2884

COI COMMUNICATIONS
(Television)
Hercules Road
London SE1 7DU
e-mail: eileen.newton@coi.gsi.gov.uk
Fax: 020-7261 8776   Tel: 020-7261 8220

COMPANY OF CRANKS
1st Floor, 62 Northfield House
Frensham Street, London SE15 6TN
e-mail: nostring@dircon.co.uk   Tel: 020-7358 0571

CONCERT ARTISTES ASSOCIATION
(See CLUB FOR ACTS & ACTORS)

CONFERENCE OF DRAMA SCHOOLS
(Flicky Ridel)
1 Stanley Avenue, Thorpe, Norwich
Norfolk NR7 0BE
e-mail: enquiries@cds.drama.ac.uk
                              Tel/Fax: 01603 702021

CRITICS' CIRCLE The
c/o 69 Marylebone Lane
London W1U 2PH   Tel: 020-7224 1410

DENVILLE HALL
62 Ducks Hill Road, Northwood
Middlesex HA6 2SB
Fax: 01923 841855   Office: 01923 825843

DEVOTEES of HAMMER The
(Fan Club)
14 Kingsdale Road
London SE18 2DG
e-mail: 07960969318@one2one.net
                              Tel: 020-8244 8640

DIRECTORS' AND PRODUCERS' RIGHTS SOCIETY The
Victoria Chambers
16-18 Strutton Ground, London SW1P 2HP
e-mail: info@dprs.org.uk
Fax: 020-7227 4755   Tel: 020-7227 4757

DIRECTORS GUILD OF GREAT BRITAIN
Acorn House
314-320 Gray's Inn Road
London WC1X 8DP
e-mail: guild@dggb.co.uk
Fax: 020-7278 4742   Tel: 020-7278 4343

D'OYLY CARTE OPERA COMPANY
The Powerhouse, 6 Sancroft Street
London SE11 5UD
e-mail: mail@doylycarte.org.uk
Fax: 020-7793 7300   Tel: 020-7793 7100

DRAMA ASSOCIATION OF WALES
(Specialist Drama Lending Library)
The Old Library, Singleton Road, Splott
Cardiff CF24 2ET
Fax: 029-2045 2277   Tel: 029-2045 2200

EDINBURGHREVIEW.COM
The Bull Theatre, 68 The High Street
Barnet, Herts EN5 5SJ
e-mail: mail@edinburghreview.com
Fax: 020-8449 5252   Tel: 020-8449 7800

ENGLISH FOLK DANCE AND SONG SOCIETY
Cecil Sharp House
2 Regent's Park Road
London NW1 7AY
e-mail: efdss@efdss.org
Fax: 020-7284 0534   Tel: 020-7485 2206

EQUITY inc Variety Artistes' Federation
Guild House, Upper St Martin's Lane
London WC2H 9EG
e-mail: info@equity.org.uk
Fax: 020-7379 7001   Tel: 020-7379 6000

EQUITY inc Variety Artistes' Federation
(North West)
Conavon Court, 12 Blackfriars Street
Salford M3 5BQ
e-mail: manchesterequity@hotmail.com
Fax: 0161-839 3133   Tel: 0161-832 3183

EQUITY inc Variety Artistes' Federation
(Scotland & Northern Ireland)
114 Union Street
Glasgow G1 3QQ
e-mail: igilchrist@glasgow.equity.org.uk
Fax: 0141-248 2473   Tel: 0141-248 2472

EQUITY inc Variety Artistes' Federation
(Wales & South West)
Transport House,
1 Cathedral Road, Cardiff CF1 9SD
e-mail: cardiffequity@altavista.net
Fax: 029-2023 0754   Tel: 029-2039 7971

ETF (Equity Trust Fund)
Suite 222, Africa House, 64 Kingsway
London WC2B 6BD
Fax: 020-7831 4953   Tel: 020-7404 6041

F.A.A.
(See FILM ARTISTS ASSOCIATION)

FILM ARTISTS ASSOCIATION
(Amalgamated with B.E.C.T.U.)
111 Wardour Street, London W1V 4AY
Fax: 020-7437 8268   Tel: 020-7437 8506

FRINGE THEATRE NETWORK
The Finborough Theatre, 118 Finborough Road
London SW10 9ED
e-mail: ftn@finboroughtheatre.freeserve.co.uk
Fax: 020-7835 1853   Tel: 020-7565 4040

GLASGOW FILM FINANCE
(Production Finance for Feature Films)
249 West George Street, Glasgow G2 4QE
Fax: 0141-302 1714   Tel: 0141-302 1757

GRAND ORDER OF WATER RATS
328 Gray's Inn Road, London WC1X 8BZ
e-mail: water.rats@virgin.net
Fax: 020-7278 1765   Tel: 020-7278 3248

GROUP LINE
(Group Bookings for London)
22-24 Torrington Place, London WC1E 7HF
Fax: 020-7436 6287   Tel: 020-7580 6793

GUY Gillian ASSOCIATES
84A Tachbrook Street, London SW1V 2NB
Fax: 020-7976 5885   Tel: 020-7976 5888

INDEPENDENT TELEVISION COMMISSION (ITC)
33 Foley Street, London W1W 7TL
e-mail: publicaffairs@itc.org.uk
                           Tel: 020-7255 3000

INDEPENDENT THEATRE COUNCIL (ITC)
12 The Leathermarket, Weston Street
London SE1 3ER
e-mail: admin@itc-arts.org
Fax: 020-7403 1745   Tel: 020-7403 1727

INTERNATIONAL FEDERATION OF ACTORS (FIA)
Guild House, Upper St Martin's Lane
London WC2H 9EG
e-mail: office@fia-actors.com
Fax: 020-7379 8260   Tel: 020-7379 0900

INTERNATIONAL THEATRE INSTITUTE
Goldsmiths College, University of London,
Lewisham Way, New Cross, London SE14 6NW
e-mail: iti@gold.ac.uk
Fax: 020-7919 7277   Tel: 020-7919 7276

INTERNATIONAL VISUAL COMMUNICATION
ASSOCIATION (IVCA)
19 Pepper Street, Glengall Bridge
London E14 9RP
e-mail: info@ivca.org
Fax: 020-7512 0591   Tel: 020-7512 0571

IRISH ACTORS' EQUITY GROUP
S.I.P.T.U. 9th Floor, Liberty Hall, Dublin 1
Fax: 00 353 1 8743691   Tel: 00 353 1 8740081

IRVING SOCIETY The
(Brien Chitty, Hon Sec)
69 Harcourt Street, Newark-on-Trent
Notts NG24 1RG
e-mail: secretary@theirvingsociety.org.uk
                           Tel: 01636 702801

ITC
(See INDEPENDENT TELEVISION COMMISSION)

ITC
(See INDEPENDENT THEATRE COUNCIL)

ITV - NETWORK Ltd
200 Gray's Inn Road, London WC1X 8HF
Fax: 020-7843 8158   Tel: 020-7843 8000

LIAISON OF ACTORS, MANAGEMENTS &
PLAYWRIGHTS (LAMP)
(W Robi)
86A Elgin Avenue
London W9   Tel: 020-7289 3031

LONDON FILM COMMISSION
20 Euston Centre
Regent's Place, London NW1 3JH
e-mail: lfc@london-film.co.uk
Fax: 020-7387 8788   Tel: 020-7387 8787

LONDON-IRISH YOUTH THEATRE The
Victor House, Marlborough Gardens
Whetstone N20 0SH
e-mail: rosemaryifbco@aol.com
Tel/Fax: 020-8361 0678   Tel: 020-8361 0549

LONDON SCHOOL OF CAPOEIRA The
Units 1 & 2 Leeds Place, Tollington Park
London N4 3RQ   Tel: 020-7281 2020

LONDON SCREENWRITERS WORKSHOP
Screenwriters' Centre, Suffolk House
1-8 Whitfield Place
London W1T 5JU
e-mail: screenoffice@cwcom.net
Tel: 020-7387 5511

LONDON SHAKESPEARE WORKOUT The
181A Faunce House
Doddington Grove, Kennington
London SE17 3TB
e-mail: londonswo@hotmail.com
Fax: 020-7735 5911   Tel: 020-7793 9755

MANDER & MITCHENSON THEATRE COLLECTION
Jerwood Library of the Performing Arts
King Charles Building
Old Royal Naval College, Greenwich
London SE10 9LW
e-mail: richard@mander-and-mitchenson.co.uk
Tel: 020-8305 3893

MECHANICAL-COPYRIGHT PROTECTION SOCIETY Ltd (MCPS)
Elgar House, 41 Streatham High Road
London SW16 1ER   Tel: 020-8664 4400

MUSICIANS' UNION
60-64 Clapham Road
London SW9 0JJ   Tel: 020-7582 5566

NATIONAL ASSOCIATION OF YOUTH THEATRES (NAYT)
Arts Centre, Vane Terrace, Darlington DL3 7AX
e-mail: naytuk@aol.com
Fax: 01325 363313   Tel: 01325 363330

NATIONAL CAMPAIGN FOR THE ARTS
Pegasus House
37-43 Sackville Street
London W1S 3EH
e-mail: nca@artscampaign.org.uk
Fax: 020-7333 0660   Tel: 020-7333 0375

NATIONAL COUNCIL FOR DRAMA TRAINING
5 Tavistock Place, London WC1H 9SS
e-mail: ncdt@lineone.net
Tel: 020-7387 3650   Fax: 020-7681 4733

NATIONAL ENTERTAINMENT AGENTS COUNCIL
PO Box 112, Seaford
East Sussex BN25 2DQ
e-mail: chrisbray@neac.org.uk
Fax: 01323 492234   Tel: 01323 492488

NATIONAL FILM THEATRE
South Bank, Waterloo
London SE1 8XT
e-mail: temp.two@bfi.org.uk   Tel: 020-7928 3535

NATIONAL RESOURCE CENTRE FOR DANCE
University of Surrey
Guildford, Surrey GU2 7XH
e-mail: nrcd@surrey.ac.uk   Tel: 01483 259316

NATIONAL YOUTH MUSIC THEATRE
5th Floor, The Palace Theatre
Shaftesbury Avenue, London W1V 8AY
e-mail: enquiries@nymt.org.uk
Fax: 020-7734 7515   Tel: 020-7734 7478

N O D A (National Operatic & Dramatic Association)
1 Crestfield Street
London WC1H 8AU
e-mail: everyone@noda.org.uk
Fax: 020-7833 0609   Tel: 020-7837 5655

NORTH AMERICAN ACTORS' ASSOCIATION
1 De Vere Cottages, Canning Place
London W8 5AA
e-mail: laurencebouvard@cs.com
                    Tel/Fax: 020-7938 4722

NORTH WEST PLAYWRIGHTS
18 St Margaret's Chambers
5 Newton Street, Manchester M1 1HL
e-mail: newplaysnw@hotmail.com
                    Tel/Fax: 0161-237 1978

NORTHERN ACTORS' CENTRE The
30 St Margaret's Chambers, 5 Newton Street
Manchester M1 1HL   Tel/Fax: 0161-236 0041

PACT (PRODUCERS ALLIANCE FOR CINEMA & TELEVISION)
(Trade Association for Independent Television, Feature Film & New Media Production Companies)
45 Mortimer Street, London W1W 8HJ
e-mail: enquiries@pact.co.uk
Fax: 020-7331 6700   Tel: 020-7331 6000

PERFORMING RIGHT SOCIETY Ltd
29-33 Berners Street
London W1T 3AB
Fax: 020-7306 4455   Tel: 020-7580 5544

PERSONAL MANAGERS' ASSOCIATION Ltd
Rivercroft, 1 Summer Road
East Molesey, Surrey KT8 9LX
e-mail: info@thepma.com
                    Tel/Fax: 020-8398 9796

RADIO AUTHORITY The
Holbrook House, 14 Great Queen Street
Holborn, London WC2B 5DG
Fax: 020-7405 7062   Tel: 020-7430 2724

ROYAL TELEVISION SOCIETY
Holborn Hall, 100 Gray's Inn Road
London WC1X 8AL
e-mail: info@rts.org.uk
Fax: 020-7430 0924   Tel: 020-7430 1000

ROYAL THEATRICAL FUND
11 Garrick Street, London WC2E 9AR
e-mail: admin@trtf.com
Fax: 020-7379 8273   Tel: 020-7836 3322

S A G
(Screen Actors Guild)
5757 Wilshire Boulevard, Los Angeles
CA 90036-3600
Fax: (323) 549-6656   Tel: (323) 954-1600

1515 Broadway
44th Floor
New York
NY 10036   Tel: (212) 944-1030

SAVE LONDON'S THEATRES CAMPAIGN
Guild House, Upper St Martin's Lane
London WC2H 9EG
Fax: 020-7379 7001   Tel: 020-7670 0270

SCOTTISH ARTS COUNCIL
12 Manor Place, Edinburgh EH3 7DD
Fax: 0131-225 9833   Tel: 0131-226 6051

SOCIETY FOR THEATRE RESEARCH
c/o The Theatre Museum
1E Tavistock Street, London WC2E 7PA
e-mail: e.cottis@btinternet.com

SOCIETY OF AUTHORS
84 Drayton Gardens, London SW10 9SB
e-mail: info@societyofauthors.org
                    Tel: 020-7373 6642

SOCIETY OF BRITISH THEATRE DESIGNERS
47 Bermondsey Street, London SE1 3XT
Fax: 020-7378 6170   Tel: 020-7403 3778

SOCIETY OF LONDON THEATRE (SOLT)
32 Rose Street, London WC2E 9ET
e-mail: enquiries@solttma.co.uk
Fax: 020-7557 6799   Tel: 020-7557 6700

SOCIETY OF TEACHERS OF SPEECH AND DRAMA The
Registered Office:
73 Berry Hill Road, Mansfield, Notts NG18 4RU
e-mail: ann.p.jones@btinternet.com
                    Tel: 01623 627636

SOCIETY OF THEATRE CONSULTANTS
47 Bermondsey Street
London SE1 3XT
Fax: 020-7378 6170   Tel: 020-7403 3778

STAGECOACH! (West Midlands) Ltd
(West Midlands Playwrights -Training & Support)
Broad Street House, 212-213 Broad Street
Birmingham B15 1AY
e-mail: stagecoach@playwriting.fsnet.co.uk
                    Tel/Fax: 0121-633 7475

STAGE CRICKET CLUB
39-41 Hanover Steps, St George's Fields
Albion Street, London W2 2YG
e-mail: brianjfilm@aol.com
Fax: 020-7262 5736   Tel: 020-7402 7543

STAGE GOLFING SOCIETY
Sudbrook Park
Sudbrook Lane, Richmond
Surrey TW10 7AS   Tel: 020-8940 8861

STAGE MANAGEMENT ASSOCIATION
47 Bermondsey Street
London SE1 3XT
e-mail: admin@stagemanagementassociation.co.uk
Fax: 020-7378 6170   Tel: 020-7403 6655

STANDING CONFERENCE OF YOUNG PEOPLES THEATRE (SCYPT)
(Office Manager: Ray Beaumont)
Valley Kids, Penygraig Community Project
1 Cross Street, Penygraig, Tonypandy
Rhonda CF40 1LD
Fax: 01443 420877   Tel: 01443 438770

THEATRE DESPATCH Ltd
Azof Hall, Azof Street, London SE10 0EG
e-mail: info@theatre.org
Fax: 08700 525915   Tel: 020-8853 0750

The Actors Centre

Providing a space of energy and inspiration where professional actors can experiment, share creativity, meet new challenges and pursue excellence.

Providing a meeting place where professional actors can develop ideas, exchange information and support one another.

Subsidised Classes

- audition technique
- dialect
- sight reading
- singing
- voice

- Alexander technique
- fencing/stage combat
- movement
- dance

- film
- musical theatre
- poetry reading
- radio
- television
- writing

- career advice
- casting sessions
- financial advice

Tristan Bates Theatre
(Under Refurbishment)

A vibrant and varied programme of play readings and showcases for invited audiences

The Green Room Bar and Restaurant
Drinks & Snacks

Audition Rooms
Available for hire - ranging from 10 x 15 to 54 x 40
Line - learning service available

If you would like a copy of our current programme please telephone:
020 7240 3940
1A Tower Street Covent Garden WC2H 9NP
or
act@actorscentre.co.uk

Founding Patron: Lord Olivier
Patron: 1983-94: Sir Alec Guinness

Patron: Alan Bates CBE
Artistic Director: Mark Wing-Davey

THEATREGOERS' CLUB OF GREAT BRITAIN
Harling House
47-51 Great Suffolk Street
London SE1 0BS
e-mail: info@theatregoers.co.uk
Fax: 020-7450 4041   Tel: 020-7450 4040

THEATRE INVESTMENT FUND Ltd
32 Rose Street
London WC2E 9ET
Fax: 020-7557 6799   Tel: 020-7557 6737

THEATRE MUSEUM The
1E Tavistock Street
London WC2E 7PA
Fax: 020-7943 4777   Tel: 020-7943 4700

THEATRES ADVISORY COUNCIL
47 Bermondsey Street
London SE1 3XT
Fax: 020-7378 6170   Tel: 020-7403 3778

THEATRES TRUST The
22 Charing Cross Road
London WC2H 0QL
e-mail: info@theatrestrust.org.uk
Fax: 020-7836 3302   Tel: 020-7836 8591

THEATRICAL GUILD The
PO Box 22712
London N22 5AG
e-mail: admin@the-theatrical-guild.org.uk
                           Tel: 020-8889 7570

THEATRICAL MANAGEMENT ASSOCIATION
(See TMA)

TMA
(Theatrical Management Association)
32 Rose Street
London WC2E 9ET
e-mail: enquiries@solttma.co.uk
Fax: 020-7557 6799   Tel: 020-7557 6700

UK ARTS EXPLORE
Media Centre
7 Northumberland Street
Huddersfield HD1 1RL
e-mail: info@ukarts-explore.com
                           Tel: 01484 350031

UK CHOREOGRAPHERS' DIRECTORY The
c/o Dance UK, Battersea Arts Centre
Lavender Hill
London SW11 5TN
e-mail: danceuk@globalnet.co.uk
Fax: 020-7223 0074   Tel: 020-7228 4990

UNITED KINGDOM COPYRIGHT BUREAU
110 Trafalgar Road
Portslade
East Sussex BN41 1GS
e-mail: info@copyrightbureau.co.uk
Fax: 0127 705451   Tel: 01273 277333

VARIETY CLUB OF GREAT BRITAIN
Variety Club House
93 Bayham Street
London NW1 0AG
e-mail: info@varietyclub.org.uk
Fax: 020-7428 8111   Tel: 020-7428 8100

VARIETY & LIGHT ENTERTAINMENT COUNCIL
54 Keyes House
Dolphin Square
London SW1V 3NA
Fax: 020-7821 0261   Tel: 020-7798 5622

WOLFF Peter THEATRE TRUST The
(Neal Foster Executive Director)
Suite 612, 162 Regent Street
London W1B 5TG
e-mail: info@peterwolfftheatretrust.org
Fax: 020-7437 3395   Tel: 020-7494 4662

WOMEN IN FILM AND TELEVISION
6 Langley Street
London WC2H 9JA
e-mail: info@wftv.org.uk
Fax: 020-7379 1625   Tel: 020-7240 4875

WRITERNET
Cabin V, Clarendon Buildings
25 Horsell Road
London N5 1XL
e-mail: writernet@btinternet.com
Fax: 020-7609 7557   Tel: 020-7609 7474

WRITERS' GUILD OF GREAT BRITAIN The
430 Edgware Road
London W2 1EH
e-mail: admin@writersguild.org.uk
Fax: 020-7706 2413   Tel: 020-7723 8074

Press Cutting Agencies

BROADCAST MONITORING COMPANY The
89¹/₂ Worship Street
London EC2A 2BF
Fax: 020-7377 6103   Tel: 020-7377 1742

DURRANTS PRESS CUTTINGS Ltd
Discovery House
28-42 Banner Street
London EC1Y 8QE
e-mail: contact@durrants.co.uk
Fax: 020-7674 0222   Tel: 020-7674 0200

INFORMATION BUREAU The
51 The Business Centre
103 Lavender Hill SW11 5QL
e-mail: infobureau@dial.pipex.com
Fax: 020-7924 4456   Tel: 020-7924 4414

INTERNATIONAL PRESS-CUTTING BUREAU
224-236 Walworth Road, London SE17 1JE
e-mail: ipcb2000@aol.com
Fax: 020-7701 4489   Tel: 020-7708 2113

McCALLUM MEDIA MONITOR
Tower House, 10 Possil Road, Glasgow G4 9SY
e-mail: presscuttings@fings.com
Fax: 0141-333 1811   Tel: 0141-333 1822

07000 BIG TOP
(Big Top, Seating, Circus)
The Arts Exchange, Congleton
Cheshire CW12 1JG
e-mail: phillipgandey@netcentral.co.uk
Fax: 01260 270777   Tel: 01260 276627

10 OUT OF 10 PRODUCTIONS Ltd
(Lighting, Sound, AV Hire, Sales and Installation)
Unit 14 Forest Hill Business Centre, Clyde Vale
London SE23 3JF
e-mail: sales@10outof10.co.uk
Fax: 020-8699 8968   Tel: 020-8291 6885

1ST CROWN
(Suppliers of T-Shirts, Baseball Caps for Crew
Publicity and Workwear)
3 Austin Court, London Road
Kent TN16 1HE   Mobile: 07903 941150

20TH CENTURY FUNFAIR FACTORY
(Fun Fair Locations, Equipment and Prop Hire)
Plot 24 The Plantation, West Park Road
New Chapel, Surrey RH7 6HT
Mobile: 07976 297735   Tel: 01342 717707

3D CREATIONS
(Production Design, Scenery Contractors,
Prop Makers & Scenic Artists)
9 Keppel Road, Gorleston-on-Sea
Great Yarmouth, Norfolk NR31 6SN
e-mail: 3dcreations@rjt.co.uk
Fax: 01493 443124   Tel: 01493 657093

A. S. DESIGNS
(Theatrical Designer, Sets, Costumes
Heads, Masks, Puppets, etc)
Fax: 01279 435642   Tel: 01279 722416

ACROBAT PRODUCTIONS
(Artistes & Advisors)
The Circus Space
Coronet Street, Hackney
London N1 6HD
e-mail: info@acrobatproductions.co.uk
          Tel/Fax: 020-7613 5259

ACTION & STUNT EQUIPMENT
(Martin Grace)
158 Christchurch Avenue, Kenton, Harrow
Middlesex HA3 8NW
Mobile: 07836 287330   Tel: 020-8907 1020

ADAMS ENGRAVING
Unit G1A, The Mayford Centre
Smarts Heath Road
Woking GU22 0PP
Fax: 01483 751787   Tel: 01483 725792

AERONAUTIC
(Function Balloons)
46 Burrage Place, Plumstead
London SE18 7BE
e-mail: sales@aeronautic.org.uk
Fax: 020-8317 1515   Mobile: 07956 369890

AFX (UK) Ltd
(Flying Systems & Specialist Aerial Effects
Rigging)
8 Greenford Avenue, Hanwell
London W7 3QP
e-mail: info@afxuk.com
Mobile: 07958 285608   Tel: 020-8723 8552

AIRBOURNE SYSTEMS INTERNATIONAL
(All Skydiving Requirements Arranged.
Parachute Hire - Period & Modern)
8 Burns Crescent, Chelmsford
Essex CM2 0TS   Tel: 01245 268772

ALCHEMICAL LABORATORIES ETC
(Medieval Science and Technology Recreated
for Museums and Films)
Oldwood Pits, Tanhouse Lane, Yate
Bristol BS37 7PZ   Tel: 01454 227164

ANCHOR MARINE FILM & TELEVISION
(Boat Location, Charter, Maritime Co-ordinators)
Spikemead Farm, Poles Lane, Lowfield Heath
West Sussex RH11 0PX
e-mail: amsfilm@aol.com
Fax: 01293 551558   Tel: 01293 538188

Properties & Trades

ANELLO & DAVIDE
(Theatrical Footwear)
Shop: 47 Beauchamp Place
Chelsea, London SW3 1NX
Fax: 020-7225 2111   Tel: 020-7225 2468

ANGLO PACIFIC INTERNATIONAL Plc
(Freight Forwarders & Removal Services)
Unit 1, Bush Industrial Estate, Standard Road
North Acton, London NW10 6DF
Fax: 020-8965 4954   Tel: 020-8965 1955

ANIMAL ARK
(Animals & Natural History Props)
Studio 29 Somerset Road, Brentford
Middlesex TW8 8BT
e-mail: info@animal-ark.co.uk
Fax: 020-8560 5762   Tel: 020-8560 3029

AQUATECH
(Camera Boats)
Epney, Gloucestershire GL2 7LN
e-mail: office@aquatech-uk.com
Tel: 01452 740559   Fax: 01452 741958

ARCHERY CENTRE The
(Archery Tuition)
PO Box 39, Battle
East Sussex TN33 0ZT
e-mail: sales@archery-centre@aol.com
          Tel: 01424 777183

ARMS & ARCHERY
(Armour, Weaponry, Chainmail, X-bows,
Longbows)
The Coach House, London Road,
Ware, Herts SG12 9QU
e-mail: tgou104885@aol.com
Fax: 01920 461044   Tel: 01920 460335

ART DIRECTORS & TRIP PHOTO LIBRARY
(Colour Slides - All Subjects)
57 Burdon Lane, Cheam, Surrey SM2 7BY
e-mail: images@artdirectors.co.uk
Fax: 020-8395 7230   Tel: 020-8642 3593

ASH Riky
(Equity Registered Stunt Performer/Co-ordinator)
c/o 65 Britania Avenue, Nottingham NG6 0EA
Mobile: 07850 471227   Tel: 0115-849 3470

ATP EUROPE Ltd
(Print & Repro)
12 Sovereign Park
London NW10 7QP
e-mail: info@atpeurope.com
Fax: 020-8961 7743   Tel: 020-8961 0001

AUTOMOTIVE ACTION STUNTS
(Stunt Rigging & Supplies/Camera Tracking
Vehicles)
2 Sheffield House, Park Road, Hampton Hill
Middlesex TW12 1HA
Mobile: 07974 919589   Tel: 020-8977 6186

BACKNUMBERS
(Papers, Magazines 1698-1998)
81 Theberton Street
London N1 0QY
Fax: 020-7704 8934   Tel: 020-7226 4711

BAD DOG DESIGN
(3D Models, Props, Sets)
Fir Tree Cottage, Fish Pool Hill, Brentry
Bristol BS10 6SW
e-mail: baddog@dircon.co.uk
Fax: 0117-959 1245   Tel: 0117-959 2011

212

BAPTY 2000 Ltd
(Weapons, Dressing, Props etc)
Witley Works, Witley Gardens
Norwood Green, Middlesex UB2 4ES
e-mail: hire@bapty.demon.co.uk
Fax: 020-8571 5700   Tel: 020-8574 7700

BARNES CATERERS Ltd
9 Ripley Drive, Normanton, Wakefield
West Yorks WF6 1QT
Fax: 01924 223730   Tel: 01924 892332

BARTON Joe
(Puppeteer, Model & Prop Maker)
7 Brands Hill Avenue
High Wycombe, Bucks   Tel: 01494 439056

BASINGSTOKE PRESS The
Digital House
The Loddon Centre, Wade Road, Basingstoke
Hants RG24 8QW
e-mail: sales@baspress.co.uk
Fax: 01256 840383   Tel: 01256 467771

BBC VISUAL EFFECTS DEPARTMENT
Room G14, Park Western, 41-44 Kendal Avenue
London W3 0RP
e-mail: visual.effects@bbc.co.uk
Fax: 020-8993 8741   Tel: 020-8993 9434

BEAT ABOUT THE BUSH
(Musical Instruments)
Unit 23, Enterprise Way
Triangle Business Centre
Salter Street, London NW10 6UG
Fax: 020-8969 2281   Tel: 020-8960 2087

BENSON'S JUMPAROUND ACTIVITY CENTRES
(Chester Benson Inflatables & Soft Play
Equipment, Bouncy Castles)
PO Box 4227
Worthing BN11 5ST
e-mail: davebensonphillips@yahoo.com
Fax: 01903 700389   Tel: 01903 248258

BIANCHERI The
(Wingbolt Safety Spanner for Techies)
T & D House, 7 Woodville Road
London E17 7ER
Mobile: 07973 663154   Tel: 020-8521 6408

BIANCHI AVIATION FILM SERVICES
(Historic and other Aircraft)
Wycombe Air Park, Booker Marlow
Bucks SL7 3DP
e-mail: bianchi@waitrose.com
Fax: 01494 461236   Tel: 01494 449810

BIDDLES Ltd
(Quality Book Binders & Printers)
Woodbridge Park Estate
Woodbridge Road, Guildford
Surrey GU1 1DA
Fax: 01483 576150   Tel: 01483 502224

BLACKOUT TRIPLE E Ltd
280 Weston Road
London SW19 2QA
e-mail: info@blackout-tabtrack.com
Fax: 020-8687 8500   Tel: 020-8687 8400

BLUEBELL RAILWAY Plc
(Steam Locomotives, Pullman Coaches
Period Stations)
Sheffield Park Station
East Sussex TN22 3QL   Tel/Fax: 01825 723777

BOSCO LIGHTING
(Design/Technical Consultancy)
63 Nimrod Road, London SW16 6SZ
e-mail: boscolx@lineone.net   Tel: 020-8769 3470

BRISTOL (UK) Ltd
(Scenic Paint & StageFloor Duo Suppliers)
12 The Arches, Maygrove Road
London NW6 2D5
Fax: 020-7372 5242   Tel: 020-7624 4370

BRISTOL OLD VIC HIRE SERVICE
(Furniture Props)
Wapping Wharf, Cumberland Road
Bristol BS1 6UP
e-mail: bov-hire-dept@lineone.net
Fax: 0117-929 1665   Tel: 0117-934 9350

BRODIE & MIDDLETON Ltd
(Theatrical Suppliers, Paints, Powders, Glitter etc)
68 Drury Lane, London WC2B 5SP
e-mail: info@brodies.net
Fax: 020-7497 8425   Tel: 020-7836 3289

BUXWORTH STEAM GROUP
Barren Clough Farm, Buxworth, Stockport
Cheshire SK12 7NS   Tel: 01663 732750

BYGONE TIMES INTERNATIONAL Plc
Grove Mill, The Green, Eccleston
Nr Chorley, Lancashire PR7 5PD
Fax: 01257 450197   Tel: 01257 453780

CANDLE MAKERS SUPPLIES
The Wax & Dyecraft Centre, 28 Blythe Road
London W14 0HA
e-mail: candles@candlemakers.co.uk
Fax: 020-7602 2796   Tel: 020-7602 4031

CAPITAL PROPERTY CARE Ltd
(Commercial Property Specialists)
44 Sheen Lane, East Sheen, London SW14 8LP
Fax: 020-8878 9637   Tel: 020-8878 2966

CHALFONT CLEANERS & DYERS Ltd
(Dry Cleaners, Launderers & Dyers
Stage Curtains & Costumes)
222 Baker Street
London NW1 5RT   Tel: 020-7935 7316

CHEVALIER EVENT DESIGN & CONTEMPORARY CUISINE
(Corporate Hospitality Caterers)
Studio 4-5, Garnett Close, Watford
Herts WD24 7GN
e-mail: enquiries@chevalier.co.uk
Fax: 01923 211704   Tel: 01923 211703

CHRISANNE Ltd
(Specialist Fabrics & Accessories for
Theatre & Dance)
Chrisanne House, 14 Locks Lane
Mitcham, Surrey CR4 2JX
e-mail: sales@chrisanne.co.uk
Fax: 020-8640 2106   Tel: 020-8640 5921

CIRCUS PROMOTIONS
(Entertainers)
36 St Lukes Road, Tunbridge Wells
Kent TN4 9JH   Tel: 01892 537964

CLARK DAVIS & Co Ltd
(Stationery & Office Equipment)
Excelda House, Unit C, Six Bridges Trading Estate
Marlborough Grove, London SE1 5JT
e-mail: steve@clarkdavis.sol.co.uk
Fax: 020-7240 2106   Tel: 020-7836 5703

CLARKE Donald
(Historical Interperter, Role Playing)
80 Warden Avenue, Rayners Lane
Harrow, Middlesex HA2 9LW
Mobile: 07811 606285   Tel: 020-8866 2997

CLAY PIGEON The
(Large Music Venue)
446 Field End Road, Eastcote
Middlesex HA4 9BP
Fax: 020-8868 1679   Tel: 020-8866 5358

CLEANING & FLAME RETARDING SERVICE The
Unit 3, Grange Farm Industrial Units, Grange
Road, Tiptree, Essex CO5 0QQ
e-mail: email@flameretarding.co.uk
Fax: 01621 819803   Tel: 01621 818477

COMPTON Mike & Rosi
(Costumes, Props & Models)
11 Woodstock Road
Croydon, Surrey CR0 1JS
Fax: 020-8681 3126   Tel: 020-8680 4364

CONCEPT ENGINEERING Ltd
(Smoke, Fog, Snow, etc)
7 Woodlands Business Park, Woodlands Park
Avenue, Maidenhead, Berks SL6 3UA
Fax: 01628 826261   Tel: 01628 825555

COOK Sheila
(Period Jewellery, Textiles, Costumes and
Accessories for Hire/Sale)
283 Westbourne Grove
London W11 2QA
e-mail: sheilacook@sheilacook.co.uk
Fax: 020-7229 3855   Tel: 020-7792 8001

CRESTA BLINDS Ltd
(Supplier of Vertical Blinds)
Crown Walks, Tetnall Street
Dudley DY2 8SA
e-mail: info@crestablindsltd.co.uk
Fax: 01384 457675   Tel: 01384 255523

CROCKSHARD FARMHOUSE
(Bed & Breakfast, Contact: Nicola Ellen)
Wingham, Canterbury, Kent CT3 1NY
Fax: 01227 721929   Tel: 01227 720464

CROFTS Andrew
(Book Writing Services)
Westlands Grange
West Grinstead, Horsham
West Sussex RH13 8LZ   Tel/Fax: 01403 864518

CUE ACTION POOL PROMOTIONS
(Advice for UK & US Pool, Snooker, Trick Shots)
PO Box 3941, Colchester, Essex CO2 8HN
e-mail: sales@cueaction.com
Fax: 01206 729480   Tel: 07000 868689

DARK SIDE
(Photographic Repro Service)
4 Helmet Row, London EC1V 3QJ
e-mail: info@darksidephoto.co.uk
Fax: 020-7250 1771   Tel: 020-7250 1200

DAVEY Brian
(See NOSTALGIA AMUSEMENTS)

DAY LIGHT DESIGNS UK Ltd
(Theatre Lantern Conversions/Recolourings
& Restoration)
Unit 163, Bruntingthorpe Industrial Estate
Nr Lutterworth, Leics LE17 5QZ
Fax: 0116-247 8070   Tel: 0116-247 8336

DEAN Audrey Vincente
(Soft Dolls, Toys & Figures to Order, No Hire)
76 Burlington Avenue
Kew, Surrey TW9 4DH
e-mail: audreymiller@waitrose.com
Tel: 020-8876 6441

DESIGN PROJECTS
Perrysfield Farm, Broadham Green
Old Oxted, Surrey RH8 9PG
Fax: 01883 723707   Tel: 01883 730262

DEVEREUX K W & Sons
(Removals)
Daimler Drive, Cowpen Industrial Estate
Billingham, Cleveland TS23 4JD
e-mail: devereux@onyxnet.co.uk
Fax: 01642 566664   Tel: 01642 560854

DIRECTFOODS.UK.COM
(British Food Export Service for
British People Working Overseas)
46 Burrage Place, Plumstead, London SE18 7BE
e-mail: sales@directfoods.uk.com
Tel/Fax: 020-8317 1515

DOBBINS Philip
(Furniture & Properties Maker)
Church Farm, Henshaw, Yeadon
Leeds LS19 7SQ
e-mail: props@dobbins.co.uk
Fax: 0113-250 6800   Tel: 0113-250 2738

DOCKLANDS PACKAGING SUPPLIES Ltd
(Custom Cut Polystyrene)
67 Stephenson Street, London E16 4SA
Fax: 020-7473 1821   Tel: 020-7474 3807

DONOGHUE Phil PRODUCTIONS
Bridge House, Three Mills Island Studios
Three Mill Lane
Bromley-by-Bow, London E3 3DU
Mobile: 07802 179801   Tel/Fax: 020-8215 0169

DORANS PROPMAKERS/SET BUILDERS
53 Derby Road, Ashbourne
Derbyshire DE6 1BH
e-mail: props@dorans.demon.co.uk
Tel/Fax: 01335 300064

DRIVING CENTRE The
(Expert Driving Instructors on All Vehicles)
6 Marlott Road, Poole, Dorset BH15 3DX
Mobile: 07860 290437   Tel: 01202 666001

DURRENT Peter
(Audition & Rehearsal Pianist, Cocktail Pianist,
Composer, Vocal Coach)
Blacksmiths Cottage, Bures Road, Little Cornard
Sudbury, Suffolk CO10 0NR   Tel: 01787 373483

EAGLES Steve
(International Sharpshooter & Firearms Lecturer)
Wivenhoe, 46 Hartwood Road, Southport
Merseyside PR9 9AW
e-mail: sn03@dial.pipex.com
Mobile: 07721 464611   Tel/Fax: 01704 547884

EAT TO THE BEAT
(Production Location Caterers)
Studio 4-5, Garnett Close, Watford
Herts WD24 7GN
e-mail: tony@eattothebeat.com
Fax: 01923 211704   Tel: 01923 211702

EATON'S SEASHELLS
30 Forest Drive West
London E11 1LA   Tel/Fax: 020-8539 5288

ECCENTRIC TRADING COMPANY Ltd
(Antique Furniture & Props) incorporating
COMPUHIRE (Computer Hire)
Unit 2, Frogmore Estate
Acton Lane
London NW10 7NQ
e-mail: info@compuhire.com   Tel: 020-8453 1125

ELECTRO SIGNS Ltd
97 Vallentin Road, London E17 3JJ
Fax: 020-8520 8127   Tel: 020-8521 8066

ELMS LESTERS PAINTING ROOMS
1-5 Flitcroft Street
London WC2H 8DH
e-mail: office@elms-lesters.demon.co.uk
Fax: 020-7379 0789   Tel: 020-7836 6747

EVANS Peter STUDIOS Ltd
(Scenic Embellishment, Vacuum Forming)
1 Frederick Street
Luton, Beds LU2 7QW
Fax: 01582 481329   Tel: 01582 725730

EVEREADY HIRE CENTRES
(Power Tool & Plant Hire)
138 Staines Road, Feltham
Middlesex TW14 9ED
Fax: 020-8751 5704   Tel: 020-8890 7590

FAB 'N' FUNKY
(Prop Hire Specialist 50's - 70's)
18-20 Brunel Road
London W3 7XR
Fax: 020-8743 2662   Tel: 020-8746 7746

FACADE
(Musical Production Services)
43A Garthorne Road
London SE23 1EP   Tel: 020-8699 8655

FAIRGROUNDS OLD & NEW
Halstead, Fovant
Salisbury, Wilts SP3 5NL
e-mail: s-vpostlethwaite@fovant.fsnet.co.uk
Mobile: 07701 287251   Tel: 01722 714786

**FALCONS STUNT DISPLAY TEAM COMBAT
THROUGH THE AGES**
(Medieval Displays, Combat Display Team,
Stunt Action Specialists)
110 Trafalgar Road, Portslade
East Sussex BN41 1GS
Tel: 01273 430323   Tel: 01273 411862

FILM MEDICAL SERVICES
Kern House, 149 Scrubs Lane, London NW10 6QX
e-mail: filmmed@aol.com
Fax: 020-8964 5855   Tel: 020-8964 5707

FIND ME ANOTHER
(Prop Hire/Location Finder specialising in
Gardenalia/Farming/Bygones/Paraphernalia)
28 Hitchin Road, Luton
Bedfordshire LU2 0ER
e-mail: info@findmeanother.co.uk
                              Tel/Fax: 01582 415 834

FIREBRAND
(Flambeaux Hire & Sales)
Leac na ban, By Lochgilphead
Argyll PA31 8PF
e-mail: alex@firebrand.fsnet.co.uk
                              Tel/Fax: 01546 870310

FLAMENCO PRODUCTIONS
(Entertainers)
Sevilla 4 Cormorant Rise
Lower Wick, Worcester   Tel: 01905 424083

FLINT HIRE & SUPPLY Ltd
Queen's Row, London SE17 2PX
e-mail: sales@flints.co.uk
Fax: 020-7708 4189   Tel: 020-7703 9786

FLYING BY FOY
(Flying Effects for Theatre, TV, Corporate Events etc)
Unit 4, Borehamwood Enterprise Centre,
Theobald Street
Borehamwood, Herts WD6 4RQ
e-mail: mail@flyingbyfoy.co.uk
Fax: 020-8236 0235   Tel: 020-8236 0234

FOXTROT PRODUCTIONS Ltd
(Armoury Services, Firearms & Weapons)
Unit 46 Canalot Production Studios
222 Kensal Road, London W10 5BN
                              Tel: 020-8964 3555

FREEDALE PRESS
(Printing)
36 Hedley Street, Maidstone, Kent ME14 5AD
e-mail: freedalepress@cableinet.co.uk
Fax: 01622 200131   Tel: 01622 200123

FROST John NEWSPAPERS
(Historical Newspaper Service)
22B Rosemary Avenue, Enfield
Middlesex EN2 0SS
e-mail: andrew@johnfrostnewspapers.com
                              Tel: 020-8366 1392

GAMBA
(Theatrical Shoes and Wholesale Danceware)
1 Northfield Industrial Estate, Beresford Avenue
Wembley HA0 1XS
Fax: 020-8903 6669   Tel: 020-8903 8177

GAMBA
(Dancewear & Ballet Shoes)
3 Garrick Street
London WC2E 9AR
Fax: 020-7497 0754   Tel: 020-7437 0704

GAV NICOLA THEATRICAL SHOES
1A Suttons Lane, Hornchurch
Essex RM12 6RD
e-mail: sales@gavnicola.freeserve.co.uk
Mobile: 07961 974278   Tel/Fax: 01708 438584

GET STUFFED
(Taxidermy)
105 Essex Road, London N1 2SL
e-mail: taxidermy@thegetstuffed.co.uk
Fax: 020-7359 8253   Tel: 020-7226 1364

GLOBAL CEILINGS & TILES
(Designers, Suppliers, Installers)
1B Argyle Road, Argyle Corner, Ealing
London W13 0LL
Mobile: 07976 159402   Tel: 020-8810 5914

GORGEOUS GOURMETS
(Caterers and Equipment Hire)
Gresham Way
Wimbledon SW19 8ED
e-mail: events@gorgeousgourmets.co.uk
Fax: 020-8946 1639   Tel: 020-8944 7771

GOULD Gillian ANTIQUES
(Scientific & Marine Antiques & Collectables)
18A Belsize Park Gardens, Belsize Park
London NW3 4LH
e-mail: gillgould@dealwith.com
Fax: 020-7419 0400   Tel: 020-7419 0500

GRADAV HIRE & SALES Ltd
(Lighting & Sound Hire/Sales)
Units C6 & C9 Hastingwood Trading Estate,
Harbet Road, Edmonton, London N18 3HR
e-mail: gradav@btinternet.com
Fax: 020-8803 5060   Tel: 020-8803 7400

GRAY Robin COMMENTARIES
(Saddles, Bridles, Racing Colours & Hunting Attire)
Comptons, Isington, Alton, Hants GU34 4PL
                    Tel/Fax: 01420 23347

GREENPROPS
(Prop Suppliers, Artificial Trees, Plants, Fruit, Grass etc)
PO Box 358A, Surbiton, Surrey KT6 4YJ
e-mail: trevor@greenprops.com
Fax: 020-8339 9251   Tel: 020-8390 4270

HANDS ON SECURITY SERVICE
65 Farnham Road, Harold Hill
Romford, Essex RM3 8ED   Tel/Fax: 01708 342186

HARLEQUIN Plc
(Floors for Stage, Opera, Dance, Concert,
Shows & Events)
Bankside House, Vale Road, Tonbridge
Kent TN9 1SJ
e-mail: sales@harlequinfloors.co.uk
Fax: 01732 367755   Tel: 01732 367666

HARLEQUIN PROMOTIONS
(Fun Casinos, Scalextric & Race Nights)
Harlequin House, 13 Gurton Road, Coggleshall,
Essex CO6 1QL
e-mail: john@harlequin-casinos.co.uk
                    Tel: 01376 563385

HAWES Joanne
(Children's Administrator for Theatre, Film & TV)
21 Westfield Road, Maidenhead
Berkshire SL6 5AU
e-mail: jo.hawes@virgin.net
Fax: 01628 672884   Tel: 01628 773048

HERON & DRIVER
(Scenic Furniture & Prop Makers)
Unit 7, Dockley Road Industrial Estate,
Rotherhithe, London SE16 3SF
e-mail: mail@herondriver.co.uk
Fax: 020-7394 8680   Tel: 020-7394 8688

HEWER Richard
(Props Maker)
7 Sion Lane
Bristol BS8 4BE   Tel/Fax: 0117-973 8760

HI-FLI (Flying Effects)
4 Boland Drive
Manchester M14 6DS
e-mail: mikefrost@hi-fli.co.uk
                    Tel/Fax: 0161-224 6082

HOTEL BROKERS
(Conference & Accommodation Consultants)
19 Bakery Place, 119 Altenburg Gardens
London SW11 1JQ
e-mail: alex@hotelbrokers.co.uk
Fax: 020-7738 0361   Tel: 020-7924 3663

HOWARD Rex DRAPES Ltd
Acton Park Industrial Estate, Eastman Road
The Vale, London W3 7QS
Fax: 020-8740 5994   Tel: 020-8740 5881

IDEAL PRODUCTION SERVICES
(Production/Stage Management, Theatre,
Conference, Presentations, etc)
94 Gordon Road, London SE15 3RP
e-mail: m-shayle@dircon.co.uk
Fax: 020-7564 3147   Tel: 020-7564 3384

IMAGERY
(Special Effects, Classical & Modern Decoration,
Scenery)
420, 9 Sims House, Commercial Road
London E1 1LB
e-mail: chrispro@freenetnames.co.uk
                         Mobile: 07956 512074

IMPACT DISTRIBUTION & MARKETING
(Leaflet & Poster Distribution & Display)
Tuscany Wharf, 4B Orsman Road, London N1 5QJ
e-mail: admin@impact.uk.com
Fax: 020-7729 5994   Tel: 020-7729 5978

IMPACT PERCUSSION
(Percussion Instruments for Sale)
Unit 7 Goose Green Trading Estate
47 East Dulwich Road, London SE22 9BN
e-mail: sales@impactpercussion.com
Fax: 020-8299 6704   Tel: 020-8299 6700

INFIDELIS (Derek New)
c/o Elspeth Cochrane Personal Management
Office 14/2, 2nd Floor
South Bank Commercial Centre
140 Battersea Park Road
London SW11 4NB
e-mail: elspeth@elspethcochrane.co.uk
                         Tel: 020-7622 0314

INTERNATIONAL CLOWNS DIRECTORY The
(Salvo The Clown)
13 Second Avenue, Kingsleigh Park
Thundersley, Essex SS7 3QD   Tel: 01268 745791

ISHAQUE
(Eastern Props Hire)
314 High Road, Chadwell Heath, Romford
Essex RM6 6AJ   Tel: 020-8599 0187

JAPAN PROMOTIONS
(Organise Japanese Events)
200 Russell Court, 3 Woburn Place
London WC1H 0ND   Tel/Fax: 020-7278 4099

JESSAMINE Bob
(Scene Painting, Prop Making)
4 Matlock Avenue, Birkdale, Southport
Merseyside PR8 5EZ
e-mail: rscsjessamine@supanet.com
                         Tel: 01704 564521

JULIETTE DESIGNS
(Diamante Jewellery Manufacturer
Necklaces, Crowns etc)
90 Yerbury Road, London N19 4RS
Fax: 020-7281 7326   Tel: 020-7263 7878

K & D
(Footwear)
Unit 7A, Thames Road Industrial Estate
Thames Road, Silvertown
London E16 2EZ
e-mail: k&d@shoemaking.co.uk
Fax: 020-7476 5220   Tel: 020-7474 0500

KEN PAUL
(Antique Prop Hire)
22-24 Englands Lane, London NW3 4TG
e-mail: kenpaul-props@easynet.co.uk
Fax: 020-7722 7553   Tel: 020-7722 5477

KEW BRIDGE STEAM MUSEUM
(Steam Museum)
Green Dragon Lane, Brentford
Middlesex TW8 0EN
e-mail: info@kbsm.org
Fax: 020-8569 9978   Tel: 020-8568 4757

KIEVE Paul
(Magical Effects for Theatre & Film)
23 Terrace Road, South Hackney, London E9 7ES
e-mail: mail@stageillusion.com
Tel/Fax: 020-8985 6188   Tel: 020-7287 9000

KIRBY'S FLYING BALLETS (LONDON)
8 Greenford Avenue, Hanwell, London W7 3QP
e-mail: info@kirbysflying.co.uk
Mobile: 07958 285608   Tel/Fax: 020-8723 8552

KIRBY'S FLYING BALLETS (SCOTLAND)
88 Leslie Street, Glasgow G41 2RR
e-mail: info@kirbysflying.co.uk
Mobile: 07767 464224   Tel/Fax: 0141-423 4672

KNEBWORTH HOUSE
(Stately Home & Country Park)
Hertfordshire   Tel: 01438 812661

KNIGHT Robert Ltd
Top of the Bill House, Queens Row
London SE17 2PX
Fax: 020-7277 1722   Tel: 020-7277 1704

K. W. PROPS
(Propmaking)
Unit J304, Tower Bridge Business Complex
100 Clements Road, London SE16 4DG
e-mail: kwprops@gmx.co.uk
                         Tel/Fax: 020-7231 2528

LAREDO Alex
(Expert with Ropes, Bullwhips, Shooting, Riding)
29 Lincoln Road, Dorking
Surrey RH4 1TE   Tel: 01306 889423

LAREDO WILD WEST TOWN
(Wild West Entertainments)
19 Surrenden Road, Staplehurst
Tonbridge, Kent TN12 0LY
e-mail: enquiries@laredo.org.uk
Tel: 01474 706129   Tel: 01580 891790

LEES-NEWSOME Ltd
(Manufacturers of Flame Retardant Fabrics)
Ashley Street, Westwood
Oldham OL9 6LT
e-mail: info@leesnewsome.co.uk
Fax: 0161-627 3362   Tel: 0161-652 1321

LEIGHTON HALL
(Historic House)
Carnforth, Lancs LA5 9ST
e-mail: leightonhall@yahoo.co.uk
Fax: 01524 720357   Tel: 01524 734474

LEVRANT Stephen
HERITAGE ARCHITECTURE Ltd
(Historic Buildings & Interiors Consultants)
363 West End Lane, West Hampstead
London NW6 1LP
e-mail: levrant@aol.com
Fax: 020-7794 9712   Tel: 020-7435 7502

LONDON BUSINESS EQUIPMENT
(Authorised Canon Dealer)
527-529 High Rd, Leytonstone, London E11 4PB
Fax: 020-8556 4865   Tel: 020-8558 0024

LONDON UNDERWATER CENTRE
(Pre-holiday Scuba Courses in Victoria)
QMSC 223 Vauxhall Bridge Road
London SW1V 1EL   Tel/Fax: 020-7630 7443

LONG Alan
(Gun Hire and Weapons Armourer)
PO Box 6079, Birmingham B28 0FF
Fax: 0121-624 9060   Mobile: 07976 953375

LYON EQUIPMENT
(Petzl & Beal Rope Access Equipment (PPE) for
Industrial & Theatrical Work)
Dent, Sedbergh, Cumbria LA10 5QL
e-mail: info@lyon.co.uk
Fax: 01539 625454   Tel: 01539 625493

M A C
(Sound Hire)
1-2 Attenburys Park, Park Road, Altrincham
Cheshire WA14 5QE
e-mail: hire@macsound.co.uk
Fax: 0161-962 9423   Tel: 0161-969 8311

MACKIE Sally LOCATIONS
(Location Finding & Management)
Cownham Farm, Broadwell, Moreton-in-Marsh
Glos GL56 0TT
e-mail: sallymackie@lokations.freeserve.co.uk
Fax: 01451 832442   Tel: 01451 830294

MADDERMARKET THEATRE
(Furniture, Props, Costumes & Accessories)
St John's Alley
Norwich NR2 1DR
e-mail: theatre@maddermarket.freeserve.co.uk
Fax: 01603 661357   Tel: 01603 626560

MAGICAL MART
(Magic, Ventriloquists' Dolls, Punch & Judy,
Hire & Advising. Callers by Appointment)
42 Christchurch Road
Sidcup, Kent DA15 7HQ   Tel/Fax: 020-8300 3579

MANSON TRASH
(Army Drill Instructor)
3 Bond Street, Chiswick
London W4 1QZ
e-mail: hayloftwoodwork@compuserve.com
                         Tel: 020-8747 3510

MARINE UNDERWATER EQUIPMENT
(Watersports Equipment)
Ocean Leisure (Main Branch)
11-14 Northumberland Avenue
London WC2N 5AQ
e-mail: info@oceanleisure.co.uk
Fax: 020-7930 3032   Tel: 020-7930 5050

MARKSON PIANOS
8 Chester Court, Albany Street, London NW1 4BU
Fax: 020-7224 0957   Tel: 020-7935 8682

McDONALD ROWE (SCULPTURE) Ltd
20 Southfield Way, St Albans, Herts AL4 9JJ
e-mail: mcdonald@stalbans01.freeserve.co.uk
                           Tel: 01727 765277

MIDNIGHT ELECTRONICS
(Sound Hire)
Off Quay Building, Foundry Lane
Newcastle NE6 1LH
e-mail: dx@compuserve.com
Fax: 0191-224 0080   Tel: 0191-224 0088

MODEL BOX Ltd
(Computer Aided Design & Design Services)
Studio 9, 75 Filmer Road, London SW6 7JF
e-mail: info@modelbox.co.uk
Fax: 020-7371 0503   Tel: 020-7371 0110

MORTON G & L
(Horses/Farming)
Hashome Carr, Holme-on-Spalding Moor
Yorks YO43 4BD   Tel: 01430 860393

NEWENS Chas MARINE Co Ltd
(Boats, Marine Props etc)
The Boathouse, Embankment, London SW15 1LB
Fax: 020-8780 2339   Tel: 020-8788 4587

NEWMAN HIRE Co
16 The Vale, Acton, London W3 7SB
e-mail: info@newman-hire.co.uk
                           Tel: 020-8743 0741

NIVOFLEX
(Theatre & Staging Equipment)
c/o Steeldeck, Barpart House
King's Cross Freight Depot, York Way
London N1 0UZ
Fax: 020-7278 3403   Tel: 020-7833 2031

NORTHERN LIGHT
79 Loanbank Quadrant, Govan
Glasgow G51 3HZ
e-mail: enquiries@northernlight.co.uk
Fax: 0141-445 4406   Tel: 0141-440 1771

NOSTALGIA AMUSEMENTS
(Brian Davey)
22 Greenwood Close, Thames Ditton
Surrey KT7 0BG
Mobile: 07973 506869   Tel: 020-8398 2141

**NOTTINGHAM JOUSTING ASSOCIATION
SCHOOL OF NATIONAL EQUITATION Ltd**
(Jousting & Medieval Tournaments, Horses &
Riders for Films & TV)
Bunny Hill Top, Costock
Loughborough
Leics LE12 6XE
e-mail: info@bunny-hill.co.uk
Fax: 01509 856067   Tel: 01509 852366

OCEAN LEISURE
(Scuba Diving, Watersports)
11-14 Northumberland Avenue
London WC2N 5AQ
Fax: 020-7930 3032   Tel: 020-7930 5050

OFFSTAGE
(Theatre & Film Bookshop)
37 Chalk Farm Road, London NW1 8AJ
e-mail: offstage@btinternet.com
Fax: 020-7916 8046   Tel: 020-7485 4996

PATERSON Helen
(Typing Services)
40 Whitelands House, London SW3 4QY
e-mail: pater@waitrose.com
                           Tel: 020-7730 6428

PENDLEBURYS CANDLE Co.
(Church Candles & Requisites)
Church House
Portland Avenue, Stamford Hill London N16 6HU
e-mail: books@pendleburys.demon.co.uk
                        Tel/Fax: 020-8809 4922

PERIOD PROPS AND LIGHTING Ltd
17-23 Stirling Road, London W3 8DJ
e-mail: pplprops@supanet.com
Fax: 020-8993 4637   Tel: 020-8992 6901

PHELPS Ltd
(Victorian & Edwardian Furniture for Hire)
133-135 St Margaret's Road
East Twickenham, Middlesex TW1 1RG
Fax: 020-8892 3661   Tel: 020-8891 2370

PHOSPHENE
(Lighting, Sound & Accessories. Design,
Sales Hire)
Milton Road South
Stowmarket, Suffolk IP14 1EZ
e-mail: cliff@phosphene.freeserve.co.uk
                           Tel: 01449 770011

PHOTOGRAPHIC RETOUCHER
(Steve McAllister)
50-54 Beak Street
London W1F 9RN   Tel: 020-7250 0951

PHYSICALITY
(Physical Artistry Specialists)
265-267 Ilford Lane
Ilford, Essex IG1 2SD
e-mail: info@physicality.co.uk
Fax: 020-8491 2801   Tel: 020-8491 2800

PICKFORDS Ltd
Heritage House
345 Southbury Road
Enfield EN1 1UP
Fax: 020-8219 8001   Tel: 020-8219 8000

PICTURES PROPS CO Ltd
(TV, Film & Stage Hire)
12-16 Brunel Road, London W3 7XR
Fax: 020-8740 5846   Tel: 020-8749 2433

PINK POINTES DANCEWEAR
1A Suttons Lane
Hornchurch, Essex RM12 6RD
e-mail: sales@gavnicola.freeserve.co.uk
                        Tel/Fax: 01708 438584

PLASTIC WARRIOR
(Model Figures)
38A Horsell Road, London N5 1XP
e-mail: figsculpt@aol.com
Fax: 020-7700 4624   Tel: 020-7700 7036

PLAYBOARD PUPPETS
2 Ockendon Mews
London N1 3JL   Tel/Fax: 020-7226 5911

POLAND Anna: MODELMAKER
(Sculpture, Models, Puppets, Masks etc)
Salterns, Old Bursledon
Southampton, Hampshire SO31 8DH
Fax: 023-8045 6364   Tel: 023-8040 5166

POLLEX PROPS / FIREBRAND
(Prop Makers)
Leac na Ban, Tayvallich, Lochgilphead
Argyll PA31 8PF
e-mail: alex@firebrand.fsnet.co.uk
Tel/Fax: 01546 870310

PRAETORIAN ASSOCIATES
(Personal Safety & Anti-Stalking Consultancy)
Suite 501, 2 Old Brompton Road
London SW7 3DG
e-mail: e17one@aol.com
Fax: 020-8923 7177   Tel: 020-8923 9075

PRAETORIAN PROCUREMENT SERVICES - SA
(Providing Services for the Film/TV Industry
within South Africa)
2 Old Brompton Road, Suite 501
London SW7 3DG
e-mail: e17one@aol.com
Fax: 020-8923 7177   Tel: 020-8923 9075

PRO-ACRO
(Acrobats/Circus Skills & Speciality Acts)
Springvale, Tutland Road, North Baddesley
Hampshire SO52 9FL
e-mail: mo@2ma.co.uk
Fax: 023-8074 1355   Tel: 023-8074 1354

PRO BLOOD
11 Mount Pleasant, Framlingham
Suffolk IP13 9HQ   Tel/Fax: 01728 723865

PROFESSOR PATTEN'S PUNCH & JUDY
(Hire & Performances/Advice on
Traditional Show)
14 The Crest, Goffs Oak
Herts EN7 5NP   Tel: 01707 873262

PROFILE PRINTS
(Photographic Processing)
Courtwood Film Service Ltd, Freepost TO55
Penzance, Cornwall TR18 2BR
e-mail: people@courtwood.co.uk
Fax: 01736 350203   Tel: 01736 365222

PROP FARM Ltd
(Pat Ward)
Grange Farm, Elmton, Nr Creswell
North Derbyshire S80 4LX
e-mail: pat/les@propfarm.free-online.co.uk
Fax: 01909 721465   Tel: 01909 723100

PROP ROTATION
41 Trelawney Road, Cotham
Bristol BS6 6DY   Tel: 0117-974 1058

PROPS GALORE
(Period Textiles/Jewellery)
15 Brunel Road
London W3 7XR
e-mail: props_galore@farley.co.uk
Fax: 020-8354 1866   Tel: 020-8746 1222

PUNCH & JUDY PUPPETS & BOOTHS
(Hire & Advisory Service, Callers by Appointment)
42 Christchurch Road
Sidcup, Kent DA15 7HQ   Tel/Fax: 020-8300 3579

PUPPET FACTORY The
Punch's Oak, Cleobury Road
Far Forest, Worcestershire DY14 9EB
Fax: 01299 266561   Tel: 01299 266634

RAINBOW PRODUCTIONS Ltd
(Manufacture & Handling of Costume
Characters)
Rainbow House
56 Windsor Avenue
London SW19 2RR
Fax: 020-8545 0777   Tel: 020-8545 0700

RENTABOOK (Norma & Ray Feather)
74 Park Chase
Wembley
Middlesex HA9 8EH   Tel: 020-8902 3659

RENT-A-CLOWN
(Mattie Faint)
37 Sekeforde Street, Clerkenwell
London EC1R 0HA   Tel/Fax: 020-7608 0312

RENT-A-SWORD
(Alan M Meek)
180 Frog Grove Lane
Wood Street Village, Guildford
Surrey GU3 3HD
Fax: 01483 236684   Tel: 01483 234084

REPLAY Ltd
(Showreels & TV Facilities Hire)
20 Greek Street
London W1D 4DU
e-mail: sales@replayfilms.co.uk
Fax: 020-7287 5348   Tel: 020-7287 5334

RETROGRAPH NOSTALGIA ARCHIVE
(Posters & Packaging 1880-1970, Picture
Library/Photo Stills/
Ephemera/Fine Arts 1870-1970)
164 Kensington Park Road
Notting Hill, London W11 2ER
e-mail: retropix1@aol.com
Fax: 020-7229 3395   Tel: 020-7727 9378

RICO THE CIRCUS CLOWN
66 Queen Elizabeth's Drive
Addington, Croydon
Surrey CR0 0HE   Tel: 01689 846887

RITCHIE Alison ASSOCIATES
16 Chessing Court, Fortis Green
London N2 9ER
Fax: 020-8883 3156   Tel: 020-8444 5983

RODEO & RIDER WESTERN WEAR
71 Windmill Road
Luton, Beds LU1 3XL   Tel: 01582 417446

ROOTSTEIN Adel Ltd
(Mannequin Hire)
9 Beaumont Avenue, London W14 9LP
Fax: 020-7381 3263   Tel: 020-7381 1447

ROYAL HORTICULTURAL HALLS & CONFERENCE CENTRE
(Film Location: Art Deco & Edwardian Buildings)
80 Vincent Square
London SW1P 2PE
e-mail: maugiel@rhs.org.uk
Fax: 020-7834 2072   Tel: 020-7828 4125

ROYAL SHAKESPEARE COMPANY COSTUME HIRE WARDROBE
Timothy's Bridge Road
Stratford-upon-Avon CV37 9UY
                              Tel: 01789 205920

ROYER Hugo INTERNATIONAL Ltd
(Hair & Wig Materials)
10 Lakeside Business Park
Swan Lake, Sandhurst
Berkshire GU47 9DN
e-mail: enquiries@royer.co.uk
Fax: 01252 878852   Tel: 01252 878811

RUDKIN DESIGN
(Design Consultants, Brochures, Advertising,
Corporate etc)
Bishop Crewe House, North Street, Daventry
Northamptonshire NN11 5PN
e-mail: studio@rudkindesign.com
Fax: 01327 872728   Tel: 01327 301770

RUMBLE Jane
(Props to Order, No Hire)
121 Elmstead Avenue, Wembley
Middlesex HA9 8NT   Tel: 020-8904 6462

SABAH
(Stylist/Designer/Co-ordinator)
155 Cholmley Gardens, Mill Lane
London NW6 1AB
e-mail: sabah.saoud@lineone.net
                              Tel/Fax: 020-7794 3213

SANDERSON Claire
(Props, Soft Props, Upholster)
1st Floor, Union Hall, 27-29 Union Street
London SE1 1SD
Mobile: 07970 032919   Tel: 020-7357 7891

SAPEX SCRIPTS
Millennium Studios, 5 Elstree Way
Borehamwood, Herts WD6 1SF
e-mail: scripts@sapex.co.uk
Fax: 020-8236 1591   Tel: 020-8236 1600

SCENA PRODUCTIONS Ltd
240 Camberwell Road, London SE5 0DP
e-mail: scena@compuserve.com
Fax: 020-7703 7012   Tel: 020-7703 4444

SCENE TWO HIRE
(Film & TV Props Hire)
18-20 Brunel Road, Acton
London W3 7XR
Fax: 020-8743 2662   Tel: 020-8740 5544

SCENICS
Copse Field Farm
Cawlow Lane, Warslow
Buxton SK17 0HE   Tel: 01298 84762

SCHULTZ & WIREMU FABRIC EFFECTS
(Screen Printing/Dyeing & Breaking Down)
Unit B202 Faircharm Studios
8-12 Creekside, London SE8 3DX
e-mail: kevin@schultz-wiremfx.demon.co.uk
                              Tel/Fax: 020-8469 0151

SCRIPTRIGHT
(S.C. Hill - Script/Manuscript Typing
Services/Script Reading Services)
6 Valetta Road, London W3 7TN
e-mail: sam_earlehill@hotmail.com
                    Tel/Fax: 020-8740 7303

SCRIPTS
(Play, Film & Book. Word Processing,
Copying & Binding)
86 Goswell Road, London EC1V 7DB
e-mail: scripts.typing@virgin.net
Fax: 020-7608 1642   Tel: 020-7253 6779

S & H TECHNICAL SUPPORT GROUP
(Star Cloths, Drapes)
Unit A The Old Laundry
Chambercombe Road
Ilfracombe, Devon EX34 9PH
e-mail: enquiries@starcloth.co.uk
Fax: 01271 865423   Tel: 01271 866832

SHAOLIN WAY
(Martial Arts, Lion Dance & Martial Arts Supplies)
10 Little Newport Street, London WC2H 7JJ
Fax: 020-7287 6548   Tel: 020-7734 6391

SHAYLE Mark
(Production Management)
Ideal Production Services
94 Gordon Road, London SE15 3RP
e-mail: m-shayle@dircon.co.uk
Fax: 020-7564 3147   Tel: 020-7564 3384

SHEEHAN Dee
(Costume Maker)
28 Lansdown Place, Lewes
East Sussex BN7 2JU
e-mail: deesheehan@onetel.net.uk
Mobile: 07801 231704   Tel: 01273 486857

SHER SYSTEM The
(Helping Skin with Acne & Rosacea)
30 New Bond Street, London W1Y 9HD
e-mail: skincare@sher.co.uk
Fax: 020-7629 7021   Tel: 020-7499 4022

SHIRLEY LEAF & PETAL Co
(Flower Makers Museum)
58A High Street, Old Town, Hastings
East Sussex TN34 3EN   Tel/Fax: 01424 427793

SHOP FITTINGS DIRECT
428 Whippendell Road
Watford, Herts WD1 7PT
Fax: 01923 232326   Tel: 01923 232425

SIDE EFFECTS
(Props, Models & FX)
Unit 4, Camberwell Trading Estate
117 Denmark Road, London SE5 9LB
e-mail: sfx@lineone.net
Fax: 020-7738 5198   Tel: 020-7738 5199

SILVER Sam KENSINGTON Ltd
(Special Eye Effects)
37 Kensington Church Street, London W8 4LL
e-mail: samsilveropticians@btinternet.com
Fax: 020-7937 8969   Tel: 020-7937 8282

SMITH Tom
(Blacksmith)
9-10 Newbury Mews
London NW5   Tel/Fax: 020-7485 0298

SNOW BUSINESS
(Snow/Winter Effects on Any Scale)
Fountain House, High Beeches, Nailsworth
Glos GL6 0AP
e-mail: snow@snowbusiness.com
                    Tel/Fax: 01453 836699

SOUND DEPARTMENT Ltd
(Importers & Distributors of Pro Audio Equipment)
Mewburn Road, Banbury, Oxon OX16 9PA
e-mail: sales@sound-dept.co.uk
Fax: 01295 817626   Tel: 01295 817625

STARTRUCK
(Location Facilities)
Grey Court, Riding Mill
Northumberland NE44 6AA
e-mail: startruck@startruck.co.uk
Mobile: 07703 494947   Tel/Fax: 01434 682160

STEELDECK SALES Ltd
(Modular Staging)
Barpart House, King's Cross Freight Depot
York Way, London N1 0UZ
Fax: 020-7278 3403   Tel: 020-7833 2031

STIRLING Rob
(Carpentry & Joinery)
Copse Field Farm, Cawlow Lane, Warslow
Buxton SK17 0HE   Tel: 01298 84762

STUDIO & TV HIRE
3 Ariel Way, Wood Lane, White City
London W12 7SL
Fax: 020-8740 9662   Tel: 020-8749 3445

STUDIO FOUR COSTUMES
4 Warple Mews, Warple Way, Acton
London W3 0RF   Tel/Fax: 020-8749 6569

223

STUNT ACTION SPECIALISTS (S.A.S.)
(Corporate Stunt Work)
110 Trafalgar Road
Portslade, Sussex BN41 1GS
Fax: 01273 708699   Tel: 01273 430323

STUNT PRO Ltd
(Stunt Equipment)
12 Forster Road
Walthamstow, London E17   Tel: 020-8509 2005

SUPERSCRIPTS
(Audio Typing, Rushes, Post Prod Scripts)
56 New Road, Hanworth
Middlesex TW13 6TQ
Mobile: 07971 671011   Tel: 020-8898 7933

14 Cambridge Grove Road, Kingston
Surrey KT1 3JJ
Mobile: 07890 972595   Tel: 020-8546 9824

TAYLOR Charlotte
(Stylist/Props Buyer)
18 Eleanor Grove, Barnes SW13 0JN
e-mail: charlotte-taylor@breathemail.net
Mobile: 07836 708904   Tel/Fax: 020-8876 9085

TECHNIQUES
(Property Makers)
15 Danehurst Avenue
Leicester LE3 6DB   Tel/Fax: 0116-285 7294

TELESCRIPT PROMPTING Ltd
The Barn, Handpost Farmhouse
Maidens Green, Bracknell, Berks RG42 6LD
Fax: 01344 890655   Tel: 01344 890470

TESTMAN P.A.T.
(Portable Electrical Appliance Testing,
Specialists in Theatre)
7 Woodville Road, London E17 7ER
Mobile: 07973 663154   Tel: 020-8521 6408

THEATRE DESPATCH Ltd
Azof Hall, Azof Street, London SE10 0EG
e-mail: info@theatre.org
Fax: 08700 525915   Tel: 020-8853 0750

THEATRESEARCH
(Theatre Consultants)
Dacre Hall, Dacre
North Yorkshire HG3 4ET
e-mail: info@theatresearch.co.uk
Fax: 01423 781957   Tel: 01423 780497

THEME TRADERS Ltd
(Props)
The Stadium, Oaklands Road, London NW2 6DL
e-mail: mailroom@themetraders.com
Fax: 020-8450 7322   Tel: 020-8452 8518

TOMLIN Mick DRAPES
(Curtain Makers)
213 Westmount Road, Eltham
London SE9 1XZ   Tel/Fax: 020-8850 8073

TOP SHOW
(Props & Scenery, Conference Specialists)
North Lane, Huntington, York YO32 9SU
                           Tel/Fax: 01904 750022

TROPICAL SURROUNDS Ltd
(Distributors and Installers of Natural
Theming Materials)
The Old Grain Store, Redenham Park Farm,
Redenham, Nr Andover, Hampshire SP11 9AQ
Tel/Fax: 01264 773660   Tel: 01264 773009

TRYFONOS Mary
(Mask Maker)
59 Shaftesbury Road
London N19 4QW
Mobile: 07711 098869   Tel: 020-7561 9880

TV UK Ltd/LATITUDE MEDIA COURSES
(Voice-Over Courses, Alan Meyer)
PO Box 2183, London W1A 1UB
e-mail: alanmeyer@tvuk.net
                           Tel: 020-7727 7447

UFX
(Event Design & Production Management)
Studio A, London, 14 Ayres Street
London SE1 1ES
e-mail: ufx@dial.pipex.com
Fax: 020-7403 6511   Tel: 020-7403 6510

VENTRILOQUIST DOLLS HOME
(Hire & Helpful Hints, Callers by Appointment)
42 Christchurch Road
Sidcup, Kent DA15 7HQ   Tel/Fax: 020-8300 3579

VENTRILOQUIST DUMMY HIRE
(Dennis Patten - Hire & Advice)
14 The Crest, Goffs Oak, Herts EN7 5NP
                           Tel: 01707 873262

VENYFLEX COMPANY
(Drapes, Tabs, Blinds)
1 Holly Road, Hampton Hill
Middlesex TW12 1QF   Tel: 020-8977 3780

VINTAGE MAGAZINE Co Ltd
(Vintage Magazines, Papers, Posters etc)
203-213 Mare Street
London E8 3QE
e-mail: piclib.vintage@ndirect.co.uk
Fax: 020-8533 7283   Tel: 020-8533 7588

VIRGIN ATLANTIC AIRWAYS Ltd
(Reservations)
The Office, Crawley Business Quarter
Manor Royal, West Sussex RH10 2NU
Fax: 01293 747699   Tel: 01293 747747

VISUALEYES IMAGING SERVICES
(Photographic Reproduction)
24 West Street
London WC2H 9NA
e-mail: imaging@visualeyes.ltd.uk
Fax: 020-7240 0050   Tel: 020-7836 3004

VOCALEYES
(Suppliers of Audio Description for Theatrical
Performance)
25 Short Street, London SE1 8LJ
e-mail: enquiries@vocaleyes.co.uk
Fax: 020-7928 2225   Tel: 020-7261 9199

WALLENDA Rudi
(Comedy Car)
33 Wesley Avenue
London NW10 7BL   Tel: 020-8965 1255

WEBBER Peter HIRE-RITZ STUDIOS
(Music Equipment Hire, Rehearsal Studios)
110-112 Disraeli Road, London SW15 2DX
Fax: 020-8877 1036   Tel: 020-8870 1335

WESTED LEATHERS Co
(Suede & Leather Suppliers/Manufacturers)
Little Wested House, Wested Lane
Swanley, Kent BR8 8EF
e-mail: wested@compuserve.com
Fax: 01322 667038   Tel: 01322 660654

WESTWARD Lynn
(Window Blind Specialist)
273 The Vale, Acton
London W3 7QA
Fax: 020-8740 9836   Tel: 020-8740 8756

WHITEHORN Simon
(Sound Design)
57 Acre Lane
London SW2 5TN
e-mail: simon@orbitalsound.co.uk
Fax: 020-7501 6869   Tel: 020-7501 6868

WILLIAMS Frank
(Bottles & Jars 1870 - 1940)
33 Enstone Road, Ickenham
Uxbridge, Middlesex   Tel: 01895 672495

WILTSHIRE A. F.
(Agricultural Engineers)
The Agricultural Centre, Alfold Road
Dunsfold, Surrey
e-mail: team@afwiltshire.fsnet.co.uk
Fax: 01483 200491   Tel: 01483 200516

WINSHIP Geoff
The Knights of Merrie England Ltd
153 Salisbury Road, Burton
Christchurch BH23 7JS
e-mail: geoff@medievaljousting.com
Fax: 01202 483666   Tel: 01202 483777

WOODEN CANAL BOAT SOCIETY
(Historic Canal Boats)
5 Oaken Clough Terrace, Limehurst
Ashton-under-Lyne, Lancs 0L7 9NY
Mobile: 07855 601589   Tel: 0161-330 2315

WORBEY Darryl STUDIOS
(Specialist Puppet Design)
e-mail: dworbey@freewire.co.uk
Fax: 020-7635 6397   Tel: 020-7639 8090

WORLD OF FANTASY
(Props and Costumes)
Swansnest, 2 Windmill Road, Hampton Hill
Middlesex TW12 1RH
e-mail: swansflight@aol.com
Fax: 020-8783 1366   Tel: 020-8941 1595

WORLD OF ILLUSION
4 Sunnyside
Wimbledon SW19 4SL
Fax: 020-8946 0228   Tel: 020-8946 9478

ACADEMY PLAYERS DIRECTORY
8949 Wilshire Blvd, 4th Floor, Beverly Hills
CA 90211
e-mail: players@oscars.org
Fax: (310) 550-5034   Tel: (310) 247-3000

A & C BLACK (Publicity Dept)
37 Soho Square, London W1D 3QZ
e-mail: publicity@acblack.com
Fax: 020-7758 0222   Tel: 020-7758 0200

A C I D PUBLICATIONS
Suite 247, 37 Store Street, London WC1E 7BS
e-mail: acidnews@aol.com
                              Tel/Fax: 07050 205206

ACTING: A DRAMA STUDIO SOURCE BOOK
(Peter Owen Publishers)
73 Kenway Road, London SW5 0RE
e-mail: admin@peterowen.com   Tel: 020-7373 5628

ACTORS' HANDBOOK
(Bloomsbury Publishing Plc)
38 Soho Square, London W1V 5DF
e-mail: webmaster@bloomsbury.com
Fax: 020-7434 0151   Tel: 020-7494 2111

AMATEUR STAGE MAGAZINE & COMMUNITY ARTS DIRECTORY
(Platform Publications Ltd)
Hampden House, 2 Weymouth Street
London W1W 5BT
e-mail: cvtheatre@aol.com
Fax: 020-7636 2323   Tel: 020-7636 4343

ANNUAIRE DU CINEMA BELLEFAYE
(French Actors Directory, Production, Technicians)
38 Rue Etienne Marcel, 75002 Paris
Fax: 00 331 42 33 39 00   Tel: 00 331 42 33 52 52

ARTISTES & AGENTS
(Richmond House Publishing Co), Douglas House, 3 Richmond Buildings, London W1D 3HE
e-mail: sales@rhpco.co.uk
Fax: 020-7287 3463   Tel: 020-7437 9556

ASSOCIATION OF PHOTOGRAPHERS AWARDS BOOK
(Variety Media Publications)
6 Bell Yard, London WC2A 2JR
e-mail: general@aophotoon.co.uk
Fax: 020-7520 5208   Tel: 020-7520 5233

AUDITION NOW
(Weekly Casting Publication)
Lifegroup Ltd, Garden Studios
11-15 Betterton Street, Covent Garden
London WC2H 9BP   Tel: 0800 0966144

AURORA METRO PRESS (1979)
(Drama, Fiction, Reference & International Literature in English Translation)
4 Osier Mews, Chiswick, London W4 2NT
e-mail: ampress@netcomuk.co.uk
Fax: 020-8742 2925   Tel: 020-8747 1953

BRITISH NATIONAL FILM & VIDEO CATALOGUE
(British Film Institute)
21 Stephen Street, London W1T 1LN
e-mail: maureen.brown@bfi.org.uk
Fax: 020-7436 7950   Tel: 020-7957 4706

BRITISH PERFORMING ARTS YEARBOOK
(Rhinegold Publishing), 241 Shaftesbury Avenue
London WC2H 8TF
e-mail: bpay@rhinegold.co.uk   Tel: 020-7333 1721

BRITISH THEATRE DIRECTORY
(Richmond House Publishing Co)
Douglas House, 3 Richmond Buildings
London W1D 3HE
e-mail: sales@rhpco.co.uk
Fax: 020-7287 3463   Tel: 020-7437 9556

BROADCAST
33-39 Bowling Green Lane
London EC1R 0DA
Fax: 020-7505 8020   Tel: 020-7505 8014

CALDER PUBLICATIONS
51 The Cut, London SE1 8LF
e-mail: info@calderpublications.com
Fax: 020-7928 5930   Tel: 020-7633 0599

CASTCALL & CASTFAX
(Casting Information Services)
106 Wilsden Avenue, Luton LU1 5HR
e-mail: admin@castcall.co.uk
Fax: 01582 480736   Tel: 01582 456213

CASTWEB
7 St Lukes Avenue, London SW4 7LG
e-mail: castweb@netcomuk.co.uk
Fax: 020-7720 2879   Tel: 020-7720 9002

CELEBRITY BULLETIN The
Rooms 203-209, 93-97 Regent Street
London W1R 7TA
e-mail: celebritylondon@aol.com
Fax: 020-7494 3500   Tel: 020-7439 9840

CELEBRITY SERVICE Ltd
Rooms 203-209, 93-97 Regent Street
London W1R 7TA
e-mail: celebritylondon@aol.com
Fax: 020-7494 3500   Tel: 020-7439 9840

CEROC ADDICT
(Fox Promotions Media Advertising Ltd)
51 Earls Court Square
London SW5 9DG   Tel: 020-7370 732

CHAPPELL OF BOND STREET
(Sheet Music, Musical Instruments, Pianos Synthesizers, Keyboards)
50 New Bond Street, London W1S 1RD
Fax: 020-7491 0133   Tel: 020-7491 2777

CONFERENCE & INCENTIVE TRAVEL MAGAZINE
174 Hammersmith Road, London W6 7JP
Fax: 020-8267 4192   Tel: 020-8267 4307

CREATIVE HANDBOOK
(Variety Media Publications)
6 Bell Yard, London WC2A 2JR
e-mail: sara@variety.demon.co.uk
Fax: 020-7520 5237   Tel: 020-7520 5233

DANCE EXPRESSION
(A. E. Morgan Publications Ltd)
51 Earls Court Square
London SW5 9DG   Tel: 020-7370 7324

DIRECTING DRAMA
(Peter Owen Publishers)
73 Kenway Road, London SW5 0RE
e-mail: admin@peterowen.com
                              Tel: 020-7373 5628

EQUITY JOURNAL
Guild House, Upper St Martin's Lane
London WC2H 9EG
e-mail: info@equity.org.uk
Fax: 020-7379 6074   Tel: 020-7379 5185

FILMLOG
(Subscriptions)
PO Box 100, Broadstairs, Kent CT10 1UJ
Tel: 01843 860885   Tel: 01843 866538

FORESIGHT
(The Profile Group)
6-7 St Cross Street, London EC1N 8UA
Fax: 020-7430 1089   Tel: 020-7405 4455

GETTING INTO FILM & TV
(See SALTCOATS PUBLISHING)

THE STAGE

www.thestage.co.uk

Stage House
47 Bermondsey St, London SE1 3XT
tel: 020 7403 1818   e-mail: info@thestage.co.uk
www.thestage.co.uk   www.showcall.co.uk

GRAPEVINE The
Armstrong Arts Ltd
9 Greville Hall, Greville Place, London NW6 5JS
e-mail: gv@armstrongarts.com
Fax: 020-7625 2213   Tel: 020-7372 7110

HOLLYWOOD REPORTER The
Endeavour House
189 Shaftesbury Avenue, London WC2H 8TJ
Fax: 020-7420 6015   Tel: 020-7420 6003

**KAY'S UK & EUROPEAN PRODUCTION
MANUALS**
Pinewood Studios, Pinewood Road
Iver Heath, Bucks SL0 0NH
e-mail: info@kays.co.uk
Fax: 01608 677811   Tel: 01608 677222

KEMP'S FILM, TV & VIDEO
(UK, International & American Editions)
(Variety Media Publications)
6 Bell Yard, London WC2A 2JR
e-mail: sara@variety.demon.co.uk
Fax: 020-7520 5237   Tel: 020-7520 5233

KNOWLEDGE The
Riverbank House, Angel Lane
Tonbridge, Kent TN9 1SE
e-mail: knowledge@ubminternational.com
Fax: 01732 368324   Tel: 01732 377041

LIMELIGHT The
(Limelight Publications, Contacts and Casting
Directory)
Postal Address: PO Box 760, Randpark Ridge,
2156, Gauteng, South Africa
e-mail: barbara@limelight.co.za
                    Tel/Fax: 00 27 11 793 7231

MAKING OF THE PROFESSIONAL ACTOR The
(Peter Owen Publishers)
73 Kenway Road, London SW5 0RE
e-mail: admin@peterowen.com
                    Tel: 020-7373 5628

MUSICAL STAGES
(Musical Theatre Magazine)
Box 8365, London W14 0GL
e-mail: editor@musicalstages.co.uk
                    Tel/Fax: 020-7603 2221

MUSIC WEEK DIRECTORY
United Business Media Entertainment Group
Ludgate House, 245 Blackfriars Road
London SE1 9UR   Tel: 020-7579 4170

OFFICIAL LONDON SEATING PLAN GUIDE The
(Richmond House Publishing Co)
Douglas House, 3 Richmond Buildings
London W1D 3HE
e-mail: sales@rhpco.co.uk
Fax: 020-7287 3463   Tel: 020-7437 9556

PA LISTINGS Ltd
292 Vauxhall Bridge Road, Victoria
London SW1V 1AE
e-mail: arts@listings.press.net
Fax: 020-7963 7800   Tel: 020-7963 7707

PANTOMIME BOOK The
(Peter Owen Publishers)
73 Kenway Road, London SW5 0RE
e-mail: admin@peterowen.com
                    Tel: 020-7373 5628

PCR
(See PRODUCTION & CASTING REPORT)

**PERFORMING ARTS YEARBOOK FOR EUROPE
(PAYE)**
(Arts Publishing International Ltd)
Lime Wharf, Vyner Street, Bethnal Green,
London E2 9DJ
Fax: 020-8709 9080   Tel: 020-8709 9050

PLAYERS' GUIDE
(In association with THE SPOTLIGHT &
BREAKDOWN SERVICES Ltd USA)
123 West 44th Street, #2J, New York NY 10036
e-mail: info@players-guide.com
Fax: (212) 302-3495   Tel: (212) 302-9474

PLAYS INTERNATIONAL
33A Lurline Gardens
London SW11 4DD   Tel/Fax: 020-7720 1950

**PRESENTER'S CONTACT FILE The/
PRESENTER'S YEAR PLANNER The**
Presenter Promotions
123 Corporation Road, Gillingham
Kent ME7 1RG
e-mail: info@presenterpromotions.com
Fax: 01634 316771   Tel: 01634 851077

PRESENTERS SPOTLIGHT
7 Leicester Place, London WC2H 7RJ
e-mail: info@spotlightcd.com
Fax: 020-7437 5881   Tel: 020-7437 7631

PRESS PLANNER
(The Profile Group), 6-7 St Cross Street
London EC1N 8UA
e-mail: info@pressplanner.co.uk
Fax: 020-7405 3123   Tel: 020-7405 4455

**PRODUCERS ALLIANCE FOR CINEMA &
TELEVISION**
(Pact Directory of Independent Producers/Art
of the Deal/Rights Clearance)
45 Mortimer Street, London W1W 8HJ
e-mail: enquiries@pact.co.uk
Fax: 020-7331 6700   Tel: 020-7331 6000

PRODUCTION & CASTING REPORT
(Subscriptions)
PO Box 100, Broadstairs, Kent CT10 1UJ
Tel: 01843 860885   Tel: 01843 866538

PRODUCTION & CASTING REPORT
(Editorial)
PO Box 11, London N1 7JZ
Fax: 020-7566 8284   Tel: 020-7566 8282

RADIO TIMES
80 Wood Lane, London W12 0TT
e-mail: radio.times@bbc.co.uk
Fax: 020-8433 3923   Tel: 0870 6084455

RICHMOND HOUSE PUBLISHING COMPANY Ltd
Douglas House, 3 Richmond Buildings
London W1D 3HE
e-mail: sales@rhpco.co.uk
Fax: 020-7287 3463   Tel: 020-7437 9556

SALTCOATS PUBLISHING
(Getting into Film & TV)
7 Saltcoats Road, London W4 1AR
e-mail: bigbenbook@aol.com
Fax: 020-8995 3376   Tel: 020-8995 0547

SCREEN INTERNATIONAL
33-39 Bowling Green Lane
London EC1R 0DA
e-mail: screeninternational@compuserve.com
Fax: 020-7505 8117   Tel: 020-7505 8080

SCRIPT BREAKDOWN SERVICE Ltd
Suite 1, 16 Sidmouth Road, London NW2 5JX
e-mail: sbsltd@talk.com
Fax: 020-8459 7442   Tel: 020-8459 2781

SHOWCALL
47 Bermondsey Street, London SE1 3XT
e-mail: info@thestage.co.uk
Fax: 020-7378 0480   Tel: 020-7403 1818

SHOWCAST: The AUSTRALASIAN CASTING DIRECTORY
PO Box 2001, Leumeah
NSW 2560 Australia
e-mail: brian@showcast.com.au
Fax: 02 4647 4167   Tel: 02 4647 4166

SIGHT & SOUND
(British Film Institute)
21 Stephen Street, London W1T 1LN
e-mail: s&s@bfi.org.uk
Fax: 020-7436 2327   Tel: 020-7255 1444

SPEECH FOR THE SPEAKER
(Peter Owen Publishers)
73 Kenway Road, London SW5 0RE
e-mail: admin@peterowen.com
                              Tel: 020-7373 5628

SPOTLIGHT CASTING DIRECTORY The
7 Leicester Place
London WC2H 7RJ
e-mail: info@spotlightcd.com
Fax: 020-7437 5881   Tel: 020-7437 7631

STAGE NEWSPAPER Ltd The
47 Bermondsey Street, London SE1 3XT
e-mail: info@thestage.co.uk
Fax: 020-7403 1418   Tel: 020-7403 1818

STAGECAST: IRISH STAGE & SCREEN DIRECTORY
15 Eaton Square, Monkstown
Dublin   Tel/Fax: 00 353 1 2808968

TANGO REVIEW
(Academia Nacional del Tango UK Ltd)
51 Earls Court Square
London SW5 9DG   Tel: 020-7370 7324

TELEVISUAL
12-26 Lexington Street, London W1R 4HQ
Fax: 020-7970 6733   Tel: 020-7970 6666

THEATRE RECORD
305 Whitton Dene
Isleworth, Middlesex TW7 7NE
e-mail: editor@theatrerecord.demon.co.uk
Fax: 020-8893 9677   Tel: 020-8737 8489

THEATRE REPORT
(Subscriptions)
PO Box 100, Broadstairs, Kent CT10 1UJ
Tel: 01843 860885   Tel: 01843 866538

TIME OUT GROUP Ltd
Universal House, 251 Tottenham Court Road
London W1T 7AB
e-mail: net@timeout.co.uk
Fax: 020-7813 6001   Tel: 020-7813 3000

TV TIMES
IPC Magazines
Kings Reach Tower, Stamford Street
London SE1 9LS
Fax: 020-7261 7888   Tel: 020-7261 7000

UK CHOREOGRAPHERS' DIRECTORY
(Dance UK)
Battersea Arts Centre, Lavender Hill
London SW11 5TF
e-mail: danceuk@globalnet.co.uk
Fax: 020-7223 0074   Tel: 020-7228 4990

VARIETY
6 Bell Yard, London WC2A 2JR
Fax: 020-7520 5217   Tel: 020-7520 5222

VOICE BOOK The
(Michael McCallion, published by
Faber & Faber)
Macmillan Distribution
e-mail: mdl@macmillan.co.uk
                              Tel: 01256 302699

WHITE BOOK The
Bank House, 23 Warwick Road
Coventry CV1 2EW   Tel: 024-7655 9590

AQUARIUS
(Picture Library/Showbusiness Press Agency)
PO Box 5, Hastings TN34 1HR
e-mail: aquarius.lib@clara.net
Fax: 01424 717704   Tel: 01424 721196

ARTHUR Anna PRESS & PR
52 Tottenham Street, London W1T 4RN
e-mail: aapr@compuserve.com
Fax: 020-7637 2984   Tel: 020-7637 2994

ASSOCIATES The
(Film & Video Publicity Specialists)
39-41 North Road, London N7 9DP
e-mail: info@the-associates.co.uk
Fax: 020-7609 2249   Tel: 020-7700 3388

AVALON PUBLIC RELATIONS
(Marketing/Arts)
4A Exmoor Street, London W10 6BD
e-mail: edt@avalonuk.com
Fax: 020-7598 7223   Tel: 020-7598 7222

BARLOW Tony ASSOCIATES
(Press & Marketing for Music, Dance & Theatre)
3 Choumert Square, London SE15 4RE
e-mail: artspublicity@hotmail.com
Mobile: 07774 407385   Tel/Fax: 020-7358 9291

BOLTON Erica & QUINN Jane Ltd
10 Pottery Lane, London W11 4LZ
e-mail: e.mail@boltonquinn.com
Fax: 020-7221 8100   Tel: 020-7221 5000

BORKOWSKI Mark PR & IMPROPERGANDA Ltd
2nd Floor, 12 Oval Road, London NW1 7DH
e-mail: nourish@borkowski.co.uk
Fax: 020-7482 5400   Tel: 020-7482 4000

CENTRESTAGE PUBLIC RELATIONS
Yeates Cottage, 27 Wellington Terrace,
Knaphill, Woking, Surrey GU21 2AP
e-mail: dellayedwards@hotmail.com
                         Tel: 01483 487808

CHAPMAN Emma PUBLICITY
2nd Floor, 18 Great Portland Street
London W1W 8QP
e-mail: pr@ecpub.com
Fax: 020-7637 0660   Tel: 020-7637 0990

CHAPMAN Guy ASSOCIATES
1-2 Henrietta Street, Covent Garden
London WC2E 8PS
e-mail: guy@g-c-a.co.uk
Fax: 020-7379 8484   Tel: 020-7379 7474

CHESTON Judith PUBLICITY
30 Telegraph Street, Shipston-on-Stour
Warks CV36 4DA
e-mail: cheston@shipstononstour1.freeserve.co.uk
Fax: 01608 663772   Tel: 01608 661198

CORBETT AND KEENE Ltd
22 Poland Street, London W1F 8QQ
Fax: 020-7734 2024   Tel: 020-7494 3478

COWAN SYMES & ASSOCIATES
83 Charlotte Street, London W1P 1LB
Fax: 020-7323 1070   Tel: 020-7323 1200

COWELL Tony
(See PRESS GROUP Ltd The)

CUE CONSULTANTS
18 Barrington Court, London N10 1QG
e-mail: jmin@globalnet.co.uk
Fax: 020-8883 4197   Tel: 020-8444 6533

DAVEY Christine Ltd
29 Victoria Road, Eton Wick, Windsor
Berkshire SL4 6LY
Fax: 01753 851123   Tel: 01753 852619

DAVIDSON Dennis ASSOCIATES
Royalty House, 72-74 Dean Street
London W1V 6QB
Fax: 020-7437 6358   Tel: 020-7439 6391

EILENBERG Charlotte ASSOCIATES
6 Balfour Road, London N5 2HB
e-mail: charlotte.eilenberg@dial.pipex.com
                    Tel/Fax: 020-7354 2155

ELSON Howard PROMOTIONS
16 Penn Avenue, Chesham
Buckinghamshire HP5 2HS
e-mail: helson1029@aol.com
Fax: 01494 784760   Tel: 01494 785873

EMM
(Epega Media Management)
11 Cosway Street, Lower Ground Level
London NW1 5NR
e-mail: epegamedia@angelfire.com
                    Tel/Fax: 020-7402 2679

GADABOUTS Ltd
(Theatre Marketing & Promotions)
54 Friary Road, London N12 9PB
e-mail: events@gadabouts.fsnet.co.uk
Tel/Fax: 020-8445 5450   Tel: 020-8445 4793

GAYNOR Avril ASSOCIATES
76 Probyn House, Page Street
London SW1P 4BQ   Tel: 020-7976 6522

GOODMAN Deborah PUBLICITY
44 Pembroke Road, London N10 2HT
e-mail: dg.pr@virgin.net
Fax: 020-8365 3557   Tel: 020-8444 2607

HATTON & RAE-SMITH
91 Southwood Lane
London N6 5TB   Tel: 020-8340 5942

HYMAN Sue ASSOCIATES Ltd
70 Chalk Farm Road, London NW1 8AN
e-mail: sue.hyman@btinternet.com
Fax: 020-7267 4715   Tel: 020-7485 8489

IMPACT AGENCY
3 Bloomsbury Place, London WC1A 2QL
e-mail: mail@impactagency.co.uk
Fax: 020-7580 7200   Tel: 020-7580 1770

INFOCOM - Information Communication Ltd
(Strategic Marketing)
6 Hornsey Lane Gardens, Highgate
London N6 5PB
e-mail: infocom@dial.pipex.com
                    Tel/Fax: 020-8374 6040

KEAN LANYON
(Sharon Kean)
Rose Cottage, The Aberdeen Centre
22-25 Highbury Grove, London N5 2EA
e-mail: sharon@keanlanyon.com
Fax: 020-7359 0199   Tel: 020-7354 3574

KELLER Don ARTS MARKETING
65 Glenwood Road, Harringay, London N15 3JS
e-mail: donkeller@waitrose.com
Fax: 020-8809 6825   Tel: 020-8800 4882

KIRWIN MEDIA
10 Tower Court, London WC2H 9NU
e-mail: office@kirwinmedia.co.uk
Fax: 020-7930 4226   Tel: 020-7930 7003

KWPR
(Kevin Wilson Public Relations)
Studio 310 The Chandlery
50 Westminster Bridge Road, London SE1 7QY
e-mail: kwshout@aol.com
Fax: 020-7721 7640   Tel: 020-7721 7621

LAKE-SMITH GRIFFIN ASSOCIATES
15 Maiden Lane
Covent Garden, London WC2E 7NG
e-mail: lakesmithgriffin@aol.com
Fax: 020-7836 1040   Tel: 020-7836 1020

LAVER Richard PUBLICITY
3 Troy Court
High Street Kensington
London W8 7RA
e-mail: richard@lavpub.u-net.com
Fax: 020-7937 5976   Tel: 020-7937 7322

MAYER Anne PR
82 Mortimer Road, London N1 4LH
e-mail: jxbird@compuserve.com
Fax: 020-7254 8227   Tel: 020-7254 7391

McDONALD Charles
(See McDONALD & RUTTER)

McDONALD & RUTTER
34 Bloomsbury Street, London WC1B 3QJ
e-mail: info@mcdonaldrutter.com
Fax: 020-7637 3690   Tel: 020-7637 2600

MITCHELL Jackie
(JM Communications)
4 Sims Cottages, The Green
Claygate, Surrey KT10 0JH
e-mail: jackiemitchell@dial.pipex.com
Fax: 01372 471073   Tel: 01372 465041

MITCHELL Sarah PARTNERSHIP The
Third Floor, 87 Wardour Street
London W1V 3TF
e-mail: sarah@thesmp.com
Fax: 020-7434 1954   Tel: 020-7434 1944

MORGAN Jane ASSOCIATES
8 Heathville Road, London N19 3AJ
e-mail: morgans@dircon.co.uk
Fax: 020-7263 9877   Tel: 020-7263 9867

NEWLEY Patrick ASSOCIATES
45 Kingscourt Road, London SW16 1JA
e-mail: patricknewley@yahoo.com
                         Tel/Fax: 020-8677 0477

PARKER James ASSOCIATES
67 Richmond Park Road
London SW14 8JY   Tel/Fax: 020-8876 1918

POWELL Martin COMMUNICATIONS
1 Lyons Court, Long Ashton Business Park
Yanley Lane, Bristol BS41 9LB
Fax: 01275 393933   Tel: 01275 394400

PRESS GROUP Ltd The
Rosemaye House
Mounts Hill, Windsor
Berks SL4 4RH
e-mail: authornews@aol.com
Fax: 01344 882651   Tel: 01344 893651

PR PEOPLE The
1 St James Drive, Sale
Cheshire M33 7QX
e-mail: pr.people@btinternet.com
Fax: 0161-976 2758   Tel: 0161-976 2729

PUBLIC EYE COMMUNICATIONS Ltd
Suite 318, Plaza, 535 Kings Road
London SW10 0SZ
e-mail: publiceye@ftech.co.uk
Fax: 020-7351 1010   Tel: 020-7351 1555

SAPIEKA Joy ASSOCIATES
JSA Studio, 8 Fitzroy Road
London NW1 8TX
e-mail: jsa.press@easynet.co.uk
Fax: 020-7586 3200   Tel: 020-7586 3100

SHIPPEN Martin MARKETING AND MEDIA
91 Dyne Road, London NW6 7DR
e-mail: m.shippen@virgin.net
Mobile: 07956 879165   Tel/Fax: 020-7372 3788

SINGER Sandra ASSOCIATES
(Corporate Services)
21 Cotswold Road, Westcliff on Sea
Essex SS0 8AA
e-mail: sandra.singer@virgin.net
Fax: 01702 339393   Tel: 01702 331616

S & X MEDIA
405F The Big Peg, Vyse Street
Birmingham B18 6NF
e-mail: roulla@sxmedia.idps.co.uk
Fax: 0121-694 6494   Tel: 0121-604 6366

TAYLOR Annie
(Festival Management and Marketing)
Spring, Washwells, Box, Wiltshire SN13 8DA
e-mail: info@greateventcompany.co.uk
Fax: 01225 744924   Mobile: 07720 444045

TAYLOR HERRING COMMUNICATIONS Ltd
107 Freston Road
London W11 4BD
e-mail: james@taylorherring.com
Fax: 020-7313 2551   Tel: 020-7313 2550

THEATRE DESPATCH Ltd
Azof Hall, Azof Street, London SE10 0EG
e-mail: info@theatre.org
Fax: 08700 525915   Tel: 020-8853 0750

THOMPSON Peter ASSOCIATES
Flat One, 12 Bourchier Street
London W1V 5HN
Fax: 020-7439 1202   Tel: 020-7439 1210

THORNBORROW Bridget
110 Newark Street, London E1 2ES
e-mail: bthornborrow@aol.com
Fax: 020-7247 4144   Tel: 020-7247 4437

TOWN HOUSE PUBLICITY Ltd
(Theatre & Television PR)
45 Islington Park Street, London N1 1QB
e-mail: thp@townhousepublicity.co.uk
Fax: 020-7359 6026   Tel: 020-7226 7450

TRE-VETT Eddie
Brink House, Avon Castle, Ringwood
Hants BH24 2BL   Tel: 01425 475544

UK ARTS EXPLORE
Media Centre, 7 Northumberland Street
Huddersfield HD1 1RL
e-mail: info@ukarts-explore.com
                         Tel: 01484 350031

WILLIAMS Tei PRESS & ARTS MARKETING
7 Acre End Street, Eynsham
Oxon OX29 4PE
e-mail: tei@artsmarketing.demon.co.uk
Fax: 01865 884011   Tel: 01865 883139

WILSON Stella PUBLICITY
130 Calabria Road
London N5 1HT
e-mail: stella@starmaker.demon.co.uk
Fax: 020-7354 2242   Tel: 020-7354 5672

WINGHAM Maureen PRESS & PUBLIC RELATIONS
PO Box 125, Stowmarket
Suffolk IP14 1PB
e-mail: mjw.wingham@virgin.net
Fax: 01449 771400   Tel: 01449 771200

WRIGHT Peter
(See CUE CONSULTANTS)

BBC RADIO Broadcasting House
London W1A 1AA Tel: 020-7580 4468

■ DRAMA
Production
Head	Gordon House
Manager	Rebecca Wilmshurst

Executive Producers
World Service	Marion Nancarrow
London	David Hunter
	Jeremy Mortimer
Manchester	Sue Roberts
Birmingham	Vanessa Whitburn

Producers - London
Sally Avens	Tracey Neale
Ned Chaillet	Jonquil Panting
Cherry Cookson	Mary Peate
Anne Edyvean	Pam Fraser Solomon
Claire Grove	Ros Ward
David Hitchinson	Janet Whitaker
Peter Kavanagh	Enyd Williams
Duncan Minshull	

Producers - Manchester
Melanie Harris	Polly Thomas

Producers - Birmingham
Keri Davies	Peter Wild
Vanessa Whitburn (Editor, Archers)	Sue Wilson

Development
	Toby Swift
	Lucy Baldwyn

New Writing
Director	Kate Rowland
Co-ordinator	Jessica Dromgoole

BROADCAST
Radio Drama - BBC Scotland
Head	Patrick Rayner
Senior Producer	Bruce Young
Management Assistant	Sue Meek

Producers
Julia Butt	Pam Wardell
Gaynor Macfarlane	David Jackson Young

Radio Drama - BBC Wales
Foz Allan	Alison Hindell

Radio Drama - BBC Northern Ireland
All enquiries to Anne Simpson

THE SPOTLIGHT®
1927 ~ 2002
Anniversary

■ LIGHT ENTERTAINMENT/RADIO PRODUCTION
Head, Light Entertainment Radio	
	John Pidgeon
Finance Manager	Sally Kirkby

Producers
Lucy Armitage	Claire Jones
Ashley Blaker	Carol Smith
Adam Bromley	Mario Stylianides
Steve Doherty	Danny Wallace
Richard Edis	Helen Williams
Maria Esposito	

Radio Administrator — Sarah Wright

■ NEWS AND CURRENT AFFAIRS
BBC News (Television & Radio)
Television Centre
Wood Lane, London W12 7RJ
Tel: 020-8576 7312   Fax: 020-8576 7120

Director News	Richard Sambrook
Deputy Director News	Mark Damazer
Head of Television News	Roger Mosey
Deputy Head of Television News	Rachel Atwell
Head of Radio News	Stephen Mitchell
Head of Political Programmes	Francesca Unsworth

■ RADIO SPORT
Head of Sport	Gordon Turnbull

■ CONTROLLERS
Director, BBC Radio	Jenny Abramsky

RADIO 1
Controller	Andy Parfitt

RADIO 2
Controller	Jim Moir

RADIO 3
Controller	Roger Wright

RADIO 4
Controller	Helen Boaden

■ BBC RADIO DRAMA
Bush House, The Strand
London WC2B 4PH   Tel: 020-7580 4468

Executive Producer	Gordon House
Head of Radio Drama	David Hitchinson
Producer	Rosalynd Ward

BBC RADIO BRISTOL
PO Box 194
Bristol BS99 7QT
Fax: 0117-923 8323   Tel: 0117-974 1111
Managing Editor: Jenny Lacey
News Editor: Dawn Trevett

BBC CAMBRIDGE
Broadcasting House
104 Hills Road
Cambridgeshire CB2 1LD
Fax: 01223 460832   Tel: 01223 259696
Managing Editor: David Martin
Assistant Editor: Patrick Davies

BBC RADIO CLEVELAND
PO Box 95 FM
Middlesbrough TS1 5DG
Tel: 01642 225211   Fax: 01642 211356
Managing Editor: Andrew Glover

BBC RADIO CORNWALL
Phoenix Wharf
Truro
Cornwall TR1 1UA
Fax: 01872 275045   Tel: 01872 275421
Managing Editor: Pauline Causey

BBC COVENTRY & WARWICKSHIRE
Holt Court
1 Greyfriars Road
Coventry CV1 2WR
Fax: 024-7657 0100   Tel: 024-7686 0086
Senior Producer: Raj Ford

BBC RADIO CUMBRIA
Annetwell Street
Carlisle
Cumbria CA3 8BB
Fax: 01228 511195   Tel: 01228 592444
Managing Editor: Nigel Dyson

BBC RADIO DERBY
PO Box 104.5
Derby DE1 3HL   Tel: 01332 361111
Editor: Mike Bettison

BBC RADIO DEVON
Linkmail 123 Plymouth
PO Box 5
Plymouth PL3 5YQ
Fax: 01752 234564   Tel: 01752 260323
Managing Editor: John Lilley

BBC ESSEX
PO Box 765 Chelmsford
Essex CM2 9XB   Tel: 01245 616000
Managing Editor: Margaret Hyde

BBC RADIO GLOUCESTERSHIRE
London Road
Glouscester GL1 1SW   Tel: 01452 308585
Managing Editor: Bob Lloyd-Smith

BBC GMR
New Broadcasting House
PO Box 951
Oxford Road
Manchester M60 1SD   Tel: 0161-200 2000
Editor: Steve Taylor

BBC RADIO GUERNSEY
Commerce House
Les Banques, St Peter Port
Guernsey
Channel Islands
e-mail: radio.guernsey@bbc.co.uk
Fax: 01481 713557   Tel: 01481 728977
Manager: Robert Wallis

BBC HEREFORD & WORCESTER
Hylton Road
Worcester WR2 5WW   Tel: 01905 748485
Managing Editor: James Coghill

BBC RADIO HUMBERSIDE
9 Chapel Street
Hull HU1 3NU
e-mail: helenthomas@bbc.co.uk
Fax: 01482 226409   Tel: 01482 323232
Managing Editor: Helen Thomas

BBC RADIO JERSEY
18 Parade Road
St Helier
Jersey JE2 3PL
Fax: 01534 732569   Tel: 01534 870000
Managing Editor: Denzil Dudley
News Editor: James Filleul

BBC RADIO KENT
The Great Hall
Mount Pleasant Road
Tunbridge Wells
Kent TN1 1QQ   Tel: 01892 670000
Managing Editor: Steve Taschini

BBC RADIO LANCASHIRE
20-26 Darwen Street, Blackburn
Lancs BB2 2EA   Tel: 01254 262411
Editor: John Clayton

BBC RADIO LEEDS
Broadcasting House
Woodhouse Lane
Leeds LS2 9PN
Fax: 0113-242 0652   Tel: 0113-244 2131
Managing Editor: Ashley Peatfield

BBC RADIO LEICESTER
Epic House, Charles Street
Leicester LE1 3SH
Fax: 0116-251 1463   Tel: 0116-251 6688
Editor: Liam McCarthy

BBC RADIO LINCOLNSHIRE
PO Box 219, Newport
Lincoln LN1 3XY
Fax: 01522 511058   Tel: 01522 511411

BBC LONDON LIVE 94.9
35C Marylebone High Street
London W1U 4QA
Fax: 020-7487 2908   Tel: 020-7224 2424
Managing Editor: David Robey
Assistant News Editor: Wyn Baptist
Assistant Editor General Programmes: Paul Leaper

BBC RADIO MERSEYSIDE
55 Paradise Street
Liverpool L1 3BP
e-mail: radio.merseyside@bbc.co.uk
Managing Editor: Mick Ord   Tel: 0151-708 5500

BBC RADIO NEWCASTLE
Broadcasting Centre
Barrack Road, Fenham
Newcastle upon Tyne NE99 1RN
Fax: 0191-232 5082   Tel: 0191-232 4141
Editor: Sarah Drummond
Senior Producer: Jon Harle

BBC RADIO NORFOLK
Norfolk Tower
Surrey Street, Norwich NR1 3PA
e-mail: david.clayton@bbc.co.uk
Fax: 01603 667949   Tel: 01603 617411
Managing Editor: David Clayton

Radio (BBC Local)

BBC NORTHAMPTON
Broadcasting House, Abington Street
Northampton NN1 2BH
e-mail: northampton@bbc.co.uk
Fax: 01604 737654   Tel: 01604 239100
Manager: David Clargo
Senior Broadcast Journalists: Mike Day, Sarah Foster

BBC RADIO NOTTINGHAM
London Road
Nottingham NG2 4UU
Fax: 0115-902 1985   Tel: 0115-955 0500
Editor: Kate Squire
Editor News Gathering: Kevin Hill

BBC RADIO SHEFFIELD
54 Shoreham Street
Sheffield S10 4RS
Fax: 0114-267 5454   Tel: 0114-273 1177
Managing Editor: Gary Keown
News SBJ: David Holmes

BBC RADIO SHROPSHIRE
2-4 Boscobel Drive
Shrewsbury, Shropshire SY1 3TT
e-mail: radio.shropshire@bbc.co.uk
Fax: 01743 271702   Tel: 01743 248484
Editor: Tony Fish
News SBJ: John Shone

BBC RADIO SOLENT
Broadcasting House
Havelock Road
Southampton SO14 7PW
e-mail: solent@bbc.co.uk
Fax: 023-8033 9648   Tel: 023-8063 1311
Managing Editor: Chris Van Schaick

BBC SOUTHERN COUNTIES RADIO
Broadcasting Centre
Guildford, Surrey GU2 5AP
e-mail: southern.counties.radio@bbc.co.uk
Fax: 01483 304952   Tel: 01483 306306
Managing Editor: Mike Hapgood
Head of Output: Sara David

BBC RADIO STOKE
Cheapside, Hanley
Stoke-on-Trent
Staffs ST1 1JJ
e-mail: radio.stoke@bbc.co.uk
Fax: 01782 289115   Tel: 01782 208080
Managing Editor: Mark Hurrell

BBC RADIO SUFFOLK
Broadcasting House
St Matthews Street
Ipswich IP1 3EP
e-mail: suffolk@bbc.co.uk
Editor: David Peel   Tel: 01473 250000

BBC THREE COUNTIES RADIO
PO Box 3CR
Luton LU1 5XL
e-mail: 3cr@bbc.co.uk
Fax: 01582 401467   Tel: 01582 637429
Managing Editor: Mark Norman

BBC RADIO WM (West Midlands)
PO Box 206
Pebble Mill Road
Birmingham B5 7SD
Fax: 0121-472 3174   Tel: 0121-432 9000
Editor Local Services: Keith Beech

BBC WILTSHIRE SOUND
Broadcasting House
56-58 Prospect Place
Swindon SN1 3RW
Fax: 01793 513650   Tel: 01793 513626
Manager: Tony Wargon

BBC RADIO YORK
20 Bootham Row
York YO30 7BR
e-mail: radio.york@bbc.co.uk
Fax: 01904 610937   Tel: 01904 641351
Managing Editor: Barrie Stephenson

Radio (Independent Local)

ABERDEEN
North Sound Radio
45 Kings Gate, Aberdeen AB15 4EL
e-mail: northsound@srh.co.uk   Tel: 01224 337000

AYR
West Sound and West FM
Radio House, 54 Holmston Road, Ayr KA7 3BE
e-mail: westfm@srh.co.uk   Tel: 01292 283662

BELFAST
Downtown Radio
Newtownards, Co Down BT23 4ES
e-mail: promotions@downtown.co.uk
                              Tel: 028-9181 5555
City Beat 96.7 FM
PO Box 967, Belfast BT9 5DF
Fax: 028-9020 0023   Tel: 028-9020 5967

BIRMINGHAM
BRMB Radio & Capital Radio
9 Brindley Place, Birmingham B1 2DJ
Fax: 0121-245 5245   Tel: 0121-245 5000

BORDERS The
Radio Borders Ltd
Tweedside Park
Galashiels TD1 3TD
Fax: 0845 3457080   Tel: 01896 759444

BRADFORD
Sunrise Radio
30 Chapel Street, Little Germany
Bradford BD1 5DN
Fax: 01274 728534   Tel: 01274 735043

BRADFORD, HUDDERSFIELD, HALIFAX, KEIGHLEY & DEWSBURY
The Pulse & West Yorkshire's Big AM
Forster Square
Bradford BD1 5NE
e-mail: general@pulse.co.uk   Tel: 01274 203040

BRIGHTON, EASTBOURNE & HASTINGS
Southern FM Radio House
PO Box 2000
Brighton BN41 2SS   Tel: 01273 430111

BRISTOL
GWR FM & Classic Gold 1260
PO Box 2000 Bristol BS99 7SN   Tel: 0117-984 3200

CAMBRIDGE & NEWMARKET
Q 103 FM
PO Box 103, The Vision Park, Chivers Way, Histon
Cambridge CB4 9WW   Tel: 01223 235255

CARDIFF & NEWPORT
Red Dragon FM & Capital Gold
Atlantic Wharf, Cardiff Bay, Cardiff CF10 4DJ
e-mail: mail@reddragonfm.co.uk
                    Tel: 029-2038 4041

CHESTER, NORTH WALES & WIRRAL
MFM & Marcher Gold
The Studios Mold Road, Wrexham LL11 4AF
e-mail: josheasby@musicradio.com
                    Tel: 01978 752202
Managing Director: Josh Easby

COVENTRY
Mercia FM
Hertford Place
Coventry CV1 3TT   Tel: 024-7686 8200

KIX 96.2 FM
Watch Close, Spon Street
Coventry CV1 3LN   Tel: 024-7652 5656

DUMFRIES
West Sound FM
Unit 40, The Loreburn Centre, High Street
Dumfries DG1 2BD   Tel: 01387 250999

DUNDEE & PERTH
Tay FM & Radio Tay AM
PO Box 123, 6 North Isla Street
Dundee DD3 7JQ
e-mail: tayfm@radiotay.co.uk Tel: 01382 200800

EDINBURGH
Radio Forth
Forth House, Forth Street
Edinburgh EH1 3LE
e-mail: info@radioforth.co.uk Tel: 0131-556 9255

EXETER & TORBAY
Gemini Radio Ltd
Hawthorn House, Exeter Business Park
Exeter EX1 3QS   Tel: 01392 444444

FALKIRK
Central FM
201-203 High Street
Falkirk FK1 1DU   Tel: 01324 611164

GLASGOW
Radio Clyde FM1 & Clyde 2 AM
3 South Avenue, Clydebank Business Park
Glasgow G81 2RX   Tel: 0141-565 2200

GLOUCESTER & CHELTENHAM
Severn Sound, FM & Classic Gold
Bridge Studios, Eastgate Centre
Gloucester GL1 1SS   Tel: 01452 313200

GREAT YARMOUTH & NORWICH
Radio Broadland FM & Classic Gold Digital
St Georges Plain, 47-49 Colegate
Norwich NR3 1DB   Tel: 01603 630621

GUILDFORD
96.4 The Eagle FM & County Sound 1566 MW
County Sound Radio Network, Dolphin House
North Street, Guildford
Surrey GU1 4AA
e-mail: eagle@countysound.co.uk
                    Tel: 01483 300964

HEREFORD & WORCESTER
Wyvern FM
5-6 Barbourne Terrace
Worcester WR1 3JZ   Tel: 01905 612212

INVERNESS
Moray Firth Radio
PO Box 271, Scorguie Place, Inverness IV3 8UJ
e-mail: mfr@mfr.co.uk
Fax: 01463 243224   Tel: 01463 224433

IPSWICH
SGR-FM: Radio House, Alpha Business Park
Whitehouse Road, Ipswich IP1 5LT
                    Tel: 01473 461000

ISLE OF WIGHT
Isle of Wight Radio
Dodnor Park Newport
Isle of Wight PO30 5XE
e-mail: admin@iwradio.co.uk
Fax: 01983 821690   Tel: 01983 822557

KENT
Invicta FM & Capital Gold
Radio House
John Wilson Business Park
Whitstable, Kent CT5 3QX
e-mail: info@invictafm.com Tel: 01227 772004

KETTERING & CORBY
Connect FM 97.2 & 107.4 FM
Centre 2000
Telford Way Industrial Estate, Kettering
Northants NN16 8PU   Tel: 01536 412413

LEEDS
96.3 Radio Aire & Magic 828
PO Box 2000, 51 Burley Road
Leeds LS3 1LR   Tel: 0113-283 5500

LEICESTER
Leicester Sound
105.4 FM, Granville House, Granville Road
Leicester LE1 7RW   Tel: 0116-256 1300

LEICESTER, NOTTINGHAM & DERBY
96 Trent FM & Classic Gold GEM
29-31 Castle Gate
Nottingham NG1 7AP   Tel: 0115-952 7000

LIVERPOOL
Radio City
St Johns Beacon, 1 Houghton Street
Liverpool L1 1RL   Tel: 0151-472 6800

LONDON

Capital Radio Plc
30 Leicester Square
London WC2H 7LA   Tel: 020-7766 6000

Choice FM
291-299 Borough High Street
London SE1 1JG   Tel: 020-7378 3969

Classic FM
7 Swallow Place, Oxford Circus
London W1B 2AG   Tel: 020-7343 9000

Heart 106.2 FM
The Chrysalis Building
Bramley Road
London W10 6SP   Tel: 020-7468 1062

ITN Radio
200 Gray's Inn Road
London WC1X 8XZ   Tel: 020-7430 4814

R

LONDON Cont'd

Jazz FM 102.2
26-27 Castlereagh Street
London W1H 6DJ
e-mail: info@jazzfm.com   Tel: 020-7706 4100

Kiss 100
Mappin House
4 Winsley Street
London W1W 8HF
Fax: 020-7975 8150   Tel: 020-7700 6100

London Greek Radio
Florentia Village
Vale Road, Haringey
London N4 1TD   Tel: 020-8800 8001

Magic 105.4 FM
4 Winsley Street
London W1W 8HF   Tel: 020-7436 1515

Millennium 106.8 FM
Harrow Manor Way
Thamesmead South
London SE2 9XH   Tel: 020-8311 3112

Virgin Radio
1 Golden Square
London W1F 9DJ   Tel: 020-7434 1215

LUTON & BEDFORD

97.6 Chiltern FM & Classic Gold 792/828
Broadcast Centre, Chiltern Road
Dunstable LU6 1HQ   Tel: 01582 676200

MANCHESTER

Key 103 FM & Magic 1152
Piccadilly Radio Ltd
Castle Quay, Castle Field
Manchester M15 4PR   Tel: 0161-288 5000

MILTON KEYNES

FM 103 Horizon
14 Vincent Avenue
Milton Keynes Broadcast Centre, Crownhill
Milton Keynes MK8 0AB   Tel: 01908 269111

NORTHAMPTON

Northhants 96/Classic Gold 1557
Northamptonshire Digital
19-21 St Edmunds Road
Northampton NN1 5DY
e-mail: reception@northants96.musicradio.com
Tel: 01604 795600

NOTTINGHAM & DERBY

96 Trent FM
29-31 Castle Gate, Nottingham NG1 7AP
e-mail: admin@musicradio.com
Tel: 0115-952 7000

OXFORD & BANBURY

Fox FM
Brush House, Pony Road
Oxford OX4 2XR   Tel: 01865 871000

PETERBOROUGH

102.7 Hereward FM
PO Box 225, Queensgate Centre
Peterborough PE1 1XJ   Tel: 01733 460460

PLYMOUTH

Plymouth Sound
Earl's Acre Alma Road
Plymouth PL3 4HX   Tel: 01752 227272

PORTSMOUTH & SOUTHAMPTON

Ocean Radio Group
Radio House, Whittle Avenue
Segensworth West, Fareham
Hants PO15 5SH   Tel: 01489 589911

PRESTON

Red Rose Radio Ltd
PO Box 301, St Paul's Square
Preston Lancs PR1 1YE   Tel: 01772 556301

READING, BASINGSTOKE & ANDOVER

2-Ten FM
PO Box 2020
Reading Berks RG31 7FG   Tel: 0118-945 4400

REIGATE & CRAWLEY

102.7 Mercury FM
9 The Stanley Centre
Kelvin Way
Manor Royal, Crawley
West Sussex RH10 9SE
e-mail: name@musicradio.com
Tel: 01293 519161

SOMERSET

Orchard FM
Haygrove House, Shoreditch
Taunton TA3 7BT   Tel: 01823 338448

SOUTH MANCHESTER

Imagine FM
Regent House, Heaton Lane, Stockport
Cheshire SK4 1BX
e-mail: recipient@imaginefm.net
Tel: 0161-609 1400

SOUTHEND

Essex Radio Group (Essex FM/The Breeze/Ten
17/Vibe FM/96.6 Oasis FM/KFM/Mercury & Fame)
Radio House, Clifftown Road
Southend-on-Sea, Essex SS1 1SX
Fax: 01702 345224   Tel: 01702 333711

STOKE-ON-TRENT & STAFFORD

Signal Radio
Stoke Road, Stoke-on-Trent
Staffordshire ST4 2SR
e-mail: info@signalradio.com   Tel: 01782 747047

SWANSEA

96.4 FM The Wave
Victoria Road, Gowerton
Swansea SA4 3AB   Tel: 01792 511964

TEESSIDE

TFM 96.6 & Magic 1170
Yale Crescent Thornaby
Stockton on Tees
Cleveland TS17 6AA   Tel: 01642 888222

TYNE & WEAR & NORTHUMBERLAND & DURHAM

Metro Radio
Newcastle upon Tyne
NE99 1BB   Tel: 0191-420 0971

WOLVERHAMPTON & BLACK COUNTRY/ SHREWSBURY & TELFORD

Beacon FM 267
Tettenhall Road
Wolverhampton WV6 0DE   Tel: 01902 461300

YORKSHIRE

Hallam FM & Magic AM
Radio House
900 Herries Road, Hillsborough
Sheffield S6 1RH   Tel: 0114-285 3333

YORKSHIRE & LINCOLNSHIRE

96.9 Viking FM & Magic 1161 AM
Commercial Road
Hull HU1 2SG   Tel: 01482 325141

R

Full Digital Audio Facility providing

Voiceover Demo Tapes
Radio Commercials
Multimedia Recordings
MOH/IVR/Concatenated Voice Prompts
Video Dubbing
Voice Casting & Search

29 Ash Grove
London W5 4AX

T: (020) 8567-5140
F: (020) 8567-5183
E: info@island41.com
W: www.island41.com

A1 VOX Ltd
(Specialising in Voices, Audio Editing,
Voice-Over Training and Demo CDs)
20 Old Compton Street
London W1D 4TW
e-mail: info@a1vox.com
Fax: 020-7434 4414   Tel: 020-7434 4404

ABBEY ROAD STUDIOS
3 Abbey Road
St John's Wood
London NW8 9AY
e-mail: info@abbeyroad.co.uk
Fax: 020-7266 7250   Tel: 020-7266 7000

AIR-EDEL RECORDING STUDIOS Ltd
18 Rodmarton Street
London W1U 8BJ
e-mail: trevorbest@air-edel.co.uk
Fax: 020-7224 0344   Tel: 020-7486 6466

AIR STUDIOS (LYNDHURST) Ltd
Lyndhurst Hall
Lyndhurst Road, London NW3 5NG
Fax: 020-7794 8518   Tel: 020-7794 0660

ANGEL RECORDING STUDIOS Ltd
311 Upper Street
London N1 2TU
e-mail: angel@angelstudio.co.uk
Fax: 020-7226 9624   Tel: 020-7354 2525

BATTERY STUDIOS
1 Maybury Gardens
London NW10 2NB
e-mail: amanda.todd@batterystudios.co.uk
Fax: 020-8459 8732   Tel: 020-8967 0013

BLACKHEATH HALLS
23 Lee Road
Blackheath
London SE3 9RQ
e-mail: mail@blackheathhalls.com
Fax: 020-8852 5154   Tel: 020-8318 9758

CHANNEL 20/20 Ltd
20/20 House
26-28 Talbot Lane
Leicester LE1 4LR
Fax: 0116-222 1113   Tel: 0116-233 2220

CRYING OUT LOUD
(Voice Over Specialists/Voice Over Demo CDs)
e-mail: simoncryer@rab.co.uk
Mobile: 07946 533108   Mobile: 07796 266265

DB POST PRODUCTIONS Ltd
1-8 Batemans Buildings
Soho Square
London W1V 5TW
e-mail: general@dbpost.com
Fax: 020-7287 9143   Tel: 020-7434 0097

DE LANE LEA SOUND
(Post Production, Re-Recording Studios)
75 Dean Street
London W1D 3PU
e-mail: dll@delanelea.com
Fax: 020-7432 3838   Tel: 020-7432 3800

ELMS STUDIOS DIGITAL
(Mac G4/Logic Platinum/Emu Systems, 02R,
Music Composing/Scoring & VO's)
Addiscombe
10 Empress Avenue
London E12 5ES
e-mail: elmsstudio@aol.com
Fax: 020-8532 9333   Tel: 020-8518 8629

ESSENTIAL MUSIC
20 Great Chapel Street
London W1V 3AQ
e-mail: essentialmusic@hotmail.com
Fax: 020-7287 3597   Tel: 020-7439 7113

FIRST BRITISH INDEPENDENT
Nomis
45-53 Sinclair Road
London W14 0NS
e-mail: first.british@virgin.net
Fax: 020-7603 5941   Tel: 020-7602 6351

ISLAND 41
(Voice-Over Recording Studio)
29 Ash Grove
London W5 4AX
e-mail: info@island41.com
Fax: 020-8567 5183   Tel: 020-8567 5140

KONK STUDIOS
84-86 Tottenham Lane
London N8 7EE
Fax: 020-8348 3952   Tel: 020-8340 7873

LADBROKE PRODUCTIONS (RADIO) Ltd
Essel House
29 Foley Street
London W1W 7TH
e-mail: mail@ladbroke-radio.co.uk
Fax: 020-7436 0948   Tel: 020-7580 8864

LANSDOWNE RECORDING STUDIOS Ltd
Lansdowne House
Lansdowne Road
London W11 3LP
e-mail: info@cts-lansdowne.co.uk
Fax: 020-7792 8904   Tel: 020-7727 0041

MAGMASTERS SOUND STUDIOS (4MC)
20 St Anne's Court
Soho
London W1V 3AW
e-mail: cmcdonald@4mc.co.uk
Fax: 020-7439 0700   Tel: 020-7439 0600

MOTIVATION SOUND STUDIOS Ltd
35A Broadhurst Gardens
London NW6 3QT
e-mail: info@motivationmultimedia.co.uk
Fax: 020-7328 6618   Tel: 020-7328 8305

SARM STUDIOS WEST Ltd
8-10 Basing Street
London W11 1ET
Fax: 020-7221 9247   Tel: 020-7229 1229

SHAW Bernard
(Specialist in Recording and
Directing Voice Tapes)
Horton Manor
e-mail: bernard@bernardshaw.co.uk
Canterbury CT4 7LG   Tel/Fax: 01227 730843

SILVER-TONGUED PRODUCTIONS
(Specialising in Voice Reels)
e-mail: silver-tongued@talk21.com
Tel/Fax: 020-8309 0659

SONY MUSIC
31-37 Whitfield Street
London W1P 5RE
Fax: 020-7580 0543   Tel: 020-7636 3434

SOUND COMPANY The
2 Lord Hills Road
London W2 6PD
e-mail: info@thesoundcompany.net
Fax: 020-7286 7377   Tel: 020-7286 7277

SOUND CONCEPTION
82-84 York Road
Bristol BS3 4AL
e-mail: soundconception@excite.co.uk
Fax: 0117-963 5059   Tel: 0117-966 2932

SOUND HOUSE POST PRODUCTION Ltd The
10th Floor
Astley House, Quay Street
Manchester M3 4AE
Fax: 0161-832 7266   Tel: 0161-832 7299

STUDIO 209
222 Kensal Road
London W10 5BN
e-mail: info@heavy-entertainment.com
Fax: 020-8960 9003   Tel: 020-8960 9001

STUDIO AVP
82 Clifton Hill
London NW8 0JT
Fax: 020-7624 9112   Tel: 020-7624 9111

SWANYARD RECORDING STUDIOS Ltd
12-27 Swanyard
London N1 1SD
Fax: 020-7226 2581   Tel: 020-7354 3737

TOUCHWOOD AUDIO PRODUCTIONS
6 Hyde Park Terrace
Leeds
W Yorks LS6 1BJ
e-mail: bruce.w@appleonline.net
Tel: 0113-278 7180

TOUCHWOOD PRODUCTION STUDIOS
(Voice-Over Showreels, Digital Editing etc)
Knightsbridge House
229 Acton Lane
Chiswick
London W4 5DD
e-mail: info@touchwoodstudios.co.uk
Fax: 020-8995 2144   Tel: 020-8995 3232

UNIVERSAL SOUND (JUST PLAY) Ltd
16 Aintree Road
Perivale
Middlesex UB6 7LA
Fax: 020-8991 9461   Tel: 020-8998 1619

VOICE CASTER
(Voice-Over Demo Tapes and Commercial
Production)   Tel: 020-8455 2211

W.F.S. Ltd
(Sound Transfer/Optical & Magnetic)
Warwick Sound
111A Wardour Street
London W1V 3TD
e-mail: info@warwicksound.com
Fax: 020-7439 0372   Tel: 020-7437 5532

WORLDWIDE SOUND Ltd
21-25 St Anne's Court
Soho, London W1V 3AW
e-mail: sound@worldwidegroup.ltd.uk
Fax: 020-7734 0619   Tel: 020-7434 1121

ACCESS STUDIOS
8-10 Creekside
London SE8 3DX
e-mail: info@accessstudios.com
Fax: 0870 120 5658   Tel: 020-7231 6185

ACRE LANE INTERNATIONAL REHEARSAL COMPLEX
57 Acre Lane, Brixton
London SW2 5TN
Fax: 020-7501 6869   Tel: 020-7501 6868

ACTORS CENTRE The (LONDON)
(Audition Space Only)
1A Tower Street
London WC2H 9NP
Fax: 020-7240 3896   Tel: 020-7240 3940

ADI The
218 Lambeth Road
London SE1 7JY
e-mail: info@adiplay.org.uk
Fax: 020-7401 2816   Tel: 020-7928 6160

ALFORD HOUSE
Aveline Street
London SE11 5DQ   Tel: 020-7735 1519

ALRA (Academy of Live and Recorded Arts)
Royal Victoria Patriotic Building
Fitzhugh Grove, Trinity Road
London SW18 3SX
e-mail: acting@alra.demon.co.uk
Fax: 020-8875 0789   Tel: 020-8870 6475

AMADEUS CENTRE The
50 Shirland Road, Little Venice
London W9 2JA
Fax: 020-7266 1225   Tel: 020-7286 1686

AMERICAN CHURCH IN LONDON The
Whitefield Memorial Church
79A Tottenham Court Road
London W1T 4TD
e-mail: amchurchuk@aol.com
Fax: 020-7580 5013   Tel: 020-7580 2791

ARGYLE PRODUCTIONS
86 Goswell Road
London EC1V 7DB
Fax: 020-7608 1642   Tel: 020-7608 2095

ARTS ADMIN
(Toynbee Studios)
28 Commercial Street
London E1 6LS
e-mail: space@artsadmin.co.uk
Fax: 020-7247 5103   Tel: 020-7247 5102

ARTS CENTRE GROUP The
59A Portobello Road, London W11 3DB
e-mail: info@artscentregroup.org.uk
Fax: 020-7221 7689   Tel: 020-7243 4550

BAC
Lavender Hill, London SW11 5TN
e-mail: mailbox@bac.org.uk
Fax: 020-7978 5207   Tel: 020-7223 6557

BELSIZE MUSIC ROOMS
(Casting, Auditioning, Filming)
67 Belsize Lane
Hampstead
London NW3 5AX
e-mail: info@belsize-music-rooms.co.uk
Fax: 020-7916 0222   Tel: 020-7916 0111

REHEARSAL HALLS
The ADI 218 Lambeth Road, London SE1 7JY

Main Hall (45' x 38' height 13' with a small stage 24' x 13') First Floor Hall (45' x 22')
Gymnasium - Sprung Floor for Dance (45' x 31')

Other Facilities - Meeting Room, Public Telephone, Drinks Machine,
2 Kitchens each with Cooker, Fridge & Microwave.
Wheelchair Access.

The Building is Fully Heated.

CONTACT: The Centre Manager or Administrator on:
020 7928 6160 Fax: 020 7401 2816 E-mail: info@adiplay.org.uk

BIG CITY STUDIOS
Montgomery House
159-161 Balls Pond Road, Islington
London N1 4BG
Fax: 020-7241 3006   Tel: 020-7241 6655

BLACKHEATH HALLS
23 Lee Road, Blackheath
London SE3 9RQ
e-mail: mail@blackheathhalls.com
Fax: 020-8852 5154   Tel: 020-8318 9758

BLOOMSBURY THEATRE
15 Gordon Street, Bloomsbury
London WC1H 0AH
e-mail: blooms.theatre@ucl.ac.uk
     Tel: 020-7679 2777

BRIXTON ST VINCENTS COMMUNITY CENTRE
Talma Road
London SW2 1AS
Fax: 020-7326 1713   Tel: 020-7326 4417

CASTING STUDIOS INTERNATIONAL Ltd
Ramillies House, 1-2 Ramillies Street
London W1F 7LN
e-mail: info@castingstudios.com
Fax: 020-7437 2080   Tel: 020-7437 2070

CASTING SUITE The
10 Warwick Street
London W1R 5RA
e-mail: sadiejenour@lineone.net
Fax: 020-7494 0803   Tel: 020-7434 2331

CECIL SHARP HOUSE
(Nicola Elwell)
2 Regent's Park Road
London NW1 7AY
e-mail: hire@efdss.org
Fax: 020-7284 0534   Tel: 020-7485 2206

CENTRAL LONDON GOLF CENTRE
Burntwood Lane
London SW17 0AT
Fax: 020-8874 7447   Tel: 020-8871 2468

CENTRAL STUDIOS
470 Bromley Road, Bromley
Kent BR1 4PN
Fax: 020-8697 8100   Tel: 020-8698 8880

CHATS PALACE ARTS CENTRE
42-44 Brooksby's Walk, Hackney
London E9 6DF
Fax: 020-8985 6878   Tel: 020-8533 0227

CHELSEA THEATRE
World's End Place
King's Road
London SW10 0DR
Fax: 020-7352 2024   Tel: 020-7352 1967

CLAPHAM COMMUNITY PROJECT
St Anne's Hall, Venn Street
London SW4 0BN
e-mail: claphamcommunityproject.org.uk
Fax: 020-7720 8731   Tel: 020-7622 2042

CLEAN BREAK CENTRE
FOR THEATRE & THE ARTS
2 Patshull Road, London NW5 2LB
Fax: 020-7482 8611   Tel: 020-7482 8600

CLUB FOR ACTS & ACTORS
(Incorporating Concert Artistes Association)
20 Bedford Street
London WC2E 9HP   Tel: 020-7836 3172

COPTIC STUDIOS Ltd
9 Coptic Street
London WC1A 1NH
Fax: 020-7436 5197   Tel: 020-7436 2248

COVENT GARDEN CASTING SUITES
& AUDITION ROOMS
29 Maiden Lane
Covent Garden
London WC2E 7JS   Tel: 020-7240 1438

CRAGRATS Ltd
The Mill, Dunford Road, Holmfirth
Huddersfield HD9 2AR
e-mail: mike@cragrats.com
Fax: 01484 686212   Tel: 01484 686451

CUSTARD FACTORY The
Gibb Street, Digbeth
Birmingham B9 4AA
e-mail: dance@clara.co.uk
Fax: 0121-604 8888   Tel: 0121-693 7777

DANCE ATTIC STUDIOS
368 North End Road
London SW6   Tel: 020-7610 2055

DANCE COMPANY The
(Sue Hann)
76 High Street, Beckenham
Kent BR3 1ED
e-mail: dancecomp@aol.com
Fax: 020-8402 1414   Tel: 020-8402 2424

DANCEWORKS
16 Balderton Street, London W1K 6TN
Fax: 020-7499 9087   Tel: 020-7629 6183

DIAMOND DANCE STUDIO
6-8 Vestry Street
London N1 7RE
e-mail: gem@diamonddance.com
Fax: 020-7251 8379   Tel: 020-7251 8858

DIORAMA ARTS
34 Osnaburgh Street
London NW1 3ND
e-mail: admin@diorama-arts.org.uk
Fax: 020-7916 5282   Tel: 020-7916 5467

DRAGON MULTIMEDIA
St Georges Theatre
49 Tufnell Park Road
London N7 0PS
e-mail: stgeorgestheatre@lineone.net
Fax: 020-7609 2427   Tel: 020-7607 7978

DRILL HALL The
16 Chenies Street
London WC1E 7EX
e-mail: admin@drillhall.co.uk
Fax: 020-7307 5062   Tel: 020-7307 5061

Artsadmin
Toynbee Studios
28 Commercial Street, London E1 6LS

Artsadmin have rehearsal spaces available in Toynbee Studios, Aldgate East. There are four spaces for hire, one of which is a 260 seat theatre with basic lighting rig and p.a. facilities.

Competitive daily and weekly rates are available and bookings of more than three weeks qualify for a discount on the weekly rate.

Artsadmin Video Resource now offers Sony digital cameras and a Media 100 LX editing suite for hire. Membership is required and Artsadmin reserve the right to refuse membership.

The Arts Cafe is on site serving light snacks, meals and a selection of drinks.

For further information and booking contact Gill Lloyd at Artsadmin
on 020 7247-5102   Fax: 020 7247-5103   e-mail: space@artsadmin.co.uk

EALING STUDIOS
Ealing Green
Ealing, London W5 5EP
e-mail: jenny.musitano@ealingstudios.com
Fax: 020-8758 8658   Tel: 020-8567 6655

ENGLISH FOLK DANCE & SONG SOCIETY
Cecil Sharp House
2 Regent's Park Road
London NW1 7AY
e-mail: efdss@efdss.org
Fax: 020-7284 0534   Tel: 020-7485 2206

ENGLISH NATIONAL OPERA
Lilian Baylis House
165 Broadhurst Gardens
London NW6 3AX
e-mail: receptionlbh@eno.org.uk
Fax: 020-7625 3398   Tel: 020-7624 7711

FBI AGENCY Ltd The
PO Box 250, Leeds LS1 2AZ
e-mail: j.spencer@fbi-agency.ltd.uk
                     Tel/Fax: 07050 222747

FSU LONDON STUDY CENTRE
100-103 Great Russell Street
London WC1B 3LA
Fax: 020-8202 6797   Tel: 020-7813 3223

HAMILTON ROAD CENTRE
1 Hamilton Road
Stratford
London E15 3AE
Fax: 020-7476 0050   Tel: 020-7473 0395

HAMPSTEAD THEATRE
98 Avenue Road, Swiss Cottage
London NW3 3EX
e-mail: admin@hampstead-theatre.com
Fax: 020-7722 3860   Tel: 020-7722 1189

HEN & CHICKENS THEATRE
Unrestricted View
Above Hen & Chickens Theatre Bar
109 St Paul's Road
London N1 2NA
e-mail: james@henandchickens.com
                     Tel: 020-7704 2001

HER MAJESTY'S THEATRE
Haymarket
London SW1Y 4QL   Tel: 020-7494 5200

HOLY INNOCENTS CHURCH
Paddenswick Road
London W6 0UB
Fax: 020-8563 8735   Tel: 020-8748 2286

ISLINGTON ARTS FACTORY
2 Parkhurst Road
London N7 0SF
Fax: 020-7700 7229   Tel: 020-7607 0561

JACKSONS LANE ARTS CENTRE
(Various spaces inc rehearsal rooms & theatre hire)
269A Archway Road
London N6 5AA
e-mail: mail@jacksonslane.org.uk
                     Tel: 020-8340 5226

JERWOOD SPACE
171 Union Street
London SE1 0LN
e-mail: space@jerwoodspace.co.uk
Fax: 020-7654 0172   Tel: 020-7654 0171

K M C AGENCIES
PO Box 122, 4th Floor
Ghulam House
16 Blossom Street
Manchester M4 5AW
e-mail: studios@kmcagencies.co.uk
Fax: 0161-237 9812   Tel: 0161-237 3009

LA MAISON VERTE
31 Avenue Henri Mas
34320 Roujan, France
e-mail: nicole.russell@wanadoo.fr
Fax: 00 334 67246998   Tel: 00 334 67248852

LIVE THEATRE The
27 Broad Chare
Quayside
Newcastle-upon-Tyne NE1 3DQ
e-mail: info@live.org.uk   Tel: 0191-261 2694

LIVELY ARTS
Aberdeen Studios
22 Highbury Grove
London N5 2EA
Fax: 020-7288 1801   Tel: 020-7288 1800

LONDON BUBBLE THEATRE COMPANY Ltd
5 Elephant Lane
London SE16 4JD
e-mail: admin@londonbubble.org.uk
Fax: 020-7231 2366   Tel: 020-7237 4434

Casting Studios International Ltd

is one of the biggest studios in London, over 2,000 sq ft all on one floor, state of the art facilities and large separate waiting areas

2 very large studios
Airconditioned and sound proofed
Simultaneous recording on
low- band Umatic and VHS
Mini DV   Chroma Key
Digital blue screen
Academy Award winning
Kino flo flourescent systems
Private viewing room with monitor

Location: situated in Soho, only three minutes walk from Oxford Circus tube station
Colour brochure and rates card on request
We offer a 24-hour service

 Wir sprechen Deutsch
Se habla Espanol
On parle Francais

Casting Studios International Ltd
Ramillies House. 1-2 Ramillies Street
London W1F 7LN
T - 020 7437 2070 F - 020 7437 2080
E - info@castingstudios.com

LONDON SCHOOL OF CAPOEIRA
Units 1 & 2 Leeds Place, Tollington Park
London N4 3RQ   Tel: 020-7281 2020

LONDON STUDIO CENTRE
42-50 York Way
London N1 9AB
e-mail: enquire@london-studio-centre.co.uk
Fax: 020-7837 3248   Tel: 020-7837 7741

LONDON WELSH TRUST Ltd
157-163 Gray's Inn Road
London WC1X 8UE
Fax: 020-7837 6268   Tel: 020-7837 3722

MACKINTOSH Cameron REHEARSAL STUDIO
The Tricycle
269 Kilburn High Road
London NW6 7JR
e-mail: admin@tricycle.co.uk
Fax: 020-7328 0795   Tel: 020-7372 6611

MADDERMARKET THEATRE
St John's Alley, Norwich
Norfolk NR2 1DR
e-mail: theatre@maddermarket.freeserve.co.uk
Fax: 01603 661357   Tel: 01603 626560

MARYMOUNT COLLEGE
22 Brownlow Mews
London WC1N 2LA
e-mail: marymount.london@mailbox.ulcc.ac.uk
Fax: 020-8202 6797   Tel: 020-8202 3311

MOBERLY SPORTS & EDUCATION CENTRE
Kilburn Lane
London W10 4AH
Fax: 020-7641 4801   Tel: 020-7641 4807

MOTIVATION SOUND STUDIOS Ltd
35A Broadhurst Gardens
London NW6 3QT
e-mail: info@motivationmultimedia.co.uk
Fax: 020-7328 6618   Tel: 020-7328 8305

MOUNTVIEW
Academy of Theatre Arts
The Ralph Richardson Memorial Studios
Kingfisher Place
Clarendon Road
London N22 6XF
e-mail: enquiries@mountview.ac.uk
Fax: 020-8829 0034   Tel: 020-8881 2201

NATIONAL YOUTH THEATRE OF GREAT BRITAIN
443-445 Holloway Road
London N7 6LW
e-mail: info@nyt.org.uk
Fax: 020-7281 8246   Tel: 020-7281 3863

NETTLEFOLD The
West Norwood Library Centre
1 Norwood High Street
London SE27 9JX
Fax: 020-7926 8071   Tel: 020-7926 8070

Commercial & Film Casting Studio

Mobile Casting, Showreels

Take Five Casting Studio
25 Ganton St • London W1F 9BP
Tel: 020 7287 2120 • Fax: 020 7287 3035

NORTH LONDON PERFORMING ARTS CENTRE
(Production & Casting Office Facilities)
76 St James Lane
Muswell Hill
London N10 3DF
e-mail: nlpac@compuserve.com
Fax: 020-8444 4040   Tel: 020-8444 4544

NORTH PADDINGTON REHEARSAL ROOMS
235 Lanark Road
London W9 1RA   Tel: 020-7624 4089

OCTOBER GALLERY
24 Old Gloucester Street
London WC1N 3AL
e-mail: rentals@ukgateway.net
Fax: 020-7405 1851   Tel: 020-7831 1618

OLD VIC THEATRE
Waterloo Road
London SE1 8NB   Tel: 020-7928 2651

OPEN DOOR COMMUNITY CENTRE
Keevil Drive
Beaumont Road
Wimbledon SW19 6TF
e-mail: opendoor_cc@lineone.net
                    Tel/Fax: 020-8871 8174

OUT OF JOINT
20-24 Eden Grove
London N7 8EA
e-mail: ojo@outofjoint.co.uk
Fax: 020-7609 0203   Tel: 020-7609 0207

OVAL HOUSE
52-54 Kennington Oval
London SE11 5SW
e-mail: admin@ovalhouse.com
                    Tel: 020-7582 0080

PAINES PLOUGH AUDITION SPACE
4th Floor
43 Aldwych
London WC2B 4DN
e-mail: office@painesplough.com
Fax: 020-7240 4534   Tel: 020-7240 4533

PEOPLE SHOW
People Show Studios
Pollard Row
London E2 6NB
e-mail: people@peopleshow.co.uk
Fax: 020-7739 0203   Tel: 020-7729 1841

PINEAPPLE STUDIOS
7 Langley Street
London WC2H 9JA
Fax: 020-7836 0803   Tel: 020-7836 4004

PLACE The (Contemporary Dance Trust)
17 Duke's Road
London WC1H 9PY
Fax: 020-7383 4851   Tel: 020-7387 0161

PLAY Ltd
(See ADI The)

PLAYGROUND The
Unit 8, Latimer Road
London W10 6RQ
e-mail: info@the-playground.co.uk
                    Tel/Fax: 020-8960 0000

POLISH YOUTH CENTRE The
238-246 King Street
London W6 0RF
e-mail: piotrk@msn.com   Tel: 020-8741 2950

POOR SCHOOL The
242-244 Pentonville Road
London N1 9JY   Tel: 020-7837 6030

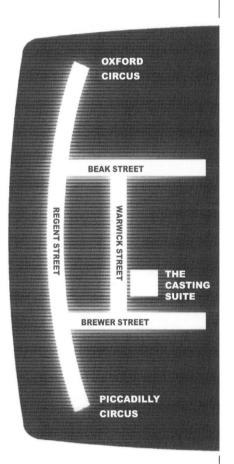

QUESTORS THEATRE EALING The
12 Mattock Lane
London W5 5BQ
e-mail: paul@questors.org.uk
Fax: 020-8567 8736   Tel: 020-8567 0011

QUICKSILVER THEATRE
The Glass House
4 Enfield Road
London N1 5AZ
e-mail: talktous@quicksilvertheatre.org
Fax: 020-7254 3119   Tel: 020-7241 2942

RAMBERT DANCE COMPANY
(Patricia Bakewell)
94 Chiswick High Road
London W4 1SH
e-mail: rdc@rambert.org.uk
Fax: 020-8747 8323   Tel: 020-8630 0600

REHEARSAL HALL
81 Camberwell Church Street
London SE5 8RB   Tel: 020-7701 9319

ROOFTOP STUDIO THEATRE
Rooftop Studio
Somerfield Arcade
Stone
Staffordshire ST15 8AU   Tel: 01785 818176

ROTHERHITHE STUDIOS
119 Rotherhithe Street
London SE16 4NF
Fax: 020-7231 2119   Tel: 020-7231 2209

ROYAL ACADEMY OF DANCING
36 Battersea Square
London SW11 3RA
e-mail: info@rad.org.uk
Fax: 020-7924 3129   Tel: 020-7326 8000

ROYAL SHAKESPEARE COMPANY
35 Clapham High Street
London SW4 7TW
Fax: 020-7374 0810   Tel: 020-7628 3351

SAVOY HILL STUDIO CASTING SUITE
Adam House
7-10 Adam Street
London WC2N 6AA
e-mail: savoyhillstudio@tabard.co.uk
Fax: 020-7497 0830   Tel: 020-7497 0850

SCHER Anna THEATRE
70-72 Barnsbury Road
Islington
London N1 0ES
Fax: 020-7833 9467   Tel: 020-7278 2101

SCREEN WEST
136-142 Bramley Road
London W10 6SR
e-mail: projectionist@johnbrown.co.uk
Fax: 020-7565 3077   Tel: 020-7565 3321

SEA CADET DRILL HALL
Fairways, Off Broom Road
Teddington   Tel: 01784 241020

SHARED EXPERIENCE THEATRE
The Soho Laundry
9 Dufours Place
London W1F 7SJ
e-mail: admin@setheatre.co.uk
Fax: 020-7287 8763   Tel: 020 7734 8570

SOHO GYMS
Covent Garden Gym
12 Macklin Street
London WC2B 5NF
Fax: 020-7242 0899   Tel: 020-7242 1290

THE SPOTLIGHT ®

CASTING ROOMS

Following a recent refurbishment The Spotlight now has five casting rooms for hire at our central location in Leicester Place, WC2.
The Spotlight Casting Rooms are light and airy with a selection of sofas/chairs and tables.

All rooms are fully air-conditioned and sound proofed and each has a TV and video. There is an extensive waiting area plus a kitchen with tea and coffee making facilities. Cameras are available to hire and access to Spotlight Casting Live is free.

The Spotlight Casting Rooms are open every weekday from 10.00am to 5.30pm and rooms can be hired on a full day or half day basis.

Large Rooms - approx. 22 x 22 feet ~ £150 full day / £75 half day

Smaller Rooms - approx. 11 x 16 feet ~ £100 full day / £50 half a day

To book a Spotlight Casting Room simply call Gini on 020 7440 5030
or email casting@spotlightcd.com

Please note that The Spotlight Casting Rooms are not available to hire for open, musical or children's auditions.

HOLY INNOCENTS CHURCH *Rehearsal Spaces Available*

Lower Hall: 900 sq feet. Kitchen. Piano
Upper Hall: 1800 sq feet. Kitchen. Piano
Church: Sympathetic Acoustics for Music Rehearsals. Max 50 Players.
Hourly & Weekly rates on request.
Paddenswick Road London W6 Tel: 020~8748 2286 Fax: 020~8563 8735

SOHO GYMS
Clapham Common Gym
95-97 Clapham High Street
London SW4 7TB   Tel: 020-7720 0321

SOHO GYMS
Camden Town Gym
193 Camden High Street
London NW1 7JY
Fax: 020-7267 0500   Tel: 020-7482 4524

SOHO GYMS
Earls Court Gym
254 Earls Court Road
London SW5 9AD
Fax: 020-7244 6893   Tel: 020-7370 1402

SOHO THEATRE & WRITERS' CENTRE
21 Dean Street
London W1V 6NE
e-mail: mail@sohotheatre.com
Fax: 020-7287 5061   Tel: 020-7287 5060

Height 5 feet 10 inches (Equity/M.U.)   *Mike Martin*

PETER DURRENT

PIANIST-ACCOMPANIST-COMPOSER-VOCALIST
AUDITION & REHEARSAL PIANIST
COCKTAIL PIANIST

01787 373483   **or c/o The Spotlight**

SOUTHALL COMMUNITY CENTRE
(Rehearsal/Location Work)
20 Merrick Road, Southall
London UB2 4AU
Fax: 020-8574 3459   Tel: 020-8574 3458

SPACE CITY STUDIOS
(Video Casting Suite)
77 Blythe Road
London W14 0HP
e-mail: louise@spacecity.co.uk
Fax: 020-7371 4001   Tel: 020-7610 5000

SPOTLIGHT The
2nd Floor, 7 Leicester Place
London WC2H 7RJ
e-mail: info@spotlightcd.com
Fax: 020-7437 5881   Tel: 020-7437 7631

STEADFAST SEA CADET CORPS
(Modern Hall Available)
Thames Side, Kingston-upon-Thames KT1 1PX
                                  Tel: 020-8541 6901

ST JAMES'S CHURCH PICCADILLY
197 Piccadilly
London W1J 9LL
e-mail: joel@jcp.fsnet.co.uk
Fax: 020-7734 7449   Tel: 020-7734 4511

ST JOHN'S CHURCH
Waterloo Road, Southbank
London SE1 8TY
Fax: 020-7928 4470   Tel: 020-7928 2003

ST JOHN'S METHODIST CHURCH
9-11 East Hill, Wandsworth
London SW18 2HT
Tel: 020-8874 4780   Tel: 020-8871 9124

ST MARY NEWINGTON CHURCH HALL
(Peter Edwards)
The Rectory, 57 Kennington Park Road
London SE11 4JQ   Tel: 020-7735 1894

ST MARY'S CHURCH HALL PADDINGTON
c/o Bill Kenwright Ltd, 106 Harrow Road
London W2 1RR
e-mail: info@kenwright.com
Fax: 020-7446 6222   Tel: 020-7446 6200

STOLL MOSS THEATRES
Manor House, 21 Soho Square
London W1D 3QP
Fax: 020-7434 1217   Tel: 020-7494 5200

TAKE FIVE CASTING STUDIO
(Casting Suite)
25 Ganton Street
London W1F 9BP
Fax: 020-7287 3035   Tel: 020-7287 2120

THEATRE ROYAL DRURY LANE
Catherine Street
London WC2B 5JF   Tel: 020-7494 5200

THRESH Melody MANAGEMENT ASSOCIATES Ltd (MTM)
MTM House
29 Ardwick Green North
Manchester M12 6DL
melody.thresh@melody-threshmanagement.co.uk
Fax: 0161-273 5455   Tel: 0161-273 5445

TRICYCLE The
269 Kilburn High Road
London NW6 7JR
e-mail: admin@tricycle.co.uk
Fax: 020-7328 0795   Tel: 020-7372 6611

TWICKENHAM SEA CADETS
Fairways, Off Broom Road
Teddington
Middlesex TW11 9PL   Tel: 01784 241020

UNION CHAPEL PROJECT
Compton Avenue
London N1 2XD
e-mail: unionchapel.project@virgin.net
Fax: 020-7354 8343   Tel: 020-7226 3750

UNION THEATRE The
204 Union Street
Southwark
London SE1 0LX
e-mail: sasha@uniontheatre.freeserve.co.uk
          Tel/Fax: 020-7261 9876

URDANG ACADEMY The
20-22 Shelton Street
Covent Garden
London WC2H 9JJ
e-mail: theurdangacademy@btinternet.com
Fax: 020-7836 7010   Tel: 020-7836 5709

WATERMANS ARTS CENTRE
40 High Street, Brentford
Middlesex TW8 0DS
Fax: 020-8232 1030   Tel: 020-8232 1020

WESTMINSTER MEETING SOCIETY OF FRIENDS (QUAKERS)
8 Hop Gardens
St Martin's Lane
London WC2N 4EH   Tel/Fax: 020-7836 7204

WHITSTABLE COMMUNITY ARTS
The Re-Assembly Rooms, Horsebridge Road
Whitstable, Kent CT5 1BU
e-mail: slappers@whitstable2000.fsnet.co.uk
          Tel/Fax: 01227 263733

WILDITCH COMMUNITY CENTRE
48 Culvert Road, Battersea, London SW11 5BB
e-mail: wilditch@wandsworth.gov.uk
          Tel/Fax: 020-8871 8172

YOUNG Sylvia THEATRE SCHOOL
Rossmore Road, Marylebone
London NW1 6NJ
e-mail: sylviayoung@freeuk.com
Fax: 020-7723 1040   Tel: 020-7723 0037

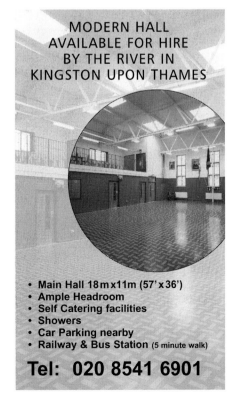

Routes To Film & Television Studios

It is essential that anyone undertaking a journey to the studios below, double checks these routes. Owing to constant changes of rail/bus companies/operators routes may change.

BBC TELEVISION

UNDERGROUND — CENTRAL LINE to WHITE CITY. Turn left from tube, cross zebra crossing. Studios outside station.

BBC South (Elstree) — BOREHAMWOOD

Trains from KINGS CROSS - Thames Link. Take stopping train to Elstree then walk (7/8 mins down Shenley High St.)
UNDERGROUND — NORTHERN LINE to EDGWARE or HIGH BARNET. 107 & 292 BUSES FROM EDGWARE VIA HIGH BARNET TO BOREHAMWOOD.

BRAY STUDIOS (BRAYSWICK)

BR Train from PADDINGTON to MAIDENHEAD. Then take taxi to studios
BR WATERLOO - WINDSOR RIVERSIDE. Take taxi. Coach from VICTORIA to WINDSOR. Take taxi.

HILLSIDE STUDIOS

Train from EUSTON (Network SE) — WATFORD JUNCTION, then taxi. UNDERGROUND — METROPOLITAN LINE to WATFORD, then taxi. Fast Trains from the Midlands & the North also stop at Watford Junction.
If catching slow train get off at Bushey/Oxhey then catch taxi from rank outside, or JUBILEE LINE to STANMORE then a taxi. METROPOLITAN LINE, change at Baker Street or Wembley.

THE LONDON STUDIOS (LONDON TELEVISION CENTRE)

UNDERGROUND (Bakerloo, Jubilee and Northern Lines) to WATERLOO then follow signs to Royal National Theatre then two buildings along.

PINEWOOD

UNDERGROUND — METROPOLITAN or PICCADILLY LINE to UXBRIDGE. Taxi rank outside station takes about 10 minutes. BRITISH RAIL WESTERN REGION — PADDINGTON to SLOUGH. Taxis from SLOUGH or BUS TO IVER HEATH.

RIVERSIDE STUDIOS

UNDERGROUND — HAMMERSMITH and CITY, DISTRICT or PICCADILLY LINE to HAMMERSMITH — then short walk to studios (behind the London Apollo Hammersmith). Numerous BUS ROUTES from the WEST END. 5 minutes from Hammersmith Broadway.

ROTHERHITHE STUDIOS

UNDERGROUND — DISTRICT LINE to WHITECHAPEL — then change to EAST LONDON LINE to ROTHERHITHE. (5 mins walk) BUS — 188 from EUSTON STATION via WATERLOO or 47 from LONDON BRIDGE or 381 from WATERLOO (best one to catch stops outside Studios).

SHEPPERTON STUDIOS

BRITISH RAIL — SOUTHERN REGION WATERLOO to SHEPPERTON then BUS Route 218 to studios

TEDDINGTON STUDIOS (THAMES TELEVISION)

BRITISH RAIL — WATERLOO to TEDDINGTON. Cross over footbridge at station. Come out of Station Road entrance. Left past Garden Centre. Nat West at right hand side TURN RIGHT walk 10 mins, then to set of lights, go over into Ferry Road, follow road then come to Studios (next to Anglers Pub on river). UNDERGROUND — DISTRICT LINE to RICHMOND — then take taxi or Bus R68 to TEDDINGTON to top of Ferry Road. Ask for Landmark Centre. Then go back to traffic lights, go across, past the Tide End Public House to Anglers Pub etc.

TWICKENHAM

BRITISH RAIL — SOUTHERN REGION — WATERLOO to ST MARGARET'S. UNDERGROUND — DISTRICT LINE to RICHMOND then SOUTHERN REGION or BUS 37 to ST MARGARET'S.

3D SET COMPANY
(Sets & Scenery Design & Construction)
Unit Q1, Buffalo Courts
Weston Park, Salford Quays
Manchester M5 2QL
Fax: 0161-876 4148   Tel: 0161-888 2225

AHEAD PRODUCTION SERVICES
Charles Taylor Works
43 Bartholomew Street, Digbeth
Birmingham B5 5QN
e-mail: enquiries@aheadps.co.uk
Mobile: 07957 470728   Tel/Fax: 0121-633 7366

ALBEMARLE OF LONDON
(Suppliers of Scenery & Costumes
Construction/Hire)
74 Mortimer Street, London W1N 7DF
e-mail: albemarle.productions@virgin.net
Fax: 020-7323 3074   Tel: 020-7631 0135

ALL SCENE ALL PROPS
(Scenery, Props & Painters)
443-445 Holloway Road, London N7 6LW
e-mail: allscene@hotmail.com
                           Tel/Fax: 020-7561 9231

BBC VISUAL EFFECTS
41-44 Kendal Avenue, Acton
London W3 0RP
Fax: 020-8993 8741   Tel: 020-8993 9434

BLACKOUT TRIPLE E Ltd
(Unitrack Track Systems, Automation,
Drape & Rigging)
280 Weston Road
London SW19 2QA
e-mail: info@blackout-tabtrack.com
Fax: 020-8681 8500   Tel: 020-8687 8400

**BOSCO LIGHTING DESIGN/TECHNICAL
CONSULTANCY**
63 Nimrod Road
London SW16 6SZ
e-mail: boscolx@lineone.net
                           Tel: 020-8769 3470

BRISTOL (UK) Ltd
(Scenic Paint & StageFloor Duo Suppliers)
12 The Arches, Maygrove Road
London NW6 2DS
e-mail: tech.sales@bristolpaint.com
Fax: 020-7372 5242   Tel: 020-7624 4370

CAMPBELL John SCENIC STUDIO
(Scenic Artist)
41 Iffley Road
London W6 0PB
e-mail: info@johncampbellscenicstudio.co.uk
Fax: 020-8748 1421   Tel: 020-8748 7266

CCT LIGHTING Ltd
(Lighting, Dimmers, Sound & Stage Machinery)
Hindle House, Traffic Street
Nottingham NG2 1NE
e-mail: office@cctlighting.co.uk
Fax: 0115-986 2546   Tel: 0115-986 2722

CLOCKWORK PRODUCTION
(Set Design & Construction, Scenic Painting
and Prop Making)
211 Beaconsfield Street, Arthurs Hill
Newcastle upon Tyne NE4 5JR
e-mail: clockwork@production10.freeserve.co.uk
Mobile: 07976 601287   Tel: 0191-245 3365

DAYLIGHT DESIGNS (UK) Ltd
(Conversions, Re-colouring & Restoration of
Luminaires)
Unit 163, Bruntingthorpe Industrial Estate
Nr Lutterworth, Leicestershire LE17 5QZ
Fax: 0116-247 8070   Tel: 0116-247 8336

DICKSON Terance and ASSOCIATES
(Scenery)
Unit 1, Michael Manley Industrial Estate
Stewarts Road
London SW8 4UB
e-mail: sales@terrydickson.com
Fax: 020-7498 9844   Tel: 020-7622 7630

DISCO ENTERTAINMENTS
(Disc Jockeys/Mobile Discos)
12 Mead Close, Grays
Essex RM16 2TR
e-mail: disco.entertainments@talk21.com
                           Tel: 01375 373886

DOVETAIL SPECIALIST SCENERY
(Scenery, Prop & Furniture Builders)
42-50 York Way
London N1 9AB
e-mail: dovetailss@cwcom.net
                           Tel/Fax: 020-7278 7379

253

S

DSA PRODUCTION SERVICES Ltd
(Sound, Light & Stage AV)
1 Addley Court, 435 Chiswick High Road
London W4 4AU
e-mail: info@dsaproductions.co.uk
Fax: 020-7734 4328   Tel: 020-7734 3121

FISHER Charles STAGING Ltd
Unit 4, Redhouse Farm, Bridgehewick, Ripon
North Yorks HG4 5AY
e-mail: info@charlesfisher.co.uk
                                    Tel: 01765 601604

FUTURIST Ltd
Trinity Business Park, Turner Way
Wakefield, West Yorks, WF2 8EF
Fax: 01924 298700   Tel: 01924 298900

GRANT INTERNATIONAL
(Period Furniture)
Dengmarsh Road, Lydd
Romney Marsh
Kent TN29 9JH
Fax: 01797 321754   Tel: 01797 321999

HARLEQUIN (British Harlequin Plc)
Bankside House, Vale Road, Tonbridge
Kent TN9 1SJ
e-mail: sales@harlequinfloors.co.uk
Fax: 01732 367755   Tel: 01732 367666

HENSHALL John
(Director of Lighting & Photography)
68 The High Street
Stanford in the Vale
Oxon SN7 8NL
e-mail: john@epi-centre.com   Tel: 01367 710191

KIMPTON WALKER Ltd
(Scenery Contractors)
10 Ellerslie Square
London SW2 5DZ
e-mail: awalker@kwscenic@aol.com
Fax: 020-7738 5517   Tel: 020-7738 3222

KNIGHT Robert
Top of the Bill House
Queen's Row
London SE17 2PX
Fax: 020-7277 1722   Tel: 020-7277 1704

LEE LIGHTING Ltd
Wycombe Road, Wembley
Middlesex HA0 1QD
e-mail: info@lee.co.uk
Fax: 020-8902 5500   Tel: 020-8900 2900

LIGHT WORKS Ltd
2A Greenwood Road
London E8 1AB
Fax: 020-7254 0306   Tel: 020-7249 3627

LIGHTING TECHNOLOGY GROUP
2 Tudor Estate
Abbey Road, Park Royal
London NW10 7UY
e-mail: info@lighting-tech.com
Fax: 020-8965 0950   Tel: 020-8965 6800

LITE IT
27 Victoria Road, Chichester
West Sussex PO19 4MY   Mobile: 07973 942027

MALTBURY Ltd
(Portable Staging Sales & Consultancy)
22 Pine Road
London NW2 6RY
e-mail: info@maltbury.com
                              Tel/Fax: 020-8208 1318

MARA Victor Ltd
(Scenic Artists & Contractors)
1-7 Newport Street
London SE11 6AJ
e-mail: info@vgroup.co.uk
Fax: 020-7735 9163   Tel: 020-7735 1518

MARPLES Ken CONSTRUCTION
(Scenery & Props)
11 Coombe Road, Chiswick
London W4 2HR
e-mail: ken@marplesk.freeserve.co.uk
Fax: 020-8995 4434   Tel: 020-8995 4446

MASSEY Bob ASSOCIATES
(Electrical & Mechanical Stage Consultants)
9 Worrall Avenue, Arnold
Notts NG5 7GN
e-mail: bm.associates@virgin.net
                              Tel/Fax: 0115-967 3969

MODELBOX
(Computer Aided Design & Design Services)
Studio 9
75 Filmer Road, Fulham
London SW6 7JF
e-mail: info@mailbox.co.uk
Fax: 020-7371 0503   Tel: 020-7371 0110

MURPHY Terry SCENERY Ltd
Western Wharf, Livesey Place
Peckham Park Road
London SE15 6SL
Fax: 020-7277 5147   Tel: 020-7277 5156

NEED Paul J
(Lighting Designer)
Unit 14, Forest Hill Business Centre
Clyde Vale
London SE23 3JF
e-mail: paul@10outof10.co.uk
Fax: 020-8699 8968   Tel: 020-8291 6885

NORTHERN LIGHT
(Lighting, Sound, Communications
& Stage Equipment)
Assembly Street, Leith
Edinburgh EH6 7RG
e-mail: enquiries@northernlight.co.uk
Fax: 0131-553 3296   Tel: 0131-553 2383

ORBITAL
(Sound Hire & Design)
57 Acre Lane, Brixton
London SW2 5TN
e-mail: hire@orbitalsound.co.uk
Fax: 020-7501 6869   Tel: 020-7501 6868

P.L. PARSONS SCENERY MAKERS
Barpart House
King's Cross Freight Depot
York Way, London N1 0UZ
Fax: 020-7278 3403   Tel: 020-7833 2031

RETROGRAPH NOSTALGIA
(Posters for interiors/exteriors 1880-1970)
164 Kensington Park Road
Notting Hill, London W11 2ER
e-mail: retropix1@aol.com
Fax: 020-7229 3395   Tel: 020-7727 9378

RWS ELECTRICAL AND AUDIO CONTRACTORS
1 Spinners Close, Biddenden
Kent TN27 8AY   Tel: 01580 291764

SCENERY JESSEL
(Scenery Builders/Stage Supplies)
Unit B, New Baltic Wharf, Oxestalls Road
Deptford, London SE8 5RJ
e-mail: sceneryjessel@ntlworld.com
Fax: 020-8694 2430   Tel: 020-8469 2777

SCOTT FLEARY Ltd
(Creative Construction Company)
Unit 2, Southside Industrial Estate
Havelock Terrace, London SW8 4AS
e-mail: scenery@scottflearyltd.demon.co.uk
Fax: 020-7622 0322   Tel: 020-7978 1787

SCOTT MYERS ASSOCIATES
(Theatre Sound Design)
14 Richmond Terrace
Cambridge CB5 8AJ
e-mail: sound.design@freeuk.com
Fax: 01223 562542   Tel: 01223 562262

SOUND COMPANY The
(Sound Hire, Design & Installation)
2 Lord Hills Road
London W2 6PD
e-mail: info@thesoundcompany.net
Fax: 020-7286 7377   Tel: 020-7286 7477

STAGECRAFT Ltd
(Hire & Sales of Lighting, Sound, Audio Visual
for Conference & Live Events)
Ashfield Trading Estate
Salisbury, Wilts SP2 7HL
e-mail: hire@stagecraft.co.uk
Fax: 01722 414076   Tel: 01722 326055

STAGE SYSTEMS
(Designers and Suppliers of Modular Staging,
Tiering & Auditorium Seating)
Stage House, Prince William Road
Loughborough LE11 5GU
e-mail: marketing@stagesystems.co.uk
Fax: 01509 233146   Tel: 01509 611021

STORM LIGHTING Ltd
Unit 6 Wintolea Industrial Estate
Monument Way West
Woking, Surrey GU21 5EN
e-mail: info@stormlighting.co.uk
Fax: 01483 757710   Tel: 01483 757211

STRAND LIGHTING Ltd
(Lighting Equipment for Stage,
Studio and Film & TV)
Unit 3, Hammersmith Studios
Yeldham Road, London W6 8JF
e-mail: sales@stranduk.com
Fax: 020-8735 9799   Tel: 020-8735 9790

SUFFOLK SCENERY
28 The Street
Brettenham, Ipswich
Suffolk IP7 7QP
e-mail: piehatch@aol.com
Fax: 01449 737620   Tel: 01449 736679

SUPOTCO GROUP
(Production - Lighting, Set Construction
& Scenery)
3-5 Valentine Place
London SE1 8QH
Fax: 020-7928 6082   Tel: 020-7928 5474

THEME PARTY COMPANY The
(Set Design Backdrops & Props)
21-37 Third Avenue
London E13 8AW
e-mail: info@themepartycompany
Fax: 020-8471 2111   Tel: 020-8471 3111

TOBEM SERVICES
(Theatrical Lighting)
Glen Orrin, Felcourt
East Grinstead
West Sussex RH19 2LE
e-mail: valerieandterry@btclick.com
          Tel: 01342 870438

TOP SHOW
(Props, Scenery, Conference Specialists)
North Lane, Huntington
York YO32 9SU   Tel: 01904 750022

TURN ON LIGHTING
(Antique Lighting c1840-1940)
116-118 Islington High Street
Camden Passage
London N1 8EG   Tel/Fax: 020-7359 7616

WEST John ASSOCIATES
(Designers & Scenic Artists - Film, TV & Display)
103 Abbotswood Close
Winyates Green
Redditch, Worcestershire B98 0QF
e-mail: johnwest@dial.pipex.com
Mobile: 07753 637451   Tel/Fax: 01527 516771

WHITEHORN Simon
(Sound Design)
57 Acre Lane
London SW2 5TN
e-mail: simon@orbitalsound.co.uk
Fax: 020-7501 6869   Tel: 020-7501 6868

WHITE LIGHT (Electrics) Ltd
(Stage & TV Lighting)
57 Filmer Road
London SW6 7JF
e-mail: info@whitelight.ltd.uk
Fax: 020-7371 0806   Tel: 020-7731 3291

WOOD Rod
(Scenic Artist, Backdrops, Scenery,
Props & Design)
41 Montserrat Road
London SW15 2LD
Mobile: 07887 697646   Tel: 020-8788 1941

BBC Television Wood Lane W12 7RJ
Tel: 020-8743 8000

■ TALENT RIGHTS GROUP
BBC PRODUCTION
172 - 178 Victoria Road, W3 6UL

Head of Rights Group   Simon Hayward-Tapp

LITERARY COPYRIGHT
Rights Manager	Ben Green
Rights Executives	Ann Kelly
	Sue Dickson
	Sally Millwood
	Julie Gallagher
	James Dundas
	Andrew Downey
	Gail Finn
	Sharon Cowley
	Fiona Nerberg
	David Knight
	Hilary Sagar
	Sarah Wade

FACTUAL, ARTS & CLASSICAL MUSIC
Rights Manager	Simon Brown
Rights Executives	Lorraine Clark
	Tristan Evans
	Gay Hedani-Palin
	Ken McHale
	Annie Pollard
	Shelagh Morrison
	John Hunter
	Pamela Wise
	Shirley Noel
	Cathy Holmes
	Penelope Davies/Alison Johnston
	Hilary Dodds/Caroline Edwards
	Costas Tanti

MUSICAL COPYRIGHT
Senior Rights Manager, Music	Claire Jarvis
Rights Executives	Nicky Bignell
	Peter Bradbury
	Sally Dunsford
	Liz Evans
	Catherine Grimes
	Debbie Rogerson

DRAMA ENTERTAINMENT & CHILDRENS
Rights Manager Performance	John Holland
Rights Executives	Maggie Anson
	Stephanie Beynon
	Mike Bickerdike
	Jo Buckingham
	Sally Dean
	Lisa Guthrie
	Marie-Louise Hagan
	Amanda Kimpton
	Lesley Longhurst
	David Marum
	Thalia Reynolds
	Lloyd Shepherd

ENGLISH REGIONS:

BIRMINGHAM - Pebble Mill
Contracts Manager	Janet Brookes

BRISTOL
Contracts Manager	
(Acting)	David Crockford

MANCHESTER
Contracts Executive	Alison Ripley

■ DRAMA
Controller of	
Drama Production	Susan Spindler
Head of Continuing Series	Mal Young
Head of Films &	
Single Drama	David Thompson
Head of Drama Serials	Laura Mackie
Executive Producers, Returning Series	
	Sue Hogg
	Simon Lewis

Executive Producers
Ruth Caleb	Hilary Salmon
Alexei de Keyzer	Tracey Scotfield
Kate Harwood	John Yorke

Executive Producer Fiction Lab
	Richard Fell

Producers
Paul Annett	Philip Leach
Chris Ballentyne	Liza Marshall
Ruth Baumgarten	Gordon Ronald
David Crean	Amanda Silvester
Beverley Dartnall	David Snodin
Victoria Fea	Joy Spink
Christopher Hall	Merryn Watson
Tim Holloway	Catherine Wearing
Kathleen Hutchinson	Pier Wilkie
Deborah Jones	Rachel Wright

■ COMMISSIONING

Controller Factual Commissioning
Nicola Moody
Controller Entertainment Commissioning
Danielle Lux
Controller Drama Commissioning
Jane Tranter

■ NEWS AND CURRENT AFFAIRS

BBC News (Television & Radio)
Television Centre
Wood Lane, London W12 7RJ
Tel: 020-8576 7312   Fax: 020-8576 7120

Director News   Richard Sambrook
Deputy Director News   Mark Damazer
Head of Television News   Roger Mosey
Deputy Head of Television News
Rachel Atwell
Head of Radio News   Stephen Mitchell
Head of Political Programmes
Francesca Unsworth

■ DOCUMENTARIES

Controller of Documentaries Group
Jeremy Gibson
Deputy Controller of Head of Development
David Mortimer
Head of Production   Marney Shears
Managing Editor   Clare Brigstocke

Creative Directors

Investigations   Alex Holmes
Crime   Seetha Kumar
General Documentaries   Olivia Lichtenstein
General Documentaries, Bristol   Tessa Finch
Consumer   Mark Killick
Digital Channels Unit   Helen O'Rahilly

■ FACTUAL & LEARNING

(All based at White City)
Leisure & Factual Entertainment (TV only)
Controller   Anne Morrison
Managing Editor   Donna Taberer

Creative Directors

Vicki Barrass
Alison Sharman
Owen Gay
Jonnine Waddell
Nick Vaughan-Barratt
Andy Batten-Foster
Mark Hill
Rachel Innes-Lumsden

■ ARTS

Creative Director   Franny Moyle
Executive Producer   Alex Graham

Editors

Editor Arena   Anthony Wall
Arts Features   Keith Alexander
Omnibus   Basil Comely

■ MUSIC

Head of Classical Music
(BBC TV/Editor of artzone)   Peter Maniura

■ CHILDREN'S PROGRAMMES

Controller CBBC   Nigel Pickard
Head of Programming, CBBC   Dorothy Prior
Editor, Blue Peter   Steve Hocking
Editor, CBBC On-Line   Rebecca Shallcross

Executive Producers

Acquisitions, CBBC   Theresa Plummer-Andrews
Drama, CBBC   Elaine Sperber
Light Entertainment, CBBC   Chris Bellinger
News & Factual Programmes, CBBC
Roy Milani
Head of CBBC, Scotland   Claire Mundell
Pre-School Programmes   Clare Elstow
Education, CBBC   Sue Nott
Development Executive, Digital Strategy
Greg Childs

■ SPORT

Director of Sport   Peter Salmon
Director, Sports Rights & Finance Dominic Coles
Controller Radio Five Live   Bob Shennan
Head of Major Events   Dave Gordon
Head of Football & Boxing   Niall Sloane
Head of Programmes & Planning   Pat Younge
Head of General Sports   Barbara Slater
Head of Radio Sport   Gordon Turnbull
Head of New Media, Sports News
& Development   Andrew Thompson

■ SCIENCE

Creative Director for Science   John Lynch
Head of Development   Sacha Baveystock
Editor Horizon   Bettina Lerner
Editor Tomorrow's World   Saul Nassé

■ BBC BRISTOL

Broadcasting House
Whiteladies Road
Bristol BS8 2LR   Tel: 0117-973 2211

NETWORK TELEVISION AND RADIO
FEATURES

Creative Directors	Tessa Finch
	Andy Batten-Foster
	Mark Hill
Executive Producers	Michael Poole
	Dick Colthurst

TELEVISION
Producers

Robert Bayley	Peter Lawrence
Mark Bristow	Christopher Lewis
Kathryn Broome	Kim Littlemore
Michelle Burgess	Jane Lomas
Roy Chapman	Susan McDermott
Linda Cleeve	Julian Mercer
Peter Firstbrook	Martin Pallthorpe
Trevor Hill	Mike Poole
Jeremy Howe	Ian Pye
Chris Hutchins	Amanda Reilly
David Hutt	Colin Rose
Sarah Johnson	Miranda Steed

RADIO

Unit Manager, Radio	Kate Chaney
Editors	Elizabeth Burke
	Fiona Cooper

Producers

Viv Beesby	Jane Greenwood
John Byrne	Jeremy Howe
Frances Byrnes	Kate McCall
Sara Davies	David Olusoga
Tim Dee	Lucy Willmore
Paul Dodgson	

NATURAL HISTORY UNIT

Head of Natural History Unit	Keith Scholey
Editor The Natural World	Neil Nightingale

Television Producers

Paul Appleby	Mike Gunton
Melinda Barker	Martin Hughes-Games
Miles Barton	Mark Jacobs
Karen Bass	Hilary Jeffkins
Vanessa Belowitz	Mark Linfield
Mike Beynon	Neil Lucas
Lucy Bowden	Sue McMillan
Andrew Byatt	Patrick Morris
Paul Chapman	Stephen Moss
Mary Colwell	Mike Salisbury
Huw Cordey	Jo Sarsby
Peter Crawford	Tim Scoones
Yvonne Ellis	Mary Summerhill
Mark Flowers	Dale Templar
Sara Ford	James Walton
Liz Green	

Managing Editor NHU Radio	Julian Hector
Director of Development	Michael Bright

■ BBC WEST

Whiteladies Road
Bristol BS8 2LR   Tel: 0117-973 2211

Head of Regional and Local Programmes,
including BBC West, Radio Bristol & Somerset
Sound, Radio Gloucestershire & BBC Wiltshire

Sound	Andrew Wilson
Editor, Newsgathering	Ian Cameron
Series Producer	
Topical Unit	James Macalpine
Editor, Political Unit	Paul Cannon
Editors, Output	Stephanie Marshall
	Jane Kingham

■ BBC SOUTH WEST

Seymour Road
Mannamead
Plymouth PL3 5BD   Tel: 01752 229201

Head of Local & Regional Programmes	Leo Devine
Editor TV Current Affairs	Simon Willis
Editor News	Roger Clark
Senior Assistant News Editor	Simon Read

■ BBC SOUTH

Havelock Road
Southampton SO14 7PU   Tel: 023-8022 6201

Head of Regional & Local Programmes (including BBC Radio Berkshire, Radio Oxford & BBC Radio Solent)	Eve Turner
Editor BBC Radio Berkshire, Radio Oxford	Phil Ashworth
Editor BBC Radio Solent	Chris van Schaik

■ BBC LONDON

PO Box 94.9
London W1A 6FL   Tel: 020-7208 9660

BBC London:
TV: Newsroom South East & (Political
Programme) Metropol
Radio: London Live 94.9 FM

Executive Editor	Jane Mote
News/Output Editor	Sandy Smith
Executive Producer, First Sight	Dippy Chaudhray
Managing Editor BBC London Live 94.9FM	David Robey
Politcal Editor	Jon Craig

■ BBC SOUTH EAST

c/o BBC Radio Kent
The Great Hall, Mount Pleasant Road
Tunbridge Wells
Kent TN1 1QQ | Tel: 01892 670000

Head of Regional & Local Programmes,
BBC South East | Laura Ellis
BBC Radio Kent & BBC Southern Counties
Managing Editor,
BBC Radio Kent | Steve Taschini
Managing Editor,
BBC Southern Counties | Mike Hapgood
Newsgathering Editor,
BBC South East | David Farwig

■ BBC NORTH WEST

New Broadcasting House
Oxford Road
Manchester M60 1SJ | Tel: 0161-200 2020

Entertainment & Features

Head of Entertainment
& Features | Wayne Garvie
Executive Producer, Factual | Alan Brown
Executive Producer,
Entertainment | Kieron Collins

Religious Broadcasting

Head of Religious Ethics | tba
Executive Producer, Talks, Debate | David Coomes

Network News & Current Affairs

Editor News & Current Affairs | Dave Stanford
Editor File on Four | David Ross

Regional & Local Programmes

Head of Regional
& Local Programmes | Martin Brooks

Leeds

Broadcasting Centre, Woodhouse Lane
Leeds LS2 9PX | Tel: 0113-244 1188
Head of Regional
& Local Programmes | Colin Philpott

Newcastle

BBC Broadcasting Centre, Barrack Road
Newcastle-upon-Tyne NE99 2NE | Tel: 0191-232 1313
Head of Regional
& Local Programmes | Olwyn Hocking

■ BBC BIRMINGHAM

BBC Birmingham
Pebble Mill Road
Birmingham B5 7QQ
Fax: 0121-432 8634 | Tel: 0121-432 8888

English Regions

Controller, English Regions. Head of Centre
(Birmingham) | Andy Griffee
Head of New Services, English Regions | John Allen
Head of Finance, English Regions | Julie Bertolini
Head of Personnel, English Regions | Liz Smith
Chief Press & Publicity Officer,
English Regions | Simon Channon
Secretary, English Regions | Louise Hall
Head of Regional & Local
Programmes West Midlands and Director of
Mailbox Project | Roy Roberts
Acting Head of Regional and Local
Programmes, West Midlands | Emma Agnew

Leisure and Factual Entertainment, BBC Birmingham

Managing Editor | Paresh Solanki
Executive Editor | Jane Booth
Creative Director, Daytime | Alison Sharman
Creative Director, Country file, Motoring &
Asian Programmes
| Andy Batten-Foster
Creative Director, Gardening | Owen Gay

Network Radio

Editor, Factual Radio & Rural Affairs
| Andrew Thorman
Editor, Specialist Programmes, Radio 2
| David Barber

Drama

Head of Production BBC
Birmingham | Trevor West
Editor Radio Drama
& The Archers | Vanessa Whitburn

■ SCOTLAND

Glasgow
Broadcasting House
Queen Margaret Drive
Glasgow G12 8DG   Tel: 0141-339 8844

SCOTTISH DIRECTION GROUP

Controller Scotland   John McCormick
Head of Network Programmes   Colin Cameron
Head of Comedy & Entertainment Mike Bolland
Executive Editor New Media   Julie Adair

Head of Radio   Maggie Cunningham
Head of Programmes Scotland   Ken McQuarrie
Head of Gaelic   Donalda Mackinnon
Head of News and Current Affairs Blair Jenkins
Head of Sport   Neil Fraser
Head of North   Andrew Jones

Head of Finance & Business Affairs   Irene Tweedie
Head of Production   Nancy Braid
Head of Human Resources and Internal
   Communications   Steve Ansell
Head of Marketing and Communications
          Mairead Ferguson
Secretary and Head of Public Policy
          Mark Leishman

Edinburgh
Broadcasting House
5 Queen Street
Edinburgh EH2 1JF   Tel: 0131-225 3131

Aberdeen
Broadcasting House
Beechgrove Terrace
Aberdeen AB15 5ZT   Tel: 01224 625233

Dumfries
BBC Dumfries
Elmbank, Lovers Walk
Dumfries DG1 1NZ   Tel: 01387 268008

Dundee
66 Nethergate
Nethergate Centre
Dundee DD1 4ER   Tel: 01382 202481

Inverness
BBC Inverness
Broadcasting House
7 Culduthel Road
Inverness IV2 4AD   Tel: 01463 720720

Orkney
BBC Radio Orkney
Castle Street
Kirkwall
Orkney KW15 1DF   Tel: 01856 873939

Portree
Clydesdale Bank Buildings
Somerled Square
Portree
Isle of Skye IV51 9BT   Tel: 01478 612005

Selkirk
BBC Selkirk
Municipal Buildings
High Street
Selkirk TD7 4BU   Tel: 01750 21884

Shetland
BBC Shetland
Bentham House
Harbour Street
Lerwick
Shetland ZE1 0DW   Tel: 01595 694747

Stornoway
Radio nan Gaidheal
Rosebank
Church Street
Stornoway
Isle of Lewis HS1 2LS   Tel: 01851 705000

■ WALES

Broadcasting House
Llandaff
Cardiff CF5 2YQ   Tel: 029-2032 2000

Controller   Menna Richards
Head of Programmes (Welsh)   Keith Jones
Head of Programmes (English)   Clare Hudson
Head of Public Affairs   Manon Williams
Head of Marketing
   & Communication   David Jones
Head of News & Current Affairs   Aled Eirug
Head of Personnel   Keith Rawlings
Head of Finance   Gareth Powell
Head of Drama   Matthew Robinson
Head of Sport   Nigel Walker
Head of North Wales   Marian Wyn Jones
Head of Factual   Adrian Davies
Head of Education   Eleri Wyn-Lewis
Editor Radio Wales   Julie Barton
Editor Radio Cymru   Aled Glynne-Davies

■ NORTHERN IRELAND

Belfast

Ormeau Avenue
Belfast BT2 8HQ   Tel: 028-9033 8000

Controller   Anna Carragher
Head of Broadcasting   Tim Cooke
Head of News &
   Current Affairs   Andrew Colman
Head of Public Affairs   Rosemary Kelly
Head of Drama   Robert Cooper
Head of Factual & Learning   Bruce Batten
Head of Entertainment
   & Events   Mike Pedger
Head of Finance &
   Business Affairs   Crawford Maclean
Head of Human Resources   Liz Torrans
Head of Marketing
   & Development   Peter Johnston
Head of Resources   Stephen Beckett

Londonderry

BBC Radio Foyle   Tel: 028-7126 2244

Managing Editor   Ana Leddy

ANGLIA TELEVISION LTD
Head Office
Anglia House Norwich NR1 3JG
Fax: 01603 631032   Tel: 01603 615151
East of England: Weekday & Weekend
Regional News Centres

Cambridge
26 Newmarket Road Cambridge CB5 8DT
Fax: 01223 467106   Tel: 01223 467076
Reporter: Matthew Hudson

Chelmsford
64-68 New London Road Chelmsford CM1 0YU
Fax: 01245 267228   Tel: 01245 357676
Reporter: Timothy Evans

Luton
16 Park Street Luton LU1 3EP
Fax: 01582 401214   Tel: 01582 729666
Reporter: Charlotte Fisher

Northampton
77B Abington Street Northampton NN1 2BH
Fax: 01604 629856   Tel: 01604 624343
Reporter: Karl Heidel

Peterborough
6 Bretton Green Village
Rightwell Bretton Peterborough PE3 8DY
Fax: 01733 269424   Tel: 01733 269440
Reporter: Linda O'Brien

Ipswich
Hubbard House Civic Drive Ipswich IP1 2QA
Fax: 01473 233279   Tel: 01473 226157
Reporters: Lindsey Brooke, Rebecca Atherstone

BORDER TELEVISION PLC
Head Office & Studios
The Television Centre
Carlisle CA1 3NT   Tel: 01228 525101
Southern Scotland, North-West England,
North Northumberland and the Isle of Man;
Weekday and Weekend

Chairman   James Graham
Managing Director   Nick Cusick
Director of Programmes   Neil Robinson

CARLTON COMMUNICATIONS
25 Knightsbridge
London SW1X 7RZ
Fax: 020-7663 6300   Tel: 020-7663 6363
Chairman   Michael Green

CARLTON TELEVISION
London
101 St Martin's Lane
London WC2N 4RF
Fax: 020-7240 4171   Tel: 020-7240 4000

Chairman, Carlton Broadcasting
  & Central Broadcasting   Nigel Walmsley
Chief Executive   Clive Jones
Director of Programmes   Steve Hewlett
Chief Executive, Carlton Sales   Martin Bowley

PRODUCTION
London
Carlton Productions
35-38 Portman Square, London W1H 0NU
Fax: 020-7486 1132   Tel: 020-7486 6688
East Midlands
Carlton Studios, Lenton Lane,
Nottingham NG7 2NA
Fax: 0115-964 5552   Tel: 0115-986 3322
West Country
West Country Television
Western Wood Way, Langage Science Park,
Plymouth PL7 5BQ
Fax: 01752 333444   Tel: 01752 333333

The Following based at
35-38 Portman Square London W1
Managing Director   Waheed Alli
Director of Programmes   Steve Hewlett
Controller, Business Affairs   Martin Baker
Director of Drama &
  Co-production   Jonathan Powell
Head of Department, Drama   Rob Pursey
Executive Producer, Drama   Sharon Bloom
Controller, Children's & Young
  People's Programmes   Michael Forte
Controller of Entertainment   Mark Wells
Controller of Comedy   Nick Symons
Controller, Factual Programmes   Polly Bide
Head of Current Affairs and
  Features   Mike Morley
Head of Regional Programmes,
  Carlton   Emma Barker
Head of Regional Programmes,
  Central   Duncan Ryecroft
Director of Programmes,
  West Country   Jane McCloskey

BROADCASTING
Carlton Broadcasting
London:
101 St Martin's Lane
London WC2N 4RF
Fax: 020-7240 4171   Tel: 020-7240 4000

London Television Centre
Upper Ground, London SE1 9LT
Fax: 020-7827 7501   Tel: 020-7620 1620

Central Broadcasting
West Midlands:
Central Court, Gas Street, Birmingham B1 2JT
Fax: 0121-634 4957   Tel: 0121-643 9898
East Midlands:
Carlton Studios, Lenton Lane
Notts NG7 2NA
Tel: 0115-986 3322   Tel: 0115-964 5552
South Midlands:
Windrush Court, Abingdon Business Park
Abingdon OX1 1SA
Fax: 01235 524024   Tel: 01235 554123

Westcountry Television:
Western Wood Way, Langage Science Park
Plymouth PL7 5BQ
Fax: 01752 333444   Tel: 01752 333333

Chairman	Clive Jones
Managing Director	Mark Haskell
Controller of News	Brad Higgins
Director of Programmes	Jane McCloskey
Controller of Features &	
Programme Development	Caroline Righton
Controller of Current Affairs	Mark Clare
Managing Director,	
Carlton Broadcasting	Colin Stanbridge
Managing Director,	
Central Broadcasting	Ian Squires
Controller Broadcasting	Coleena Reid
Head of Planning & Acquisitions	David Joel
Head of Presentation	Wendy Chapman
Head of Presentation & Programme	
Planning (Central)	David Burge
Controller, News & Operations	
(Central)	Laurie Upshon
Controller, Sport (Central)	Gary Newbon
Editor, Central News West	John Boileau
Editor, Central News East	Dan Barton
Editor, Central News South	Phil Carrodus

FACILITIES AND STUDIOS
Outside Broadcasting
Carlton 021
12-13 Gravelly Hill Industrial Estate
Gravelly Hill, Birmingham B24 8HZ
Fax: 0121-327 7021   Tel: 0121-327 2021
Managing Director   Ed Everest

Carlton Studios
Lenton Lane, Nottingham NG7 2NA
Fax: 0115-964 5552   Tel: 0115-986 3322
Managing Director   Ian Squires

SALES
London
101 St Martin's Lane
London WC2N 4RF   Tel: 020-7270 4000

Manchester
Brazenose House West
Lincoln Square
Manchester M2 5AS
Fax: 0161-237 1970   Tel: 0161-237 1811

Westcountry
Westcountry Television
Western Wood Way
Langage Science Park
Plymouth PL7 5BQ
Fax: 01752 333316   Tel: 01752 333311

Birmingham
Central Court, Gas Street
Birmingham B1 2JT
Fax: 0121-634 4414   Tel: 0121-643 9898

Chief Executive	Martin Bowley
Managing Director	Steve Platt
Sales Director	Gary Digby
Marketing Director	Fran Cassidy

CHANNEL TELEVISION LTD
Registered Office
The Television Centre
La Pouquelaye
St Helier Jersey JE1 3ZD
Channel Islands
Fax: 01534 816817   Tel: 01534 816816
Channel Islands: Weekday and Weekend

Managing Director	Michael Lucas
Director of Programmes	Karen Rankine
Director of Sales	Gordon de Ste.Croix
Director of Transmission	
& Resources	Kevin Banne
Director of Finance	Amanda Trotman
News Editor	Allan Watts

CHANNEL FOUR TELEVISION CORPORATION
London Office
124 Horseferry Road
London SW1P 2TX
Fax: 020-7306 8116   Tel: 020-7396 4444

Members of the Board
Chairman   Vanni Treves
Deputy Chairman   Barry Cox
Chief Executive   Michael Jackson
Managing Director   David Scott
Director of Programmes   Tim Gardam
Commercial Director   Andy Barnes
Director of Strategy
    & Development   David Brook
Director of Finance &
    Business Affairs   Janet Walker
Millie Banerjee   Ian Ritchie
Peter Bazalgette   Joe Sinyor
Andrew Graham   Rob Woodward
Robin Miller
Company Secretary: Andrew Brown

Heads of Department
Head of Airtime Management   Merlin Inkley
Head of Commercial Development & Research
    Hugh Johnson
Head of Agency Sales   Matt Shreeva
Head of Information Systems   Ian Dobb
Controller of Human Resources   Peter Meier
Head of Presentation   Steve White
Acting MD, 124 Facilities   David Mann
Head of Business Affairs   Andrew Brann
Head of Programme Finance
    Maureen Semple-Piggot
Head of Legal & Comliance   Jan Tomalin
Head of Finance   Tony Moore
MD 4 Learning Ltd/
    Deputy Director of Programmes   Karen Brown
Managing Editor Commissioning   Janey Walker
Head of Programmes
    (Nations & Regions)   Stuart Cosgrove
Controller of
    Programme Acquisition   June Dromgoole
Head of Science & Education   Sara Ramsden
Head of News, Current Affairs
    & Business   David Lloyd
Head of Entertainment   Daniella Lux
Head of Drama   Tessa Ross
Director of Marketing &
    Commercial Development   Polly Cochrane
Chief Executive - FilmFour Ltd   Paul Webster
Head of Corporate Relations   John Newbigin
Head of Programme Planning
    & Strategy   Rosemary Newell
Head of Press & Publicity   Matt Baker

Commissioning Editors
Documentaries   Peter Dale
Art & Religion   Janice Hadlow
Multicultural (Docs & Factual)   Yasmin Anwar
Multicultural (Education &
    Current Affairs)   Patrick Younge
Independent Film & Video   Adam Baker
Daytime   Jo McGrath
4 Learning   Paul Ashton
Schools Programmes   John Richmond
Adult Interactive Learning   Paula Snyder
News, Current Affairs & Business   Dorothy Byrne
Entertainment   Caroline Leddy
T4   Andi Peters
Drama   Johnathan Young

CHANNEL 5 BROADCASTING
22 Long Acre
London WC2E 9LY
Fax: 020-7550 5554   Tel: 020-7550 5555

Chief Executive   Dawn Airey
Director of Programmes   Kevin Lygoe
Director of Marketing
    and Communications   Jim Hytner
Deputy Chief Executive   Nick Milligan
Controller of Drama   Corinne Hollingworth
Senior Programme Controller   Michael Attwell
Senior Programme Controller   Chris Shaw
Controller of Entertainment   Alan Nixon
Controller of Special Events   Adam Perry
Controller of Sport   Robert Charles
Controller of Children's
    Programmes   Nick Wilson
Director of Broadcasting   Ashley Hill
Controller of Acquisitions   Jeff Ford

GMTV
London Television Centre
Upper Ground
London SE1 9TT
Fax: 020-7827 7001   Tel: 020-7827 7000

Chairman   Nigel Walmsley
Managing Director   Paul Corley
Director of Programmes   Peter McHugh
Finance Director   Simon Davey
Director of Sales   Clive Crouch
Head of Press   Sue Brealey
Managing Editor   John Scammell
Editor   Martin Frizell
Chief Engineer   Geoff Wright

GRAMPIAN TELEVISION PLC

Head Office & Studios
Queen's Cross
Aberdeen AB15 4XJ
Fax: 01224 846800   Tel: 01224 846846

Dundee Office & Studios
Harbour Chambers
Dock Street
Dundee DD1 3HW
Fax: 01382 591010   Tel: 01382 591000

Inverness Office & Studios
23-25 Huntly Street
Inverness IV3 5PR
Fax: 01463 223637   Tel: 01463 242624
North Scotland: Weekday and weekend

Chairman   Calum A MacLeod CBE LLD
Managing Director   Derrick Thomson
Head of News & Current Affairs   Henry Eagles
Production Resources Manager   Avril Shannon

GRANADA TELEVISION LTD
Granada TV Centre
Quay Street
Manchester M60 9EA   Tel: 0161-832 7211

London
London Television Centre
Upper Ground
London SE1 9LT   Tel: 020-7620 1620

Liverpool
Granada News Centre
Albert Dock
Liverpool L3 4BA
Fax: 0151-709 3389   Tel: 0151-709 9393

Chester
Granada News Centre
Bridgegate House
5 Bridge Place
Lower Bridge Street
Chester CH1 1SA
Fax: 01244 320599   Tel: 01244 313966

Lancaster
Granada News Centre
White Cross
Lancaster LA1 4XQ
Fax: 01524 67607   Tel: 01524 60688

Blackburn
Granada News Centre
Daisyfield Business Centre
Appleby Street
Blackburn BB1 3BL
Fax: 01254 699299   Tel: 01254 690099

Granada plc - Executive Board

Executive Chairman	Charles Allen
Chief Executive	Steve Morrison
Finance Director & Deputy Chairman, Media Ventures	Henry Staunton
Commercial Director	Graham Parrott
Director Operations	Jules Burns
Executive Chair, Granada Creative	Andrea Wonfor
Managing Director, Granada Broadcasting	Stewart Butterfield
Managing Director, Granada Broadband	Simon Shaps
Chief Executive, Enterprises	Mick Desmond

Granada Television

Chairman	Charles Allen
Managing Director	Brenda Smith
Director of Programmes	Grant Mansfield
Director of Broadcasting	Susan Woodward
Controller of Production	Claire Poyser
Controller of Current Affairs & Features	Jeff Anderson
Controller of Documentaries, History & Science	Bill Jones
Controller of Drama & Comedy	Andy Harries
Controller of Childrens	Steven Andrew
Controller of Entertainment	Duncan Gray
Controller of Lifestyle	James Hunt
Executive Producer Coronation Street	Jane Macnaught
Head of Regional Affairs	Jane Luca
Head of Media Relations, North	Sallie Ryle
Haad of Granada Film	Pippa Cross
Head of Regional Programmes	Eamonn O'Neal
Head of Factual Drama	Jeff Pope
Head of Sport	Don Jones
Financial Controller	Kevan Taylor

HTV GROUP LTD
Television Centre, Culverhouse Cross
Cardiff CF5 6XJ   Tel: 029-2059 0590

Television Centre, Bath Road
Bristol BS4 3HG   Tel: 0117-972 2722

Wales/West of England: All week

Group Managing Director	Jeremy Payne
Controller, HTV Wales	Elis Owen
Controller, HTV West	Sandra Jones
HTV Wales Head of Drama Development	Peter Edwards
HTV Wales Head of Factual Development	Clare Hudson

INDEPENDENT TELEVISION NEWS
200 Gray's Inn Road
London WC1X 8XZ   Tel: 020-7833 3000

Chief Executive	Stewart Purvis
Editor-in-Chief	Richard Tait
Editor, ITV News	Nigel Dacre
Editor, Channel 4 News	Jim Gray
Editor 5 News	Gary Rogers
Marketing Director	David Robinson
Director of Public Affairs	Mark Gallasher

LWT

LWT HOLDINGS PLC
The London Television Centre
Upper Ground
London SE1 9LT   Tel: 020-7620 1620

London 5.10 pm Friday to 6 am Monday

Executives of the LWT Group

Controller of Arts & Features LWT Productions Ltd	Melvyn Bragg
Controller of Drama LWT & United Productions	Michelle Buck
Controller of Factual, LWT	Jim Allen

Directors

Executive Chairman, Granada	Charles Allen
Chief Executive, Granda	Steve Morrison
Managing Director, Granada Broadcasting	Stewart Butterfield
Managing Director, LWT	Lindsay Charlton
Director of Programmes	Marcus Plantin

How to Draw Attention to Oneself

Place a free line entry in Contacts®

To be included in the 2003 edition of Contacts, published in October 2002, send the following details on company headed paper before July 2002 stating: Company Name, Address, Telephone Number, Fax Number and the SECTION in which you wish to be included.

Contacts Listings

The Spotlight, 7 Leicester Place London WC2H 7RJ
e-mail: info@spotlight.cd.com Fax: 020-7437 5881
Advertising rates available from May 2002. Please telephone: 020-7437 7631

MERIDIAN BROADCASTING LTD

Television Centre, Southampton SO14 0PZ
Fax: 023-8033 5050   Tel: 023-8022 2555

Board

Chairman	Charles Allen
MD Granada Broadcasting	Stewart Butterfield
Finance Director, Granada Broadcasting	Mike Fegan
Director of Sales, Granada Enterprises	David Croft
Managing Director, Meridian	Mary McAnally
Director of Broadcasting	Mark Southgate
Director of News	Andy Cooper
Director of Regional & Commercial Affairs	Martin Morrall

Executives

Managing Director, Meridian	Mary McAnally
Director of Broadcasting	Mark Southgate
Director of News	Andy Cooper
Director of Regional & Commercial Affairs	Martin Morrall
General Manager	Jan Beal
Controller of Sport	Tony Baines
Controller of Personnel	Peter Ashwood
Finance Controller	Steve Godwin
Head of Current Affairs & Social Action	Trish Powell

S4C

S4C-THE WELSH FOURTH CHANNEL

Parc Tŷ Glas, Llanisien Cardiff CF14 5DU
Fax: 029-2075 4444   Tel: 029-2074 7444

The Welsh Fourth Channel Authority

Chair	Elan Closs Stephens
Members	Cefin Campbell
Enid Rowlands	Peter Davies CBE
Huw Wynne-Griffiths	Janet Lewis Jones
Nic Parry	Janice Rowlands

Senior Staff

Chief Executive	Huw Jones
Director of Corporate Affairs	Alun Davies
Director of Programming	Huw Eirug
Director of Engineering	Arshad Rasul
Director of Marketing	Eleri Twynog Davies
Director of Finance	Kathryn Morris
Director of Commercial Affairs	Wyn Innes
Head of Corporate Press & Public Relations	David Meredith
Director of Personnel	Ifan Roberts

SCOTTISH TELEVISION

Glasgow

200 Renfield Street, Glasgow G2 3PR
Fax: 0141-300 3030   Tel: 0141-300 3000

London Office

3 Waterhouse Square, 138-142 Holborn,
London EC1N 2YN
Fax: 020-7882 1014   Tel: 020-7882 1010

Chairman	Don Cruickshank
Chief Executive	Andrew Flanagan
Chief Executive, Television	Donald Emslie
Managing Director, Scottish TV	Sandy Ross
Managing Director, Grampian TV	Derrick Thompson
Managing Director, SMGTV Productions	Jagdip Jagpal
Head of Drama	Eric Coulter

TYNE TEES TELEVISION

TYNE TEES TELEVISION

The Television Centre, City Road
Newcastle upon Tyne NE1 2AL
Fax: 0191-261 2302   Tel: 0191-261 0181

Teeside Studio

Pavilion 13 Belasis Hall Technology Park
Greenwood Rd
Billingham

Cleveland TS23 4EG
Fax: 01642 566560   Tel: 01642 566999
North East and North Yorkshire: Weekday and Weekend

Chairman	Charles Allen
Managing Director	Margaret Fay
Director of Broadcasting	Graeme Thompson
Managing Editor, News	Graham Marples
Head of Network Features	Malcolm Wright
Head of Young People's Programmes	Lesley Oakden
Head of Sport	Roger Tames

ULSTER TELEVISION PLC

Havelock House
Ormeau Road
Belfast BT7 1EB
Fax: 028-9024 6695   Tel: 028-9032 8122

Northern Ireland: Weekday and Weekend

Chairman	J B McGuckian BSc (Econ)
Managing Director	J McCann BSc, FCA
Financial Director	Jim Downey
Director of Programming	A Bremner
Head of Press & Public Relations	Orla McKibbin
Head of News & Current Affairs	R Morrison
Sales Director	P Hutchinson

YORKSHIRE TELEVISION LTD

The Television Centre
Leeds LS3 1JS
Fax: 0113-244 5107   Tel: 0113-243 8283

London Office

Global House
96-108 Great Suffolk Street
London SE1 0BE
Fax: 020-7578 4320   Tel: 020-7578 4304

Hull Office

23 Brook Street
The Prospect Centre
Hull HU2 8PN   Tel: 01482 24488

Sheffield Office

Charter Square
Sheffield S1 3EJ   Tel: 0114-272 3262

Lincoln Office

88 Bailgate
Lincoln LN1 3AR   Tel: 01522 530738

Grimsby Office

Alexandra Dock Business Centre
Fisherman's Wharf
Alexandra Dock, Grimsby
N E Lincs DN31 1UL   Tel: 01472 357026

York Office

8 Coppergate
York YO1 1NR   Tel: 01904 610066

Executives

Director of Broadcasting	Mike Best
Controller, Features	Bridget Boseley
Executive Producer, Entertainment	Jim Brown

Controller of Factual Programmes, Yorkshire-Tyne Tess Productions	Chris Bryer
Director of Business Affairs for Granada Productions & YTTP	Filip Cieslik
Head of International Factual, & YAP	Pauline Duffy
Executive Producer, Documentaries	Nick Finnis
Managing Director	Richard Gregory
Head of News & Current Affairs	Clare Morrow
Controller of Drama, YTV	Carolyn Reynolds
Controller of Comedy Drama & Drama Features	David Reynolds
Controller of Drama, Yorkshire-Tyne Tees Productions	Keith Richardson
Director of Finance, Yorkshire-Tyne Tees Productions	Ian Roe
Executive Producer, Factual Programmes	Simon Schofield
Controller, Documentaries & Factual Programmes	Helen Scott
Joint Controller of Broadcast Operations	Helen Stevens
Controller of Production	John Surtees
Deputy Controller of Children's, Granada Media Group	Patrick Titley
Director of Programmes	John Whiston
Head of Regional Features	Mark Witty

SKY Satellite Television
BRITISH SKY BROADCASTING LIMITED (BSkyB)

6 Centaurs Business Park
Grant Way
Isleworth
Middlesex TW7 5QD
Fax: 020-7705 3030   Tel: 020-7705 3000

Chief Executive	Tony Ball
Chief Operating Officer	Richard Freudenstein
Managing Director, Sky Sports	Vic Wakeling
Director of Broadcasting & Production	Mark Sharman
Head of Sky News	Nick Pollard
Director of Public Affairs	Ray Gallagher
Director of Communications	Julian Eccles

30 BIRD PRODUCTIONS
Studio Voltaire
1A Nelson's Row, London SW4 7JR
e-mail: thirtybird.productions@virgin.net
Fax: 020-7622 6707   Tel: 020-7622 6745

ABA DABA PRODUCTIONS
30 Upper Park Road
London NW3 2UT   Tel/Fax: 020-7722 5395

ACORN ENTERTAINMENTS Ltd
PO Box 64, Cirencester, Glos GL7 5YD
e-mail: acornents@btconnect.com
Fax: 01285 642291   Tel: 01285 644622

ACTORS OF DIONYSUS
26 Charlton Street, York YO23 1JN
e-mail: info@actors-of-dionysus.co.uk
Fax: 01904 541749   Tel: 01904 642912

ACTORS TOURING COMPANY (ATC)
Alford House, Aveline Street, London SE11 5DQ
e-mail: atc@cwcom.net   Tel: 020-7735 8311

ACT PRODUCTIONS Ltd
20-22 Stukeley Street, London WC2B 5LR
e-mail: info@act.tt
Fax: 020-7242 3548   Tel: 020-7438 9500

AD PRODUCTIONS
(See HILTON Adrian Ltd)

AKA PRODUCTIONS
Gloucester Mansions
140A Shaftesbury Avenue, London WC2H 8HD
e-mail: aka@akauk.com
Fax: 020-7836 8787   Tel: 020-7836 4747

ALBERY Ian
c/o Sadler's Wells Theatre
Rosebery Avenue, London EC1R 4TN
e-mail: ceo@sadlerwells.com
Fax: 020-7863 8031   Tel: 020-7863 8034

AMBASSADOR THEATRE GROUP
Duke of York's Theatre
104 St Martin's Lane, London WC2N 4BG
e-mail: atglondon@theambassadors.com
Fax: 020-7854 7001   Tel: 020-7854 7000

ANDROMEDA PRODUCTIONS
4 The Old School, 146 York Way
London N1 0AE   Tel/Fax: 020-7278 3799

ANGELIC CHARGE PRODUCTIONS
41 Highlands Close, Crouch Hill, Islington
London N4 4SE
e-mail: angelicharge@hotmail.com
          Tel: 020-7263 3294

ARENA PRODUCTIONS
111 Blackfriars Foundry
156 Blackfriars Road, London SE1 8EN
Fax: 020-7721 8541   Tel: 020-7721 8540

ARMSTRONG ARTS Ltd
9 Greville Hall, Greville Place
London NW6 5JS
e-mail: info@armstrongarts.com
Fax: 020-7625 2213   Tel: 020-7372 7110

ARTS MANAGEMENT
Redroofs, Littlewick Green
Maidenhead, Berks
Fax: 01628 822461   Tel: 01628 822982

ASH PRODUCTIONS
8 Valley Road, Streatham, London SW16 2XN
e-mail: ashproductions@hotmail.com
          Tel/Fax: 020-8677 6171

A. T. P. Ltd
PO Box 24182, London SW18 2WY
e-mail: prompt@atpmedia.com
          Tel/Fax: 020-7738 9886

ATTIC THEATRE COMPANY (LONDON) Ltd
Wimbledon Theatre, The Broadway
London SW19 1QG
e-mail: info@attictheatre.com
          Tel/Fax: 020-8543 7838

BACK ROW PRODUCTIONS
The Garrick Theatre, 2 Charing Cross Road
London WC2H 0HH   Tel: 020-7240 4282

BACKGROUND PRODUCTION Ltd
Second Floor, Lafone House
11-13 Leathermarket Street, London SE1 3HN
e-mail: insight@background.co.uk
Fax: 020-7357 9520   Tel: 020-7357 9515

BARKING PRODUCTIONS/INSTANT WIT
(Comedy Improvisation/Corporate
Entertainment & Training)
PO Box 597, Bristol BS99 2BB
e-mail: info@barkingproductions.co.uk
Fax: 0117-908 5384   Tel: 0117-939 3171

BEE & BUSTLE ENTERPRISES
32 Exeter Road, London NW2 4SB
e-mail: info@beeandbustle.co.uk
Fax: 020-8450 1057   Tel: 020-8450 0371

BHJ Ltd
(Brian Hewitt-Jones)
The Studio, No. 1 Barrington Road
London N8 8QR
Fax: 020-8374 5163   Tel: 020-8374 6970

BIG DOG PRODUCTIONS Ltd
16 Kirkwick Avenue, Harpenden, Herts AL5 2QN
e-mail: bigdog@kirkwick.demon.co.uk
Fax: 01582 467349   Tel: 01582 467344

BLACK THEATRE CO-OPERATIVE
(See NITRO)

BLUE ORANGE THEATRE COMPANY The
43 Mendip Court, Riverside Plaza
Chatfield Road, London SW11 3UZ
e-mail: blueorangetc@aol.com
          Tel/Fax: 020-7223 1100

BORDERLINE THEATRE COMPANY
North Harbour Street, Ayr KA8 8AA
e-mail: enquiries@borderlinetheatre.co.uk
          Tel: 01292 281010

BREAKWITH PRODUCTIONS Ltd
1 Kensington Church Walk, London W8 4NB
          Tel/Fax: 020-7938 2803

BRIDGE LANE THEATRE COMPANY Ltd
Bridge Lane, Battersea, London SW11 3AD
e-mail: bridgelanetheatre@aol.com
Mobile: 07977 225198   Tel: 020-7228 5185

BRIGHT Ltd
(Guy Chapman, Paul Spyker)
1-2 Henrietta Street, Covent Garden
London WC2E 8PS
e-mail: guy@g-c-a.co.uk
Fax: 020-7379 5888   Tel: 020-7379 3666

BRIGHTON REVUE COMPANY The
139 Freshfield Road, Brighton BN2 2YE
e-mail: enquiries@brightonrevue.fsnet.co.uk
          Fax: 01273 672646

BRIGHTON THEATRE EVENTS
40 Upper Gardner Street, Brighton BN1 4AN
e-mail: brightontheatreevents@supanet.com
          Tel/Fax: 01273 819184

BRISTOL EXPRESS THEATRE COMPANY Ltd
24 Well's House Road, East Acton
London NW10 6EE
e-mail: andyjandyjordan@aol.com
Fax: 020-8838 4482   Tel: 020-8963 9171

BRITISH STAGE PRODUCTIONS
Victoria Buildings, 1B Sherwood Street
Scarborough, North Yorks YO11 1SR
Fax: 01723 501328　　　　Tel: 01723 507186

BROOKS Sacha Ltd
3rd Floor, 55 Greek Street, London W1D 3DT
e-mail: letterbox@sacha.com
Fax: 020-7437 0930　　　　Tel: 020-7437 2900

B & R PRODUCTIONS Ltd
1st Floor, 66A Great Titchfield Street
London W1W 7QH
Fax: 020-7436 6603　　　　Tel: 020-7580 5277

BUSH THEATRE
Shepherd's Bush Green, London W12 8QD
e-mail: info@bushtheatre.co.uk
　　　　　　　　　　　　Tel: 020-7602 3703

CAPRICORN STAGE (& SCREEN) DIRECTIONS
1A Wedderburn House, Wedderburn Road
Hampstead, London NW3 5QR
　　　　　　　　　Tel/Fax: 020-7794 5843

CASSANDRA THEATRE COMPANY
(Vanessa Mildenberg, Clare Bloomer)
79 Brondesbury Villas, London NW6 6AG
e-mail: cassandraprod@hotmail.com
Mobile: 07796 264828　　　Tel: 020-7372 0733

CAVALCADE THEATRE COMPANY Ltd
(Plays, Musicals & Tribute Shows,
Children's Shows)
57 Pelham Road, London SW19 1NW
Fax: 020-8540 2243　　　　Tel: 020-8540 3513

CELEBRATION
(Theatre Company for the Young)
48 Chiswick Staithe, London W4 3TP
　　　　　　　　　　　　Tel: 020-8994 8886

CENTRELINE PRODUCTIONS
Unit 7, 93 Paul Street, London EC2A 4NY
e-mail: c-line@dircon.co.uk
Fax: 020-7251 9255　　　　Tel: 020-7251 9251

CHANNEL THEATRE COMPANY
Central Studios, 130 Grosvenor Place
Margate, Kent CT9 1UY
e-mail: info@channel-theatre.co.uk
Fax: 01843 280088　　　　Tel: 01843 280077

CHAPMAN Duggie ASSOCIATES
(Pantomime, Concerts, Musicals)
The Old Coach House
202 Common Edge Road
Blackpool FY4 5DG
Mobile: 07976 925504　　　Tel/Fax: 01253 691823

CHAPMAN Guy
(See BRIGHT Ltd)

CHICHESTER FESTIVAL THEATRE
Oaklands Park, Chichester
West Sussex PO19 4AP
e-mail: admin@cft.org.uk
Fax: 01243 787288　　　　Tel: 01243 784437

CHURCHILL THEATRE BROMLEY Ltd
Churchill Theatre, High Street, Bromley
Kent BR1 1HA
Fax: 020-8290 6968　　　　Tel: 020-8464 7131

CITY CONCERT ORGANISATION Ltd The
Head Office, King Edward House
82 Stourbridge Rd, Halesowen
Birmingham B63 3UP
e-mail: admin@cityconcert.co.uk
　　　　　　　　　Tel/Fax: 0121-501 1065

CODRON Michael PLAYS Ltd
Aldwych Theatre Offices, London WC2B 4DF
Fax: 020-7240 8467　　　　Tel: 020-7240 8291

COGO-FAWCETT Robert
28 Shire House, Lambs Passage
London EC1Y 8TE
e-mail: cogo@cogo.freeserve.co.uk
　　　　　　　　　　　　Tel: 020-7628 1324

COLE KITCHENN Ltd
Nederlander House, 7 Great Russell Street
London WC1B 3NH
Fax: 020-7580 2992　　　　Tel: 020-7580 2772

COMPASS THEATRE COMPANY
Carver Street Institute
24 Rockingham Lane, Sheffield S1 4FW
e-mail: info@compasstheatrecompany.com
Fax: 0114-278 6931　　　　Tel: 0114-275 5328

CONCORDANCE
(Neil McPherson)
7 Defoe House, Barbican, London EC2Y 8DN
e-mail: concordance@gohip.com
　　　　　　　　　Tel/Fax: 020-7638 9073

CONTEMPORARY STAGE COMPANY
3 Etchingham Park Road, Finchley
London N3 2DU
Fax: 020-8349 2458　　　　Tel: 020-8349 4402

CONWAY Clive ASSOCIATES
(See ENGLISH CHAMBER THEATRE)

CONWAY Clive & THE ENGLISH CHAMBER THEATRE
32 Grove Street, Oxford OX2 7JT
e-mail: cliveconway.ect@ntlworld.com
Fax: 01865 514409　　　　Tel: 01865 514830

COONEY Ray PLAYS
Everglades, 29 Salmons Road
Chessington, Surrey KT9 2JE
e-mail: alan@raycooneyplays.co.uk
Fax: 020-8397 0070　　　　Tel: 020-8397 0021

CRISP THEATRE
8 Cornwallis Crescent, Clifton, Bristol BS8 4PL
e-mail: crisptheatre@hotmail.com
　　　　　　　　　Tel/Fax: 0117-973 7106

C T G COTSWOLD THEATRE GROUP
Sandford Cottage, Shipton Road
Milton-under-Wychwood, Oxon OX7 6JT
　　　　　　　　　　　　Fax: 01993 776071

DAVID GRAHAM PRODUCTIONS Ltd
3-5 Latimer Road, Teddington
Middlesex TW11 8QA
e-mail: info@davidgraham.co.uk
Fax: 020-8977 6909　　　　Tel: 020-8977 8707

DAVIES-WILLIAMS Alma
1756 Broadway, #29K, New York, NY 10019
Fax: (212) 977-7116　　　Tel: (212) 245-5396

DEAD EARNEST THEATRE
c/o The Burton Street Project
57 Burton Street, Sheffield S6 2HH
e-mail: dead-earnest@pop3.poptel.org.uk
　　　　　　　　　　　　Tel: 0114-231 0687

DEAN Lee
PO Box 10703, London WC2H 9ED
Fax: 020-7836 6968　　　　Tel: 020-7497 5111

DELFONT MACKINTOSH THEATRES Ltd
(Theatre Owners)
Prince of Wales Theatre
Coventry Street, London W1D 6AS
e-mail: info@delfont-mackintosh.com
Fax: 020-7930 8970　　　　Tel: 020-7930 9901

DISNEY Walt THEATRICAL (UK) Ltd
The Lyceum Theatre, 21 Wellington Street
London WC2E 7DA
Fax: 020-7845 0999　　　　Tel: 020-7845 0900

DIZZY HEIGHTS / UK ARTS EXPLORE
Media Centre, 7 Northumberland Street
Huddersfield HD1 1RL
e-mail: info@ukarts-explore.com
Tel: 01484 350031

DONNA MARIA COMPANY
16 Bell Meadow, Dulwich, London SE19 1HP
e-mail: info@donna-marias-world.co.uk
Tel: 020-8670 7814

DOODAH THEATRE
27 St Peter's Way, Ealing, London W5 2QR
e-mail: doodahtc@aol.com
Fax: 020-8991 5903   Tel: 020-8997 9757

DORE Katharine MANAGEMENT (KDM Ltd)
Suite 3, 140A Gloucester Mansions
Cambridge Circus, London WC2H 8HD
Fax: 020-7836 8717   Tel: 020-7836 8716

DRAMATIS PERSONAE Ltd
(Nathan Silver, Nicolas Kent)
19 Regency Street, London SW1P 4BY
e-mail: nathan.silver@ntlworld.com
Tel: 020-7834 9300

DUAL CONTROL OPERA & BALLET INTERNATIONAL
Historic Dockyard, Chatham, Kent ME4 4TE
e-mail: opera.international@virgin.net
Fax: 01634 819149   Tel: 01634 819141

EACH WORLD PRODUCTIONS
43 Moormead Road, St Margaret's
Twickenham TW1 1JS
Fax: 020-8744 0676   Tel: 020-8892 0908

EASTERN ANGLES THEATRE COMPANY
(Touring)
Sir John Mills Theatre
Gatacre Road, Ipswich Suffolk IP1 2LQ
Fax: 01473 250954   Tel: 01473 218202

ELLIOTT Paul Ltd
(Triumph Entertainment Ltd), Suite 3
Waldorf Chambers, 11 Aldwych
London WC2B 4DG
e-mail: pelliott@paulelliott.ltd.uk
Fax: 020-7379 4860   Tel: 020-7379 4870

EMPTY SPACE THEATRE COMPANY
7-15 Greatorex Street, London E1 5NF
e-mail: estc@dircon.co.uk
Fax: 0870 9090103   Tel: 0870 9090102

ENGLISH NATIONAL OPERA
London Coliseum, St Martin's Lane
London WC2N 4ES
Fax: 020-7845 9277   Tel: 020-7836 0111

ENGLISH STAGE COMPANY Ltd
Royal Court, Sloane Square, London SW1W 8AS
e-mail: info@royalcourttheatre.com
Fax: 020-7565 5001   Tel: 020-7565 5050

ENGLISH THEATRE COMPANY Ltd
(TMA Member)
Nybrogatan 35, 114 39 Stockholm, Sweden
e-mail: etc.ltd@telia.com
Fax: 00 46 8660 1159   Tel: 00 46 8662 4133

ENGLISH TOURING THEATRE
25 Short Street, London SE1 8LJ
e-mail: admin@englishtouringtheatre.co.uk
Fax: 020-7450 1998   Tel: 020-7450 1990

ENTERTAINMENT BUSINESS Ltd The
199 Piccadilly, London W1J 9HA
Fax: 020-7287 5144   Tel: 020-7734 8555

EUROPEAN THEATRE COMPANY The
39 Oxford Avenue, London SW20 8LS
Fax: 020-8544 1999   Tel: 020-8544 1994

FACADE
(Musicals)
43A Garthorne Road
London SE23 1EP   Tel: 020-8699 8655

FACE TO FACE THEATRE PRODUCTIONS Ltd
(Write)
10 St Fillans Road, Stepps, Glasgow G33 6LW
e-mail: robinfacetoface@hotmail.com

FARRAH Paul PRODUCTIONS
Strand Theatre Offices, London WC2B 4LD
e-mail: pfpltd@aol.com
Fax: 020-7240 4451   Tel: 020-7240 4431

FELL Andrew Ltd
7 Upper St Martin's Lane, London WC2H 9DL
e-mail: hq@andrewfell.co.uk
Fax: 0207-240 2499   Tel: 0207-240 2420

FIELDING Harold
69 Strand on the Green
London W4 3PF   Tel: 020-8673 4323

FIFTH AMENDMENT Ltd
2nd Floor, 6 Shaw Street
Worcester WR1 3QQ
e-mail: janryan@amendmnt.demon.co.uk
Fax: 01905 22868   Tel: 01905 26424

FLEIGHTON PRODUCTIONS Ltd
Top of the Bill House, Queen's Row
London SE17 2PX
Fax: 020-7277 1722   Tel: 020-7277 1704

FLUXX
(Improvised Theatre)
7-15 Greatorex Street, London E1 5NF
e-mail: admin@fluxx.co.uk
Fax: 0870 0566376   Tel: 020-7247 9072

FORD Vanessa PRODUCTIONS Ltd
Upper House Farm, Upper House Lane
Shamley Green, Surrey GU5 0SX
e-mail: gvfr@dialstart.net
Tel/Fax: 01483 278203   Tel: 01483 268530

FOX Robert Ltd
6 Beauchamp Place, London SW3 1NG
e-mail: rf@robertfoxltd.com
Fax: 020-7225 1638   Tel: 020-7584 6855

FREEDMAN Bill Ltd
Room 311, Bedford Chambers, The Piazza
Covent Garden, London WC2E 8HA
Fax: 020-7836 9903   Tel: 020-7836 9900

FUTURA MUSIC (PRODUCTIONS) Ltd
(Write only)
29 Emanuel House, Rochester Row
London SW1P 1BS

GALE PRODUCTIONS Ltd
24 Wimbledon Park Road, London SW18 1LT
e-mail: gale.prod@which.net
Fax: 020-8875 1582   Tel: 020-8870 1149

GALLEON THEATRE COMPANY Ltd
Greenwich Playhouse, Greenwich BR Station
Forecourt, 189 Greenwich High Road
London SE10 8JA
Fax: 020-8969 2910   Tel: 020-8858 9256

GLASS David ENSEMBLE
Unit 422, The Leathermarket
Weston Street London SE1 3ER
e-mail: dg.ensemble@virgin.net
Fax: 020-7357 9199   Tel: 020-7357 9200

GOOD COMPANY
46 Quebec Street, Brighton, Sussex BN2 2UZ
e-mail: gco@goodcompany.idps.co.uk
Fax: 01273 606926   Tel: 01273 606652

GOSS Gerald Ltd
Dudley House, 169 Piccadilly, London W1J 9EH
Fax: 020-7499 7227   Tel: 020-7499 7447

GRAEAE THEATRE COMPANY
Interchange Studios, Hampstead Town Hall
Centre, 213 Haverstock Hill, London NW3 4QP
e-mail: info@graeae.org
Fax: 020-7681 4756   Tel: 020-7681 4755

GREEN & LENAGAN Ltd
285-287 Gray's Inn Road, London WC1X 8QF
Fax: 020-7713 6384   Tel: 020-7713 6696

HALE Ivan Ltd
5 Denmark Street, London WC2H 8LP
e-mail: ivanhaleltd@hotmail.com
Fax: 01923 492772   Tel: 01923 492992

HAMPSTEAD THEATRE PRODUCTIONS Ltd
98 Avenue Road, Swiss Cottage
London NW3 3EX
e-mail: admin@hampstead-theatre.com
Fax: 020-7722 3860   Tel: 020-7722 9224

HANDSTAND PRODUCTIONS
13 Hope Street, Liverpool L1 9BH
e-mail: info@handstand-uk.com
Fax: 0151-709 3515   Tel: 0151-708 7441

HARLEY CINE LIBRE PRODUCTIONS
68 New Cavendish Street, London W1G 8TE
e-mail: harleyprods@aol.com
Fax: 020-8202 8863   Tel: 020-7580 3247

HAYMARKET THEATRE Co Ltd
Wote Street, Basingstoke, Hants RG21 7NW
e-mail: info@haymarket.org.uk
Fax: 01256 357130   Tel: 01256 323073

HAZEMEAD Ltd
(Entertainment Consultants)
3rd Floor, 18 Hanover Street, London W1R 9HG
Fax: 020-7629 5668   Tel: 020-7629 4817

HENDERSON Glynis PRODUCTIONS
69 Charlotte Street, London W1T 4PJ
e-mail: info@ghmp.co.uk
Fax: 020-7436 1489   Tel: 020-7580 9644

HESTER John (INTIMATE MYSTERIES THEATRE COMPANY)
105 Stoneleigh Park Road, Epsom
Surrey KT19 0RF
e-mail: hester92@hotmail.com
                        Tel/Fax: 020-8393 5705

HILTON Adrian Ltd
(Write Only)
Priory House, Amersham Road
Beaconsfield, Bucks HP9 2HA

HISS & BOO COMPANY Ltd The
(Ian Liston)
Nyes Hill, Wineham Lane, Bolney
West Sussex RH17 5SD
e-mail: hissboo@msn.com
Fax: 01444 882057   Tel: 01444 881707

HOLMAN Paul ASSOCIATES Ltd
20 Deane Avenue, South Ruislip
Middlesex HA4 6SR
e-mail: paulholmanassociates@blueyonder.co.uk
Fax: 020-8582 2557   Tel: 020-8845 9408

HOLT Thelma Ltd
Waldorf Chambers, 11 Aldwych
London WC2B 4DG
e-mail: thelma@dircon.co.uk
Fax: 020-7836 9832   Tel: 020-7379 0438

HOUSE OF GULLIVER
(Write)
77 Longfield Road, Tring, Herts HP23 4DF

HULL TRUCK THEATRE
Spring Street, Hull HU2 8RW
e-mail: admin@hulltruck.co.uk
Fax: 01482 581182   Tel: 01482 224800

HUTT RUSSELL PRODUCTIONS Ltd
PO Box 64, Cirencester, Glos GL7 5YD
e-mail: shows@huttrussellorg.com
Fax: 01285 642291   Tel: 01285 644622

IMAGE THEATRE COMPANY
23 Sedgeford Road, Shepherd's Bush
London W12 0NA
e-mail: brianthresh@image-theatre-co.demon.uk
Fax: 020-8749 9294   Tel: 020-8743 9380

IMAGINATION ENTERTAINMENTS
25 Store Street, South Crescent
London WC1E 7BL
e-mail: entertainments@imagination.com
Fax: 020-7323 5801   Tel: 020-7323 3300

IMPACT
Sovereign Business Centre, Lockwood
Huddersfield HD4 6BL
Fax: 01484 518100   Tel: 01484 516132

INCISOR
30 Brondesbury Park, London NW6 7DN
e-mail: enquiries@startek-uk.com
Fax: 020-8830 4992   Tel: 020-8830 0074

INDIGO PRODUCTIONS INTERNATIONAL
(Write Only)
Tynymynydd, Bryneglwys, Corwen
Denbighshire LL21 2NP
e-mail: indigo.productions@virgin.net

INSIDE INTELLIGENCE
13 Athlone Close, London E5 8HD
e-mail: admin@inside-intelligence.org.uk
                        Tel/Fax: 020-8986 8013

INTERNATIONAL THEATRE & MUSIC Ltd
(Piers Chater Robinson)
Shakespeare House, Theatre Street
London SW11 5ND
e-mail: inttheatre@aol.com
Fax: 020-7801 6317   Tel: 020-7801 6316

ISLEWORTH ACTORS COMPANY
38 Eve Road, Isleworth, Middlesex TW7 7HS
Tel/Fax: 020-8891 1073   Tel: 020-8892 4207

JACKSON Richard
48 William Mews, London SW1X 9HQ
                        Tel: 020-7235 3759

JAMES Bruce PRODUCTIONS Ltd
89A West Road, Westcliff-on-Sea, Essex SS0 9AY
e-mail: bjamesprods@onet.co.uk
                        Tel/Fax: 01702 335970

JENKINS Andrew THEATRE PRODUCTION
63 Kidbrooke Park Road, Blackheath
London SE3 0EE
e-mail: andrew-j@lineone.net
Fax: 08701 349590   Tel: 020-8856 7106

JORDAN Richard PRODUCTIONS Ltd
Mews Studios, 16 Vernon Yard, London W11 2DX
e-mail: richard.jordan@virgin.net
Fax: 020-7313 9667   Tel: 020-7243 9001

KENWRIGHT Bill Ltd
BKL House, 106 Harrow Road, Off Howley Place
London W2 1RR
e-mail: info@kenwright.com
Fax: 020-7446 6222   Tel: 020-7446 6200

KING'S HEAD THEATRE PRODUCTION Ltd
115 Upper Street, London N1 1QN
Fax: 020-7226 8507   Tel: 020-7226 8561

KIRK David
12 Panmuir Road
Wimbledon SW20 0PZ   Tel: 020-8947 0130

**KNIGHTSBRIDGE THEATRICAL
PRODUCTIONS Ltd**
21 New Fetter Lane, London EC4A 1JJ
Fax: 020-7583 1040   Tel: 020-7583 8687

**KRAFT Susannah THEATRE ADMINISTRATION
(SKTA)**
(Tours and Administration for Small/
Middle Scale Theatre Co's)
28 Bournevale Road, London SW16 2BA
e-mail: s-nskraft@online.rednet.co.uk
Fax: 020-7564 8138   Tel: 020-8677 7952

LADDER TO THE MOON ENTERTAINMENT
66A St Ann's Hill, London SW18 2SB
e-mail: enquiries@laddertothemoon.co.uk
                    Mobile: 07711 984 378

LEWIS Richard PRODUCTIONS Ltd
Limelight, Trident International
40 Victoria Way, London SE7 7QS
Fax: 020-8305 2684   Tel: 020-8858 6141

LINNIT PRODUCTIONS Ltd
123A Kings Road, London SW3 4PL
Fax: 020-7352 3450   Tel: 020-7352 7722

LIVE THEATRE COMPANY
7-8 Trinity Chare, Quayside
Newcastle-upon-Tyne NE1 3DF
                    Tel: 0191-261 2694

LLOYD-JAMES Adrian
310 Cowley Mansions
Mortlake High Street, London SW14 8SL
e-mail: tabsproductions@bushinternet.com
Fax: 020-8255 1632   Tel: 020-8255 1332

LONDON BUBBLE THEATRE COMPANY Ltd
5 Elephant Lane, London SE16 4JD
e-mail: admin@londonbubble.org.uk
Fax: 020-7231 2366   Tel: 020-7237 4434

**LONDON COMPANY INTERNATIONAL PLAYS
Ltd The**
(No CV's please)
PO Box 4458, London SW1X 8XP
e-mail: glynne@dial.pipex.com
Fax: 020-7486 2164   Tel: 020-7486 3166

LONDON GREEK THEATRE GROUP The
(Write)
86C Sinclair Road, London W14 0NJ

LONDON PRODUCTIONS Ltd
PO Box 10703, London WC2H 9ED
Fax: 020-7836 6968   Tel: 020-7497 5111

LONDON STAGE COMPANY The
Suite 612, 162 Regent Street, London W1R 5TB
Fax: 020-7437 3395   Tel: 020-7437 3391

LYRIC HAMMERSMITH PRODUCTIONS
28 Shire House, Lambs Passage, London EC1Y 8TE
e-mail: cogo@cogo.freeserve.co.uk
                    Tel: 020-7628 1324

MACKINTOSH Cameron Ltd
1 Bedford Square, London WC1B 3RA
Fax: 020-7436 2683   Tel: 020-7637 8866

MACNAGHTEN Marianne
Dundarave, Bushmills, Co. Antrim
N Ireland BT57 8ST
Fax: 028-2073 2575   Tel: 028-2073 1215

MALCOLM Christopher Ltd
1 Calton Road, Bath BA2 4PP
e-mail: cmalcolm@btconnect.com
Fax: 01225 427778   Tel: 01225 445459

MANS Johnny PRODUCTIONS Ltd
The Maltings, Brewery Road, Hoddesdon
Herts EN11 8HF
Fax: 01992 470516   Tel: 01992 470907

MASTERSON Guy PRODUCTIONS
(Write)
The Bull Theatre, 68 High Street, Barnet
Herts EN5 5SJ
e-mail: admin@guymasterson.com
Fax: 020-8449 5252   Tel: 020-8449 7800

MATTHEWS Barbara
12 Mercer Street, London WC2H 9DQ
e-mail: bmmassociates@msn.com
Fax: 01825 766415   Tel: 020-7836 9674

MEADOW Jeremy
(See TEG PRODUCTIONS Ltd)

MENZIES Lee Ltd
118-120 Wardour Street
London W1V 3LA
e-mail: leemenzies@leemenzies.co.uk
Fax: 020-7734 4224   Tel: 020-7734 9559

METRO ENTERTAINMENT Ltd
Strand Theatre Offices
London WC2B 4LD
e-mail: info@metroent.co.uk
Fax: 020-7240 4451   Tel: 020-7240 4431

METRO PRODUCTIONS
11 Keyford Place, Frome
Somerset BA11 1JE   Tel: 01373 462812

MICHAEL ROSE Ltd
The Old Dairy, Throop Road, Holdenhurst
Bournemouth, Dorset BH8 0DL
e-mail: mrl@mrltheatre.u-net.com
Fax: 01202 522311   Tel: 01202 522711

MIDDLE GROUND THEATRE COMPANY
3 Gordon Terrace, Malvern Wells, Malvern
Worcs WR14 4ER
e-mail: middleground@tinyworld.co.uk
Fax: 01684 574472   Tel: 01684 577231

MILLENNIUM ARTISTES MANAGEMENT Ltd
(Personal Management & Event Co-ordinators)
PO Box 2001, Caterham
Surrey CR3 6UA
e-mail: mamlimited@aol.com
                    Tel/Fax: 01883 347790

MILLFIELD THEATRE
Silver Street, Edmonton, London N18 1PJ
e-mail: info@millfieldtheatre.co.uk
                    Tel: 020-8807 6186

MITCHELL Matthew Ltd
Flat 5, 65 Cumberland Street, London SW1V 4LY
e-mail: mmitch@dircon.co.uk
Fax: 020-7834 8738   Tel: 020-7630 8881

MOVING THEATRE
16 Laughton Lodge, Laughton, Nr Lewes
East Sussex BN8 6BY
e-mail: info@movingtheatre.com
Fax: 01323 815736   Tel: 01323 815726

MU-LAN THEATRE COMPANY
The Albany, Douglas Way
London SE8 4AG
e-mail: mailbox@mu-lan.org.uk
Fax: 020-8694 0618   Tel: 020-8694 0557

MUSIC THEATRE LONDON
Chertsey Chambers, 12 Mercer Street
London WC2H 9QD
e-mail: musictheatre.london@virgin.net
Fax: 020-7240 0805   Tel: 020-7240 0919

NEW OLYMPUS PRODUCTIONS Ltd
17 Wood Lodge Lane
West Wickham, Kent BR4 9LY
e-mail: newolympus@yahoo.com
                        Tel/Fax: 020-8776 2386

NEW SHAKESPEARE COMPANY Ltd The
Open Air Theatre, The Iron Works, Inner Circle
Regent's Park, London NW1 4NR
Fax: 020-7487 4562   Tel: 020-7935 5756

NEW VIC THEATRE OF LONDON INC.
Suite 42, 91 St Martin's Lane
London WC2H 0DL   Tel/Fax: 020-7240 2929

NEW VIC WORKSHOP Ltd
23 Hampton Place, Brighton BN1 3DA
e-mail: newvicworkshop@lineone.net
                        Tel/Fax: 01273 328112

NEWPALM PRODUCTIONS
26 Cavendish Avenue, London N3 3QN
Fax: 020-8346 8257   Tel: 020-8349 0802

NITRO
(Formerly Black Theatre Co-operative)
6 Brewery Road, London N7 9NH
e-mail: btc@dircon.co.uk
Fax: 020-7609 1221   Tel: 020-7609 1331

NORTHERN STAGE (THEATRICAL PRODUCTIONS) Ltd
Newcastle Playhouse, Barras Bridge
Newcastle-upon-Tyne NE1 7RH
e-mail: info@northernstage.com
Fax: 0191-261 8093   Tel: 0191-232 3366

NORWELL LAPLEY ASSOCIATES
Lapley Hall, Lapley, Staffs ST19 9JR
e-mail: norwelllapley@freeuk.com
Fax: 01785 841992   Tel: 01785 841991

NOT THE NATIONAL THEATRE
(Write) (Small/Mid-Scale Touring - UK & Abroad)
101 Broadhurst Gardens, London NW6 3BJ

NTC TOURING THEATRE COMPANY
The Playhouse, Bondgate Without, Alnwick
Northumberland NE66 1PQ
e-mail: admin@ntc-touringtheatre.co.uk
Fax: 01665 605837   Tel: 01665 602586

O'BRIEN Barry (1968) Ltd
26 Cavendish Avenue, London N3 3QN
Fax: 020-8346 8257   Tel: 020-8346 8011

OPEN AIR THEATRE
(See NEW SHAKESPEARE COMPANY)

OPERA AND BALLET INTERNATIONAL Ltd
(International Opera & Ballet Producers)
The Historic Dockyard
Chatham
Kent ME4 4TE
e-mail: opera.international@virgin.net
Fax: 01634 819149   Tel: 01634 819141

ORIGINAL SHAKESPEARE COMPANY Ltd
52 Barrowgate Road, London W4 4QY
e-mail: original@easynet.co.uk
Fax: 020-8747 8754   Tel: 020-8747 0443

O'SHEA Patrick Ltd
57 Lancaster Grove, London NW3 4HD
Fax: 020-7419 1059   Tel: 020-7916 5797

OUT OF JOINT
20-24 Eden Grove, London N7 8EA
e-mail: ojo@outofjoint.co.uk
Fax: 020-7609 0203   Tel: 020-7609 0207

OUT OF THE BLUE PRODUCTIONS Ltd
48 Conduit Street, London W1S 2YR
e-mail: info@otbp.com
Fax: 020-7734 3678   Tel: 020-7734 1345

OXFORD STAGE COMPANY
131 High Street, Oxford OX1 4DH
e-mail: info@oxfordstage.co.uk
Fax: 01865 790625   Tel: 01865 723238

PAINES PLOUGH
Fourth Floor, 43 Aldwych
London WC2B 4DN
e-mail: office@painesplough.com
Fax: 020-7240 4534   Tel: 020-7240 4533

PARASOL PRODUCTIONS
Garden House, 4 Sunnyside
Wimbledon SW19 4SL
Fax: 020-8946 0228   Tel: 020-8946 9478

PENDLE PRODUCTIONS
39 Ermine Close, Blackburn BB2 3UW
e-mail: theatre@pendle.u-net.com
                        Tel/Fax: 01254 59590

PEOPLE SHOW
People Show Studios, Pollard Row
London E2 6NB
e-mail: people@peopleshow.co.uk
Fax: 020-7739 0203   Tel: 020-7729 1841

PERICLES
(Paddy Wilson), Cambridge Theatre
Seven Dials, London WC2H 9HU
Fax: 020-7240 1939   Tel: 020-7240 3030

PLANTAGENET PRODUCTIONS
Westridge (Open Centre),
(Drawing Room Recitals)
Star Lane, Andover Road, Highclere
Nr Newbury RG20 9PJ   Tel: 01635 253322

PLAYERS' THEATRE The
(Victorian Music Hall)
The Arches, Villiers Street
London WC2N 6NL
e-mail: info@playerstheatre.co.uk
Fax: 020-7839 8067   Tel: 020-7839 1134

PLUNGE PRODUCTIONS Ltd
9 Whittington Road, London N22 8YS
e-mail: info@plungeproductions.com
                        Tel/Fax: 020-8888 6608

POLKA THEATRE FOR CHILDREN
240 The Broadway, Wimbledon SW19 1SB
e-mail: admin@polkatheatre.com
Fax: 020-8545 8365   Tel: 020-8545 8320

POSTER Kim
The Penthouse, Charles House
7 Leicester Place
London WC2H 7RJ   Tel: 020-7734 3128

PROMENADE PRODUCTIONS Ltd
6 Russell Grove, London SW9 6HS
e-mail: promenadeproductions@msn.com
Fax: 020-7564 3026   Tel: 020-7582 9354

P&S PRODUCTIONS
Unit 48, St Gabriel's Manor
25 Cormont Road, London SE5 9RH
e-mail: timsawers@msn.com
Tel/Fax: 020-8780 9115

PUGH David Ltd
Canaletto Yard, 41-45 Beak Street
London W1F 9SB
e-mail: dpl@davidpughltd.freeserve.co.uk
Fax: 020-7287 8856   Tel: 020-7434 9757

PURSUED BY A BEAR PRODUCTIONS
6 Glenluce Road, Blackheath
London SE3 7SB
e-mail: pbab@pbab.freeserve.co.uk
Tel/Fax: 020-8480 9514

PW PRODUCTIONS Ltd
The Penthouse, 7 Leicester Place
London WC2H 7RJ
e-mail: info@pwprods.co.uk
Fax: 020-7734 7185   Tel: 020-7734 7184

QDOS ENTERTAINMENT (THEATRE) Ltd
8 King Street, London WC2E 8HN
Fax: 020-7379 4892   Tel: 020-7836 2795

Qdos House, Queen Margaret's Road
Scarborough, North Yorks YO11 2SA
Fax: 01723 361958   Tel: 01723 500038

QUANTUM THEATRE
Unit S9, The Shakespeare Centre
245A Coldharbour Lane
London SW9 8RR
e-mail: quantumtheatre@btinternet.com
Tel: 020-7733 8150

RAGGED RAINBOW PRODUCTIONS Ltd
45 Nightingale Lane, Crouch End
London N8 7RA
e-mail: rainbowrp@ukgateway.net
Tel/Fax: 020-8341 6241

RAIN OR SHINE T.C.
25 Paddock Gardens, Longlevens
Gloucester GL2 0ED
Tel: 0870 1281900   Tel: 01452 521575

RE:ACTORS
15 Montrose Walk, Weybridge
Surrey KT13 8JN
e-mail: michael@reactors.co.uk
Fax: 01932 830248   Tel: 01932 888885

REALLY USEFUL GROUP Ltd The
22 Tower Street, London WC2H 9TW
Fax: 020-7240 1204   Tel: 020-7240 0880

REALLY USEFUL THEATRES
(Theatre Operators)
Manor House, 21 Soho Square, London W1D 3QP
e-mail: info@rutheatres.com
Fax: 020-7434 1217   Tel: 020-7494 5200

RED LEAF
Ground Floor, 384 Hanworth Road, Hounslow,
Middlesex TW3 3SN   Tel/Fax: 020-8577 5138

RED ROSE CHAIN
1A Cauldwell Avenue, Ipswich IP4 4EB
e-mail: info@redrosechain.co.uk
Tel: 01473 723804

RED SHIFT THEATRE COMPANY
TRG2 Trowbray House
108 Weston Street, London SE1 3QB
e-mail: mail@redshifttheatreco.co.uk
Fax: 020-7378 9789   Tel: 020-7378 9787

REDINGTON Michael Ltd
10 Maunsel Street, London SW1P 2QL
Fax: 020-7828 6947   Tel: 020-7834 5119

274

RELEASE THEATRE COMPANY
(Small Scale, Fringe Venues, TIE Touring)
PO Box 34512, London SE15 2FZ
e-mail: releasetheatreco@yahoo.co.uk
Mobile: 07720 600126

REVEAL THEATRE COMPANY
40 Pirehill Lane, Walton, Stone
Staffordshire ST15 0JN   Tel: 01785 814052

RICHMOND PRODUCTIONS
47 Moor Mead Road, St Margaret's
Twickenham TW1 1JS   Tel/Fax: 020-8891 2280

ROCKET THEATRE COMPANY
245 Broadfield Road
Manchester M14 7JT
e-mail: martin@rockettheatre.co.uk
Mobile: 07788 723570   Tel: 0161-226 8788

ROSENTHAL Suzanna Ltd
61 Talbot Road, London N6 4QX
e-mail: admin@suzannarosenthal.com
Tel/Fax: 020-8340 4421

ROYAL COURT THEATRE PRODUCTIONS Ltd
Sloane Square, London SW1W 8AS
e-mail: info@royalcourttheatre.com
Fax: 020-7565 5001   Tel: 020-7565 5050

ROYAL EXCHANGE THEATRE COMPANY
St Ann's Square
Manchester M2 7DH   Tel: 0161-833 9333

ROYAL NATIONAL THEATRE
South Bank, London SE1 9PX
e-mail: marketing@nationaltheatre.org.uk
Fax: 020-7452 3344   Tel: 020-7452 3333

ROYAL SHAKESPEARE COMPANY
Barbican Theatre, Silk Street, London EC2Y 8BQ
Fax: 020-7374 0818   Tel: 020-7628 3351

ROYAL SHAKESPEARE THEATRE
Stratford-upon-Avon CV37 6BB
Fax: 01789 294810   Tel: 01789 296655

SALBERG & STEPHENSON
2nd Floor, The White House
26 Mortimer Street
London W1N 7RA
Fax: 020-8342 9835   Tel: 020-7253 5232

SANDPIPER PRODUCTIONS Ltd
49A Ossington Street, London W2 4LY
e-mail: sandpipe@dircon.co.uk
Fax: 020-7229 6710   Tel: 020-7229 6708

S F X
35 Grosvenor Street
London W1R 4QX
Fax: 020-7529 4301   Tel: 020-7529 4300

SHAMMAS Sam PRODUCTIONS Ltd
c/o Regina House
124 Finchley Road, London NW3 5JS
e-mail: contacts.samshammas.com
Fax: 020-7823 1905   Tel: 020-7823 1904

SHARED EXPERIENCE THEATRE
(National/International Touring)
The Soho Laundry, 9 Dufour's Place
London W1F 7SJ
e-mail: admin@setheatre.co.uk
Fax: 020-7287 8763   Tel: 020-7434 9248

SHARLAND Elizabeth
Suite 12, 30 New Compton Street
London WC2H 8DN   Tel: 020-7836 4203

SHAW Vincent ASSOCIATES Ltd
20 Jay Mews, London SW7 2EP
e-mail: vincentshaw@clara.net
Fax: 020-7225 1079   Tel: 020-7581 8215

SHOW OF STRENGTH
74 Chessel Street, Bedminster
Bristol BS3 3DN
Fax: 0117-902 0196   Tel: 0117-902 0235

SINDEN Marc PRODUCTIONS
Albery Theatre, St Martin's Lane
London WC2N 4AU
e-mail: mail@sindenproductions.com
Fax: 020-7836 3669   Tel: 020-7836 3667

SNAPE EDWARD Ltd / FIERY ANGEL Ltd
22-24 Torrington Place, London WC1E 7HF
e-mail: esnape@groupline.com
Fax: 020-7580 6652   Tel: 020-7907 7040

SOHO THEATRE COMPANY
21 Dean Street, London W1V 6NE
e-mail: mail@sohotheatre.com
Fax: 020-7287 5061   Tel: 020-7287 5060

SOLE A.R.M. PRODUCTIONS
151A Field End Road, Eastcote
Middlesex HA5 1QL
e-mail: sole.file@virgin.net   Tel: 020-8868 7960

SPHINX THEATRE COMPANY The
25 Short Street, London SE1 8LJ
Fax: 020-7401 9995   Tel: 020-7401 9993

SPIEGEL Adam PRODUCTIONS
2nd Floor, 35-39 Old Street, London EC1V 9HX
e-mail: claudia@adamspeigel.demon.co.uk
Fax: 020-7336 6096   Tel: 020-7336 0306

SPYKER Paul
(See BRIGHT Ltd)

STACEY Barrie UK PRODUCTIONS Ltd
Flat 8, 132 Charing Cross Road
London WC2H 0LA
Fax: 020-7836 2949   Tel: 020-7836 4128

STAGE FURTHER PRODUCTIONS Ltd
22 High Street, Market Lavington, Devizes
Wilts SN10 4AG
e-mail: garthsfp@aol.com Tel/Fax: 01380 816555

STANHOPE PRODUCTIONS Ltd
The Penthouse, Charles House, 7 Leicester Place
London WC2H 7RJ   Tel: 020-7734 3128

STEAM INDUSTRY The
The Finborough Theatre, 118 Finborough Road
London SW10 9ED
steamindustry@finboroughtheatre.freeserve.co.uk
Fax: 020-7835 1853   Tel: 020-7244 7439

STEPHENS Charles
20 Fitzroy Square, London W1P 5HJ
Fax: 020-7387 1677   Tel: 020-7387 7200

STIGWOOD Robert ORGANISATION Ltd The
Write
Barton Manor, Whippenham, East Cowes
Isle of Wight PO32 6LB

STRAYDOGS
55 Monmouth Street, London WC2H 9DG
e-mail: info@straydogs.org.uk
Fax: 020-7395 6110   Tel: 020-7395 6113

SWALLOW PRODUCTIONS (UK) Ltd
32 Blenheim Gardens, Wembley Park
Middlesex HA9 7NP
e-mail: swproduk@aol.com Tel/Fax: 020-8904 7024

TABS PRODUCTIONS
310 Cowley Mansions, Mortlake High Street
London SW14 8SL
e-mail: tabsproductions@bushinternet.com
Fax: 020-8255 1632   Tel: 020-8255 1332

TALAWA THEATRE COMPANY
23-25 Great Sutton Street, London EC1V 0DN
e-mail: hq@talawa.com
Fax: 020-7251 5969   Tel: 020-7251 6644

TAMASHA THEATRE COMPANY Ltd
Unit E, 11 Ronalds Road, London N5 1XJ
e-mail: info@tamasha.org.uk
Fax: 020-7609 2722   Tel: 020-7609 2411

TAMBAR Ltd
PO Box LB689, London W1A 9LB
e-mail: tambarltd@hotmail.com
Fax: 020-7252 0822   Tel: 020-7232 0519

TBA MUSIC Ltd
111 Church Street, London NW8 8HA
e-mail: peter@tbamusic.freeserve.co.uk
Fax: 020-7724 7287   Tel: 020-7723 1307

TEG PRODUCTIONS Ltd
11-15 Betterton Street
London WC2H 9BP
e-mail: teg@plays.demon.co.uk
Fax: 020-7836 9454   Tel: 020-7379 1066

Winnington Hall, Winnington, Northwich
Cheshire CW8 4DU
Fax: 01606 872701   Tel: 01606 872700

TEMPLE Richard PRODUCTIONS
Revolver House
15 Kensington High Street, London W8 5NP
e-mail: richardtempleproductions@yahoo.com
Fax: 020-7376 0916   Tel: 020-7376 0915

TEN PENCE PRODUCTIONS
Ground Floor, 384 Hanworth Road
Hounslow, Middlesex TW3 3SN
e-mail: tenpenceproductions@yahoo.co.uk
                    Tel/Fax: 020-8577 5138

TENTH PLANET PRODUCTIONS
75 Woodland Gardens, London N10 3UD
e-mail: admin@tenthplanetproductions.com
Tel: 020-8442 2659   Fax: 020-8883 1708

THEATRE ABSOLUTE
57-61 Corporation Street
Coventry CV1 1GQ
e-mail: julia@theatreabsolute.demon.co.uk
                    Tel: 024-7625 7380

THEATRE DE COMPLICITE
14 Angler's Lane, London NW5 3DE
e-mail: email@complicite.co.uk
Fax: 020-7485 7701   Tel: 020-7485 7700

THEATRE MACHINE
13 Dunbar Road, London N22 5BG
e-mail: izzy@theatremachine.freeserve.co.uk
                    Tel/Fax: 020-8888 5335

THEATRE OF COMEDY COMPANY Ltd
Shaftesbury Theatre, 210 Shaftesbury Avenue
London WC2H 8DP
Fax: 020-7836 8181   Tel: 020-7379 3345

THEATRE ROYAL STRATFORD EAST
Gerry Raffles Square, Stratford
London E15 1BN
e-mail: theatreroyal@stratfordeast.com
                    Tel: 020-8534 7374

THEATRE SET-UP Ltd
(International Touring)
12 Fairlawn Close, Southgate
London N14 4JX   Tel/Fax: 020-8886 9572

THRESHOLD THEATRE COMPANY Ltd
Flat 5, 65 Cumberland Street
London SW1V 4LY
Fax: 020-7834 8738   Tel: 020-7630 8881

TRADING FACES
(Mask & Physical Theatre)
2 Bridge View, Bridge Street
Abingdon OX14 3HN
e-mail: office@tradingfaces.demon.co.uk
Fax: 01235 553403   Tel: 01235 550829

TRAVELLING LIGHT SHAKESPEARE Co
102 Plantation Road, Amersham
Bucks HP6 6HW
e-mail: tl@shake.free-online.co.uk
                    Tel/Fax: 01494 725186

TRENDS PRODUCTIONS Ltd
54 Lisson Street, London NW1 5DF
e-mail: linda@trendsgroup.co.uk
Fax: 020-7258 3591   Tel: 020-7723 8001

TRESTLE THEATRE COMPANY
(Touring Mask Theatre)
Birch Centre, Hill End Lane
St Albans AL4 0RA
e-mail: admin@trestle.org.uk
Fax: 01727 855558   Tel: 01727 850950

TRIUMPH ENTERTAINMENT Ltd
Suite 4, Waldorf Chambers
11 Aldwych, London WC2B 4DG
e-mail: dcwtpp@aol.com
Fax: 020-7343 8801   Tel: 020-7343 8800

TROY PRODUCTIONS
17 Talbot Meadows, Talbot Village, Poole
Dorset BH12 5DG
e-mail: lulu_2013@yahoo.co.uk
Mobile: 07710 431741   Tel: 01202 516696

TUDOR David PRODUCTIONS
17 St Marys Avenue, Purley-on-Thames
Berks RG8 8BJ   Tel/Fax: 0118-942 1144

TURTLE KEY ARTS
Ladbroke Hall, 79 Barlby Road
London W10 6AZ
e-mail: turtlek@globalnet.co.uk
Fax: 020-8964 4080   Tel: 020-8964 5060

TWO HATS MIDLANDS THEATRE COMPANY
2 The Countess' Croft
Coventry CV3 5ET
e-mail: twohatz@yahoo.com Tel: 024-7650 5098

TWO'S COMPANY
244 Upland Road, London SE22 0DN
e-mail: 2scompany@britishlibrary.net
Fax: 020-8299 3714   Tel: 020-8299 4593

UNRESTRICTED VIEW
Above Hen & Chickens Theatre Bar
109 St Paul's Road, London N1 2NA
e-mail: james@henandchickens.com
                    Tel: 020-7704 2001

VAGABOND HEART
Above Hen & Chickens Theatre Bar
2 Grassmere Road, Hornchurch
Essex RM11 3DP
e-mail: vagabondheart@virgin.net
                    Tel: 01708 781994

VANCE Charles
CV Productions Ltd
Hampden House, 2 Weymouth Street
London W1W 5BT
e-mail: cvtheatre@aol.com
Fax: 020-7636 2323   Tel: 020-7636 4343

VANDER ELST Anthony PRODUCTIONS
The Studio, 14 College Road, Bromley
Kent BR1 3NS
Fax: 020-8313 0443   Tel: 020-8466 5580

VENUS PRODUCTIONS
51 Church Road
London SE19 2TE   Tel: 020-8653 7735

VOLCANO THEATRE COMPANY Ltd
176 Hanover Street, Swansea SA1 6BP
e-mail: volcano.tc@virgin.net
Fax: 01792 648230   Tel: 01792 472772

WALLBANK John ASSOCIATES
60 Barclay Road, London E11 3DG
Fax: 020-8928 0339   Tel: 020-8530 7386

WAREHOUSE THEATRE COMPANY
Dingwall Road, Croydon CR0 2NF
e-mail: warehous@dircon.co.uk
Fax: 020-8688 6699   Tel: 020-8681 1257

WARRICK PRODUCING CONSULTANTS
2nd Floor, 40-42 Parker Street
London WC2B 5PQ
e-mail: chris@trackview.co.uk
Fax: 020-7404 1555   Tel: 020-7404 0546

WAX Kenneth H Ltd
The Penthouse, 7 Leicester Place
London WC2H 7RJ
Fax: 020-7734 7185   Tel: 020-7734 7184

WEAVER-HUGHES ENSEMBLE
565 Lordship Lane, London SE22 8LB
e-mail: ensemble@weaverhughesensemble.co.uk
                    Tel/Fax: 020-8693 5614

WHITE Michael
48 Dean Street, London W1D 5BF
e-mail: contact@michaelwhite.co.uk
Fax: 020-7734 7727   Tel: 020-7734 7707

WILDCARD THEATRE COMPANY
PO Box 267, High Wycombe
Bucks HP11 1PF
e-mail: wtc@britishlibrary.net
Fax: 07092 024967   Tel: 01494 439375

WILLS Newton MANAGEMENT
The Studios, 17 Church Street, Belton
Rutland LE15 9JU
e-mail: csocci@compuserve.com
                    Tel/Fax: 01572 717314

WIZARD PRESENTS
2 Lord Hills Road, London W2 6PD
e-mail: info@wizardpresents.co.uk
Fax: 020-7286 7377   Tel: 020-7286 7277

WOMENS PLAYHOUSE TRUST (WPT)
Wapping Hydraulic Power Station
Wapping Wall, London E1W 3ST
e-mail: info@wapping.wpt.com
Fax: 020-7680 2081   Tel: 020-7680 2096

WOOD Kevin PRODUCTIONS
5 Archery Square, Walmer
Deal, Kent CT14 7JA
e-mail: kevin.wood.organisation@dial.pipex.com
Fax: 01304 381192   Tel: 01304 365515

WRESTLING SCHOOL The
(The Howard Baker Company)
42 Durlston Road
London E5 8RR   Tel/Fax: 020-8442 4229

X-PRODUCTIONS AT THE SHAW THEATRE
Write
100-110 Euston Road, London NW1 2AJ
e-mail: mike@the-shaw.co.uk

YOUNG VIC COMPANY
66 The Cut, London SE1 8LZ
e-mail: info@youngvic.org
Fax: 020-7928 1585   Tel: 020-7633 0133

6.15 THEATRE COMPANY
22 Brookfield Mansions, Highgate West Hill
London N6 6AS
e-mail: six15@dircon.co.uk
Fax: 020-8340 5696   Tel: 020-8342 8239

7:84 THEATRE COMPANY SCOTLAND
333 Woodlands Road, Glasgow G3 6NG
e-mail: admin@784theatre.fsnet.co.uk
Fax: 0141-334 3369   Tel: 0141-334 6686

ABERYSTWYTH ARTS CENTRE
Penglais, Aberystwyth, Ceredigion SY23 3DE
e-mail: lla@aber.ac.uk
Fax: 01970 622883   Tel: 01970 622882

ACTION TRANSPORT - THE YOUNG PEOPLE'S THEATRE
Whitby Hall, Stanney Lane, Ellesmere Port
South Wirral CH65 9AE
e-mail: all@actiontransporttheatre.co.uk
                              Tel: 0151-357 2120

ACTORCLUB Ltd
17 Inkerman Road
London NW5 3BT   Tel: 020-7267 2759

AGE EXCHANGE THEATRE TRUST
The Reminiscence Centre
11 Blackheath Village, London SE3 9LA
e-mail: age-exchange@lewisham.gov.uk
Fax: 020-8318 0060   Tel: 020-8318 9105

ALLEGRESSE
3 Hampden Road, Muswell Hill, London N10 2HP
e-mail: sara@allegresse.demon.co.uk
                              Tel: 020-8361 5556

ALTERNATIVE ARTS
Top Studio, Bethnal Green Training Centre
Deal Street, London E1 5HZ
e-mail: info@alternativearts.co.uk
Fax: 020-7375 0484   Tel: 020-7375 0441

ANGLES THEATRE The
Alexandra Road, Wisbech, Cambs PE13 1HQ
Fax: 01945 481768   Tel: 01945 585587

ASHCROFT YOUTH THEATRE
Ashcroft Academy of Dramatic Art,
Bellenden Old School, Bellenden Road,
London SE15 4DG   Tel/Fax: 020-8693 8088

ATTIC THEATRE COMPANY (LONDON) Ltd
Wimbledon Theatre, The Broadway
                              London SW19 1QG
e-mail: info@attictheatre.com
Tel/Fax: 020-8543 7838

BANNER THEATRE
Friends Institute, 220 Moseley Road
Highgate, Birmingham B12 0DG
e-mail: voices@btinternet.com
Fax: 0121-440 0459   Tel: 0121-440 0460

BESHT TELLERS
33 Abbey Road, London NW8 0AT
e-mail: info@besht-tellers.org
                              Tel/Fax: 020-8340 4421

BLUNDERBUS THEATRE COMPANY Ltd
The Mick Jagger Centre, Shepherds Lane
Dartford DA1 2JZ
e-mail: admin@blunderbus.co.uk
Fax: 01322 286285   Tel: 01322 286284

BORDERLINE THEATRE COMPANY
North Harbour Street, Ayr KA8 8AA
Fax: 01292 263825   Tel: 01292 281010

BRAVE NEW WORLD THEATRE COMPANY
Write
2nd Floor, 79 Highbury Hill, London N5 1SX
e-mail: spencer.hinton@virgin.net

BRIGHTON THEATRE EVENTS
40 Upper Gardner Street
Brighton BN1 4AN   Tel: 01273 819184

BRISTOL EXPRESS THEATRE COMPANY Ltd
24 Well's House Road, East Acton
London NW10 6EE
e-mail: andyjandyjordan@aol.com
Fax: 020-8838 4482   Tel: 020-8963 9171

BRITISH ASIAN THEATRE COMPANY
Star Studios, 38 Leabridge Road
London E5 9QD   Tel: 020-8986 4470

BRUVVERS THEATRE COMPANY
(Touring on Tyneside)
Ouseburn Warehouse Workshops, 36 Lime
Street, Newcastle-upon-Tyne NE1 2PQ
                              Tel: 0191-261 9230

BUSH THEATRE
Shepherd's Bush Green, London W12 8QD
e-mail: info@bushtheatre.co.uk
                              Tel: 020-7602 3703

CAPITAL ARTS YOUTH THEATRE
Wyllyotts Centre, Darkes Lane, Potters Bar
Herts EN6 2HN
e-mail: capitalartstheatre@genie.co.uk
Mobile: 07885 232414   Tel/Fax: 020-8449 2342

CARIB THEATRE COMPANY
73 Lancelot Road, Wembley
Middlesex HA0 2AN
e-mail: caribtheatre@aol.com
                              Tel/Fax: 020-8795 0576

CASSANDRA THEATRE COMPANY
79 Brondesbury Villas, London NW6 6AG
e-mail: cassandraprod@hotmail.com
Mobile: 07796 264828   Tel: 020-7372 0733

CAVALCADE THEATRE COMPANY
(Touring Shows - Musicals, Pantomimes,
Music Hall, Comedy & Rock 'n' Roll)
57 Pelham Road, London SW19 1NW
Fax: 020-8540 2243   Tel: 020-8540 3513

CENTRE FOR PERFORMANCE RESEARCH
6 Science Park, Aberystwyth SY23 3AH
e-mail: cprwww@aber.ac.uk
Fax: 01970 622132   Tel: 01970 622133

CHANGELING The
14 The Terrace, Rochester, Kent ME1 1XN
e-mail: mail@thechangeling.com
                              Tel: 01634 831957

CHATS PALACE ARTS CENTRE
42-44 Brooksby's Walk, Hackney
London E9 6DF
Fax: 020-8985 6878   Tel: 020-8533 0227

CHERUB COMPANY LONDON The
Arch 5-6 Midland Road, London NW1 2AD
e-mail: visnevski@cherub.org.uk
                              Tel/Fax: 020-7383 0947

CLASSIC MUSICALS UK
Chequers, Station Road, Petworth
West Sussex GU28 0ES
e-mail: cmuk@gibenterprises.com
Fax: 01798 343611   Mobile: 07776 195357

CLEAN BREAK THEATRE COMPANY
2 Patshull Road, London NW5 2LB
Fax: 020-7482 8611   Tel: 020-7482 8600

CLOSE FOR COMFORT THEATRE CO
34 Boleyn Walk, Leatherhead, Surrey KT22 7HU
e-mail: close4comf@aol.com   Tel: 01372 378613

COMMON PULSE THEATRE
c/o Cardiff Casting, Chapter Arts Centre
Market Road, Canton, Cardiff CF5 1QE
e-mail: admin@cardiffcasting.co.uk
Fax: 029-2023 3380   Tel: 029-2023 3321

COMPANY OF CRANKS The
1st Floor, 62 Northfield House, Frensham Street
London SE15 6TN
e-mail: mimetic@london.com Tel: 020-7358 0571

COMPLETE WORKS THEATRE COMPANY Ltd The
27 Prospect Road, London NW2 2JU
e-mail: info@tcw.org.uk Tel: 020-7435 4718

CORNELIUS AND JONES ORIGINAL PRODUCTIONS
49 Carters Close, Sherington, Newport Pagnell
Bucks MK16 9NW
e-mail: admin@corneliusjones.com
Fax: 01908 216400 Tel: 01908 612593

CRAGRATS Ltd
The Mill, Dunford Road, Holmfirth
Huddersfield HD9 2AR
e-mail: mike@cragrats.com
Fax: 01484 686212 Tel: 01484 686451

CTC
Arts Centre, Vane Terrace, Darlington, Co
Durham DL3 7AX
e-mail: ctc@clevelandtheatre.demon.co.uk
Fax: 01325 369404 Tel: 01325 352004

CUT-CLOTH THEATRE
41 Beresford Road
London N5 2HR Tel: 020-7503 4393

DEPTFORD ALBANY
Douglas Way, Deptford, London SE8 4AG
Fax: 020-8469 2253 Tel: 020-8692 0231

DIZZY HEIGHTS (UK ARTS EXPLORE)
Media Centre, 7 Northumberland Street
Huddersfield HD1 1RL
e-mail: info@ukarts-explore.com
Tel: 01484 350031

DRAGON MULTIMEDIA
St Georges Theatre
49 Tufnell Park Road, London N7 0PS
e-mail: stgeorgestheatre@lineone.net
Fax: 020-7609 2427 Tel: 020-7607 7978

DRAMA CLUB
12 Hardy Close, Surrey Quays, London SE16 6RT
e-mail: samanthahgiblin@hotmail.com
Fax: 0870 1645895 Tel: 020-7231 6083

ELAN WALES
(European Live Arts Network)
Chapter, Market Road, Canton, Cardiff CF5 1QE
e-mail: fire@elanw.demon.co.uk
Tel/Fax: 029-2034 5831

EMPTY SPACE THEATRE COMPANY
7-15 Greatorex Street, London E1 5NF
e-mail: estc@dircon.co.uk
Fax: 0870 9090103 Tel: 0870 9090102

ESCAPE ARTISTS
42 Woodlark Road, Cambridge CB3 0HS
e-mail: houdini@escapeartists.co.uk
Fax: 01223 522301 Tel: 01223 301439

EUROPEAN THEATRE COMPANY The
39 Oxford Avenue, London SW20 8LS
Fax: 020-8544 1999 Tel: 020-8544 1994

FAMILY CURIOSO THEATRE COMPANY
334A High Road, London N22 8JW
e-mail: familycurioso@hotmail.com
Tel: 020-8888 2095

FIGURE & GROUND
10 Cleveland Avenue, Wimbledon Chase
London SW20 9EW
e-mail: fandg@caso.clara.net Tel: 020-8543 5939

FLOATING POINT SCIENCE THEATRE
10 Warren Drive, Chelsfield, Kent BR6 6EX
e-mail: stevemesure@ic24.net
Tel: 01689 812200

FLUXX
(Improvised Theatre)
7-15 Greatorex Street, London E1 5NF
e-mail: admin@fluxx.co.uk
Fax: 0870 0566376 Tel: 020-7247 9072

FORBIDDEN THEATRE COMPANY
Diorama Arts Centre
34 Osnaburgh Street
London NW1 3ND
e-mail: info@forbidden.org.uk
Tel/Fax: 020-7813 1025

FOREST FORGE THEATRE COMPANY
The Theatre Centre
Endeavour Park, Crow Arch Lane
Ringwood, Hampshire BH24 1SF
e-mail: theatre@forestforge.demon.co.uk
Fax: 01425 471158 Tel: 01425 470188

FOURSIGHT THEATRE Ltd
Newhampton Arts Centre, Dunkley Street
Wolverhampton WV1 4AN
e-mail: foursight.theatre@cwcom.net
Fax: 01902 428413 Tel: 01902 714257

FRANTIC THEATRE COMPANY
32 Woodlane, Falmouth TR11 4RF
e-mail: frantic@btinternet.com
Tel/Fax: 01326 312985

FUTURES THEATRE COMPANY
St Peter's Centre, Cranfield Road, Brockley
London SE4 1UF
e-mail: futures@ukonline.co.uk
Fax: 020-8694 0289 Tel: 020-8694 8655

GALLEON THEATRE COMPANY Ltd
Greenwich Playhouse, Greenwich BR Station
Forecourt, 189 Greenwich High Road
London SE10 8JA
Fax: 020-8969 2910 Tel: 020-8858 9256

GAZEBO TIE COMPANY Ltd
The Multipurpose Centre, Victoria Road
Darlaston, West Midlands WS10 8AP
e-mail: gazebo@ukgateway.net
Tel: 0121-526 6877

GRANGE ARTS
Rochdale Road, Oldham
Greater Manchester OL9 6EA
e-mail: joanne.draper@oldham.ac.uk
Fax: 0161-785 4263 Tel: 0161-785 4239

GREASEPAINT ANONYMOUS
4 Gallus Close, Winchmore Hill
London N21 1JR
e-mail: info@greaspaintanonymous.co.uk
Fax: 020-8882 9189 Tel: 020-8886 2263

GREENWICH & LEWISHAM'S YOUNG PEOPLES THEATRE (GYPT)
Burrage Road, London SE18 7JZ
e-mail: postbox@gypt.co.uk
Fax: 020-8317 8595 Tel: 020-8854 1316

GWENT TIE COMPANY
The Drama Centre Pen-y-pound
Abergavenny, Gwent NP7 5UD
e-mail: gwenttie@aol.com
Fax: 01873 853910 Tel: 01873 853167

HACKNEY YOUNG PEOPLE'S YOUTH THEATRE
Hoxton Hall Theatre & Arts Centre
130 Hoxton Street, London N1 6SH
e-mail: office@hoxtonhall.dabsol.co.uk
Fax: 020-7729 3815 Tel: 020-7684 0060

HALF MOON YOUNG PEOPLE'S THEATRE
43 White Horse Road, London E1 0ND
e-mail: info@halfmoon.org.uk
Fax: 020-7709 8914   Tel: 020-7265 8138

HIJINX THEATRE
(Adults with Learning Disabilities, Community)
Bay Chambers, West Bute Street
Cardiff Bay CF10 5BB
e-mail: info@hijinx.org.uk
Fax: 029-2030 0332   Tel: 029-2030 0331

HORLA
The Rose and Crown Theatre
59-61 High Street, Hampton Wick, Surrey KT1 4DG
e-mail: info@horla.co.uk   Tel/Fax: 020-8296 0242

IMAGE THEATRE COMPANY
23 Sedgeford Road, Shepherd's Bush
London W12 0NA
e-mail: brian@image-theatre-co.demon.co.uk
Fax: 020-8749 9294   Tel: 020-8743 9380

IMMEDIATE THEATRE
C1/62 Beechwood Road, London E8 3DY
e-mail: immediatejo@aol.com
Fax: 020-7683 0247   Tel: 020-7683 0233

IN TOTO PRODUCTIONS
PO Box 2247, Brighton BN1 3DQ
e-mail: admin@intoto.freeserve.co.uk
Tel/Fax: 01273 205863

INOCENTE ART AND FILM Ltd
(Fashion Shows, Film, Multimedia)
5 Denmans Lane, Lindfield, Sussex RH16 2LA
e-mail: rikki.tarascas@virginnet.com
Mobile: 07973 518132

INTERPLAY THEATRE COMPANY
Armley Ridge Road, Leeds LS12 3LE
e-mail: info@interplaytheatre.org
Tel: 0113-263 8556

IRISH YOUTH THEATRE The
Victor House, Marlborough Gardens
Whetstone N20 0SH
e-mail: rosemaryifbco@aol.com
Mobile: 07956 855512   Tel/Fax: 020-8361 0678

ISOSCELES COMEDY COMPANY
7 Amity Grove, Raynes Park
London SW20 0LQ   Tel: 020-8946 3905

KABOODLE PRODUCTIONS Ltd
(National/International Small/Mid-Scale Touring)
15 Hope Street, Liverpool L1 9BQ
e-mail: admin@kaboodle.freeserve.co.uk
Tel: 0151-709 2818

KOMEDIA
44-47 Gardner Street, Brighton BN1 1UN
e-mail: info@komedia.co.uk
Fax: 01273 647102   Tel: 01273 647101

LANGUAGE ALIVE!
The Play House, Longmore Street
Birmingham B12 9ED
e-mail: theplayhouse@saqnet.co.uk
Tel/Fax: 0121-446 4301

LATCHMERE THEATRE
(Chris Fisher)
Unit 5A, Abbey Business Centre, Ingate Place
London SW8 3NS
e-mail: fisherfalcon@compuserve.com
Fax: 020-7978 2631   Tel: 020-7978 2620

LIVE THEATRE COMPANY
(New Writing)
7-8 Trinity Chare, Quayside
Newcastle-upon-Tyne NE1 3DF
e-mail: info@live.org.uk
Fax: 0191-232 2224   Tel: 0191-261 2694

LOGOS THEATRE COMPANY
48 Taybridge Road
London SW11 5PT   Tel: 020-7228 4374

LONDON ACTORS THEATRE COMPANY
Unit 5A, Abbey Business Centre, Ingate Place
London SW8 3NS
e-mail: fisherfalcon@compuserve.com
Fax: 020-7978 2631   Tel: 020-7978 2620

LONDON BUBBLE THEATRE COMPANY Ltd
5 Elephant Lane, London SE16 4JD
e-mail: admin@londonbubble.org.uk
Fax: 020-7231 2366   Tel: 020-7237 4434

LSW: JUNIOR INTER-ACT
181A Faunce House
Doddington Grove, London SE17 3TB
e-mail: londonswo@hotmail.com
Fax: 020-7735 5911   Tel: 020-7793 9755

LSW: PRISON PROJECT
181A Faunce House
Doddington Grove
London SE17 3TB
e-mail: londonswo@hotmail.com
Fax: 020-7735 5911   Tel: 020-7793 9755

LSW: SENIOR RE-ACTION
181A Faunce House
Doddington Grove, London SE17 3TB
e-mail: londonswo@hotmail.com
Fax: 020-7735 5911   Tel: 020-7793 9755

LUNG HAS THEATRE COMPANY
Central Hall, West Tollcross, Edinburgh EH3 9BP
e-mail: lungha@ednet.co.uk
Fax: 0131-229 8965   Tel: 0131-228 8998

M6 THEATRE COMPANY
Hamer CP School, Albert Royds Street
Rochdale OL16 2SU
e-mail: info@m6theatre.freeserve.co.uk
Fax: 01706 711700   Tel: 01706 355898

MADDERMARKET THEATRE
(Resident Community Theatre Company and
Small-Scale Producing & Receiving House)
St John's Alley, Norwich NR2 1DR
e-mail: theatre@maddermarket.freeserve.co.uk
Fax: 01603 661357   Tel: 01603 626560

MADE IN WALES
Chapter, Market Road, Canton
Cardiff CF5 1QE
e-mail: madein.wales@mail.virgin.net
Fax: 029-2034 4738   Tel: 029-2034 4737

MAGIC CARPET THEATRE
18 Church Street, Sutton-on-Hull HU7 4TS
e-mail: jon@magiccarpettheatre.com
Fax: 01482 787362   Tel: 01482 709939

MAN MELA THEATRE COMPANY
(Admin Contact: Caroline Goffin)
e-mail: man-mela@dircon.co.uk
Mobile: 07973 349101   Mobile: 07966 215090

MANCHESTER ACTORS COMPANY
PO BOX 54
Manchester M60 7AB   Tel: 0161-227 8702

MAYA PRODUCTIONS Ltd
156 Richmond Road, London E8 3HN
e-mail: mayachris@aol.com
Tel/Fax: 020-7923 0675

MERSEYSIDE YOUNG PEOPLE'S THEATRE COMPANY
13 Hope Street, Liverpool L1 9BH
e-mail: mail@mypt.co.uk
Fax: 0151-707 9950   Tel: 0151-708 0877

MIKRON THEATRE COMPANY Ltd
(Canal Touring Nationally)
Marsden Mechanics, Peel Street, Marsden
Huddersfield HD7 6BW
e-mail: admin@mikron.org.uk   Tel: 01484 843701

MONTAGE THEATRE
45 Chalsey Road
London SE4 1YN
e-mail: info@montagetheatre.com
Tel: 020-8694 9497

MOVING THEATRE
16 Laughton Lodge, Laughton, Nr Lewes
East Sussex BN8 6BY
e-mail: info@movingtheatre.com
Fax: 01323 815736   Tel: 01323 815726

NATIONAL ASSOCIATION OF YOUTH THEATRES (NAYT)
Arts Centre, Vane Terrace
Darlington, County
Durham DL3 7AX
e-mail: naytuk@aol.com
Tel: 01325 363330   Fax: 01325 363313

NATIONAL STUDENT THEATRE COMPANY
20 Lansdowne Road, London N10 2AU
e-mail: clive@nsdf.org.uk
Fax: 020-8883 7142   Tel: 020-8883 4586

NATIONAL YOUTH MUSIC THEATRE
5th Floor, The Palace Theatre
Shaftesbury Avenue
London W1V 8AY
e-mail: enquiries@nymt.org.uk
Fax: 020-7734 7515   Tel: 020-7734 7478

NATIONAL YOUTH THEATRE OF GREAT BRITAIN
443-445 Holloway Road
London N7 6LW
e-mail: info@nyt.org.uk
Fax: 020-7281 8246   Tel: 020-7281 3863

NATURAL THEATRE COMPANY
Widcombe Institute, Widcombe Hill
Bath BA2 6AA
e-mail: naturals@dircon.co.uk
Fax: 01225 442555   Tel: 01225 469131

NAVRANG THEATRE
130 Goodman Park, Slough SL2 5NL
e-mail: chaandig@hotmail.com
Tel: 07050 105625

NETI-NETI THEATRE COMPANY
Quintin Kynaston School, Marlborough Hill
London NW8 0NL
Tel/Fax: 020-7483 4239 (Minicom)

NETTLEFOLD The
West Norwood Library Centre
1 Norwood High Street, London SE27 9JX
Fax: 020-7926 8071   Tel: 020-7926 8070

NEW PERSPECTIVES THEATRE COMPANY
(Touring and Community Theatre Projects)
The Old Library, Leeming Street, Mansfield
Notts NG18 1NG
e-mail: info@newperspectives.co.uk
Tel: 01623 635225

NORTHERN STAGE PROJECTS
(See NORTHERN STAGE THEATRICAL PRODUCTIONS Ltd)

NORTHERN STAGE THEATRICAL PRODUCTIONS Ltd
Newcastle Playhouse
Barras Bridge, Haymarket
Newcastle-upon-Tyne NE1 7RH
e-mail: info@northernstage.com
Fax: 0191-261 8093   Tel: 0191-232 3366

NTC TOURING THEATRE COMPANY
The Playhouse, Bondgate Without, Alnwick
Northumberland NE66 1PQ
e-mail: admin@ntc-touringtheatre.co.uk
Fax: 01665 605837   Tel: 01665 602586

NUFFIELD THEATRE EDUCATION
University Road, Southampton SO17 1TR
e-mail: education@nuffieldtheatre.co.uk
Fax: 023-8090 0950   Tel: 023-8034 4515

OCTOBER GALLERY The
24 Old Gloucester Street, London WC1N 3AL
e-mail: octobergallery@compuserve.com
Fax: 020-7405 1851   Tel: 020-7242 7367

OFF THE CUFF THEATRE COMPANY
First Floor, 52 Crowndale Road
London NW1 1TP
e-mail: otctheatre@aol.com   Tel: 020-7691 1577

ONATTI THEATRE COMPANY
9 Field Close, Warwick, Warwickshire CV34 4QD
e-mail: info@onatti.co.uk   Tel: 01926 495220

OPEN STAGE PRODUCTIONS
49 Springfield Road, Moseley
Birmingham B13 9NN   Tel/Fax: 0121-777 9086

OXFORDSHIRE TOURING THEATRE COMPANY
Unit 1 St John Fisher School, Sandy Lane West
Oxford OX4 5LD
e-mail: manager@ottc.oxfordshire.co.uk
Fax: 01865 714822   Tel: 01865 778119

PANDEMONIUM TOURING PARTNERSHIP
228 Railway Street
Cardiff CF24 2NJ   Tel: 029-2047 2060

PASCAL THEATRE COMPANY
35 Flaxman Court, Flaxman Terrace
Bloomsbury, London WC1H 9AR
e-mail: pascaltheatreco@aol.com
Fax: 020-7419 9798   Tel: 020-7383 0920

PAUL'S THEATRE COMPANY
Fairkytes Arts Centre
51 Billet Lane, Hornchurch
Essex RM11 1AX   Tel: 01708 447123

PENTABUS
Bromfield, Ludlow, Shropshire SY8 2JU
e-mail: tree@pentabus.co.uk
Fax: 01584 856254   Tel: 01584 856564

PERFORMANCE PROJECT The
32 Kenbrook House, Leighton Road
London NW5 2QN   Tel: 020-7482 1850

PHANTOM CAPTAIN The
618B Finchley Road, London NW11 7RR
e-mail: ziph@appleonline.net
Tel/Fax: 020-8455 4564

PIED PIPER COMPANY (TIE)
(In association with The Yvonne Arnaud Theatre Guildford)
1 Lilian Place, Coxcombe Lane, Chiddingfold
Surrey GU8 4QA
e-mail: twpiedpiper@aol.com
Tel/Fax: 01428 684022

PILOT THEATRE COMPANY
Glasshoughton Cultural Centre
Redhill Avenue, Castleford, Wakefield
West Yorkshire WF10 4QH
e-mail: info@pilot-theatre.com
Fax: 01977 512819   Tel: 01977 604852

PLAYTIME THEATRE COMPANY
18 Bennells Avenue, Whitstable, Kent CT5 2HP
e-mail: playtime@dircon.co.uk
Fax: 01227 266648   Tel: 01227 266272

PRAXIS THEATRE COMPANY Ltd
24 Wykeham Road, London NW4 2SU
e-mail: praxisco@globalnet.co.uk
Tel/Fax: 020-8203 1916

PRIME PRODUCTIONS
54 Hermiston, Currie EH14 4AQ
e-mail: mheller@primeproductions.fsnet.co.uk
Tel/Fax: 0131-449 4055

PROTEUS THEATRE COMPANY
Fairfields Arts Centre, Council Road
Basingstoke RG21 3DH
e-mail: proteus@dircon.co.uk   Tel: 01256 354541

PUMBLECHOOK
(Singing Duo)
1 Clifford Avenue, Bletchley
Milton Keynes MK2 2LT
e-mail: andy.collier@euphony.net
Mobile: 07733 118889   Tel/Fax: 01908 374223

PURSUED BY A BEAR PRODUCTIONS
6 Glenluce Road, Blackheath, London SE3 7SB
e-mail: pbab@pbab.freeserve.co.uk
Tel/Fax: 020-8480 9514

Q20 THEATRE COMPANY
19 Wellington Crescent, Shipley
West Yorks BD18 3PH
e-mail: john.lambert.q20@cwcom.net
Tel: 01274 591417

QUAKER YOUTH THEATRE
Ground Floor, 1 The Lodge, 1046 Bristol Road
Birmingham B29 6LJ
e-mail: qyt@leaveners.org.uk
Fax: 0121-414 0090   Tel: 0121-414 0099

QUANTUM THEATRE FOR SCIENCE
Unit S9, The Shakespeare Centre
245A Coldharbour Lane, London SW9 8RR
e-mail: quantumtheatre@btinternet.com
Tel: 020-7733 8150

QUEST THEATRE COMPANY
(Artistic Director David Craik)
3C Mecklenburgh Street, Bloomsbury
London WC1N 2AH   Tel/Fax: 020-7713 0342

QUICKSILVER THEATRE
The Glasshouse, 4 Enfield Road
London N1 5AZ
e-mail: talktous@quicksilvertheatre.org
Fax: 020-7254 3119   Tel: 020-7241 2942

RAGS & FEATHERS THEATRE COMPANY
80 Summer Road, Thames Ditton
Surrey KT7 0QP
e-mail: jill@ragsandfeathers.freeserve.co.uk
Mobile: 07958 724374   Tel: 020-8224 2203

RED LADDER THEATRE COMPANY Ltd
3 St Peters Buildings, York Street
Leeds LS9 8AJ
e-mail: wendy@redladder.co.uk
Fax: 0113-245 5351   Tel: 0113-245 5311

RIDICULUSMUS
Edenderry Industrial Estate, Crumlin Road
Belfast BT14
e-mail: ridiculusmus@altavista.net
Tel: 0708 1756694

RIDING LIGHTS THEATRE CO.
Friargate Theatre, Lower Friargate, York YO1 9SL
e-mail: info@rltc.org.uk
Fax: 01904 651532   Tel: 01904 655317

ROSE THEATRE COMPANY The
10 Riverside Forest Row, Sussex RH18 5HB
e-mail: dan.skinner@btinternet.com
Tel/Fax: 01342 825639

ROYAL COURT YOUNG WRITERS PROGRAMME
The Site, Royal Court Theatre, Sloane Square
London SW1W 8AS
e-mail: ywp@royalcourttheatre.com
Fax: 020-7565 5001   Tel: 020-7565 5050

SALAMANDER THEATRE COMPANY Ltd
333 Chiswick High Road, Chiswick
London W4 4HS
e-mail: salamander.theatre@btinternet.com
Fax: 020-8742 3923   Tel: 020-8994 4969

SALTMINE THEATRE COMPANY
St James House, Trinity Road, Dudley
West Midlands DY1 1JB
e-mail: stc@saltmine.org   Tel: 01384 454807

SCARLET THEATRE
Studio 4, The Bull, 68 High Street, Barnet
Herts EN5 5SJ
e-mail: admin@scarlettheatre.co.uk
Fax: 020-8447 0075   Tel: 020-8441 9779

SCOTTISH YOUTH THEATRE
3rd Floor, Forsyth House, 111 Union Street
Glasgow G1 3TA
e-mail: info@scottishyouththeatre.org
Fax: 0141-221 9123   Tel: 0141-221 5127

SHARED EXPERIENCE YOUTH THEATRE
The Soho Laundry, 9 Dufours Place
London W1F 7SJ
e-mail: youththeatre@setheatre.co.uk
Fax: 020-7287 8763   Tel: 020-7434 9248

SKINNING THE CAT AERIAL THEATRE COMPANY
Woolston House, 3 Tetley Street
Bradford BD1 2NP
e-mail: skats@globalnet.co.uk
Fax: 01274 770352   Tel: 01274 770300

SNAP PEOPLE'S THEATRE TRUST
45-47 South Street, Bishops Stortford
Herts CM23 3AG
Fax: 01279 506694   Tel: 01279 461607

SOHO THEATRE AND WRITERS' CENTRE
21 Dean Street, London W1V 6NE
e-mail: mail@sohotheatre.com
Fax: 020-7287 5061   Tel: 020-7287 5060

SPANNER IN THE WORKS
155 Station Road, Sidcup
Kent DA15 7AA
e-mail: rapieruk@aol.com
Mobile: 07850 313986   Tel: 020-8304 7660

SPARE TYRE THEATRE COMPANY
(Community Drama & Music Projects)
Hampstead Town Hall, 213 Haverstock Hill
London NW3 4QP   Tel: 020-7419 7007

SPECTACLE THEATRE
Pontyprid College, Rhondda Campus
Llwynypia, Tonypandy CF40 2TQ
e-mail: info@spectacletheatre.co.uk
Fax: 01443 423080   Tel: 01443 430700

SPRINGBOARD THEATRE COMPANY
20 Lansdowne Road, London N10 2AU
e-mail: clive@nsdf.org.uk
Fax: 020-8883 7142   Tel: 020-8883 4586

TAG THEATRE COMPANY
18 Albion Street
Glasgow G1 1LH
e-mail: info@tag-theatre.co.uk
Fax: 0141-552 0666   Tel: 0141-552 4949

TARA ARTS GROUP
356 Garratt Lane, London SW18 4ES
Fax: 020-8870 9540   Tel: 020-8333 4457

THEATRE CENTRE YOUNG PEOPLE'S THEATRE COMPANY
(National Touring)
Units 7 & 8, Toynbee Workshops
3 Gunthorpe Street, London E1 7RQ
e-mail: admin@theatre-centre.co.uk
Fax: 020-7377 1376   Tel: 020-7377 0379

THEATRE EXPRESS
PO Box 94, Chipping Norton
Oxon OX7 3YL
e-mail: perform@theatre-express.com
Tel/Fax: 01608 676024

THEATRE OF LITERATURE The
(Dramatised Readings)
51 The Cut, London SE1 8LF
e-mail: info@calderpub.demon.co.uk
Tel/Fax: 020-7633 0599

THEATRE RE:PUBLIC
1 Mellor Road, Leicester LE3 6HN
e-mail: mellor@ntlworld.com   Tel: 0116-233 8432

THEATRE VENTURE
(Alternative/Multimedia)
Stratford Circus, Theatre Square, London E15 1BX
e-mail: info@theatre-venture.org
Fax: 020-8519 8769   Tel: 020-8519 6678

THEATRE WORKSHOP
34 Hamilton Place, Edinburgh EH3 5AX
Fax: 0131-220 0112   Tel: 0131-225 7942

THEATRE WORKSHOP NORTH-WEST AND MIDLANDS
18 Weston Lane, Crewe
Cheshire CW2 5AN
e-mail: theatrew@globalnet.co.uk
Fax: 070 2098 2098   Tel: 070 2096 2096

THEATR NA N'OG
Unit 3, Milland Road Industrial Estate, Neath
West Glamorgan SA11 1NJ
e-mail: cwmni@theatr-nanog.co.uk
Fax: 01639 647941   Tel: 01639 641771

THEATR POWYS
The Drama Centre, Tremont Road
Llandrindod Wells, Powys LD1 5EB
e-mail: theatr.powys@powys.gov.uk
Fax: 01597 824381   Tel: 01597 824444

THIRD PARTY PRODUCTIONS Ltd
87 St Thomas' Road, Hastings
East Sussex TN34 3LD
e-mail: agleave@thirdparty.demon.co.uk
Tel/Fax: 01424 719320

THREE COUNTIES YOUTH THEATRE
1 Clifford Avenue, Bletchley
Milton Keynes MK2 2LT
e-mail: andy.collier@euphony.net
Mobile: 07733 118889   Tel: 01908 374223

TIE TOURS
Holloway School, Hilldrop Road, Islington
London N7 0JG
e-mail: tie@tietours.com
Fax: 020-7700 3697   Tel: 020-7619 9115

TIME OF OUR LIVES MUSIC THEATRE Ltd
(Formerly Gilt and Gaslight Music Theatre Ltd)
5 Monkhams Drive, Woodford Green
Essex IG8 0LG
e-mail: dympna@giltandgaslight.com
Tel/Fax: 020-8491 6695

TITHE BARN MUSIC & DRAMA SOCIETY
Shiplake College
Henley-on-Thames RG9 4BW
e-mail: tithe@shiplake.org.uk   Tel: 0118-940 2455

TRICYCLE THEATRE
269 Kilburn High Road, London NW6 7JR
e-mail: admin@tricycle.co.uk
Fax: 020-7328 0795   Tel: 020-7372 6611

TROY PRODUCTIONS
17 Talbot Meadows, Talbot Village, Poole
Dorset BH12 5OG
e-mail: lulu_2013@yahoo.co.uk
Tel: 01202 516696

VOLCANO THEATRE COMPANY Ltd
176 Hanover Street, Swansea SA1 6BP
e-mail: volcano.tc@virgin.net
Fax: 01792 648230   Tel: 01792 472772

WAREHOUSE THEATRE COMPANY
Dingwall Road, Croydon CR0 2NF
e-mail: warehous@dircon.co.uk
Fax: 020-8688 6699   Tel: 020-8681 1257

WEAVER-HUGHES ENSEMBLE
565 Lordship Lane
London SE22 8LB
e-mail: ensemble@weaverhughesensemble.co.uk
Tel/Fax: 020-8693 5614

WEIRD SISTERS The
4 Shamrock Street, Clapham North
London SW4 6HE
e-mail: weirdsists@aol.com
Mobile: 07715 360021   Tel/Fax: 020-7720 4252

WIGAN PIER THEATRE COMPANY
The 'Way We Were' Museum
Wigan Pier, Trencherfield Mill, Wigan
Lancs WN3 4EF
e-mail: paul@wptc.co.uk   Tel: 01942 709305

WINCHESTER HAT FAIR, FESTIVAL OF STREET THEATRE
5A Jewry Street, Winchester, Hants SO23 8RZ
e-mail: cat@hatfair.co.uk
Fax: 01962 868957   Tel: 01962 849841

WOMEN & THEATRE BIRMINGHAM Ltd
220 Moseley Road, Highgate
Birmingham B12 0DG
e-mail: womenandtheatre@btinternet.com
Fax: 0121-446 4280   Tel: 0121-440 4203

Y TOURING THEATRE COMPANY
8-10 Lennox Road, Finsbury Park
London N4 3NW
e-mail: ytouring@ytouring.demon.co.uk
Fax: 020-7272 8413   Tel: 020-7272 5755

YORICK INTERNATIONALIST THEATRE ENSEMBLE
(Yorick Theatre & Film)
4 Duval Court, 36 Bedfordbury, Covent Garden
London WC2N 4DQ
e-mail: yorick.internationalist.theatre@ukgateway.net
Tel/Fax: 020-7836 7637

YORKSHIRE WOMEN THEATRE COMPANY
(Touring Theatre in Health Education)
F10 Host, 21 Savile Mount, Leeds LS7 3HZ
e-mail: admin@ywtheatre.com
Tel: 0113-200 7200

YOUNG VIC COMPANY
66 The Cut, Waterloo, London SE1 8LZ
e-mail: info@youngvic.org
Fax: 020-7928 1585   Tel: 020-7633 0133

ZENANA THEATRE COMPANY
40 Barrie House, Hawksley Court, Albion Road
London N16 0TX   Tel: 020-7249 4487

ZIP THEATRE
Dunkley Street, Wolverhampton WV1 4AN
e-mail: cathy.zip@dial.pipex.com
Fax: 01902 572251   Tel: 01902 712251

A.R.C. ENTERTAINMENTS
34 Bishopton Court, Fairfield
Stockton on Tees, Cleveland TS19 7HJ
e-mail: info@arcentertainments.co.uk
Fax: 01642 800465   Tel: 01642 641852

BAC
(Workshops thoughout Year & Theatre
on Saturdays)
Lavender Hill, Battersea
London SW11 5TF
e-mail: mailbox@bac.org.uk
Fax: 020-7978 5207   Tel: 020-7223 6557

BARKING DOG THEATRE COMPANY
18 Hayleybell Gardens, Bishop's Stortford
Herts CM23 3HB
e-mail: pat@barkingdog.co.uk
Fax: 01279 465386   Tel: 01279 465550

BITESIZE THEATRE COMPANY
8 Green Meadows, New Broughton
Wrexham LL11 6SG
Administrator: Bill Robertson   Tel: 01978 756308

BLUE HAT PRODUCTIONS
43 Radwinter Road, Saffron Walden
Essex CB11 3HU
e-mail: sweeneybluehat@aol.com
Mobile: 07811 175351   Tel: 01799 502569

BLUNDERBUS THEATRE COMPANY
The Mick Jagger Centre, Shepherds Lane
Dartford, Kent DN1 2JZ
e-mail: admin@blunderbus.co.uk
Fax: 01322 286285   Tel: 01322 286284

BOOSTER CUSHION THEATRE COMPANY
1st Floor, Building B, Chocolate Factory
Clarendon Road, London N22 6JX
e-mail: bct@faxvia.net
Fax: 020-8365 8686   Tel: 020-8888 4545

DANCE FOR EVERYONE Ltd
30 Sevington Road
London NW4 3RX
e-mail: orders@dfe.org.uk   Tel: 020-8202 7863

DAYLIGHT THEATRE
66 Middle Street, Stroud
Glos GL5 1EA   Tel: 01453 763808

DONNA MARIA COMPANY
16 Bell Meadow, Dulwich
London SE19 1HP
e-mail: info@donna-marias-world.co.uk
Tel: 020-8670 7814

DRAGON DRAMA
(Theatre Company, Tuition, Film, Parties)
1B Station Road, Hampton Wick, Kingston
Surrey KT1 4HG
e-mail: dragondrama@hotmail.com
Tel/Fax: 020-8943 1504

EUROPA CLOWN THEATRE SHOW
36 St Lukes Road, Tunbridge Wells
Kent TN4 9JH   Tel: 01892 537964

IMAGE THEATRE COMPANY
23 Sedgeford Road, Shepherd's Bush
London W12 0NA
e-mail: brianthresh@image-theatre-co.demon.uk
Fax: 020-8749 9294   Tel: 020-8743 9380

IRISH (London-Irish) YOUTH THEATRE The
St Joseph's Youth Centre, Highgate Hill
London N19 0SH
Mobile: 07956 855512   Tel/Fax: 020-8361 0678

MAGIC MIRROR THEATRE COMPANY (UK) Ltd
(Musical Theatre for 5-11's)
17 Short Road, Leytonstone
London E11 4RH
Fax: 020-8556 2525   Tel: 020-8556 7216

NETTLEFOLD The
West Norwood Library Centre
1 Norwood High Street
London SE27 9JX
Fax: 020-7926 8071   Tel: 020-7926 8070

OILY CART COMPANY
Smallwood School Annexe, Smallwood Road
London SW17 0TW
e-mail: oilycart@globalnet.co.uk
Fax: 020-8672 0792   Tel: 020-8672 6329

PANDEMONIUM TOURING PARTNERSHIP
228 Railway Street
Cardiff CF24 2NJ   Tel: 029-2047 2060

PARASOL THEATRE FOR CHILDREN
Artistic Director: Richard Gill
Garden House, 4 Sunnyside, Wimbledon
London SW19 4SL
Fax: 020-8946 0228   Tel: 020-8946 9478

PAUL'S THEATRE COMPANY
Fairkytes Arts Centre
51 Billet Lane, Hornchurch
Essex RM11 1AX   Tel: 01708 447123

PIED PIPER THEATRE COMPANY
(In association with The Yvonne Arnaud
Theatre Guildford)
1 Lilian Place, Coxcombe Lane, Chiddingfold
Surrey GU8 4QA
e-mail: twpiedpiper@aol.com
Tel/Fax: 01428 684022

PLAYTIME THEATRE COMPANY
18 Bennells Avenue, Whitstable, Kent CT5 2HP
e-mail: playtime@dircon.co.uk
Fax: 01227 266648   Tel: 01227 266272

POLKA THEATRE FOR CHILDREN
240 The Broadway, Wimbledon SW19 1SB
e-mail: administration@polkatheatre.com
Fax: 020-8545 8365   Tel: 020-8545 8320

Q20 THEATRE COMPANY
19 Wellington Crescent, Shipley
West Yorks BD18 3PH
e-mail: john.lambert.q20@cwcom.net
Tel: 01274 591417

QUANTUM THEATRE FOR SCIENCE
Unit S9, The Shakespeare Centre
245A Coldharbour Lane, London SW9 8RR
e-mail: quantumtheatre@btinternet.com
Tel: 020-7733 8150

QUERCUS THEATRE COMPANY
33 Broadlands Avenue, Shepperton
Middlesex TW17 9DJ
e-mail: quercus@quercustheatrecompany.org.uk
Tel: 01932 252182

QUICKSILVER THEATRE COMPANY
(National Touring - New Writing for the
under 12's)
4 Enfield Road, London N1 5AZ
e-mail: talktous@quicksilvertheatre.org
Fax: 020-7254 3119   Tel: 020-7241 2942

REDROOFS THEATRE COMPANY
The Novello Theatre, Sunninghill, Nr Ascot
Berks SL5 9NE   Tel: 01344 20881

SCOTTISH YOUTH THEATRE
3rd Floor, Forsyth House, 111 Union Street
Glasgow G1 3TA
e-mail: info@scottishyouththeatre.org
Fax: 0141-221 9123   Tel: 0141-221 5127

SEAGULL THEATRE OF THE GORGE Ltd
(Theatre in Education)
Artistic Directors: Margo Cooper & Sian Murray
16 Victoria Road, Much Wenlock
Salop TF13 6AL   Tel/Fax: 01952 727803

SHAKESPEARE 4 KIDZ THEATRE COMPANY Ltd
27 Station Road West
Oxted
Surrey RH8 9EE
e-mail: office@shakepeare4kidz.com
Fax: 01883 730384   Tel: 01883 723444

THE GOOD THE BAD & THE CUDDLY THEATRE COMPANY
140 Manor Road
New Milton
Hants BH25 5ED
e-mail: j.sinclair@cwcom.net   Tel: 01425 612830

TICKLISH ALLSORTS SHOW
Cremyll
Marshmead Close
Clarendon
Salisbury, Wilts SP5 3DD
e-mail: garynunn@lineone.net
                           Tel/Fax: 01722 711800

TIEBREAK TOURING THEATRE
Heartsease High School
Marryat Road, Norwich NR7 9DF
e-mail: info@tiebreak-theatre.com
Fax: 01603 435184   Tel: 01603 435209

TRICYCLE THEATRE
269 Kilburn High Road, London NW6 7JR
e-mail: admin@tricycle.co.uk
                           Tel: 020-7372 6611

UNICORN THEATRE FOR CHILDREN The
St Mark's Studios, Chillingworth Road
London N7 8QJ
e-mail: admin@unicorntheatre.com
Fax: 020-7700 3870   Tel: 020-7700 0702

WHIRLIGIG THEATRE
(National Touring Company)
14 Belvedere Drive, Wimbledon SW19 7BY
e-mail: whirligig.theatre@virgin.net
Fax: 020-8879 7648   Tel: 020-8947 1732

Theatre - English Speaking in Europe

■ **AUSTRIA**
VIENNA
Vienna's English Theatre
English Agent: VM Theatre Productions Ltd
16 The Street, Ash, Kent CT3 2HJ
                           Tel/Fax: 01304 813330

■ **DENMARK**
COPENHAGEN
The English Theatre of Copenhagen
London Toast Theatre, Kochsvej 18, 1812 Fred C
Copenhagen Denmark
e-mail: londontoast@get2net.dk
                           Tel: + 45 33 22 8686
Artistic Director: Vivienne McKee
Admin: Soren Hall

■ **FRANCE**
PARIS
ACT Company
51 rue Hoche, 92 240 Malakoff, France
e-mail: andrew.wilson.wanadoo.fr
Fax: +33 1 46 56 23 18   Tel: +33 1 46 56 20 50
Artistic Director: Andrew Wilson
Administrator: Anne Wilson
Secretary: Sanya Dzeba

■ **FRANCE**
PARIS
Dear Conjunction Theatre Company
6 rue Arthur Rozier, 75019 Paris
e-mail: dearconjunction@wanadoo.fr
                           Tel: + 33 1 44 70 06 69
Artistic Directors: Barbara Bray, Leslie Clack,
Patricia Kessler

■ **FRANCE**
Amandla Theatre Company
(Bi-lingual Touring Theatre Company
12 Bis Rue Nicolas Abram
88130 xaronval, France
                           Tel: + 33 6 86 37 48 92 (Mobile)
e-mail: amandlatheatreco@aol.com
Artistic Director: Caroline Benamza
Administrator: Jean-Marie Degove

■ **GERMANY**
FRANKFURT
English Theater
25 Rattray Road, London SW2 1AZ
Fax: 020-7326 1713   Tel: 020-7326 4417
London Contact: Caroline Funnell

■ **GERMANY**
HAMBURG
The English Theatre of Hamburg
Lerchenfeld 14, 22081 Hamburg, Germany
                           Tel: + 49 40 227 7089
Contact: Robert Rumpf, Clifford Dean

■ **GERMANY**
TOURING GERMANY
White Horse Theatre
Boerdenstrasse 17
59494 Soest-Muellingsen, Germany
e-mail: theatre@whitehorse.de
Fax: + 49 2921 76581   Tel: + 49 2921 76488
Contact: Peter Griffith, Michael Dray

■ **HUNGARY**
BUDAPEST
Merlin International Theatre
Gerloczy Utca 4, 1052 Budapest, Hungary
e-mail: merlin.szinhaz@matavnet.hu
Tel/Fax: + 36 1 317 9338 Tel/Fax: + 36 1 206 0904
Contact: Tamas Jordan, Laszlo Magacs

■ **ICELAND**
REYKJAVIK
Light Nights - The Summer Theatre
The Travelling Theatre
Baldursgata 37, IS-101 Reykjavik, Iceland
Fax: + 354 551 5015   Tel: + 354 551 9181
Artistic Director: Kristine G Magnus

■ **NORWAY**
OSLO
The English Speaking Theatre-Oslo (TESTO)
Jacob Aalls Gate 30, 0364 Oslo, Norway
e-mail: testo-no@online.no
Fax: + 47 22466249   Tel: + 47 22466248
Artistic Director: Simon Lay
Director: Kristin Zachariassen

■ **SWEDEN**
STOCKHOLM
The English Theatre Company Ltd
(TMA Member) Nybrogatan 35
114 39 Stockholm, Sweden
e-mail: etc.ltd@telia.com
Fax: + 46 8 660 1159   Tel: + 46 8 662 4133
Artistic Director: Christer Berg

■ **UNITED KINGDOM**
THEATRE FROM OXFORD Touring Europe and Beyond
69-71 Oxford Street, Woodstock
Oxford OX20 1TJ
Contact: Robert Southam (Write)

ADELPHI
Strand
London WC2R 0NS

Manager:	020-7836 1166
Stage Door:	020-7836 1166
Box Office:	020-7836 1166
Artists:	020-7836 1166

ALBERY
St Martin's Lane
London WC2N 4AU

Manager:	020-7438 9700
Stage Door:	020-7438 9700
Box Office:	020-7369 1740
Artists:	020-7438 9700

ALDWYCH
Aldwych
London WC2B 4DF

Manager:	020-7379 6736
Stage Door:	020-7836 5537
Box Office:	0870 4000805
Artists:	020-7836 5537

ALMEIDA
Almeida Street
London N1 1TA

Manager:	020-7226 7432
Stage Door:	--------------------
Box Office	020-7359 4404
Artists:	--------------------

APOLLO
Shaftesbury Avenue
London W1D 7EZ

Manager:	020-7734 2987
Stage Door:	020-7437 3435
Box Office:	0870 4000800
Artists:	--------------------

APOLLO VICTORIA
17 Wilton Road
London SW1V 1LG

Manager	020-7834 6318
Stage Door:	020-7834 7231
Box Office:	020-7416 6059
Artists:	--------------------

ARTS THEATRE
6-7 Great Newport Street, London WC2H 7JB

Manager:	--------------------
Stage Door:	020-7836 2132
Box Office:	020-7836 3334
Artists:	--------------------
e-mail:	natalie@the-arts.fsnet.co.uk

BARBICAN
Barbican
London EC2Y 8BQ

Manager:	020-7628 3351
Stage Door:	020-7628 3351
Box Office:	020-7638 8891
Artists:	020-7628 3351

BLOOMSBURY
15 Gordon Street, London WC1H 0AH

Manager:	020-7679 2777
Stage Door:	020-7679 2922
Box Office:	020-7388 8822
Artists:	--------------------
e-mail:	blooms.theatre@ucl.ac.uk

CAMBRIDGE
Earlham Street
Seven Dials, Covent Garden, London WC2 9HH

Manager:	020-7850 8711
Stage Door:	020-7850 8710
Box Office:	020-7494 5040
Artists:	--------------------

COLISEUM (English National Opera)
St Martin's Lane
London WC2N 4ES

Manager:	020-7836 0111
Stage Door:	020-7836 1416
Box Office:	020-7632 8300
Artists:	020-7836 1416

COMEDY
Panton Street
London SW1Y 4DN

Manager:	020-7321 5310
Stage Door:	020-7321 5300
Box Office:	020-7321 5305
Artists:	020-7321 5317

CRITERION
Piccadilly
London W1

Manager:	020-7839 8811
Stage Door:	020-7839 8811
Box Office:	020-7413 1437
Artists:	020-7839 8811

DOMINION
268-269 Tottenham Court Road
London W1T 7AQ

Manager:	020-7580 1889
Stage Door:	020-7927 0900
Box Office:	0870 6077400
Artists:	--------------------

DONMAR WAREHOUSE
41 Earlham Street, London WC2H 9LX

Manager:	020-7438 9200
Stage Door:	020-7438 9200
Box Office:	020-7369 1732
Admin:	020-7240 4882
e-mail:	office@donmar.demon.co.uk

DRURY LANE
(Theatre Royal)
Catherine Street, London WC2B 5JF

Manager:	020-7836 3687
Stage Door:	020-7836 3352
Box Office:	020-7494 5060
Artists:	020-7836 3352

DUCHESS
Catherine Street
London WC2B 5LA

Manager:	020-7379 5717
Stage Door:	020-7379 0495
Box Office:	020-7494 5075
Artists:	--------------------

DUKE OF YORK'S
St Martin's Lane
London WC2N 4BG

Manager:	020-7836 4615
Stage Door:	020-7836 4615
Box Office:	020-7836 5122
Artists:	020-7836 4615

FORTUNE
Russell Street
Covent Garden, London WC2B 5HH

Manager:	020-7836 6260
Stage Door:	020-7836 0441
Box Office:	020-7836 2238
Artists:	020-7836 0441

GARRICK
Charing Cross Road
London WC2H 0HH

Manager:	020-7836 9396
Stage Door:	020-7836 8271
Box Office:	020-7494 5085
Artists:	020-7836 8271

GIELGUD
Shaftesbury Avenue
London W1V 8AR
Manager: 020-7439 1912
Stage Door: 020-7437 6003
Box Office: 020-7494 5065
Artists: 020-7437 5163

HACKNEY EMPIRE
291 Mare Street
London E8 1EJ
Manager: 020-8510 4500
Stage Door: 020-8510 4515
Box Office: 020-8985 2424
Artists: -------------------

HAMPSTEAD THEATRE
98 Avenue Road, Swiss Cottage London NW3 3EX
Manager: 020-7722 9224
Stage Door: 020-7722 1189
Box Office: 020-7722 9301
Artists: 020-7722 1189
e-mail: admin@hampstead-theatre.com

HAYMARKET
(Theatre Royal)
London SW1Y 4HT
Manager: 020-7930 8890
Stage Door: -------------------
Box Office: 0870 9013356
Artists: -------------------

HER MAJESTY'S
Haymarket
London SW1Y 4QR
Manager: 020-7930 5343
Stage Door: 020-7930 5337
Box Office: 020-7494 5400
Artists: -------------------

LONDON APOLLO HAMMERSMITH
Queen Caroline Street
London W6 9QH
Manager: 020-8748 8660
Stage Door: -------------------
Box Office: 0870 6063400
Artists: -------------------

LYCEUM THEATRE
21 Wellington Street
London WC2E 7RQ
Manager: 020-7420 8191
Stage Door: 020-7420 8100
Box Office: 020-7420 8114
Artists: -------------------

LYRIC
Shaftesbury Avenue
London W1D 7ES
Manager: 020-7437 3694
Stage Door: 020-7437 5443
Box Office: 020-7494 5045
Artists: -------------------

LYRIC THEATRE HAMMERSMITH
King Street, London W6 0QL
Manager: 020-8741 0824
Stage Door: 020-8041 0824
Box Office: 020-8741 2311
Artists: 020-8741 0824
e-mail: enquiries@lyric.co.uk

NEW AMBASSADORS
West Street, London WC2H 9ND
Manager: 020-7565 6471
Stage Door: 020-7836 4105
Box Office: 020-7369 1761
Artists: 020-7836 4105

NEW LONDON
Drury Lane
London WC2B 5PW
Manager: 020-7242 9802
Stage Door: 020-7242 9802
Box Office: 020-7405 0072
Artists: 020-7242 9802

OLD VIC The
Waterloo Road, London SE1 8NB
Manager: 020-7928 2651
Stage Door: 020-7928 2651
Box Office: 020-7928 7616
Artists: 020-7928 2651
e-mail: old.vic@pobox.com

OPEN AIR THEATRE
(Regent's Park)
London
Manager: 020-7935 5756
Stage Door: 020-7935 5756
Box Office: 020-7486 2431
Artists: -------------------

PALACE
Shaftesbury Avenue, London W1
Manager: 020-7434 0088
Stage Door: 020-7434 0088
Box Office: 020-7434 0909
Artists: -------------------
e-mail: thepalacetheatre@hotmail.com

PALLADIUM
Argyll Street
London W1F 7TF
Manager: 020-7437 6678
Stage Door: 020-7437 1278
Box Office: 020-7494 5020
Artists: -------------------

PEACOCK
(See
SADLER'S
WELLS
in the
West End)

PHOENIX
Charing Cross Road
London WC2H 0JP
Manager: 020-7438 9600
Stage Door: 020-7438 9610
Box Office: 020-7438 9605
Artists: -------------------

PICCADILLY
Denman Street
London W1D 7DY
Manager: 020-7478 8810
Stage Door: 020-7478 8800
Box Office: 020-7478 8805
Artists: 020-7478 8800

PLAYERS'
The Arches, Villiers Street, London WC2N 6NL
Manager: 020-7976 1307
Stage Door: 020-7976 1307
Box Office: 020-7839 1134
Artists: 020-7976 1307
e-mail: info@playerstheatre.co.uk

PLAYHOUSE
Northumberland Avenue, London WC2N 5DE
Manager: -------------------
Stage Door: 020-7839 4292
Box Office: 020-7839 4401
Artists: -------------------

Scenery contractors specialising in all aspects of
engineering, carpentry, scenic art and prop making.
Recent projects include The King & I, Witches of Eastwick
and sets for ITN and Channel 4 News.

Kimpton Walker

Theatre, Film and Television Scenery

10 Ellerslie Square
Lyham Road, London SW2 5DZ
Telephone: 020 7738 3222 Telefax: 020 7738 5517
E-mail: info@kimptonwalker.co.uk
Web Site: http://www.kimptonwalker.co.uk

PRINCE EDWARD
Old Compton Street
London W1V 6HS
Manager:	020-7437 2024
Stage Door:	020-7439 3041
Box Office:	020-7447 5400
Artists:	--------------------

PRINCE OF WALES
Coventry Street
London W1D 6AS
Manager:	020-7930 1867
Stage Door:	020-7930 1432
Box Office:	020-7839 5972
Artists:	020-7930 1432

QUEEN'S
51 Shaftesbury Avenue
London W1D 6BA
Manager:	020-7734 0869
Stage Door:	020-7734 1348
Box Office:	020-7494 5040
Artists:	--------------------

ROYAL COURT THEATRE
Sloane Square, London SW1W 8AS
Manager:	020-7565 5050
Stage Door:	020-7565 5050
Box Office:	020-7565 5000
Artists:	020-7565 5050
e-mail:	info@royalcourttheatre.com

ROYAL NATIONAL
South Bank
London SE1 9PX
Admin:	020-7452 3333
Stage Door:	020-7452 3333
Box Office:	020-7452 3000
Artists:	020-7452 3333

ROYAL OPERA HOUSE
Bow Street
Covent Garden, London WC2E 9DD
Manager:	020-7240 1200
Stage Door:	--------------------
Box Office:	020-7304 4000
Artists:	--------------------

SADLER'S WELLS
Rosebery Avenue
London EC1R 4TN
Manager:	--------------------
Stage Door:	020-7863 8198
Box Office:	020-7863 8000
Artists:	--------------------
e-mail:	info@sadlerswells.com

SADLER'S WELLS IN THE WEST END
Peacock Theatre
Portugal Street, Kingsway, London WC2A 2HT
Manager:	--------------------
Stage Door:	020-7863 8268
Box Office:	020-7863 8222
Artists:	--------------------

SAVOY
Strand
London WC2R 0ET
Manager:	020-7836 8117
Stage Door:	020-7836 8117
Box Office:	020-7836 8888
Artists:	020-7836 8117

SHAFTESBURY
210 Shaftesbury Avenue, London WC2H 8DP
Manager:	020-7379 3345
Stage Door:	020-7379 3345
Box Office:	020-7379 5399
Artists:	020-7379 3345
e-mail:	cflatman@toc.dltentertainment.co.uk

SHAKESPEARE'S GLOBE
21 New Globe Walk
Bankside London SE1 9DT
Manager:	020-7902 1400
Stage Door:	020-7902 1400
Box Office:	020-7401 9919
Artists:	020-7902 1400

ST MARTIN'S
West Street
London WC2H 9NZ
Manager:	020-7497 0578
Stage Door:	020-7836 1086
Box Office:	020-7836 1443
Artists:	020-7836 1086

STRAND
Aldwych
London WC2B 4LD
Manager:	020-7836 4144
Stage Door:	020-7836 4144
Box Office:	020-7930 8800
Artists:	020-7836 4144

VAUDEVILLE
404 Strand
London WC2R 0NH
Manager:	020-7836 1820
Stage Door:	020-7836 3191
Box Office:	020-7836 9987
Artists:	020-7836 3191

VICTORIA PALACE
Victoria Street
London SW1E 5EA
Manager:	020-7834 2781
Stage Door:	020-7834 2781
Box Office:	020-7834 1317
Artists:	020-7834 2781

WHITEHALL
14 Whitehall
London SW1A 2DY
Manager:	020-7321 5400
Stage Door:	020-7321 5400
Box Office:	020-7369 1735
Artists:	020-7321 5400
e-mail:	whitehall@theambassadors.com

WYNDHAM'S
Charing Cross Road
London WC2H 0DA
Manager:	020-7438 9700
Stage Door:	020-7438 9700
Box Office:	020-7369 1736
Artists:	020-7438 9700

YOUNG VIC
66 The Cut, London SE1 8LZ
Manager:	020-7633 0133
Stage Door:	--------------------
Box Office:	020-7928 6363
Artists:	--------------------
e-mail:	info@youngvic.org.uk

ARCOLA THEATRE
(Artistic Director - Mehmet Ergen)
27 Arcola Street, Dalston
(Off Stoke Newington Road), London E8 2DJ
e-mail: info@arcolatheatre.com
Fax: 020-7503 1645
BO: 020-7503 1646   Admin: 020-7503 1645
Route: Victoria Line to Highbury & Islington, then
North London Line to Dalston Kingsland BR - 5 min
walk. Buses: 38 from West End, 149 from London
Bridge or 30, 5, 67, 76, 243

ASHCROFT THEATRE
Fairfield Halls Park Lane, Croydon CR9 1DG
e-mail: dbarr@fairfield.co.uk
BO: 020-8688 9291   Admin & SD: 020-8681 0821
Route: Victoria (BR) to East Croydon then 5 min
walk

BAC
Lavender Hill, London SW11 5TN
e-mail: mailbox@bac.org.uk
Fax: 020-7978 5207
BO: 020-7223 2223   Admin: 020-7223 6557
Route: Victoria or Waterloo (BR) to Clapham
Junction then 5 min walk or Northern Line to
Clapham Common then 20 min walk

BARONS COURT THEATRE
'The Curtain's Up'
28A Comeragh Road, West Kensington
London W14 9RH
Fax: 020-7603 8935   Admin/BO: 020-8932 4747
Route: West Kensington or Barons Court tube

BECK THEATRE
Grange Road, Hayes, Middlesex UB3 2UE
BO: 020-8561 8371   Admin: 020-8561 7506
Route: Central Line to Ealing Broadway then bus
207 to Theatre (30 min) or Paddington (BR) to
Hayes Harlington then buses 90, H98 or 195 (10
min)

BEDLAM THEATRE
11B Bristo Place, Edinburgh EH1 1EZ
e-mail: info@bedlamtheatre.co.uk
                              Tel: 0131-225 9873

BELLAIRS PLAYHOUSE
(Guildford School of Acting)
Millmead Terrace, Guildford GU2 4YT
e-mail: enquiries@gsa.drama.ac.uk
                              Admin: 01483 560701

BLOOMSBURY THEATRE
15 Gordon Street, Bloomsbury, London WC1H 0AH
e-mail: blooms.theatre@ucl.ac.uk
BO: 020-7388 8822   Admin: 020-7679 2777
Route: Tube to Euston, Euston Square or Warren
Street

BRENTWOOD THEATRE
(Theatre Administrator Karen Fisher)
15 Shenfield Road, Brentwood, Essex CM15 8AG
Stage Door: 01277 226658
BO: 01277 200300   Admin/Fax: 01277 230833
Route: Liverpool Street (BR) to Brentwood, then 15
min walk

BRIDEWELL THEATRE The
Bride Lane, Fleet Street, London EC4Y 8EQ
e-mail: admin@bridewelltheatre.co.uk
Fax: 020-7583 5289
BO: 020-7936 3456   Admin: 020-7353 0259
Route: Blackfriars, St Paul's: City Thameslink.
Fifteen different bus routes

BULLION ROOM THEATRE
(Behind Hackney Empire Theatre)
117 Wilton Way, London E8 1BH
BO: 020-8985 2424   Press/Admin: 020-8510 4500

BUSH THEATRE
(Mike Bradwell)
Shepherd's Bush Green, London W12 8QD
BO: 020-7610 4224
Production: 020-8743 5050 Admin: 020-7602 3703
Route: Central Line to Shepherd's Bush or
Hammersmith & City Line to Goldhawk Road or
buses 12, 49, 94, 207 or 220

CAMDEN PEOPLE'S THEATRE
(Artistic Director - Olivia Jackson)
58-60 Hampstead Road, London NW1 2PY
e-mail: cpt@dircon.co.uk
Fax: 020-7813 3889   Tel: 020-7916 5878
Route: Victoria or Northern Line to Warren Street,
Metropolitan or Circle Line to Euston Square
(1 min walk either way)

CANAL CAFE THEATRE The
(Artistic Director - Emma Taylor)
The Bridge House, Delamere Terrace
Little Venice, London W2 6ND
e-mail: mail@canalcafetheatre.com
Fax: 020-7266 1717
BO: 020-7289 6054   Admin: 020-7289 6056

CAPITAL ARTS THEATRE COMPANY
Capital Arts, Wyllyotts Centre, Darkes Lane
Potters Bar, Herts EN6 12HN
e-mail: capitalartstheatre@genie.co.uk
Mobile: 07885 232414   Tel/Fax: 020-8449 2342

CHANTICLEER THEATRE
(Webber Douglas Academy)
30 Clareville Street, London SW7 5AP
Fax: 020-7373 5639   Tel: 020-7370 4154
Route: Piccadilly, District or Circle Line to
Gloucester Road, turn right, walk for 300 yards
then turn left into Clareville Street

CHATS PALACE ARTS CENTRE
(Nick Reed)
42-44 Brooksby's Walk, Hackney, London E9 6DF
BO: 020-8986 6714   Admin: 020-8533 0227

CHELSEA THEATRE
(Francis Alexander)
World's End Place, King's Road, SW10 0DR
e-mail: chelseatheatre@btinternet.com
Fax: 020-7352 2024   Tel: 020-7352 1967
Route: District or Circle Line to Sloane Square
then short bus ride 11 or 22 down King's Road

CHRIST'S HOSPITAL THEATRE
(Director Jeff Mayhew)
Horsham, West Sussex RH13 7LW
e-mail: jmayhew@christs_hospital.org.uk
BO: 01403 247434   Admin: 01403 247435

CLUB FOR ACTS & ACTORS The
(Concert Artistes Association)
(Pamela Cundell, Barbara Daniels)
20 Bedford Street
London WC2E 9HP   Admin: 020-7836 3172
Route: Piccadilly or Northern Line to Leicester
Square then few mins walk

COCHRANE THEATRE
(Deirdre Malynn)
Southampton Row, London WC1B 4AP
e-mail: cochranetheatre@linst.ac.uk
BO: 020-7242 7040   Admin: 020-7430 2500
Route: Central or Piccadilly Line to Holborn then 1
min walk

COCKPIT THEATRE
Gateforth Street, London NW8 8EH
e-mail: dave.wybrow@awc.ac.uk
Fax: 020-7258 2921
BO: 020-7258 2925   Admin: 020-7258 2920
Route: Tube to Marylebone/Edgware Road then
short walk or bus 139 to Lisson Grove & 6, 8, or 16
to Edgware Road

CORBETT THEATRE
(East 15 Acting School)
Rectory Lane, Loughton, Essex IG10 3RY
e-mail: east15.acting@ukonline.co.uk
Fax: 020-8508 7521   BO & Admin: 020-8508 5983
Route: Central Line (Epping Branch) to Debden
then 6 min walk

COURTYARD THEATRE The
(June Abbott - Artistic Director,
Tim Gill - General Manager)
10 York Way, King's Cross, London N1 9AA
e-mail: info@courtyardtheatre.freeserve.co.uk
Admin/Fax: 020-7833 0870   BO: 020-7833 0876
Route: Route: Side of King's Cross Station

CUSTARD FACTORY
Gibb Street, Digbeth
Birmingham B9 4AA
e-mail: custardfactory@clara.net
Fax: 0121-604 8888   Tel: 0121-693 7777

DARTFORD ORCHARD THEATRE
Home Gardens, Dartford, Kent DA1 1ED
Fax: 01322 227122
BO: 01322 220000   Admin: 01322 220099
Route: Route: Charing Cross (BR) to Dartford

DENCH Judi THEATRE
(See MOUNTVIEW THEATRE)

DIORAMA STUDIO THEATRE
(Mark Ross)
34 Osnaburgh Street, London NW1 3ND
e-mail: admin@diorama-arts.org.uk
Fax: 020-7916 5282
BO: 020-7419 2000   Admin: 020-7916 5467
Route: Circle & District Line to Great Portland
Street then 1 min walk or Victoria/Northern line to
Warren Street then 5 min walk

DRAGON MULTIMEDIA
St Georges Theatre
49 Tufnell Park Road, London N7 0PS
e-mail: stgeorgestheatre@lineone.net
Fax: 020-7609 2427   Tel: 020-7607 7978

DRILL HALL The
16 Chenies Street, London WC1E 7EX
e-mail: admin@drillhall.co.uk
Fax: 020-7307 5062
BO: 020-7307 5060   Admin: 020-7307 5061
Route: Northern Line to Goodge Street then 1 min
walk

EDINBURGH FESTIVAL FRINGE
180 High Street, Edinburgh EH1 1QS
e-mail: admin@edfringe.com
Fax: 0131-220 4205   Tel: 0131-226 5257

EDINBURGH UNIVERSITY THEATRE COMPANY
(See BEDLAM THEATRE)

EMBASSY THEATRE & STUDIOS
(Central School of Speech & Drama)
64 Eton Avenue, Swiss Cottage
London NW3 3HY
BO: 020-7559 3935   Admin: 020-7559 3999
Route: Jubilee Line to Swiss Cottage then 1 min
walk

ETCETERA THEATRE CLUB
(Kirsty Housley - Director,
Rob McIndoe - Literary Manager)
Oxford Arms, 265 Camden High St, London NW1 7BU
e-mail: etceteratheatre@hotmail.com
Fax: 020-7482 0378   Admin/BO: 020-7482 4857

FINBOROUGH THEATRE
(Neil McPherson)
Finborough Arms, 118 Finborough Road
London SW10 9ED
steamindustry@finboroughtheatre.freeserve.co.uk
Fax: 020-7835 1853
BO: 020-7373 3842   Admin: 020-7244 7439
Route: District or Piccadilly Line to Earls Court then
5 min walk. Buses 30, 74, C3 or 31 then 3 min walk

GATE THEATRE
(Erica Whyman)
Above Prince Albert Pub
11 Pembridge Road, London W11 3HQ
e-mail: gate@gatetheatre.freeserve.co.uk
Fax: 020-7221 6055
BO: 020-7229 0706   Admin: 020-7229 5387
Route: Central, Circle or District Line to Notting
Hill Gate then 1 min walk

GRACE THEATRE The
(Artistic Director - Ruth Carney)
The Latchmere, 503 Battersea Park Road
London SW11 3BW
e-mail: carneyruth@hotmail.com
BO: 020-7794 0022   Admin: 020-7228 5011
Route: Victoria or Waterloo (BR) to Clapham
Junction then 10 min walk or buses 44, 219, 319,
344, 345 or tube to South Kensington then buses
45a or 49

GREENWICH PLAYHOUSE
(Alice de Sousa)
Greenwich BR Station Forecourt
189 Greenwich High Road
London SE10 8JA
Fax: 020-8969 2910   Tel: 020-8858 9256
Route: BR from Charing Cross, Waterloo East or
London Bridge, DLR-Greenwich

GREENWICH THEATRE
(Executive Director - Hilary Strong)
Crooms Hill, Greenwich
London SE10 8ES
e-mail: info@greenwichtheatre.org.uk
Fax: 020-8858 8042
BO: 020-8858 7755   Admin: 020-8858 4447
Route: Jubilee Line (change Canary Wharf) then
DLR to Greenwich Cutty Sark, 3 minute walk or
Charing Cross (BR) to Greenwich, 5 minute walk

GUILDHALL SCHOOL OF MUSIC & DRAMA
Silk Street, Barbican
London EC2Y 8DT
e-mail: info@gsmd.ac.uk
Fax: 020-7256 9438   Tel: 020-7628 2571
Route: Hammersmith & City, Circle or
Metropolitan line to Barbican or Moorgate
(also served by Northern line) then 5 min walk

HEN & CHICKENS THEATRE
Unrestricted View,
Above Hen & Chickens Theatre Bar
109 St Paul's Road, Islington
London N1 2NA
e-mail: james@henandchickens.com
Tel: 020-7704 2001
Route: Route: Victoria Line or Main Line to
Highbury & Islington directly opposite station

HORLA
(Artistic Director - Alistair Green,
General Manager - Dave Roberts)
The Rose and Crown Theatre, 59-61 High Street
Hampton Wick, Surrey KT1 4DG
e-mail: info@horla.co.uk
BO: 020-8296 9100   Admin/Fax: 020-8296 0242

HUNT THEATRE
Felsted School, Felsted, Nr Dunmow
Essex CM6 3JG
e-mail: crsl@felsted.essex.sch.uk
Fax: 01371 821232
BO: 01371 820258   Admin: 01371 821078

ICA THEATRE
The Mall, London SW1
Fax: 020-7839 6213
BO: 020-7930 3647   Admin: 020-7930 0493
Route: Nearest stations Piccadilly & Charing Cross

JACKSONS LANE THEATRE
269A Archway Road
London N6 5AA   Tel: 020-8340 5226

JERMYN STREET THEATRE
(Administator - Penny Horner)
16B Jermyn Street, London SW1Y 6ST
BO: 020-7287 2875   Fax/Admin: 020-7434 1443

KING'S HEAD THEATRE
(Dan Crawford)
115 Upper Street, Islington, London N1 1QN
BO: 020-7226 1916   Admin: 020-7226 8561
Route: Northern Line to Angel then 5 min walk.
Approx halfway between Angel and Highbury &
Islington tube stations

KING'S LYNN CORN EXCHANGE
Tuesday Market Place, King's Lynn
Norfolk PE30 1JW
e-mail: suzanne.hopp@west-norfolk.gov.uk
Fax: 01553 762141
BO: 01553 764864   Admin: 01553 765565

KOMEDIA
(Artistic Directors David Lavender - Theatre &
Comedy, Marina Cobler - Music & Cabaret)
44-47 Gardner Street, Brighton BN1 1UN
e-mail: info@komedia.co.uk
Fax: 01273 647102
BO: 01273 647100   Tel: 01273 647101

LANDMARK ARTS CENTRE
Ferry Road, Teddington Lock
Middlesex TW11 9NN
e-mail: landmarkz1@aol.com
Fax: 020-8977 4830   Tel: 020-8977 7558

LANDOR THEATRE The
(Artistic Director - Linda Edwards,
General Manager - Robert McWhir)
70 Landor Road, London SW9 9PH
                         Admin/BO: 020-7737 7276
Route: Northern Line Clapham North then 2 min
walk

LEIGHTON BUZZARD
(Lois Wright - Theatre Manager)
Leighton Buzzard Theatre, Lake Street
Leighton Buzzard
Beds LU7 8RX   Tel: 01525 850290

LILIAN BAYLIS THEATRE
(Information: Sadler's Wells)
Rosebery Avenue, London EC1R 4TN
e-mail: info@sadlerswells.com
BO: 020-7863 8000   SD: 020-7863 8198

LIVE THEATRE The
27 Broad Chare, Quayside
Newcastle-upon-Tyne NE1 3DQ
e-mail: info@live.org.uk
Fax: 0191-232 2224
BO: 0191-232 1232   Admin: 0191-261 2694

MACOWAN THEATRE
(LAMDA)
1-2 Logan Place, London W8 6QN
Fax: 020-7370 1980
BO: 020-7244 2000   Admin: 020-7373 9883
Route: District or Piccadilly Line to Earl's Court
then 6 min walk

MADDERMARKET THEATRE
(Clare Goddard - Artistic Director,
Michael Lyas - General Manager)
St John's Alley, Norwich NR2 1DR
e-mail: theatre@maddermarket.freeserve.co.uk
Fax: 01603 661357
BO: 01603 620917   Admin: 01603 626560

MAN IN THE MOON THEATRE
392 King's Road, London SW3 5UZ
Fax: 020-7351 1873
BO: 020-7351 2876   Admin: 020-7351 5701
Route: Tube to Sloane Square then short bus ride
11, 22 or 19 down King's Road or tube to South
Kensington then bus 49 or 345 to junction of
Beaufort Street & King's Road

MERMAID THEATRE
(Conference & Events Centre)
Puddle Dock, Blackfriars
London EC4V 3DB
e-mail: info@the-mermaid.co.uk
                         Tel: 020-7236 1919
Route: Route: Tube to Blackfriars or St Paul's, buses
45 or 63 or Thameslink to Blackfriars

MILLFIELD THEATRE
Silver Street, London N18 1PJ
e-mail: info@millfieldtheatre.co.uk
Fax: 020-8803 2801
BO: 020-8807 6680   Admin: 020-8803 5283
Route: Liverpool Street (BR) to Silver Street or tube
to Turnpike Lane then buses 444, 144A, 217 or 231.
10 min to Cambridge roundabout

MOUNTVIEW THEATRE
104 Crouch Hill
London N8 9EA   Admin/BO: 020-8347 3601
Route: Piccadilly or Victoria Line to Finsbury Park
(18 min) then W7 bus to Dickenson Road (5 min)

MYERS STUDIO THEATRE The
(Trevor Mitchell - Venues Manager)
The Epsom Playhouse, Ashley Avenue
Epsom, Surrey KT18 5AL
Fax: 01372 726228
BO: 01372 742555   Tel: 01372 742226

NETHERBOW The
(Donald Smith)
43-45 High Street
Edinburgh EH1 1SR   Tel: 0131-556 9579

NETTLEFOLD The
West Norwood Library Centre
1 Norwood High Street, London SE27 9JX
Fax: 020-7926 8071   Admin/BO: 020-7926 8070
Route: Victoria, West Croydon or London Bridge
(BR) to West Norwood then 2 min walk, or tube to
Brixton then buses 196, 2, 68

NEW END THEATRE
27 New End, Hampstead
London NW3 1JD
Fax: 020-7472 5808
BO: 020-7794 0022   Admin: 020-7794 9963
Route: Northern Line to Hampstead then 2 min
walk off Heath Street

NORTHBROOK THEATRE The
Littlehampton Road, Goring-by-Sea
Worthing, West Sussex BN12 6NU
e-mail: box.office@nbcol.ac.uk
Fax: 01903 606316　　　　　　BO: 01903 606162
　　　　　Marketing & Publicity: 01903 606230
　　　　　Theatre Manager: 01903 606287

NOVELLO THEATRE The
(Redroofs Theatre Company)
2 High Street, Sunninghill
Nr Ascot Berks　　　　　　Tel: 01344 20881
Route: Waterloo (BR) to Ascot then 1 mile from
station

OLD RED LION
(Ken McClymont - Artistic Director)
418 St John Street, Islington, London EC1V 4NJ
BO: 020-7837 7816　　Admin/Fax: 020-7833 3053
Route: Northern Line to Angel then 1 min walk

ORANGE TREE
(Sam Walters - Artistic Director)
1 Clarence Street, Richmond TW9 2SA
e-mail: admin@orange-tree.demon.co.uk
Fax: 020-8332 0369
BO: 020-8940 3633　　　　　Admin: 020-8940 0141
Route: District Line, Waterloo (BR) or North London
Line, then virtually opposite station

OVAL HOUSE THEATRE
52-54 Kennington Oval, London SE11 5SW
e-mail: admin@ovalhouse.com
BO: 020-7582 7680　　　　Admin: 020-7582 0080
Route: Northern Line to Oval then 1 min walk,
Victoria Line & BR to Vauxhall then 5 min walk

PENTAMETERS
Three Horseshoes
28 Heath Street, London NW3 6TE
e-mail: pentameters@ptheatre.freeserve.co.uk
　　　　　　　BO/Admin: 020-7435 3648
Route: Northern Line to Hampstead then 1 min
walk

PLACE The
(Main London Venue for Contemporary Dance)
17 Duke's Road, London WC1H 9PY
e-mail: placetheatre@easynet.co.uk
BO: 020-7387 0031　　　　Admin: 020-7380 1268
Route: Northern or Victoria Lines to Euston or
King's Cross then 5 min walk (Opposite rear of St
Pancras Church)

PLEASANCE LONDON
(Christopher Richardson)
Carpenters Mews, North Road
(Off Caledonian Road), London N7 9EF
e-mail: info@pleasance.co.uk
Fax: 020-7700 7366
BO: 020-7609 1800　　　　Admin: 020-7700 6877
Route: Piccadilly Line to Caledonian Road, turn
left, walk 50 yds, turn left into North Road, 2 min
walk, buses 10, 17, 46, 91, 259, N21 or N91

POLISH THEATRE
Polish Social & Cultural Assoc. Ltd
238-246 King Street, London W6 0RF
BO: 020-8741 0398　　　　Admin: 020-8741 1940
Route: District Line to Ravenscourt Park, or District
& Piccadilly or Metropolitan Lines to
Hammersmith then 7 min walk. Buses 27, 267, 190,
391 or H91

POLKA THEATRE FOR CHILDREN
240 The Broadway, Wimbledon SW19 1SB
e-mail: administration@polkatheatre.com
Fax: 020-8545 8365
BO: 020-8543 4888　　　　Admin: 020-8545 8320
Route: Waterloo (BR) or District Line to
Wimbledon then 10 min walk. Northern Line to
South Wimbledon then 10 min walk

PRINCESS THEATRE HUNSTANTON
The Green, Hunstanton, Norfolk PE36 5AH
Fax: 01485 534463
BO: 01485 532252　　　　Admin: 01485 535937

QUEEN'S THEATRE
(Artistic Director - Bob Carlton,
Administrator - Henrietta Duckworth)
Billet Lane, Hornchurch, Essex RM11 1QT
e-mail: info@queens-theatre.co.uk
Fax: 01708 452348　　　　　SD: 01708 442078
BO: 01708 443333　　　　Admin 01708 456118
Route: District Line to Hornchurch, BR to
Romford/Gidea Park. 15 miles from West End
take A13, A1306 then A125 or A12 then A127

QUESTORS THEATRE EALING The
12 Mattock Lane, London W5 5BQ
e-mail: enquiries@questors.org.uk
Fax: 020-8567 8736
BO: 020-8567 5184　　　　Admin: 020-8567 0011
Route: Central or District Line to
Ealing Broadway then 5 min walk

RICHMOND THEATRE
(Karin Gartzke)
The Green, Richmond, Surrey TW9 1QJ
e-mail: richmondtheatre@theambassadors.com
Fax: 020-8948 3601
BO: 020-8940 0088　　Admin & SD: 020-8940 0220
Route: District Line, Waterloo (BR) or
North London Line to Richmond then 2 min walk

RIDWARE THEATRE
(Alan & Margaret Williams)
Wheelwright's House, Pipe Ridware
Rugeley, Staffs WS15 3QL
e-mail: alanw@smr-group.com
　　　　　　　　　　　　Tel: 01889 504380

RIVERSIDE STUDIOS
Crisp Road, London W6 9RL
e-mail: jonfawcett@riversidestudios.co.uk
BO: 020-8237 1111　　　　Admin: 020-8237 1000
Route: District, Piccadilly or Hammersmith & City
Line to Hammersmith Broadway then 5 min walk.
Buses 9, 11, 27, 73, 91, 220, 283 or 295

ROSEMARY BRANCH THEATRE
2 Shepperton Road
London N1 3DT
e-mail: cecilia@rosemarybranch.co.uk
　　　　　　　　　　　　Tel: 020-7704 6665

SEVENOAKS STAG THEATRE
London Road, Sevenoaks
Kent TN13 1ZZ
BO: 01732 450175　　　　Admin: 01732 451548
Route: Charing Cross (BR) to Sevenoaks then 15
mins up the hill from station

SHAW THEATRE The
The Shaw Park Plaza Hotel
100-110 Euston Road, London NW1 2AJ
e-mail: admin@the-shaw.co.uk
BO: 0870 7301180　　　Tel/Fax: 020-7387 6864

SOHO THEATRE COMPANY
21 Dean Street, London W1V 6NE
Fax: 020-7493 8051　　　　Tel: 020-7493 8050
Route: Route: Tube to Tottenham Court Road
then 2nd left up Oxford Street

SOUTH HILL PARK ARTS CENTRE
Ringmead
Bracknell, Berks RG12 7PA
e-mail: admin@southillpark.org.uk
BO: 01344 484123　　Admin & SD: 01344 484858
Route: Waterloo (BR) to Bracknell then 10 min bus
ride or taxi rank at station

SOUTH LONDON THEATRE
(Bell Theatre & Prompt Corner)
2A Norwood High Street
London SE27 9NS
e-mail: southlondontheatre@yahoo.co.uk
Tel: 020-8670 3474
Route: A) Victoria or London Bridge (BR) to W Norwood then 2 min walk. Route B) Victoria Line to Brixton then buses 2, 68, 196 or 322

SOUTHWARK PLAYHOUSE
(Artistic Director - Thea Sharrock
Hon. Directors - Juliet Alderdice, Tom Wilson)
62 Southwark Bridge Road
London SE1 0AS
e-mail: skplay@globalnet.co.uk
BO: 020-7620 3494   Admin: 020-7652 2224
Route: Northern Line to Borough or Jubilee Line to Southwark (BR) & London Bridge. Buses 133, 35, 344, 40, P3

STANSTED PARK
The Little Theatre, Stansted Park
Rowlands Castle, Hants PO9 6DX
e-mail: enquiry@stanstedpark.co.uk
Fax: 023-9241 3773   Tel: 023-9241 2265

TABARD THEATRE
(Hamish Gray - Artistic Director)
2 Bath Road, Turnham Green
London W4 1LW
e-mail: hamish@hgray68.freeserve.co.uk
BO 020-8995 6035   Admin/Fax: 020-8994 5985
Route: District Line to Turnham Green then 1 min walk

THEATRE ROYAL STRATFORD EAST
(Philip Hedley)
Gerry Raffles Square
London E15 1BN
e-mail: theatreroyal@stratfordeast.com
Fax: 020-8534 8381
BO: 020-8534 0310   Admin: 020-8534 7374
Route: Central Line and Jubilee Line to Stratford then 2 min walk)

THEATRO TECHNIS
(George Eugeniou)
26 Crowndale Road
London NW1   BO & Admin: 020-7387 6617
Route: Northern Line to Mornington Crescent then 3 min walk

TOWER THEATRE
(Tavistock Repertory Company)
Canonbury Place, Islington
London N1 2NQ
BO: 020-7226 3633 (2.00pm-8.00pm)
Admin: 020-7226 5111
Route: Victoria Line to Highbury and Islington then 5 min walk

TRICYCLE THEATRE
(Nicolas Kent - Artistic Director,
Mary Lauder - General Manager)
269 Kilburn High Road, London NW6 7JR
e-mail: admin@tricycle.co.uk
Fax: 020-7328 0795
BO: 020-7328 1000   Admin: 020-7372 6611
Route: Jubilee Line to Kilburn then 5 min walk or buses 16, 189 or 32 pass the door, 28, 98, 31, 206, 316 & 139 pass nearby

TRON THEATRE
(Neil Murray - Administrative Director)
63 Trongate, Glasgow G1 5HB
e-mail: neil@tron.co.uk
Fax: 0141-552 6657
BO: 0141-552 4267   Admin: 0141-552 3748

UNION THEATRE The
(Artistic Director - Sasha Regan)
204 Union Street
Southwark, London SE1 0LX
e-mail: sasha@uniontheatre.freeserve.co.uk
Tel/Fax: 020-7261 9876
Route: Jubilee line to Southwark then 2 min walk

UPSTAIRS AT THE GATEHOUSE
(Ovation Theatres Ltd)
The Gatehouse Pub
North Road, London N6 4BD
e-mail: ovationgb@aol.com
BO: 020-8340 3488   Admin: 020-8340 3477

WAREHOUSE THEATRE
(Ted Craig)
Dingwall Road
Croydon CR0 2NF
e-mail: warehous@dircon.co.uk
Fax: 020-8688 6699
BO: 020-8680 4060   Admin: 020-8681 1257
Route: Adjacent to East Croydon (BR). Direct from Victoria (15 mins), Clapham Junction (10 mins) or by Thameslink from West Hampstead, Kentish Town, Kings Cross, Blackfriars & London Bridge

WATERMANS
(Jan Lennox)
40 High Street, Brentford
Middlesex TW8 0DS
e-mail: enquiries@watermans.org.uk
Fax: 020-8232 1030
BO: 020-8232 1010   Admin: 020-8232 1020
Route: Buses: 237, 267, 65 or N97
Tube: Gunnersbury or South Ealing BR:
Kew Bridge then 5 min walk, Gunnersbury then 10 min walk, or Brentford

WESTRIDGE OPEN CENTRE
(Showcase Window for Drawing Room Rrecitals)
Star Lane, Andover Road, Highclere
Nr Newbury, Berks RG20 9PJ   Tel: 01635 253322

WHITE BEAR THEATRE
(Favours New Writing)
138 Kennington Park Road
London SE11 4DJ
e-mail: micwbear@hotmail.com
Admin/BO: 020-7793 9193

WILTON'S MUSIC HALL
Graces' Alley, London E1 8JB
e-mail: opera@broomhill.demon.co.uk
BO: 020-7420 0222   Manager: 020-7702 9555

WIMBLEDON THEATRE
The Broadway
London SW19 1QG
Fax: 020-8543 6637
BO: 020-8540 0362   Admin: 020-8543 4549
Route: BR or District Line to Wimbledon BR and Tube, then 3 min walk. Buses 57, 93, 155

WIMBLEDON STUDIO THEATRE
(Wimbledon Theatre)
103 The Broadway
London SW19 1QG
Fax: 020-8543 6637
BO: 020-8540 0362   Admin: 020-8543 4549
Route: BR or District Line to Wimbledon BR and Tube, then 3 min walk. Buses 57,93,155

WYCOMBE SWAN
St Mary Street, High Wycombe
Bucks HP11 2XE
e-mail: enquiries@wycombeswan.co.uk
BO: 01494 512000   Admin: 01494 514444

See London Underground Map - inside back cover   293

ABERDEEN

His Majesty's Theatre
Rosemount Viaduct AB25 1GL
Box Office:	01224 641122
Stage Door:	01224 638677
Admin:	01224 637788
e-mail:	dhendry@arts-rec.aberdeen.net.uk

ABERYSTWYTH

Aberystwyth Arts Centre
Penglais Road
SY23 3DE
Box Office:	01970 623232
Stage Door:	01970 624239
Admin:	01970 622882

ASHTON-UNDER-LYNE

Tameside Hippodrome
Oldham Road
OL6 7SE
Box Office:	0161-308 3223
Stage Door:	0161-330 9256
Admin:	0161-330 2095

AYR

Gaiety Theatre
Carrick Street
KA7 1NU
Box Office:	01292 611222
Stage Door:	01292 611222
Admin:	01292 617400

BACUP

Royal Court Theatre
Rochdale Road, Lancs OL13 9NR
Box Office:	01706 874080
Stage Door:	------------------
Admin:	01706 870652
e-mail:	directoraw@aol.com

BASINGSTOKE

Haymarket Theatre
Wote Street RG21 7NW
Box Office:	01256 465566
Stage Door:	01256 323073
Admin:	01256 323073
e-mail:	info@haymarket.org.uk

BATH

Theatre Royal
Sawclose BA1 1ET
Box Office:	01225 448844
Stage Door:	01225 448815
Admin:	01225 448815
e-mail:	forename.surname@theatreroyal.org.uk

BELFAST

Grand Opera House
Great Victoria Street BT2 7HR
Box Office:	028-9024 1919
Stage Door:	028-9024 0411
Admin:	028-9024 0411
e-mail:	info@goh.co.uk

BILLINGHAM

Forum Theatre
Town Centre
TS23 2LJ
Box Office:	01642 552663
Stage Door:	------------------
Admin:	01642 551389

BIRMINGHAM

Alexandra Theatre
Station Street
B5 4DS
Box Office:	0870 6077533
Stage Door:	0121-230 9102
Admin:	0121-643 5536

BIRMINGHAM

Hippodrome
Hurst Street
B5 4TB
Box Office:	0870 7301234
Stage Door:	------------------
Admin:	0870 7305555

BLACKPOOL

Grand Theatre
33 Church Street FY1 1HT
Box Office:	01253 290190
Stage Door:	01253 294571
Admin:	01253 290111
e-mail:	geninfo@blackpoolgrand.co.uk

BLACKPOOL

Opera House
Church Street
FY1 1HW
Box Office:	01253 292029
Stage Door:	01253 625252 ext 148
Admin:	01253 625252

BOURNEMOUTH

Pavilion Theatre
Westover Road
BH1 2BX
Box Office:	01202 456456
Stage Door:	01202 451863
Admin:	01202 456400

BRADFORD

Alhambra Theatre
Morley Street
BD7 1AJ
Box Office:	01274 752000
Stage Door:	01274 752375
Admin:	01274 752375

BRADFORD

Theatre in the Mill
University of Bradford, Shearbridge Road BD7 1DP
Box Office:	01274 233200
Stage Door:	------------------
Admin:	01274 233188
e-mail:	theatre-manager@brad.ac.uk

BRIGHTON

The Dome, Corn Exchange & Pavilion Theatres
29 New Road
BN1 1UG
Box Office:	01273 709709
Stage Door:	------------------
Admin:	01273 700747

BRIGHTON

Theatre Royal
New Road
BN1 1SD
Box Office:	01273 328488
Stage Door:	01273 764400
Admin:	01273 764400

For accommodation see The Good Digs Guide Listings

BRISTOL

Hippodrome
St Augustines Parade
BS1 4UZ
Box Office: 0870 6077500
Stage Door: 0117-927 3077
Admin: 0117-926 5524

BROXBOURNE (Herts)

Civic Hall
High Street
Hoddesdon
EN11 8BE
Box Office: 01992 441946
Stage Door: --------------------
Admin: 01992 441931

BURY ST EDMUNDS

Theatre Royal
Westgate Street IP33 1QR
Box Office: 01284 769505
Stage Door: 01284 755127
Admin: 01284 755127
e-mail: admin@theatreroyal.org

BUXTON

Opera House
Water Street, Derbyshire SK17 6XN
Box Office: 01298 72190
Stage Door: 01298 71382
Admin: 01298 72050
e-mail: admin@buxton-opera.co.uk

CAMBRIDGE

Arts Theatre
6 St Edward's Passage
CB2 3PJ
Box Office: 01223 503333
Stage Door: 01223 578951
Admin: 01223 578933

CAMBRIDGE

Mumford Theatre
Anglia Polytechnic University, East Road CB1 1PT
Box Office: 01223 352932
Stage Door: 01223 352932
Admin: 01223 352932
e-mail: mumford@apu.ac.uk

CANTERBURY

Gulbenkian Theatre
University of Kent
CT2 7NB
Box Office: 01227 769075
Stage Door: 01227 769565
Admin: 01227 827861

CANTERBURY

The Marlowe Theatre
The Friars CT1 2AS
Box Office: 01227 787787
Stage Door: 01227 786867
Admin: 01227 763262
e-mail: markeverett@canterbury.gov.uk

CARDIFF

New Theatre
Park Place
CF10 3LN
Box Office: 029-2087 8889
Stage Door: 029-2087 8900
Admin: 029-2087 8787

CHELTENHAM

Everyman Theatre
Regent Street GL50 1HQ
Box Office: 01242 572573
Stage Door: 01242 512515
Admin: 01242 512515
e-mail: admin@everymantheatre.org.uk

CHICHESTER

Festival Theatre
Oaklands Park
PO19 4AP
Box Office: 01243 781312
Stage Door: 01243 784437
Admin: 01243 784437
e-mail: admin@cft.org.uk

CRAWLEY

The Hawth
Hawth Avenue RH10 6YZ
Box Office: 01293 553636
Stage Door: 01293 510022
Admin: 01293 552941
e-mail: info@hawth.co.uk

CREWE

Lyceum Theatre
Heath Street
CW1 2DA
Box Office: 01270 537333
Stage Door: 01270 537336
Admin: 01270 537243

DARLINGTON

Civic Theatre
Parkgate
DL1 1RR
Box Office: 01325 486555
Stage Door: 01325 467743
Admin: 01325 468006

DUBLIN

Gaiety Theatre
South King Street
Dublin
Box Office: 00 353 1 6771717
Stage Door: -------------------------
Admin: 00 353 1 6795622

DUBLIN

Gate Theatre
1 Cavendish Row Dublin 1
Box Office: 00 353 1 8744045
Stage Door: -------------------------
Admin: 00 353 1 8744368
e-mail: info@gate-theatre.ie

DUBLIN

Olympia Theatre
72 Dame Street, Dublin 2
Box Office: 00 353 1 6777744
Stage Door: 00 353 1 6771400
Admin: 00 353 1 6725883
e-mail: aideen@olympia.ie

EASTBOURNE

Congress Theatre
Admin: Winter Garden, Compton Street BN21 4BP
Box Office: 01323 412000
Stage Door: 01323 410048
Admin: 01323 415500
e-mail: theatres@eastbourne.gov.uk

EASTBOURNE

Devonshire Park Theatre
Admin: Winter Garden
Compton Street BN21 4BP
Box Office: 01323 412000
Stage Door: 01323 410074
Admin: 01323 415530
e-mail: theatres@eastbourne.gov.uk

EDINBURGH

King's Theatre
2 Leven Street
EH3 9LQ
Box Office: 0131-529 6000
Stage Door: 0131-229 3416
Admin: 0131-662 1112
e-mail: admin@eft.co.uk

EDINBURGH

Playhouse Theatre
18-22 Greenside Place
EH1 3AA
Box Office: 0870 6063424
Stage Door: 0131-557 2692
Admin: 0131-557 2692

GLASGOW

King's Theatre
297 Bath Street
G2 4JN
Box Office: 0141-287 5511
Stage Door: 0141-248 5153
Admin: 0141-287 5429

GLASGOW

Theatre Royal
Hope Street
G2 3QA
Box Office: 0141-332 9000
Stage Door: 0141-332 3321
Admin: 0141-332 3321

GRAYS THURROCK

Thameside Theatre
Orsett Road RM17 5DX
Box Office: 01375 383961
Stage Door: -------------------
Admin: 01375 382555
e-mail: mallinson@thurrock.gov.uk

HARLOW

The Playhouse
Playhouse Square, Essex CM20 1LS
Box Office: 01279 431945
Stage Door: -------------------
Admin: 01279 446760
e-mail: philip.dale@harlow.gov.uk

HARROGATE

Harrogate International Centre
Kings Road
HG1 5LA
Box Office: 01423 537230
Stage Door: 01423 537222
Admin: 01423 537200

HARROGATE

Royal Hall
Ripon Road
HG1 2RD
Box Office: 01423 537230
Stage Door: -------------------
Admin: 01423 537200

HASTINGS

White Rock Theatre
White Rock
TN34 1JX
Box Office: 01424 781000
Stage Door: 01424 434091
Admin: 01424 781010

HAYES (Middlesex)

Beck Theatre
Grange Road
UB3 2UE
Box Office: 020-8561 8371
Stage Door: -------------------
Admin: 020-8561 7506

HEREFORD

The Courtyard
Edgar Street
HR4 9JR
Box Office: 01432 359252
Stage Door: -------------------
Admin: 01432 346500

HIGH WYCOMBE

Wycombe Swan
St Mary Street HP11 2XE
Box Office: 01494 512000
Stage Door: 01494 514444
Admin: 01494 514444
e-mail: enquiries@wycombeswan.co.uk

HUDDERSFIELD

Lawrence Batley Theatre
Queen's Square, Queen Street HD1 2SP
Box Office: 01484 430528
Stage Door: -------------------
Admin: 01484 425282
e-mail: theatre@lbt-uk.org

HULL

Hull Truck Theatre
Spring Street HU2 8RW
Box Office: 01482 323638
Stage Door: -------------------
Admin: 01482 224800
e-mail: admin@hulltruck.co.uk

HULL

New Theatre
Kingston Square HU1 3HF
Box Office: 01482 226655
Stage Door: 01482 320244
Admin: 01482 613818
e-mail: theatre.management@hullcc.gov.uk

ILFORD

Kenneth More Theatre
Oakfield Road IG1 1BT
Box Office: 020-8553 4466
Stage Door: 020-8553 4465
Admin: 020-8553 4464
e-mail: kmtheatre@aol.com

IPSWICH

Sir John Mills Theatre (Hire Only)
Gatacre Road IP1 2LQ
Box Office: 01473 211498
Stage Door: -------------------
Admin: 01473 218202
e-mail: admin@easternangles.co.uk

JERSEY

Opera House
Gloucester Street St Helier JE2 3QR
Box Office: 01534 511115
Stage Door: -------------------
Admin: 01534 511100
e-mail: istephens-je@yahoo.co.uk

KIRKCALDY

Adam Smith Theatre
Bennochy Road
KY1 1ET
Box Office: 01592 412929
Stage Door: 01592 266193
Admin: 01592 412567

LEEDS

City Varieties Music Hall
Swan Street
LS1 6LW
Box Office: 0113-243 0808
Stage Door: -------------------
Admin: 0113-391 7777

LEEDS

Grand Theatre
46 New Briggate
LS1 6NZ
Box Office: 0113-222 6222
Stage Door: -------------------
Admin: 0113-245 6014

LINCOLN

Theatre Royal
Clasketgate
LN2 1JJ
Box Office: 01522 525555
Stage Door: 01522 523303
Admin: 01522 523303

LIVERPOOL

Empire Theatre
Lime Street
L1 1JE
Box Office: 0870 6063556
Stage Door: 0151-708 3200
Admin: 0151-708 3200

LIVERPOOL

Neptune Theatre
Hanover Street L1 3DY
Box Office: 0151-709 7844
Stage Door: 0151-709 7844
Admin: 0151-709 7844
e-mail: neptune.theatre@liverpool.gov.uk

MALVERN

Malvern Theatres (Festival & Forum Theatres)
Grange Road WR14 3HB
Box Office: 01684 892277
Stage Door: -------------------
Admin: 01684 569256
e-mail: post@malvern-theatres.co.uk

MANCHESTER

Apollo Theatre
Ardwick Green
M12 6AP
Box Office: 0161-242 2560
Stage Door: 0161-273 2416
Admin: 0161-273 6921

MANCHESTER

Forum Theatre Wythenshawe
Leningrad Sq, Wythenshawe
M22 5RT
Box Office: 0161-437 9663
Stage Door: 0161-935 4070
Admin: 0161-234 1913

MANCHESTER

Opera House
Quay Street
M3 3HP
Box Office: 0161-242 2509
Stage Door: 0161-834 1787
Admin: 0161-834 1787

MANCHESTER

Palace Theatre
Oxford Street
M1 6FT
Box Office: 0161-242 2503
Stage Door: 0161-228 6255
Admin: 0161-228 6255

MILTON KEYNES

Milton Keynes Theatre
500 Marlborough Gate
Central Milton Keynes MK9 3NZ
Box Office: 01908 606090
Stage Door: 01908 547500
Admin: 01908 547500

NEWARK

Palace Theatre
Appletongate NG24 1JY
Box Office: 01636 655755
Stage Door: -------------------
Admin: 01636 655750
e-mail: david.piper@newark-sherwooddc.gov.uk

NEWCASTLE UPON TYNE

Newcastle Opera House
111 Westgate Road NE1 4AG
Box Office: 0191-232 0899
Stage Door: 0191-232 1551
Admin: 0191-261 1725
e-mail: webmaster@newcastleoperahouse.com

NEWCASTLE UPON TYNE

Playhouse & Gulbenkian Studio Theatre
Barras Bridge, Haymarket NE1 7RH
Box Office: 0191-232 5151
Stage Door: -------------------
Admin: 0191-232 3366
e-mail: info@northernstage.com

NEWCASTLE UPON TYNE

Theatre Royal
Grey Street
NE1 6BR
Box Office: 0191-232 2061
Stage Door: 0191-261 8815
Admin: 0191-232 0997

NORTHAMPTON

Northampton Theatre Trust
19-21 Guildhall Road NN1 1DP
Box Office: 01604 624811
Stage Door: 01604 626289
Admin: 01604 626222
e-mail: postbox@ntt.org.uk

NORWICH

Theatre Royal
Theatre Street
NR2 1RL
Box Office: 01603 630000
Stage Door: 01603 598500
Admin: 01603 598500

NOTTINGHAM

Theatre Royal & Royal Concert Hall
Theatre Square NG1 5ND
Box Office: 0115-989 5555
Stage Door: 0115-989 5500
Admin: 0115-989 5500
e-mail: enquiry@royalcentre-nottingham.co.uk

OXFORD

Apollo Theatre
George Street
OX1 2AG
Box Office: 0870 6063500
Stage Door: 01865 241631
Admin: 01865 243041

OXFORD

Oxford Playhouse
Beaumont Street OX1 2LW
Box Office: 01865 798600
Stage Door: 01865 792758
Admin: 01865 247134
e-mail: admin@oxfordplayhouse.co.uk

PAIGNTON

Palace Theatre
Palace Ave TQ3 3HF
Box Office: 01803 665800
Stage Door: 01803 558367
Admin: 01803 296296
e-mail: palace.theatre@torbay.gov.uk

PLYMOUTH

Athenaeum
Derry's Cross
PL1 2SW
Box Office: 01752 266104
Stage Door: -------------------
Admin: 01752 266079

POOLE

Towngate Theatre,
Poole Arts Centre
Kingland Road BH15 1UG
Box Office: 01202 685222
Stage Door: -------------------
Admin: 01202 665334

READING

The Hexagon
Queen's Walk
RG1 7UA
Box Office: 0118-960 6060
Stage Door: 0118-939 0018
Admin: 0118-939 0390

RICHMOND (N Yorks)

Georgian Theatre Royal
Victoria Road
DL10 4DW
Box Office: 01748 823021
Stage Door: -------------------
Admin: 01748 823710

RICHMOND (Surrey)

Richmond Theatre
The Green
TW9 1QJ
Box Office: 020-8940 0088
Stage Door: 020-8940 0220
Admin: 020-8940 0220

SHEFFIELD

Crucible, Lyceum & Crucible Studio
55 Norfolk Street
S1 1DA
Box Office: 0114-249 6000
Stage Door: 0114-249 5999
Admin: 0114-249 5999

SOUTHAMPTON

Mayflower Theatre
Commercial Road SO15 1GE
Box Office: 023-8071 1811
Stage Door: 023-8033 0071
Admin: 023-80711800
e-mail: info@the-mayflower.com

ST ALBANS

Abbey Theatre
Holywell Hill AL1 2DL
Box Office: 01727 857861
Stage Door: 01727 861731
Admin: 01727 847472
e-mail: manager@abbeytheatre.freeserve.co.uk

ST ALBANS

Alban Arena
Civic Centre AL1 3LD
Box Office: 01727 844488
Stage Door: 01727 850345
Admin: 01727 861078
e-mail: info@alban-arena.co.uk

ST HELENS

Theatre Royal
Corporation Street
Lancs WA10 1LQ
Box Office: 01744 756000
Stage Door: -------------------
Admin: 01744 756333

STEVENAGE

Gordon Craig Theatre
Arts & Leisure Centre, Lytton Way SG1 1LZ
Box Office: 08700 131030
Stage Door: 01438 242629
Admin: 01438 242642
e-mail: gordoncraig@stevenage-leisure.co.uk

STOCKPORT

Peter Barkworth Theatre The
Stockport College
Wellington Road SK1 4UQ
Box Office: 0161-958 3114
Stage Door: 0161-958 3429
Admin: 0161-429 7413

STRATFORD-UPON-AVON

Royal Shakespeare Theatre
Waterside, Warwickshire CV37 6BB
Box Office: 01789 403403
Stage Door: 01789 296655
Admin: 01789 296655
e-mail: info@rsc.org.uk

STRATFORD-UPON-AVON

The Other Place
Southern Lane
CV37 6BH
Box Office: 01789 403403
Stage Door: 01789 296655
Admin: 01789 296655

STRATFORD-UPON-AVON

Swan Theatre
Waterside CV37 6BB
Box Office: 01789 403403
Stage Door: 01789 296655
Admin: 01789 296655
e-mail: info@rsc.org.uk

SUNDERLAND

Empire Theatre
High Street West
SR1 3EX
Box Office: 0191-514 2517
Stage Door: 0191-565 6750
Admin: 0191-510 0545

SWANAGE

Mowlem Theatre
Shore Road
BH19 1DD
Box Office: 01929 422239
Stage Door: --------------------
Admin: 01929 422229

SWANSEA

Volcano Theatre Co Ltd
176 Hanover Street SA1 6BP
Box Office: --------------------
Stage Door: --------------------
Admin: 01792 472772
e-mail: volcano.tc@virgin.net

TEWKESBURY

The Roses
Sun Street GL20 5NX
Box Office: 01684 295074
Stage Door: --------------------
Admin: 01684 290374
e-mail: arts@rosestheatre.org.uk

TORQUAY

Babbacombe Theatre
Babbacombe Downs TQ1 3LU
Box Office: 01803 328385
Stage Door: 01803 328385
Admin: 01803 322233
e-mail: matpro@btinternet.com

TORQUAY

Princess Theatre
Torbay Road TQ2 5EZ
Box Office: 0870 2414120
Stage Door: 01803 290068
Admin: 01803 290288
e-mail: princess@sfx.com

WATFORD

Palace Theatre
Clarendon Road, WD17 1JZ
Box Office: 01923 225671
Stage Door: --------------------
Admin: 01923 235455
e-mail: enquiries@watfordtheatre.co.uk

WINCHESTER

Theatre Royal
Jewry House, Jewry Street SO23 8RZ
Box Office: --------------------
Stage Door: --------------------
Admin: 01962 820220
e-mail: ingridr@trwinchester.fsnet.co.uk

WOKING

New Victoria Theatre, The Ambassadors
The Peacocks Centre GU21 1GQ
Box Office: 01483 545900
Stage Door: 01483 545855
Admin: 01483 545800
e-mail: boxoffice@theambassadors.com

WOLVERHAMPTON

Grand Theatre
Lichfield Street WV1 1DE
Box Office: 01902 429212
Stage Door: 01902 573320
Admin: 01902 573300
e-mail: annp@grandtheatre.co.uk

WORTHING

Connaught Theatre
Union Place
BN11 1LG
Box Office: 01903 206206
Stage Door: --------------------
Admin: 01903 231799

YEOVIL

Octagon Theatre
Hendford BA20 1UX
Box Office: 01935 422884
Stage Door: 01935 431075
Admin: 01935 422836
e-mail: octagontheatre@southsomerset.gov.uk

YORK

Grand Opera House
Cumberland Street
YO1 9SW
Box Office: 01904 671818
Stage Door: 01904 671857
Admin: 01904 655441

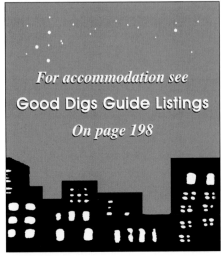

For accommodation see

Good Digs Guide Listings

On page 198

AUTHENTIC PUNCH & JUDY
Puppets, Booths & Presentations (John Styles)
42 Christchurch Road, Sidcup
Kent DA15 7HQ   Tel/Fax: 020-8300 3579

BROOKER David
(Punch & Judy)
75 Northcote Road
New Malden
Surrey KT3 3HF   Tel: 020-8949 5035

BUCKLEY Simon
(Freelance Puppeteer/Presenter)
c/o Talent Artists Ltd
4 Mews House
Princes Lane
London N10 3LU
e-mail: puppet.buckley@virgin.net
                         Tel: 020-8444 4088

CORNELIUS & JONES
49 Carters Close, Sherington
Newport Pagnell
Bucks MK16 9NW
e-mail: admin@corneliusjones.com
Fax: 01908 216400   Tel: 01908 612593

DYNAMIC NEW ANIMATION
19 Royal Close, Manor Road
London N16 5SE
e-mail: dnaanimation@unforgettable.com
                         Mobile: 07976 946003

GRIFFITHS Marc
(Ventriloquist)
The Mega Centre
Bernard Road
Sheffield S2   Tel: 0114-272 5077

JACOLLY PUPPET THEATRE
Kirkella Road, Yelverton
West Devon PL20 6BB
e-mail: theatre@jacolly-puppets.co.uk
                         Tel: 01822 852346

LITTLE ANGEL THEATRE
14 Dagmar Passage
Cross Street
London N1 2DN
Fax: 020-7359 7565   Tel: 020-7226 1787

NORWICH PUPPET THEATRE
St James, Whitefriars
Norwich NR3 1TN
e-mail: norpuppet@hotmail.com
Fax: 01603 617578   Tel: 01603 615564

PARAPHERNALIA PUPPETS
Church Studios
Common Road
Stafford ST16 3EQ
Fax: 01785 220460   SD: 01785 226326

PARASOL PUPPET THEATRE
Garden House, 4 Sunnyside
Wimbledon SW19 4SL
Fax: 020-8946 0228   Tel: 020-8946 9478

PEEL John PUPPETS
c/o Downham Montessori School
The Old Rectory
Stow Bardolph, Lynn Road
Kings Lynn, Norfolk PE34 3HT
                         Mobile: 07953 770070

PEKKO'S PUPPETS
28 Dorset Road
London W5 4HU   Tel: 020-8579 7651

PICCOLO PUPPET COMPANY
Maythorne Higher Park Road
Braunton
North Devon EX33 2LF
Tel: 01271 815984   Tel: 020-8342 8555

PIP CRITTEN
12 Trelawney Avenue
St Budeaux
Plymouth PL5 1RH   Tel: 01752 208242

PLAYBOARD PUPPETS
94 Ockendon Road
London N1 3NW
Fax: 020-7704 1081   Tel: 020-7226 5911

POM POM PUPPETS
10 Fulham Park Gardens
London SW6 4JX
Mobile: 07974 175247   Tel: 020-7736 6532

PROFESSOR PATTEN'S PUNCH & JUDY
(Puppetry & Magic)
14 The Crest, Goffs Oak
Herts EN7 5NP   Tel: 01707 873262

PUNCH & JUDY
(Des Turner, President Punch & Judy Fellowship)
Richmond House
2 Benington Road, Aston
Stevenage, Herts SG2 7DX
e-mail: desturner@aol.com   Tel: 01438 880376

PUPPET CENTRE TRUST
BAC Lavender Hill
London SW11 5TN
e-mail: pct@puppetcentre.demon.co.uk
Fax: 020-7228 8863   Tel: 020-7228 5335

STERENBERG Neil
(Television Puppeteer & Puppet Designer/Builder)
16 Wolverton Close
Redditch
Worcs B98 0AR   Tel: 01527 518969

**THE GOOD THE BAD & THE CUDDLY THEATRE
COMPANY**
140 Manor Road
New Milton
Hants BH25 5ED
e-mail: j.sinclair@cwcom.net
                         Tel: 01425 612830

**THEATR PYPEDAU SBLOT/SPLOTT PUPPET
THEATRE**
1 Gwendoline Place
Cardiff CF24 2AW   Tel: 029-2049 0160

TICKLISH ALLSORTS SHOW
Cremyll, Marshmead Close
Clarendon, Salisbury
Wilts SP5 3DD
e-mail: garynunn@lineone.net
                         Tel/Fax: 01722 711800

TOPPER Chris PUPPETS
(Puppets Created & Performed)
75 Barrows Green Lane, Widnes
Cheshire WA8 0JH   Tel: 0151-424 8692

Where appropriate, Rep periods are indicated, e.g. (4 Weekly) and matinee times e.g. Th 2.30 for Thursday 2.30pm.

SD - Stage Door
BO - Box Office
TIE - Theatre in Education (For further details of TIE/YPT see Theatre - TIE/YPT Companies).

ALDEBURGH
Summer Theatre The Jubilee Hall
(July & August)
Crabbe Street
Aldeburgh IP15 5BW
> BO: 01728 453007 Mon-Fri: 11-4
> BO: 01728 454022 Mon-Fri: 6-9
> Admin: (Oct-May) 020-7724 5432
> Admin: (June-Sept) 01502 723077/722688

Jill Freud

BASINGSTOKE
Haymarket Theatre Company
Wote Street
Basingstoke RG21 7NW
Fax: 01256 357130
BO: 01256 465566   Tel:01256 323073
e-mail: info@haymarket.org.uk

Theatre Director: Alasdair Ramsay

BELFAST
Lyric Theatre
55 Ridgeway Street, Belfast BT9 5FB
Fax: 028-9038 1395
BO: 028-9038 1081   Tel: 028-9066 9660
e-mail: info@lyrictheatre.co.uk

House Manager: May Arnott

BIRMINGHAM
Birmingham Stage Company
The Old Rep Theatre
Station Street
Birmingham B5 4DY
Fax: 0121-643 8099
BO: 0121-236 5622   Admin: 0121-643 9050
e-mail: info@birminghamstage.net

Actor/Manager: Neal Foster
Administrator: Rebecca Shallard

London Office:
Suite 612, 162 Regent Street, London W1B 5TG
Fax: 020-7437 3395   Admin: 020-7437 3391
e-mail: info@birminghamstage.net

Administration: Rebecca Shallard

BIRMINGHAM
Repertory Theatre
(4-5 Weekly Thurs & Sat 2.30pm
Centenary Square
Broad Street, Birmingham B1 2EP
Press Office: 0121-245 2075
BO: 0121-236 4455   Tel: 0121-245 2000
e-mail: tickets@birmingham-rep.co.uk

Artistic Director: Jonathan Church
Chief Executive: John Stalker

BOLTON
Octagon Theatre
Howell Croft South, Bolton BL1 1SB
Fax: 01204 556502
BO: 01204 520661   Admin: 01204 529407

Artistic Director: Mark Babych
Executive Director: John Blackmore

BRISTOL
Theatre Royal & New Vic Studio
(3/4 Weekly) Sat 2.30pm
(Bristol Old Vic Co)
King Street, Bristol BS1 4ED
Fax: 0117-949 3996
BO: 0117-987 7877   Tel: 0117-949 3993
e-mail: the.bristol.old.vic@cableinet.co.uk

Executive Director: Sarah Smith

BROMLEY
Churchill Theatre (Administration)
High Street, Bromley, Kent BR1 1HA
Fax: 020-8290 6968
BO: 020-8460 6677   Tel: 020-8464 7131

General Manager: Lori D Dorman

CARDIFF
Sherman Theatre & Sherman Studio
Senghennydd Road CF24 4YE
Fax: 029-2064 6902
BO: 029-2064 6900   Tel: 029-2064 6901

Director: Phil Clark
General Manager: Margaret Jones

CHELMSFORD
Civic Theatre
(2 Weekly) (Oct-Mar) Sat 5pm
Fairfield Road, Chelmsford
Essex CM1 1JG
Tel: 020-8349 0802 (London)
> Admin: 01245 268998

Artistic Director: John Newman
(Newpalm Prods)

CHESTER
Gateway Theatre
(3-4 Weekly)
Hamilton Place, Chester
Cheshire CH1 2BH
Fax: 01244 317277
BO: 01244 340392   Admin: 01244 344238
e-mail: admin@gateway-theatre.org.uk

Acting Chief Executive: Charles Bishop

CHICHESTER
Chichester Festival Theatre
(May-Oct & Touring) Eves 7.30pm
Thurs & Sat Mats 2.30pm
Oaklands Park, Chichester
West Sussex PO19 4AP
Fax: 01243 787288
BO: 01243 781312   SD & Admin: 01243 784437
e-mail: admin@cft.org.uk

Theatre Director: Andrew Welch
Theatre Manager: Janet Burton

CHICHESTER
Minerva Theatre at Chichester Festival Theatre
(June-Oct) Eves 7.45pm
Weds & Sat Mats 2.45pm
Oaklands Park, Chichester
West Sussex PO19 4AP
Fax: 01243 787288
BO: 01243 781312   SD & Admin: 01243 784437
e-mail: admin@cft.org.uk

Theatre Director: Andrew Welch
Theatre Manager: Janet Burton

COLCHESTER
Mercury Theatre
(3-4 Weekly) Thurs & Sat Mats 2.30pm
Balkerne Gate
Colchester, Essex CO1 1PT
Fax: 01206 769607
BO: 01206 573948   Admin: 01206 577006
e-mail: mercury.theatre@virgin.net

Chief Executive: Dee Evans
Artistic Producer: Gregory Floy

COVENTRY
Belgrade Theatre & Belgrade Studio
(3 Weekly) Weds 2.30pm
Belgrade Square, Coventry
Warwickshire CV1 1GS
BO: 024-765 3055   Admin: 024-762 6431
e-mail: admin@belgrade.co.uk

Theatre Director: Bob Eaton
Associate Producer: Jane Hytch
General Manager: David Beidas
Acting Head of Marketing: Nancy Mules

DERBY
Derby Playhouse
(3 1/2 Weekly)
Theatre Walk
Eagle Centre
Derby DE1 2NF
Fax: 01332 547200   SD: 01332 363271
BO: 01332 363275   Admin: 01332 363271
e-mail: admin@derbyplayhouse.demon.co.uk

Artistic Director: Mark Clements
Executive Director: David Edwards

DUBLIN
Abbey Theatre & Peacock Theatre
The National Theatre Society Limited
26 Lower Abbey Street, Dublin 1
Fax: 00 353 1 872 9177   BO: 00 353 1 878 7222
                         Admin: 00 353 1 887 2200
e-mail: mail@abbeytheatre.ie

Artistic Director: Ben Barnes
General Manager: Martin Fahy
Managing Director: Richard Wakely

DUNDEE
Dundee Repertory Theatre
Tay Square, Dundee DD1 1PB
Fax: 01382 228609
BO: 01382 223530   Admin: 01382 227684

Artistic Director: Hamish Glen
Administrative Director: Joanna Reid

EDINBURGH
Royal Lyceum Theatre Company
Grindlay Street
Edinburgh EH3 9AX
Fax: 0131-228 3955
BO: 0131-248 4848   SD & Admin: 0131-248 4800
e-mail: royallyceumtheatre@cableinet.co.uk

Artistic Director: Kenny Ireland

EDINBURGH
Traverse Theatre
(New Writing, Own Productions & Visiting
Companies)
Cambridge Street, Edinburgh EH1 2ED
Fax: 0131-229 8443
BO: 0131-228 1404   Admin: 0131-228 3223
e-mail: admin@traverse.co.uk

Artistic Director: Philip Howard
Administrative Producer: Lucy Mason

EXETER
Northcott Theatre
(3/4 Weekly)
Stocker Road
Exeter, Devon EX4 4QB
Fax: 01392 223996
BO: 01392 493493   Admin: 01392 223999

Artistic Director: Ben Crocker

EYE THEATRE
Eye Theatre
(4 Weekly) Sat 4.00pm
Broad Street
Eye, Suffolk IP23 7AF
Fax: 01379 871142   Tel: 01379 870519
e-mail: tomscott@eyetheatre.freeserve.co.uk

Artistic Director: Tom Scott
Associate Director: Janeena Sims

FRINTON
Frinton Summer Theatre
(July-Sept)
Ashlyns Road, Frinton, Essex
        Admin: 01255 674443 (During Season Only)

Producer: Seymour Matthews

GLASGOW
Citizens Theatre
Gorbals, Glasgow G5 9DS
Fax: 0141-429 7374
BO: 0141-429 0022   Admin: 0141-429 5561
e-mail: anna@citz.co.uk

Artistic Director: Giles Havergal
General Manager: Anna Stapleton

GUILDFORD
Yvonne Arnaud Theatre
Millbrook
Guildford
Surrey GU1 3UX
Fax: 01483 564071
BO: 01483 440000   Admin: 01483 440077
e-mail: yat@yvonne-arnaud.co.uk

Director: James Barber

HARROGATE
Harrogate Theatre
(3-4 weekly) 2.30pm Sat
Oxford Street, Harrogate HG1 1QF
Fax: 01423 563205
BO: 01423 502116   Admin: 01423 502710
e-mail: staff.name@harrogatetheatre.demon.co.uk

Artistic Director: Rob Swain
Executive Director: Sheena Wrigley

IPSWICH
The New Wolsey Theatre
Civic Drive, Ipswich
Suffolk IP1 2AS
BO: 01473 295900   Admin: 01473 295911
e-mail: tickets@wolseytheatre.co.uk

KESWICK
Theatre by the Lake (Cumbria Theatre Trust)
Lakeside, Keswick
Cumbria CA12 5DJ
Fax: 017687 74698
BO: 017687 74411   Admin: 017687 72282
e-mail: enquiries@theatrebythelake.com

Artistic Director: Ian Forrest

LANCASTER
The Dukes
Moor Lane, Lancaster, Lancs LA1 1QE
Fax: 01524 598519
BO: 01524 598500   Admin: 01524 598505

Artistic Director: Ian Hastings
Chief Executive: Amanda Belcham

LEEDS
The West Yorkshire Playhouse
Inc Schools Company
Playhouse Square, Quarry Hill
Leeds LS2 7UP
Fax: 0113-213 7250
BO: 0113-213 7700   Admin: 0113-213 7800

Artistic Director (Chief Executive): Jude Kelly
Managing Director: Maggie Saxon
Associate Producer: Paul Crewes

LEICESTER
Leicester Haymarket Theatre & Studio
Belgrave Gate
Leicester LE1 3YQ
Fax: 0116-251 3310
BO: 0116-253 9797   Admin: 0116-253 0021
e-mail: enquiry@leicesterhaymarkettheatre.org

Artistic Director: Paul Kerryson, Kully Thiarai
Executive Director: Mandy Stewart

LIVERPOOL
Everyman and Playhouse Theatres
Everyman: 13 Hope Street, Liverpool L1 9BH

Playhouse: Williamson Square
Liverpool L1 1EL
Fax: 0151-709 0398
BO: 0151-709 4776   Admin: 0151-708 0338
e-mail: info@everymanplayhouse.com

Director: Jo Beddoe

MANCHESTER
Contact Theatre Company
(3/4 Weekly)
Oxford Road
Manchester M15 6JA
Fax: 0161-274 0640
BO: 0161-274 0600   Admin: 0161-274 3434
e-mail: info@contact-theatre.org.uk

Chief Executive/Artistic Director:
John Edward McGrath

MANCHESTER
Library Theatre Company
St Peter's Square
Manchester M2 5PD
Fax: 0161-228 6481
BO: 0161-236 7110   Admin: 0161-234 1913
e-mail: ltc@libraries.manchester.gov.uk

Artistic Director: Chris Honer
General Manager: Adrian J. P. Morgan

MANCHESTER
Royal Exchange Theatre
St Ann's Square
Manchester M2 7DH
Fax: 0161-832 0881
BO: 0161-833 9833   SD & Admin: 0161-833 9333

Artistic Directors: Braham Murray,
Gregory Hersov, Matthew Lloyd, Marianne Elliot
Executive Director: Patricia Weller
General Manager: Richard Morgan
Casting Director: Sophie Marshall

MILFORD HAVEN
Torch Theatre
St Peter's Road
Milford Haven
Pembrokeshire SA73 2BU
Fax: 01646 698919
BO: 01646 695267   Admin: 01646 694192
e-mail: torchtheatre@cwcom.net

Artistic Director: Peter Doran

MOLD
Clwyd Theatr Cymru
(Repertoire, 4 Weekly, also touring)
Mold, Flintshire
North Wales CH7 1YA
Fax: 01352 758323
BO: 01352 755114   Admin: 01352 756331
e-mail: drama@celtic.co.uk

MUSSELBURGH
The Brunton Theatre
(2/3/4 Weekly) (Sept-April)
Ladywell Way
Musselburgh EH21 6AA
Fax: 0131-665 3665
BO: 0131-665 2240   Admin: 0131-665 9900

Artistic Director: David Mark Thomson
General Manager: Lesley Smith

NEWBURY
Watermill Theatre
(4-7 Weekly) (Feb-Jan)
Bagnor, Nr Newbury
Berks RG20 8AE
Fax: 01635 523726   SD: 01635 44532
BO: 01635 46044   Admin: 01635 45834
e-mail: admin@watermill.org.uk

Artistic Director: Jill Fraser

NEWCASTLE UPON TYNE
Northern Stage (Theatrical Productions) Ltd
Newcastle Playhouse
Barras Bridge
Haymarket NE1 7RH
Fax: 0191-261 8093
BO: 0191-230 5151   Admin: 0191-232 3366
e-mail: info@northernstage.com

Artistic Director: Alan Lyddiard

NEWCASTLE-UNDER-LYME
New Vic Theatre
(3-4 Weekly)
Theatre in the Round
Etruria Road
Newcastle-under-Lyme
Staffs ST5 0JG
Fax: 01782 712885
BO: 01782 717962   Tel: 01782 717954
e-mail: victheatre@aol.com

Artistic Director: Gwenda Hughes

NORTHAMPTON
Northampton Theatres, The Royal & Derngate
Guildhall Road, Northampton
Northants NN1 1DP
BO: 01604 624811   Casting: 01604 638343
TIE: 01604 627566   Admin: 01604 626222

Chief Executive: Symon Easton
Artistic Producer: Natasha Betteridge
Associate Director: Simon Godwin

NOTTINGHAM
Nottingham Playhouse
(3/4 Weekly)
(Nottingham Theatre Trust Ltd)
Wellington Circus
Nottingham NG1 5AF
Fax: 0115-947 5759
BO: 0115-941 9419   Admin: 0115-947 4361

Executive Director: Venu Dhupa
Artistic Director: Giles Croft
Administrative Director: Jim Robertson
Roundabout TIE Director: Andrew Breakwell

OLDHAM
Coliseum Theatre
(3-4 Weekly)
Fairbottom Street
Oldham, Lancs OL1 3SW
Fax: 0161-624 5318
BO: 0161-624 2829
Admin: 0161-624 1731
e-mail: mail@thecoliseum.fsnet.co.uk

Chief Executive: Kenneth Alan Taylor

PERTH
Perth Repertory Theatre
(2-3 Weekly)
185 High Street
Perth PH1 5UW
Fax: 01738 624576   SD: 01738 621435
BO: 01738 621031   Admin: 01738 472700
e-mail: theatre@perth.org.uk

Artistic Director: Michael Winter
General Manager: Paul Hackett

PETERBOROUGH
Key Theatre
(Touring & Occasional Seasonal)
Embankment Road
Peterborough
Cambs PE1 1EF
Fax: 01733 567025   SD: 01733 565040
BO: 01733 552439   Admin: 01733 552437
e-mail: keytheatre@freenetname.co.uk

PITLOCHRY FESTIVAL THEATRE
Pitlochry Festival Theatre
(May-Oct)
Pitlochry
Perthshire PH16 5DR
Fax: 01796 484616
BO: 01796 484626   Admin: 01796 484600
e-mail: admin@pitlochry.org.uk

Festival Director: Clive Perry
General Manager: Nikki Axford

PLYMOUTH
Theatre Royal & Drum Theatre
Royal Parade
Plymouth
Devon PL1 2TR
Fax: 01752 671179   Admin: 01752 668282
e-mail: s.stokes@theatreroyal.com

Artistic Director: Simon Stokes
Chief Executive: Adrian Vinken

SALISBURY
Playhouse & Salberg Studio
(3-4 Weekly)
Malthouse Lane
Salisbury
Wilts SP2 7RA
Fax: 01722 421991   SD: 01722 327670
BO: 01722 320333   Admin: 01722 320117
e-mail: info@salisburyplayhouse.com

Artistic Director: Joanna Read
Executive Director: Rebecca Morland

SCARBOROUGH
Stephen Joseph Theatre
(Repertoire/Repertory)
Westborough
Scarborough
North Yorks YO11 1JW
Fax: 01723 360506   SD: 01723 507047
BO: 01723 370541   Admin: 01723 370540
e-mail: response@sjt.uk.com

Artistic Director: Alan Ayckbourn
General Administrator: Stephen Wood

SHEFFIELD
Crucible Theatre & Studio Theatre
55 Norfolk Street
Sheffield S1 1DA
Admin Fax: 0114-249 6003
BO: 0114-249 6000   Admin: 0114-249 5999

Associate Director: Michael Grandage
Chief Executive: Grahame Morris

SIDMOUTH
Manor Pavilion
(Weekly) (July-Sept)
Manor Road
Sidmouth
Devon EX10 8RP
BO: 01395 579977 (Season Only)
                    Tel: 020-7636 4343 Charles Vance

SONNING THEATRE
The Mill at Sonning Theatre
(5-6 Weekly)
Sonning Eye
Reading RG4 6TY
SD: 0118-969 5201
BO: 0118-969 8000   Admin: 0118-969 6039

Artistic Director: Sally Hughes
Assistant Administrator: Ann Seymour

SOUTHAMPTON
Nuffield Theatre
(Sept-July, Sunday Night Concerts, Occasional
Tours)
University Road
Southampton SO17 1TR
Fax: 023-8031 5511   SD: 023-8055 5414
BO: 023-8067 1771   Admin: 023-8031 5500

Artistic Director: Patrick Sandford
Administrative Director: Kate Anderson

SOUTHWOLD
Summer Theatre
(July-Sept)
St Edmund's Hall
Cumberland Road
Southwold IP18 6JP   Admin: 020-7724 5432

Jill Freud & Company

ST ANDREWS
Byre Theatre
Abbey Street
St Andrews KY16 9LA
Fax: 01334 475370
BO: 01334 475000   Admin: 01334 476288
e-mail: enquiries@byretheatre.com

Artistic Director: Ken Alexander
Managing Director: Tom Gardner

STRATFORD-UPON-AVON
Swan Theatre & Royal Shakespeare Theatre
Waterside
Stratford-upon-Avon CV37 6BB
Fax: 01789 294810
BO: 01789 403403   Admin: 01789 296655
e-mail: info@rsc.org.uk

STRATFORD-UPON-AVON
The Other Place
Southern Lane
Stratford-upon-Avon CV37 6BH
Fax: 01789 415192
BO: 01789 403403   Admin: 01789 296655
e-mail: info@rsc.org.uk

WATFORD
Palace Theatre
(3-4 Weekly) Weds 2.30pm, Sat 3pm
Clarendon Road
Watford
Herts WD17 1JZ
Fax: 01923 819664
BO: 01923 225671   Admin: 01923 235455
e-mail: enquiries@watfordtheatre.co.uk

Artistic Director: Lawrence Till
Administrative Director: Mary Caws
Casting: Andrea Bath

WESTCLIFF
Palace Theatre & Dixon Theatres
London Road
Westcliff-on-Sea
Essex SS0 9LA
Fax: 01702 435031
BO: 01702 342564   Admin: 01702 347816
e-mail: palacetheatre@hotmail.com

Artistic Director: Roy Marsden

WINDSOR
Theatre Royal
(2-3 Weekly) (Thurs 2.30 Sat 4.45pm)
Thames Street
Windsor
Berks SL4 1PS
Fax: 01753 831673
BO: 01753 853888   Admin/SD: 01753 863444
e-mail: info@theatreroyalwindsor.co.uk

Executive Director: Mark Piper

WORCESTER
Swan Theatre
The Moors
Worcester WR1 3EF
Fax: 01905 723738
BO: 01905 27322   Admin: 01905 726969
e-mail: swan_theatre@lineone.net

Artistic Director: Jenny Stephens
General Manager: Deborah Rees

YORK
Theatre Royal
St Leonard's Place
York YO1 7HD
Fax: 01904 611534
BO: 01904 623568   Admin: 01904 658162
e-mail: admin@theatreroyalyork.fsnet.co.uk

Artistic Director: Damian Cruden
Chief Executive: Ludo Keston

For accommodation see The Good Digs Guide Listings

6:15 THEATRE COMPANY
22 Brookfield Mansions, Highgate West Hill
London N6 6AS
e-mail: six15@dircon.co.uk
Fax: 020-8340 5696   Tel: 020-8342 8239

BLAH BLAH BLAH THEATRE COMPANY The
East Leeds Family Learning Centre
Brooklands View, Leeds LS14 6SA
e-mail: admin@blahs.co.uk
Fax: 0113-224 3685   Tel: 0113-224 3171

BLUNDERBUS THEATRE COMPANY Ltd
The Mick Jagger Centre, Shepherd's Lane
Dartford, Kent DA1 2JZ
e-mail: admin@blunderbus.co.uk
Tel/Fax: 01322 286285   Tel: 01322 286284

BORDERLINE THEATRE COMPANY
North Harbour Street
Ayr KA8 8AA
e-mail: enquiries@borderlinetheatre.co.uk
Fax: 01292 263825   Tel: 01292 281010
Artistic Director: Leslie Finlay

CHANNEL THEATRE COMPANY
TIE Company
Central Studios, 130 Grosvenor Place
Margate, Kent CT9 1UY
e-mail: info@channel-theatre.co.uk
Fax: 01843 280088   Tel: 01843 280077
Artistic Director: Philip Dart

COMPLETE WORKS THEATRE COMPANY The
27 Prospect Road, London NW2 2JU
e-mail: info@tcw.org.uk   Tel: 020-7435 4718
Artistic Director: Phil Evans

CRAGRATS Ltd
The Mill, Dunford Road, Holmfirth
Huddersfield HD9 2AR
e-mail: jill@cragrats.com
Fax: 01484 686212   Tel: 01484 686451

C T C
Arts Centre, Vane Terrace, Darlington
Co Durham DL3 7AX
e-mail: ctc@clevelandtheatre.demon.co.uk
Fax: 01325 369404   Tel: 01325 352004

ENGLISH TEACHING THEATRE The
c/o 26 Petley Road, London W6 9ST
e-mail: ett@arcinter.net   Tel: 020-7254 9199

EUROPEAN THEATRE COMPANY The
39 Oxford Avenue, London SW20 8LS
Fax: 020-8544 1999   Tel: 020-8544 1994

M6 THEATRE COMPANY
Hamer CP School, Albert Royds Street
Rochdale OL16 2SU
e-mail: info@m6theatre.freeserve.co.uk
Fax: 01706 711700   Tel: 01706 355898

NATIONAL TRUST THEATRE The
(TMA Member)
2 & 4 Homerton High Street, Hackney
London E9 6JQ
Fax: 020-8985 2343   Tel: 020-8986 0242

NEW KINETIC THEATRE FOR SCIENCE
Suite H, The Jubilee Centre, Lombard Road
Wimbledon, London SW19 3TZ
e-mail: sarah@kinetictheatre.co.uk
Tel/Fax: 020-8672 8609
Contact: Dr Oliver Thalmann

ONATTI THEATRE COMPANY
9 Field Close, Warwick, Warwickshire CV34 4QD
e-mail: info@onatti.co.uk   Tel: 01926 495220
Artistic Director: Andrew Bardwell

QUANTUM THEATRE FOR SCIENCE
Unit S9, The Shakespeare Centre
245A Coldharbour Lane, London SW9 8RR
e-mail: quantumtheatre@btinternet.com
Tel: 020-7733 8150
Artistic Directors:
Michael Whitmore, Jessica Selous

QUERCUS THEATRE COMPANY
33 Broadlands Avenue
Shepperton, Middlesex TW17 9DJ
e-mail: quercus@quercustheatrecompany.org.uk
Tel: 01932 252182
Director: Therese Kitchin

ROUNDABOUT THEATRE IN EDUCATION
Nottingham Playhouse, Wellington Circus
Nottingham NG1 5AF
e-mail: admin@roundabout.org.uk
Fax: 0115-953 9055   Tel: 0115-947 4361

ROYAL THEATRE IN EDUCATION
19-21 Guildhall Road
Northampton NN1 1DP
e-mail: education@ntt.org   Tel: 01604 627566

SALAMANDER THEATRE COMPANY Ltd
333 Chiswick High Road, Chiswick
London W4 4HS
e-mail: salamander.theatre@btinternet.com
Fax: 020-8742 3923   Tel: 020-8994 4969

SHEFFIELD THEATRES EDUCATION COMPANY
55 Norfolk Street, Sheffield S1 1DA
Admin Fax: 0114-249 6003   Tel: 0114-249 5999
Education Administator: Sue Burley
Youth Theatre Director: Nick Nuttgens

SNAP PEOPLE'S THEATRE TRUST
45-47 South Street, Bishop's Stortford
Herts CM23 3AG
e-mail: info@snaptheatre.co.uk
Fax: 01279 506694   Tel: 01279 461607

SPECTACLE THEATRE
Pontypridd College, Rhondda Campus
Llwynypia, Tonypandy CF40 2TQ
e-mail: info@spectacletheatre.co.uk
Fax: 01443 423080   Tel: 01443 430700

TAG THEATRE COMPANY
18 Albion Street, Glasgow G1 1LH
e-mail: info@tag-theatre.co.uk
Fax: 0141-552 0666   Tel: 0141-552 4949

THEATR IOLO Ltd
The Old School Building, Cefn Road, Mynachdy
Cardiff CF14 3HS
e-mail: admin@theatriolo.com
Fax: 029-2052 2225   Tel: 029-2061 3782

TIEBREAK TOURING THEATRE
Heartsease High School, Marryat Road
Norwich NR7 9DF
e-mail: info@tiebreak-theatre.com
Fax: 01603 435184   Tel: 01603 435209

TIE TOURS
Holloway School, Hilldrop Road, Islington
London N7 0JG
e-mail: tie@tietours.com
Fax: 020-7619 9115   Tel: 020-7700 3697

WEST YORKSHIRE PLAYHOUSE SCHOOLS TOURING COMPANY
West Yorkshire Playhouse, Playhouse Square
Quarry Hill, Leeds LS2 7UP   Tel: 0113-213 7800

ACTION CARS Ltd
(Steven Royffe)
Units 3 & 4 Rosslyn Crescent, Harrow
Middlesex HA1 2SP
Fax: 020-8861 4876   Tel: 020-8863 6889

AIRLINE CREWING SERVICES Ltd
(Celebrity Services)
8 Maunsell Park, Pound Hill, Crawley
West Sussex RH10 7AD
Fax: 01737 271446   Tel: 01737 271440

ANCHOR MARINE FILM & TELEVISION
(Boat Location, Charter, Marine Co-ordinators)
Spike Mead Farm, Poles Lane, Lowfield Heath
West Sussex RH11 0PX
e-mail: amsfilms@aol.com
Fax: 01293 551558   Tel: 01293 538188

ANGLO PACIFIC INTERNATIONAL Plc
(Freight Forwarders to the Performing Arts)
Unit 1 Bush Industrial Estate, Standard Road
North Acton, London NW10 6DF
Fax: 020-8965 4954   Tel: 020-8965 1234

AUTOMATIVE ACTION TRACKING DIVISION
(Supplier)
2 Sheffield House, Park Road, Hampton Hill
Middlesex TW12 1HA
Mobile: 07974 919589   Tel: 020-8977 6186

AZTEC OF BRISTOL
20 Walnut Lane, Kingswood
Bristol BS15 4JG   Tel/Fax: 0117-940 7712

BIANCHI AVIATION FILM SERVICES
(Historic & Other Aircraft)
Wycombe Air Park, Booker Nr Marlow
Bucks SL7 3DP
Fax: 01494 461236   Tel: 01494 449810

BICYCLES UNLIMITED
(John Pinkerton)
522 Holly Lane, Erdington
Birmingham B24 9LY
e-mail: pinkertn@mwfree.net Tel: 0121-350 0685

BLUEBELL RAILWAY Plc
(Steam Locomotives, Pullman Coaches,
Period Stations)
Sheffield Park Station
East Sussex TN22 3QL   Tel/Fax: 01825 723777

BRUNEL'S THEATRICAL SERVICES
Unit 4, Crown Industrial Estate, Crown Road
Warmley, Bristol BS30 8JB
Fax: 0117-907 7856   Tel: 0117-907 7855

BUXWORTH STEAM GROUP
(Steam Driven Victorian Fairground)
Barren Clough Farm, Buxworth, Stockport
Cheshire SK12 7NS   Tel: 01663 732750

CELEBRITY CARS FOR ALL OCCASIONS
(Chauffeur Driven American Cars of the 50's
featuring 1958 Buick Ltd)
71 Fairlands Road, Limefield, Bury
Lancashire BL9 6QB   Tel/Fax: 0161-761 7906

CENTRAL FILM FACILITIES
(Film Transport/Period & Modern
Vehicles for Hire)
Marshbrook Business Park
Church Stretton
Shropshire SY6 6QE
Fax: 01694 781468   Tel: 01694 781418

CLASSIC CAR AGENCY The
(Film, Promotional, Advertising, Publicity)
Foxholt, Sheephouse Lane, Leith Hill
Surrey RH5 6LP
e-mail: theccaltd@cs.com
Mobile: 07788 977655   Tel: 01306 731052

CLASSIC COACHES
Binders Industrial Estate
Cryers Hill Road, Cryers Hill
High Wycombe HP15 6LJ
Fax: 01494 717575   Tel: 01494 521994

CLASSIC HIRE
(Rolls Royce Phantoms, Bentleys, Alvis &
Daimlers for hire 1920-70)
Garrick House
161 High Street
Hampton Hill, Middlesex   Tel: 020-8941 5414

CLASSIC OMNIBUS
(Vintage Open-Top Buses & Coaches)
44 Welson Road
Folkestone, Kent CT20 2NP
Fax: 01303 241245   Tel: 01303 248999

CRESTAR YACHTS Ltd
Colette Court, 125 Sloane Street
London SW1X 9AU
e-mail: charters@crestaryachts.com
Fax: 020-7824 8691   Tel: 020-7730 9962

DEVEREUX K. W. & SONS
(Removals)
Daimler Drive
Cowpen Industrial Estate, Billingham
Cleveland TS23 4JD
e-mail: devereux@onyxnet.co.uk
Fax: 01642 566664   Tel: 01642 560854

DORFGAR CHAUFFEUR DRIVE
(Uniformed Experienced Chauffeurs
Discretion Assured, Air Conditioning)
16 Gallows Hill Lane
Abbots Langley
Herts WD5 0DA   Tel/Fax: 01923 270555

EAST LONDON MOTORCYCLES
249 Barking Road
East Ham
London E6 1LB   Tel: 020-8472 8301

EST Ltd
(Trucking - Every Size & Country)
Marshgate Sidings, Marshgate Lane
London E15 2PB
e-mail: delr@est-uk.com
Fax: 020-8522 1002   Tel: 020-8522 1000

FAHREN WIDE
(Coach Company)
15 Darwin Close, Orpington
Kent BR6 7EP   Tel: 01689 851565

FELLOWES Mark TRANSPORT SERVICES
(Transport/Personal Storage)
59 Sherbrooke Road, London SW6 7QL
Mobile: 07850 332818   Tel: 020-7386 7005

FRANKIE'S YANKEES
(Classic 1950's American Cars, Memorabilia &
New Superstretch Limos)
1768-1770 Pershore Road, Birmingham B30 3BG
Fax: 0121-459 0009   Tel: 0121-458 7000

IMPACT
(Private & Contract Hire of Coaches -
Terry Morley)
1 Leighton Road, Ealing
London W13 9EL
Fax: 020-8840 4880   Tel: 020-8579 9922

JASON'S LADY ROSE
(Up-market Cruising Canal Wideboat)
Opp. 42 Blomfield Road, Little Venice
London W9 2PD
e-mail: enquiries@jasons.co.uk
Fax: 020-7266 4332   Tel: 020-7286 3428

**KEIGHLEY & WORTH VALLEY
LIGHT RAILWAY Ltd**
(Engines, Stations, Carriages, Props & Crew)
The Railway Station, Haworth, Keighley
West Yorkshire BD22 8NJ
e-mail: admin@kwvr.co.uk
Fax: 01535 647317   Tel: 01535 645214

LUCKING G. H. & SONS
(Transporters/Storage/Stage Hands)
Commerce Road, Brentford, Middlesex TW8 8LX
Fax: 020-8569 9847   Tel: 020-8569 9030

MAINSTREAM LEISURE GROUP
(Riverboat/Canal Boat Hire)
5 The Mews, 6 Putney Common
London SW15 1HL
Fax: 020-8788 0073   Tel: 020-8788 2669

McNEILL Brian
(Vintage Truck & Coaches)
Hawk Mount, Kebcote, Todmorden
Lancs OL14 8SB
e-mail: autotrams@currantbun.com
Fax: 01706 812292   Tel: 01706 812291

MOTORHOUSE HIRE Ltd
(Period Vehicles 1900-80)
Weston Underwood, Olney, Bucks MK46 5LD
e-mail: john@motorhouseltd.co.uk
Fax: 01234 240393   Tel: 020-7495 1618

M. V. DIXIE QUEEN
Thames Luxury Charters
5 The Mews, 6 Putney Common
London SW15 1HL
e-mail: sales@thamesluxurycharters.co.uk
Fax: 020-8788 0072   Tel: 020-8780 1562

NATIONAL MOTOR MUSEUM
John Montagu Building
Beaulieu, Nr Brockenhurst
Hants SO42 7ZN   Tel: 01590 612345

NINE-NINE CARS Ltd
Hyde Meadow Farm
Hyde Lane
Hemel Hempstead HP3 8SA
e-mail: sales@nineninecars.demon.co.uk
Tel: 01923 266373

PICKFORDS REMOVALS Ltd
Heritage House
345 Southbury Road
Enfield
Middlesex EN1 1UP
Fax: 020-8219 8001   Tel: 020-8219 8000

PLUS FILM SERVICES
(All Periods Vehicle Hire)
1 Mill House Cottages
Winchester Road
Bishop's Waltham SO32 1AH
e-mail: stephen@plusfilms.freeserve.co.uk
Tel/Fax: 01489 895559

RADCLIFFE'S TRANSPORT
(see LUCKING G. H. & SONS)

SCOOTABOUT MOTORCYCLE HIRE CENTRE
1-3 Leeke Street
London WC1X 9HZ
Fax: 020-7833 4613   Tel: 020-7833 4607

STOKE BRUERNE BOAT COMPANY
(Passenger & Commercial Boats)
29 Main Road, Shutlanger
Northants NN12 7RU
Fax: 01604 864098   Tel: 01604 862107

THAMES LUXURY CHARTERS Ltd
5 The Mews
6 Putney Common
London SW15 1HL
e-mail: sales@thamesluxurycharters.co.uk
Fax: 020 8788 0072   Tel: 020 8780 1562

THEATRE PICK-UPS
(Theatre Transport, Storage & Stage
Tabs/Curtain Hire)
PO Box 232
London WC2B 5SY
e-mail: pickups@orange.net Tel: 020-7387 7200

TOWN TYRE SERVICES Ltd
(Tug Boat for Hire)
Valley Way
Swansea Enterprise Park Llansamcet
Swansea SA6 8QP   Tel: 01792 773431

VINTAGE CARRIAGES TRUST
(Owners of the Museum of Rail Travel at Ingrow
Railway Centre)
Keighley
West Yorks BD22 8NJ
e-mail: vct@mwdjcope.demon.co.uk
Fax: 01535 610796   Tel: 01535 680425

VIRGIN ATLANTIC AIRWAYS
(Reservations)
The Office, Crawley Business Quarter
Manor Royal
West Sussex RH10 2NU
Fax: 01293 747699   Tel: 01293 747747

Notes

Notes

Notes